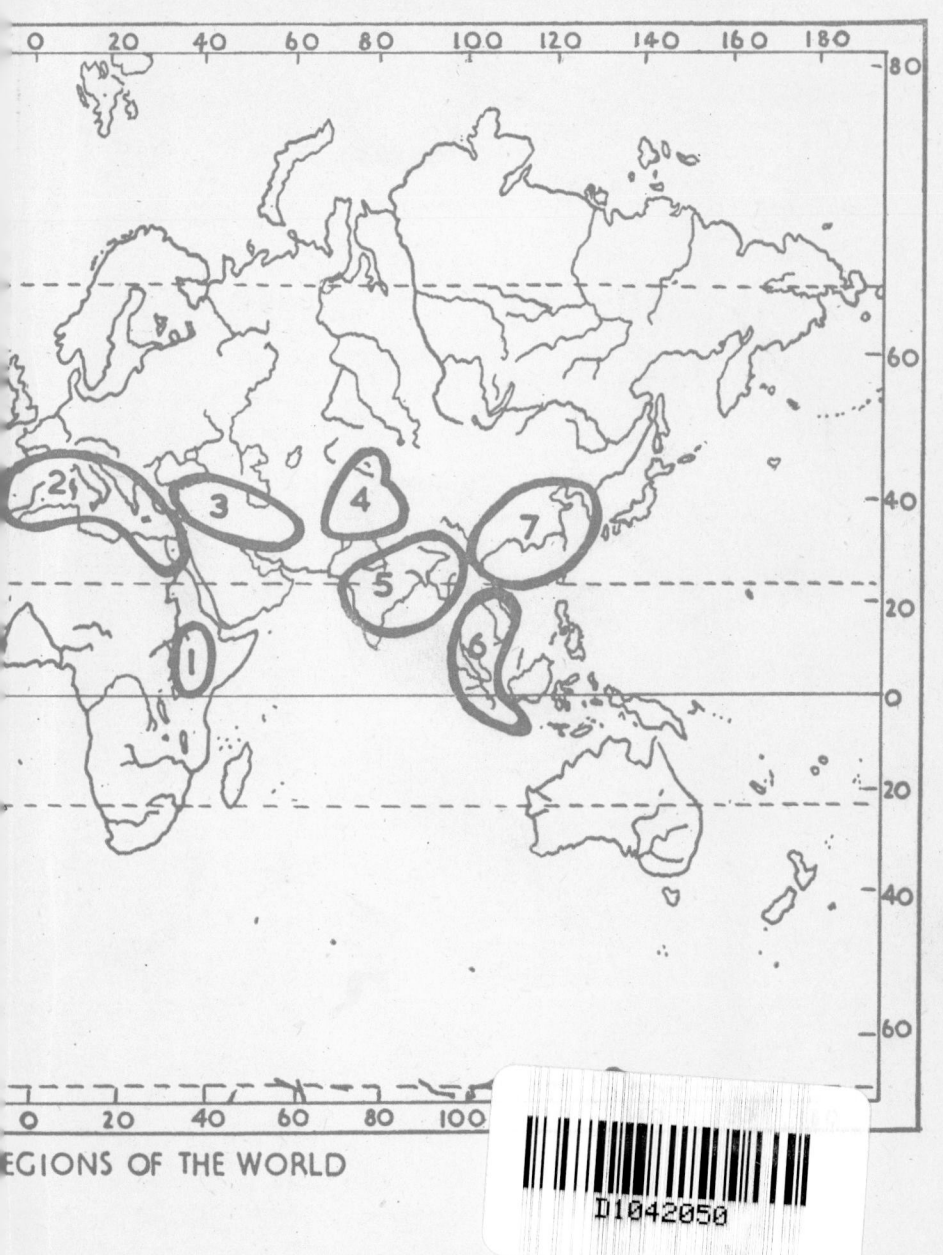

EGIONS OF THE WORLD

CHROMOSOME ATLAS OF FLOWERING PLANTS

by C. D. DARLINGTON, F.R.S.

CHROMOSOMES AND PLANT BREEDING
Macmillan 1932

RECENT ADVANCES IN CYTOLOGY
2nd ed. *Churchill* 1937

THE EVOLUTION OF GENETIC SYSTEMS
2nd impression *Cambridge University Press* 1946

THE CONFLICT OF SCIENCE AND SOCIETY
Watts 1948

THE FACTS OF LIFE
Allen and Unwin 1953

CHROMOSOME BOTANY
Allen and Unwin 1956

with E. K. Janaki Ammal
CHROMOSOME ATLAS OF CULTIVATED PLANTS
Allen and Unwin 1945

with L. F. La Cour, M.B.E.
THE HANDLING OF CHROMOSOMES
2nd ed. *Allen and Unwin* 1947

with K. Mather, F.R.S.
THE ELEMENTS OF GENETICS
Allen and Unwin 1949

GENES, PLANTS AND PEOPLE
Allen and Unwin 1950

CHROMOSOME ATLAS
of Flowering Plants

C. D. Darlington
and
A. P. Wylie

LONDON
GEORGE ALLEN & UNWIN LTD
Ruskin House Museum Street

FIRST EDITION (WITH E. K. JANAKI AMMAL)
PUBLISHED IN 1945
SECOND EDITION (WITH A. P. WYLIE) 1955

PRINTED IN GREAT BRITAIN
in Times Roman type
AT THE UNIVERSITY PRESS
ABERDEEN

To

NIKOLAI IVANOVICH VAVILOV

1886 - 1942

President of the Lenin Academy of Agricultural Sciences

1921 - 1940

For. Mem. R.S.

1945

PREFACE

TEN years have passed since the publication of the *Chromosome Atlas of Cultivated Plants* by C. D. Darlington and E. K. Janaki Ammal. During these years our knowledge has widened, deepened and developed. Some of the most significant developments have been due to the work of Dr. Janaki Ammal, first in the Royal Horticultural Society's Gardens at Wisley and latterly with the Indian Botanical Survey at Calcutta.

In this interval the known chromosome numbers have been nearly doubled. They have now been studied in some fifty thousand flowering plants belonging to nearly twenty thousand species. In this time too the physical means by which chromosomes change their forms and numbers have been experimentally demonstrated. The evolutionary consequences of these changes have become much clearer. Chromosome systematics has been brought into a fertile union with plant geography and plant ecology.

In view of this growth and transformation the title of the book has been changed in this new edition and its scope extended to include all flowering plants. Its purpose is threefold.

First, for the systematist it is intended to show how chromosome numbers can be used as a basis of the classification of species, genera and families. Secondly, for the plant breeder it is intended to show, in general, the genetic structure of groups of plants and in particular what species may be crossed and with what results. Thirdly, for the cytologist it is intended to show what work has been done and where it has been published. Perhaps we may also disclose a fourth purpose, the personal interest of the authors in which some readers may join us. This is to discover something of value for the geneticist and evolutionist, namely, the rules or laws of chromosome variation.

The first edition of this book already revealed the important principle that the stability of chromosome numbers is a function of the length of the life cycle. Woody plants are immensely stable. Comparison of their chromosome numbers therefore clarifies remote evolutionary relationships. Ephemeral plants are in varying degrees unstable. Comparison of their chromosome numbers therefore clarifies the origins of living species and the foundations of ecological genetics. This principle is useful to us at once for, in producing the atlas, we are enabled to abbreviate the uniform and stable genera and expand the more interesting unstable genera.

The present edition has gone further in indicating the widespread existence with unstable genera of two types of chromosomes: the A chromosomes which maintain heredity and the B chromosomes which stimulate variation. Exploring this distinction offers us an important field of research.

The means of interpreting and exploiting the materials in the Chromosome Atlas were discussed in a lengthy introduction to the first edition. This has now grown to need a separate volume, a companion volume entitled *Chromosome Botany*. Each volume separately will be useful to a particular group of individuals. The two together should be of interest rather to libraries and research laboratories.

C. D. DARLINGTON
Department of Botany
Oxford

A. P. WYLIE
Department of Botany
Manchester

ACKNOWLEDGMENTS

WE are indebted to Dr. W. B. Turrill of the Royal Botanic Gardens, Kew and Dr. P. S. Hudson of the Imperial Bureau of Plant Breeding and Genetics for the unrestricted use of their libraries.

We are also indebted to numerous collaborators apart from those already mentioned.

Dr. N. W. Simmonds of the Imperial College of Tropical Agriculture, Trinidad, checked uses and distributions of the Musaceae; Miss N. Burbidge of the Herbarium, Kew, the *Eucalyptus* and *Acacia* sections; Mr. G. D. Rowley the succulents (Ficoidaceae, Cactaceae and Crassulaceae); Major Albert Pam the Amaryllidaceae. Colonel F. C. Stern provided the preliminary list of *Iris* species.

The sources of the ILLUSTRATIONS are given in the Contents (p. xviii) and we wish to thank the authors acknowledged for the use of their figures both published and unpublished.

INTRODUCTION

How to Use the Atlas

The families of Angiosperms follow the order and bear the numbers of Hutchinson's " Families of Flowering Plants " (Dicotyledons, 1926; Monocotyledons, 1934). 241 out of 332 families are represented. To facilitate reference the whole are divided into 25 groups of orders, as listed in the Contents. Three exceptions are made to Hutchinson's subdivision. (i) We have, on account of their chromosome affinities, retained the Tribes Allieae and Agapantheae in the heterogeneous Liliaceae. (ii) On account of the chromosome evidence we have followed the suggestion of H. P. Traub (1946) and taken the Tribe Hemerocallideae out of the Liliaceae in the Atlas, putting *Hemerocallis* into the Amaryllidaceae and *Hosta* into the Agavaceae. (iii) We have kept the Nolanaceae separate from the Convolvulaceae. We have resisted the temptation, however, to put the Garryaceae back into the Cornaceae.

The families of Gymnosperms are taken from Pilger in Engler and Prantl's *Die Natürlichen Pflanzenfamilien* (1926) and follow our own order. Large families of Angiosperms we have subdivided as follows:

(i) Divided into Tribes:

Ranunculaceae, after W. C. Gregory (1941).

Cruciferae, after Schulz, in Engler and Prantl (1936).

Papilionaceae, after Taubert, 1894, cf. Willis 1931 (but putting *Abrus* out of the Vicieae into the Phaseoleae, following Senn, 1938).

Umbelliferae, after Engler, cf. Willis 1931.

Compositae, after Hoffman, in Engler and Gilg (Syllabus der Pflanzenfamilien, 1919).

Liliaceae, after Hutchinson, 1934.

Gramineae, after Hubbard (unpublished).

(ii) Divided into sub-families, etc.:

Caryophyllaceae, after Pax, cf. Willis, 1931.

Euphorbiaceae, after Pax, cf. Willis, 1931.

Rosaceae, partly after Focke, cf. Willis, 1931 and Clapham, Tutin and Warburg 1952.

Scrophulariaceae, into Parasites and Non-Parasites.

Myrtaceae, after Niedenzu, in Engler and Prantl (1898).

A synopsis of the tribes given before the families indicates the pattern of variation in chromosome number. The order in which we have taken them generally follows our rule which is to proceed from the lower to the higher basic numbers. Genera within families or tribes we have likewise, with special exceptions, taken in ascending order of basic numbers. Groups are headed by their basic numbers, primary x, secondary x_2.

Individual genera are likewise subdivided where necessary according to basic number and ploidy. The exceptions are certain large genera which have been, in our view, satisfactorily divided into sections on other grounds, e.g. *Prunus, Rosa, Primula, Crepis, Rhododendron, Nicotiana, Bellevalia, Tulipa, Calochortus* and *Iris*. Genera in which apomixis is known are noted since its occurrence is usually related to ploidy.

Synonyms or old alternatives corresponding to the whole or part of a genus are given in brackets. The name given by the chromosome author may then be either the first or the second. If the second, a more recent authority has been found in Willis, Bailey, Rehder or Clapham, Tutin and Warburg, confirmed sometimes by the chromosome evidence itself. In particular, Dr. Hubbard corrected the whole of the Gramineae for the first edition in the light of this evidence.

We have not put the conventional × before the name of an alleged hybrid since in our view this usage has no exact meaning without experimental and cytological control. Such forms often appear in the sixth column as *cult*.

The specific name of a plant without the name of the describer refers to a group of plants resembling the available descriptions or illustrations of the type specimen. When the name of the describer is attached it refers to plants identical in all significant respects with this type specimen. Since type specimens are dead plants in herbaria their chromosome numbers cannot be certainly known. They may often differ from those of plants which seem to be identical with them when lying dead in herbaria. This is proved by the fact that two plants with widely different chromosome numbers are assigned to the same species without qualification by competent systematists. In these circumstances the use of the authority's name in conjunction with the chromosome number would be misleading for the person who made the observation on the chromosomes. And its insertion by a compiler after the event would be actually fraudulent. The chromosome number itself constitutes a new independent criterion of classification. It must not be identified with the Linnean system but must be kept independent if its value is to be utilised in approaching the distant goal of putting the classification of plants and animals on a natural, that is a genetic, basis.

In all, over 15,000 species in 2,500 genera are included in the catalogue. About half the larger genera, those with the greatest constancy, have been abbreviated. The names of species have been omitted where many have the same chromosome number, especially in stable genera, amounting altogether to about 3,000. These genera are indicated by an asterisk. About half the species summarised in this way will be found in the first edition, and the remainder in the references which have always been retained. Similarly the names of some 500 economically important species, which were included in the first edition and whose chromosome numbers are not yet known, have been left out. The remainder, those of greatest interest, amount to about 12,000 species. These are recorded in detail. Some of these have been the subject of extensive study and experiment. The majority, however, have been examined merely from single and even unrepresentative specimens. The effect is that only a part of the natural wealth of variation in chromosome numbers is now revealed. Much remains to be discovered.

SECOND COLUMN: POPULAR NAMES

Important economic or decorative species, or their useful products, have been given their popular, vernacular or commercial names, English and American, Spanish and Portuguese, Hindustani and Hottentot. These names often have a priority over the scientific names and may, we fear, often survive them. In some genera, like *Brassica* and *Iris*, where systematics has been defeated by plant breeding, the popular names often alone have any meaning. On the other hand, we have tried (with partial success) to avoid the many bogus popular names given in reference books which are either scholastic translations or attempts to impose botanical rules on the common speech. Secondary or borrowed popular names such as " Papaw ", applied in America since 1760 to *Asimina*, as well as to *Carica papaya* we have placed in quotation marks.

THIRD COLUMN: NUMBERS

The somatic or " diploid " number, and not the gametic or haploid number, is given in all cases. It varies from 6 to 500, and may have been either directly observed or calculated from observations of mitosis in the pollen or of meiosis in the pollen mother cells. The chromosome numbers of experimentally produced haploids and polyploids are put in brackets. Supernumerary chromosomes whose numbers are presumed to be unstable are indicated by B.

Errors. A proportion of the ascriptions of chromosome numbers to names of species are undoubtedly incorrect. In the first edition we estimated the proportion of errors as 5 per cent. In the present edition it is probably reduced to about 3 per cent., divided, we believe, between miscounting, misnaming, and the accidents of hybridisation and labelling in botanic gardens. Where the author is uncertain we prefix *c.* (*circa*). Where we are uncertain of the number, or of its attachment to the botanical name given, we add a question mark. Where the name seems clearly incorrect we put it in quotation marks or add a query.

A more important source of error remains, however, not in the ascription but in the interpretation, where insufficient facts have been given by enthusiasts interested only in accumulating lists of numbers. Where, for example, two numbers not in a polyploid series have been ascribed to one species by different authors we often do not know whether the difference is made up of paired or unpaired chromosomes or of supernumerary or B chromosomes, either new and sporadic or old and well-established. One of the purposes of the Atlas is to reveal these dangers and show how to deal with them: how, in other words, a true chromosome number can be authentically attached to a significant name.

FOURTH COLUMN: AUTHORS

Where two accounts differ in number for the same species we have quoted both. We have omitted only ancient and obvious errors. Where accounts agree, we have reversed the rule of botanical priority and quoted the last important reference, since from this the earlier sources can usually be obtained.

Previous summaries of chromosome numbers are referred to by the following initials as abbreviations:

Delay: D. 1951 (general).

Ishikawa: I. 1916 (general).

Kihara *et alii:* K. 1931 (Japanese cultivated plants).

Löve and Löve: L. & L. 1942, 1944, 1948 (Scandinavian Flora).

Matsuura and Suto: M. & S. 1935 (personal counts).

Maude: M. 1939 (British Flora).

Tischler: T. 1922, 1926, 1931, 1937, 1938 (general), 1950 (Central European Flora).

Most of these lists contain otherwise unpublished information, and Tischler's and Delay's lists form a series of catalogues of nearly all numbers published up to 1950.

In addition we are indebted for some unpublished counts to our colleagues Messrs. L. F. La Cour, R. D. Brock, J. B. Hair, B. Snoad and R. de V. Pienaar and to many correspondents. For special lists we are indebted to:

Professor H. N. Barber and members of the Botany Department, University of Hobart (many Australian plants).

Professor P. T. Thomas, University of Wales, Aberystwyth (African grasses).

Dr. S. Smith-White and other members of the Botany Department, University of Sydney (many Australian plants).

Dr. O. H. Frankel, F.R.S. (*Hebe*).

Dr. H. G. Baker (Geraniaceae, Plumbaginaceae).

Dr. Harlan Lewis (*Clarkia*).

Some 150 unpublished counts by Dr. E. K. Janaki-Ammal for the first edition are initialled EKJ*. These are chiefly grasses and the neglected economic plants of the tropics.

FIFTH COLUMN: USES OF PLANTS

The known or supposed uses of all the more useful plants are summarised. We should have liked to include a similar classification for habits and reproductive methods, but this must be left for a later work. In preparing the catalogue of uses we have chiefly relied on the valuable works listed in the Special References. We have used the Guide to the Kew Museums of Economic Botany and, in addition, various special works and nurserymen's catalogues.

The following initials show our classification of uses:

A   *Alcoholic Liquors*, produced by fermentation (barley for malting, grapes for wine, cocoanut sap for arrak).

B   *Beverages*, produced by infusion (tea, coffee, cocoa).

C   *Carnivorous Plants* (Droseraceae, Sarraceniaceae).

D   *Dyes and Tannins* (indigo, madder, annatto, cassia, wattle, oak bark).

F   *Fruits*, edible by man (apple, mango, orange, banana, lichi, fig, melon, tomato, date palm).

Fs   *Stocks* for fruit and flowering trees (*Atalantia*, *Crataegus*, *Prunus*, *Rosa*).

Fo   *Fodder*, green for cattle, sheep, elephants, etc. (grasses, legumes, roots and trees).

Fo_1 *Fodder*, for insects (mulberry and *Ricinus* for silkworm, *Opuntia* for cochineal, *Cassia* for shellac insect).

G   *Grains* and *Pulses* for cattle and man (cereals and legumes, buckwheat).

H   *Horticultural Plants,* grown for decoration, instruction, experiment, protection, curiosity or religious edification, including hedge-plants and lawn grasses.

I   *Insecticides* and *Vermifuges,* for infusion or dusting (nicotine, derris, *Pyrethrum,* santonine).

M   *Medicinal Plants,* drugs and poisons including fish-poisons (cascara, quinine, cocaine, nux vomica, hemp).

Ma   *Green Manure,* chiefly leguminous crops.

N   *Nuts,* edible by man (walnut, chestnut, cocoanut, pistachio).

O   *Oil Seeds* and *Waxes* (linseed, sunflower, rape, cotton-seed, castor oil, sesame, palms).

P   *Perfumes* and *Essential Oils,* naturally volatile (rose, violet, jasmine, lavender, sandalwood, eucalyptus, lemongrass).

Par   *Parasites* and *Semi-Parasites* (Orobanchaceae, Mistletoe, sandalwood tree).

R   *Roots, Tubers* and *Bulbs,* edible or extractable (potato, turnip, radish, arrowroot, tapioca, yam).

Re   *Resins,* extracted from trees (damar, copal, mastics, balsams, frankincense and myrrh).

Ru   *Rubber* from latex of roots or stems (Euphorbiaceae, Compositae, Asclepiadaceae, Apocynaceae and Sapotaceae).

Sb   *Sand-binders* (bindweeds, grasses and trees).

Sh   *Shade Trees* for parks, avenues, nurseries and plantations (*Grevillea, Erythrina, Ficus, Eucalyptus, Cedrus*).

Sp   *Spices* and *Condiments* (peppers, cinnamon, cloves, ginger, herbs of Umbelliferae, Labiatae and Compositae).

St   *Starch,* extracted from stems (*Caryota, Cycas*).

Su   *Sugar,* extracted from stems or roots (sugar-cane, sugar-beet and palms). Also sweeteners (liquorice, etc.).

T   *Textile Fibres,* for weaving fabrics, carpets, mats, baskets, ropes and cords and for paper-making and thatching (cotton, jute, hemp, raffia, bamboo).

To   *Tools:* weapons, vessels, pipes, strainers, cleaners, beads, made directly from fruits and stems (gourd, lufa, bamboo, teasel, *Coix*).

V   *Vegetables,* green crops and salads, not roots (cabbage, celery, lettuce, cucurbits).

Vit   *Vitamin C* sources, fruits and stems (*Actinidia*, walnut, rose, paprika).

W   *Wood*, timber, cork and charcoal-wood trees (Gymnosperms, palms, hardwoods).

SIXTH COLUMN: DISTRIBUTIONS

The distributions have been taken primarily from the Index Kewensis, whose main geographical divisions are shown on the back end-papers. This source has been enlarged and amended in the light of more recent authorities particularly Vavilov (1926, 1933, 1950), Bailey's *Hortus Second* (1941), Chittenden's *Dictionary of Gardening* (1951), Laufer's historical " Sino-Iranica " (1919), and special systematic works many of them included in the chromosome studies quoted.

We have translated the ancient and modern Latin localities in the Index Kewensis as follows:

Amphig., Cosmopolitan.

Amphig. Trop., Tropics.

Byzant., S. W. Asia.

Dahuria, Amur.

Geront. Trop., Old World Tropics.

Ind. or., India (not East Indies).

Masc. Ins. (Mascarene Islands), Madagascar, etc.

N. Granat., New Granada, i.e. Colombia.

Oriens., S. W. Asia (including Nile Delta).

Cilicia, Galatia, Pisidia, Asia Minor.

Soongaria, Turkestan.

Taurus, Taurus Mountains.

Mistakes have frequently been made in putting these names into English since no one has undertaken to define them, and their original meaning is now obscured by the process of time.

Forms labelled *cult* are those effectively distinct from wild species. They are chiefly derived from hybridisation of two or more races or species with later selection and with or without later changes of chromosome number.

CONTENTS

Examples of Categories used in The Atlas in their order of importance

1	Class	I GYMNOSPERMS
		II DICOTYLEDONS
		III MONOCOTYLEDONS
2	Group	(1-10 Orders) XIII ERICALES
3	Family	143 ROSACEAE
4	Sub-family	SF 1: ROSOIDEAE
5	Tribe	*TRIBE II: HELIANTHEAE* (in Compositae)
6	Genus	ROSA
7	Subgenus	SUBGENUS 4 : EUROSA (in *Rosa*)
8	Section	S 2: RETICULATA (in *Iris*)
9	Series	Series: LAPPONICUM (only in Rhododendron)
10	Species	*persica* (in *Rosa*)
11	Variety	v. *bicolor* (of *Rosa foetida*)

REFERENCES FOR THE INTRODUCTION

BAILEY, L. H. and BAILEY, E. Z. 1941. *Hortus Second.* New York.

BURKILL, I. H. 1935. *A Dictionary of the Economic Products of the Malay Peninsula.* London.

CHITTENDEN, F. J. 1951. *Dictionary of Gardening.* Oxford.

CLAPHAM, A. R., TUTIN, T. G. and WARBURG, E. F. 1952. *Flora of the British Isles.* Cambridge.

DALZIEL, J. M. 1948. *Useful Plants of West Tropical Africa.* London.

DEY, K. L. 1896. *Indigenous Drugs of India.* Calcutta.

GREGORY, W. C. 1941. *Trans. Amer. Phil. Soc.,* N.S. **31**, 443.

HITCHCOCK, A. S. 1935. *Manual of the Grasses of the United States.* Washington.

HOLLAND, J. H. 1937. *Overseas Plant Products.* London.

MACMILLAN, H. F. 1925. *Tropical Gardening and Planting.* Colombo.

MEDSGER, O. P. 1947. *Edible Wild Plants.* New York.

NICHOLSON, G. *Illustrated Dictionary of Gardening* (N.D.). London.

REHDER, A. 1940. *Manual of Cultivated Trees and Shrubs.* 2nd edn. New York.

SAMPSON, H. C. 1936. Cultivated Crop Plants of the British Empire, etc. *Kew. Bull. Misc. Inf. Add. Series* 12.

SHERY, R. W. 1954. *Plants for Man.* London.

DE SORNAY, P. 1916. *Green Manures and Manuring in the Tropics.* (Trans. Flattely)· London.

STURTEVANT, E. L. 1919. *Notes on Edible Plants.* Albany, New York.

TRAUB, H. P. 1946. *Review of Chromosome Atlas,* 1st edn. *Plant Life,* **2**, 99.

WILLIS, J. C. 1931. *A Dictionary of Flowering Plants and Ferns.* 6th edn. Cambridge.

CONTENTS OF THE ATLAS

XVIII: 250-264	Solanales, Personales, Lamiales	*Glechoma hederacea* × 3000 Rutland 1941

MONOCOTYLEDONS

I: 265-285	Butomales, Alismatales, Triuridales, Juncaginales, Aponogetonales, Potamogetonales, Najadales, Commelinales, Xyridales, Eriocaulales	*Hydrocharis morsus-ranae* × 2100 Maude 1940
II: 286-292	Bromeliales, Zingiberales	*Musa paradisiaca* Banana " Gros Michel " × 3950 Larter 1935
III: 293-307	Liliales, Alstroemeriales, Arales, Typhales, Amaryllidales, Iridales	*Puschkinia libanotica* × 3600 Darlington 1937a
IV: 308-316	Discoreales, Agavales, Palmales, Pandanales, Cyclanthales	*Dioscorea batatas* × 3700 B. W. Smith 1937
V: 317-326	Haemodorales, Burmanniales, Orchidales	*Cephalanthera erecta* × 1250 Miduno 1938
VI: 327-332	Juncales, Cyperales, Graminales	*Sieglingia decumbens* × 2100 Maude 1940

GYMNOSPERMS

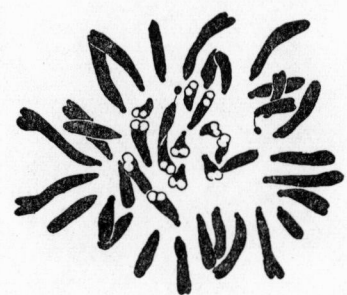

Welwitschia mirabilis

I CYCADACEAE

CERATOZAMIA $x = 8$
mexicana		16 Resende 1937	H	Mexico

STANGERIA $x = 8$
paradoxa (eriopus)		16 Sax & B. 1934	H	S. Africa

ZAMIA $x = 8, 9$
floridana	Coontie	16 Sax & B. 1934	H	Bah., S. Fla.
media		16 ,, ,,	H	W. Indies
loddigesii		18 Resende & R. 1948	H	Mexico

BOWENIA $x = 9$
serrulata	18 Sax & B. 1934	H	Australia
spectabilis	18 Resende & R. 1948	H	,,

DIOON (DION) $x = 9$
edule	18 Viveiros 1951	N	Mexico
spinulosum	18 Sax & B. 1934	H	,,

ENCEPHALARTOS $x = 9$
altensteinii	Hottentot B.	18 Resende 1940	NH	S. Africa
caffer	Kaffir Bread	18 Viveiros 1951	NSt	,,
horridus		18 Resende 1940	H	,,
latifrons		18 ,, ,,	H	?
lehmannii		18 Viveiros 1951	H	S. Africa
villosus		18 ,, ,,	H	,,

MACROZAMIA $x = 9$
miquelii	18 Sax & B. 1934	H	Australia
moorei	18 ,, ,,	H	,,
tridentata	18 ., ,,	H	,,

CYCAS $x = 11, 12$
circinalis	Eenthu	22 Sax & B. 1934	HNSt	S.E. As., E. Ind.
rumphii		22 ,, ,,	H	Mal., Austr.
revoluta		22 ,, ,, 22, 24 T. Nakamura 1929	HNSt	S. Japan

MICROCYCAS $x = 13$
calocoma	Corcho	26 Sax & B. 1934	H	Cuba

2 GINGKOACEAE

GINGKO $x = 12$
biloba	24 Lee 1954	H	E. China

3 TAXACEAE

TORREYA $x = 11$
macrosperma	22 Nakajima 1942	W	Japan
nucifera	22 Hirayoshi 1942	NOW	,,

TAXUS $x = 12$

baccata	English Yew	24	Dark 1932a	HW	N. Temp.
	Irish Yew	24	,, ,,	H	*cult*
canadensis	Ground	24 + 1B	,, ,,	H	N. America
	Hemlock				
cuspidata	Japanese Y.	24	,, ,,	HW	Japan
hunnewelliana		24	Sax & S. 1933	H	*cult*
media		24	,, ,,	H	,,

4 PODOCARPACEAE

PODOCARPUS $x = 19 (12, 20)$

falcatus		24	Flory 1936	H	S. Africa
neriifolius		38	,, ,,	H	Himalayas
nivalis	Alpine Totara	38	Snoad 1952	H	N. Zealand
macrophyllus	Kusamaki	38	Hirayoshi 1942	H	China, Japan
as *chinensis*		40	Flory 1936		
andinus		c. 40	,, ,,	FH	Chile

5 ARAUCARIACEAE

AGATHIS $x = 13$

robusta	Queensland	26	Flory 1936	W	Australia
	Kauri Pine				

ARAUCARIA $x = 13$

bidwillii	Bunya-Bunya	26	Flory 1936	H	Australia
brasiliana	Parana P.	26	,, ,,	H	Brazil
cunninghamii	Hoop P.	26	,, ,,	H	Australia

6 CEPHALOTAXACEAE

CEPHALOTAXUS $x = 12$

drupacea	Jap. Plum Yew	24	Sugihara 1940	H	Japan
fortunei	Chinese P.Y.	24	Sax & S. 1933	H	C. China

7 TAXODIACEAE

SCIADOPITYS $x = 10$

verticillata	Umbrella Pine	20	Tahara 1937	H	Japan

ATHROTAXIS $x = 11$

cupressoides		22	Gulline 1952	H	Tasmania
laxifolia		22	,, ,,	H	,,
selaginoides	King William P.	22	,, ,,	H	,,

CRYPTOMERIA $x = 11$

japonica		22	Sax & S. 1933	HW	Japan
		(44)	Zinnai & C. 1951		

CUNNINGHAMIA $x = 11$

lanceolata	China Fir	22	Sugihara 1941	H	S. & W. China

4

TAIWANIA x = 11
cryptomerioides — 22 Sax & S. 1933 — H — Formosa, Yunnan

TAXODIUM x = 11
distichum Bald Cypress 22 Stebbins 1948 H N. America

METASEQUOIA x = 11
glyptostroboides 22 Stebbins 1948 H C. China

SEQUOIADENDRON x = 11
giganteum Big Tree 22 (44) Jensen & L. 1941 HW California

SEQUOIA x = 11
sempervirens Redwood {66 Hirayoshi & N. '43 / 66 Stebbins 1948} HW California

8 PINACEAE

SF1: ABIETOIDEAE

PSEUDOLARIX x = 11
amabilis Golden Larch 44 Sax & S. 1933 HW China

TSUGA x = 12
canadensis Hemlock 24 Sax & S. 1933 DW N. America
caroliniana 24 ,, ,, W ,, ,,
diversifolia 24 ,, ,, W Japan

ABIES x = 12
balsamea Balsam F. 24 Miyake 1903 HW N. America
cephalonica Greek Fir 24 Sax & S. 1933 HW Greece
concolor White Fir 24 ,, ,, HW N. America
nordmanniana Caucasian F. 24 ,, ,, HW Caucasus
veitchii 24 ,, ,, HW Japan
pindrow 24 Mehra & K. 1948b H Himalayas

CEDRUS x = 12
deodara Deodar 24 Mehra & K. 1948b HMW Himalayas
libanensis Lebanon C. 24 Sax & S. 1933 HW Syria

KETELEERIA x = 12
davidiana 24 Sugihara 1943 H China
as *evelyniana* 24 Wang 1948 H W. China

LARIX x = 12
decidua Common Larch {24 Sax & S. 1933 / 24,48 Christiansen 1950} HW Eur., W. Asia
  (*europaea*)
eurolepis Dunkeld L. 24 Sax 1932 W cult
dahurica (*gmelinii*) 24 Woycicki 1906 HW Siberia
leptolepis Jap. L. 24 Sax & S. 1933 H Japan
  (*kaempferi*)
occidentalis W. Amer. L. 24 ,, ,, — W: N. Amer.
polonica 24 Hruby 1933 — Poland
sibirica Siberian L. 24 L. & L. 1948 — Siberia
sudetica 24 Hruby 1933 — Europe
decidua × *sibirica* (36) Larsen & W. 1938 H cult

5

PICEA $x = 12$

abies	Norway Spruce	24	Sax & S. 1933	ReW	Europe
		24,48	L. & L. 1948		
glauca	White S.	24	Sax & S. 1933	W	N. America
mariana (nigra)	Black S.	24	,, ,,	W	,,
pungens		24	,, ,,	W	W. N. America
sitchensis	Sitka S.	24	Thomas 1945*	W	,, ,,

PSEUDOTSUGA $x = 13$

taxifolia	Douglas Fir	26	Sax & S. 1933	W	W. N. America

SF2: PINOIDEAE

PINUS * $x = 12$

canariensis	Canary Is. P.	24	Bowden 1945b	HW	Canary Is.
caribaea	Cuban P.	24	Mehra & K. 1948b	ReW	S.E: U.S.A., C. Amer.
contorta	Shore P.	24	Langlet 1934	W	W: N. Amer.
densiflora	Jap. Red P.	24	Hirayoshi 1942	ReW	Japan
gerardiana	Nepal Nut P.	24	Mehra & K. 1948b	NW	Himalayas
halepensis	Aleppo P.	24	,, ,,	Re	Medit.
lambertiana	Sugar P.	24	,, ,,	SuW	W: N. Amer.
nigra (laricio)	Corsican P.	24	Sax & S. 1933	ReW	S. Europe
sylvestris	& 17 spp.	24	,, ,,	W	N. Eur., Alps
palustris	Longleaf P.	24	Mathews 1932	OReW	E: N. Amer.
patula		24	Bowden 1945b	—	Mexico
pinaster	Cluster P.	24	Saxton 1909	ReW	Medit.
pinea	Stone P.	24	Lane unp.	ReW	,,
radiata	Monterey P.	24	Mehra & K. 1948b	W	S. Calif.
roxburghii	Chir P.	24	Sethi 1928	NReW	Himalayas
wallichiana	Blue P.	24	Mehra & K. 1948b	HSuW	,,

9 CUPRESSACEAE

CALLITRIS $x = 11$

rhomboidalis		22	Gulline unp.	HReW	Australia

CHAMAECYPARIS $x = 11$

lawsoniana	L. Cypress	22	Sax & S. 1933	HW	W: N. Amer.
obtusa	Hinoki C.	22 / 22 (44)	Hirayoshi 1942 / Kanezawa 1951	HW	Japan

CUPRESSUS $x = 11$

funebris	Mourning Cyp.	22	Mehra & K. 1948b	H	C. China
lusitanica	Cedro do Buçaco	22	Camara & de J. 1946	H	Mexico, Guat.
sempervirens	Medit. C.	22	Mehra & K. 1948b	HPW	S. Eur., S.W. Asia
torulosa	Bhutan C.	22	,, ,,	HW	Himalayas

LIBOCEDRUS $x = 11$

plumosa (doniana)	Kawaka	22	Lane unp.	HW	New Zealand

THUJA $x = 11$

occidentalis	Arbor-Vitae, White Cedar	22	Sax & S. 1933	BH	E: N. Amer.
orientalis	Chinese A.-V.	22	,, ,,	H	N. & W. China

THUJA (*cont.*)

plicata	West. Red C.	22	Sax & S. 1933	StW	W: N. Amer.
(*gigantea*)					
standishii	Japanese A.-V.	22	„ „	HW	Japan

JUNIPERUS *x* = 11

communis	Juniper	22	Sax & S. 1933	BHSp	N. Temp. Arctic
(*sibirica*)					
horizontalis	Creeping J.	22	Ross & D. 1949	H	N. America
rigida	Needle J.	22	Sax & S. 1933	H	Jap., Kor., Manch.
sabina	Savin	22-24	Reese 1952a	HMO	Eur., W. Asia
virginiana	Red Cedar	22, 33	Stiff 1951	HORe	N. America
chinensis	Chinese J.	44	Sax & S. 1933	H	Ch., Japan, Mong.

10 EPHEDRACEAE

EPHEDRA *x* = 7

americana (*andina*)		14	Resende 1937	—	S. America
equisetina	Mongolian E.	14	Florin 1932	M	C.Asia—N.China
foliata		14	Mehra 1946	—	S.W. Asia
fragilis (*campylopoda*)		14	Geitler 1929a	—	Mediterranean
major (*nebrodensis*)		14	„ „	—	Medit.—Himal.
gerardiana		{ 14	Mehra 1946		Himal.,
		{ 28	„ 1934		S.W. China
altissima (*algerica*)		28	„ 1946	—	N. Africa
distachya	Sea Grape	28	Florin 1932	FM	Eur., N. Asia
intermedia		28	Mehra 1946	—	C. Asia
likiangensis		28	„ „	—	Yun., Szech.
saxatilis		28	„ „	—	China
sinica	Ma-huang	28	Resende 1937	M	„

11 GNETACEAE

GNETUM *x* = 12

africanum		*c.* 24	Pearson 1912	—	Trop. Africa
gnemon		{ 24	Coulter 1908	N	Malaya
		{ 48	EKJ unp.		

12 WELWITSCHIACEAE

WELWITSCHIA *x* = (7)

bainesii (*mirabilis*)		{ 42	Florin 1932	—	Trop. S.W. Africa
		{ 42, 84	Fernandes 1936		

DICOTYLEDONS

Group 1

MAGNOLIALES
1–7
ST

ANNONALES
8–9
ST

LAURALES
10–14
ST

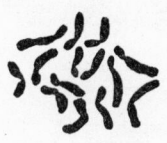

Annona squamosa

I MAGNOLIACEAE

LIRIODENDRON $x = 19$

chinense		38	Janaki Ammal 1953c	HW	China
tulipifera	Tulip T.	38	Whitaker 1933c	BHSpW	S.E: U.S.A.

MANGLIETIA $x = 19$

hookeri	38	Janaki Ammal 1953c	H	Yunnan, Burma
insignis	38	,, ,, ,,	H	E. Himal., China

MICHELIA $x = 19$

champaca	Champak	38	Janaki Ammal 1953c	HMPW	India—China
compressa		38	,, ,, ,,	HP	Japan
doltsopa		38	,, ,, ;,	H	Himalayas
figo (fuscata)	Banana Shrub	38	,, ,, ,,	H	China
lanuginosa		38	,, ,, ,,	H	Assam, Yunnan

PACHYLARNAX $x = 19$

pleiocarpa	38	Janaki Ammal 1953c	H	Assam

TALAUMA $x = 19$

hodgsoni	38	Janaki Ammal 1953c	HT	Nepal
phellocarpa	38	,, ,, ,,	H	Assam

MAGNOLIA $x = 19$

1. Evergreen

delavayi		38	Janaki Ammal 1953c	H	Yunnan
griffithii		38	,, ,, ,,	H	Assam
hamori		38	,, ,, ,,	H	Hispaniola
nitida		38	,, ,, ,,	H	Yun., Tib., Burma
pterocarpa		38	,, ,, ,,	H	E Himal., Burma
grandiflora	Bull Bay	114	,, ,, ,,	HPSp	S.E: U.S.A.
schiedeana		114	,, ,, ,,	H	Mexico

2. Deciduous

ashei		38	,, ,, ,,	H	Florida
fraseri		38	,, ,, ,,	H	Alleghenies
macrophylla		38	,, ,, ,,	H	S.E: U.S.A.
tripetala	Umbrella T.	38	,, ,, ,,	HW	E. U.S.A.
virginiana	Am. Sweet Bay	38	,, ,, ,,	H	,,
globosa		38	,, ,, ,,	H	Yunnan, Sikkim
kobus		38	,, ,, ,,	H	Japan
obovata		38	,, ,, ,,	HP	,,
officinalis		38	,, ,, ,,	HM	China
rostrata		38	,, ,, ,,	H	Yunnan
salicifolia		38	,, ,, ,,	H	Japan
sieboldi		38	,, ,, ,,	H	Jap.—Manch.
sinensis		38	,, ,, ,,	H	W. Szechuan
stellata		38	,, ,, ,,	H	Japan
tsarongensis		38	,, ,, ,,	H	Tibet
wilsoni		38	,, ,, ,,	H	W. Szechuan
acuminata	Cucumber T.	76	,, ,, ,,	HW	S.E: U.S.A.
cordata		76	,, ,, ,,	H	Georgia
liliiflora		76	,, ,, ,,	HP	Java, China
campbellii		114	,, ,, ,,	H	E. Himalayas
dawsoniana		114	,, ,, ,,	H	W. Szechuan
denudata	Yulan	114	,, ,, ,,	HPSp	China
mollicomata		114	,, ,, ,,	H	Yunnan

3

MAGNOLIA (*cont.*)

sargentiana	114	Janaki Ammal 1953c	H	Yun., Szechuan
sprengeri	114	,, ,, ,,	H	China

3. Garden Forms

watsoni (*obovata* × *sieboldi*)	38	,, ,, ,,	H	*cult*
stellata rubra (*st.* × *liliiflora*)	57	,, ,, ,,	H	,,
soulangerna (*denudata* × *liliiflora*)	95	,, ,, ,,	H	,,
,, var. *lenneana*	114	,, ,, ,,	H	,,
veitchii (*campbellii* × *denudata*)	114	,, ,, ,.	H	,,
raffili (*camp.* × *molli.*)	114	,, ,, ,,	H	,,

2 WINTERACEAE

ILLICIUM $x = 7$

anisatum	Chinese A. T.	28	Morinaga *et al.* 1929	HOSp	E. Asia
(*religiosum*)					
floridanum	Aniseed T.	28	Whitaker 1933c	HSp	S.E: U.S.A.

DRIMYS $x = ?$

lanceolata		26	Smith-White unp.	—	Tasmania
		28	Gulline unp.		
aromatica	Pepper Tree	38?	EKJ unp.	HSp	,,
winteri	Winter's Bark	*c.* 76	Whitaker 1933c	HM	S. America

3 SCHISANDRACEAE

SCHISANDRA $x = 7$

chinensis	28	EKJ unp.	H	N.E. Asia, Japan
sphenanthera	28	Whitaker 1933c	H	C. & W. China

KADSURA $x = 7$

japonica	28	Whitaker 1933c	H	Japan, Korea

6 TROCHODENDRACEAE

EUPTELEA $x = 7?$

polyandra	14?	Sugiura 1936b	H	Japan

TROCHODENDRON $x = 19$

aralioides	38	Whitaker 1933c	H	Japan, Korea

7 CERCIDIPHYLLACEAE

CERCIDIPHYLLUM $x = 19$

japonicum	38	Whitaker 1933c	W	Japan

TETRACENTRON $x = 19$

sinense	38	Whitaker 1933c	—	China

8 ANNONACEAE

ANNONA $x = 7$

cherimolia	Cherimoyer	{ 14 Kumar & R. 1941, EKJ* 16? Bowden 1948	F	Trop. America
muricata	Sour-sop	{ 14 Kumar & R. 1941, EKJ* 16? Bowden 1945a	F	„ „
reticulata	Custard Apple	{ 14 Asana & A. 1945, EKJ* 16? Bowden 1945a	F	„ „
squamosa	Sweet-sop	{ 14 Kumar & R. 1941 14 Asana & A. 1945 16? Bowden 1945a 14 (28) Islam 1953	FM	„ „
montana		16? Bowden 1945a	—	Jamaica
glabra (*palustris*)	Alligator Pear	28 „ „ , EKJ*	Fs	Trop. America

CANANGIUM (CANANGA) $x = 8$
odoratum	Ylang Ylang	16 Bowden 1945a	HP	E. Trop. Asia

ARTABOTRYS $x = 8, 9$
odoratissimus	Climbing Y.Y.	{ 16 Asana & A. 1945 18 Bowden 1948, EKJ*	HMP	Trop. Asia

ASIMINA* $x = 9$
obovata and 5 spp.		18 Bowden 1945a, 1948	—	Florida
triloba	Papaw	18, 27 „ 1948	F	S.E: U.S.A.

POLYALTHIA $x = 9$
longifolia	Asoth	18 Asana & A. 1945	ShW	India

SACCOPETALUM $x = 9$
tomentosum		18 Adatia & C. 1951	—	India

ROLLINIA $x = ?$
orthopetala?		48 Bowden 1948	—	Trop America

9 EUPOMATIACEAE

EUPOMATIA $x = 10$
bennettii		20 A. T. Hotchkiss unp.	—	E. Australia
laurina		20 „ „	W	„ „

11 LAURACEAE

CINNAMOMUM $x = 12$
camphora	Camphor Tree	24 Sugiura 1936b	MW	Jap.,Form., China
japonicum (*pedunculatum*)	Khoga T.	24 „ „	O	Japan
linearifolium	Chinese C.	24 EKJ*	MSp	China

15

CINNAMOMUM (*cont.*)
loureiri	Tonkin C.	24	Sugiura 1936b	MSp	Jap., Form.
obtusifolium	Tej C.	24	EKJ*	MSp	Himal., Burma
sieboldii (*burmanni*)		24	Täckholm & S. 1917	MSp	Java, Sum.
zeylanicum	Cinnamon	24	EKJ*	MSpW	S. Ind., Cey., Mal.

LINDERA (BENZOIN) $x = 12$
benzoin (*aestivale*) Spice Bush		24	Jensen 1941b	HMP	N. America
glauca		24	Sugiura 1936b	MPSp	E. Asia
praecox		24	EKJ unp.	H	Japan

PERSEA* $x = 12$
americana	Avocado Pear	⎰24 ⎱24	Bowden 1940b, EKJ*	FO	E: N. America, W. Indies
drymifolia	Mexican A.	24	Krishnaswamy & R. 1949	F	Mexico
palustris (*pubescens*) Red Bay		24	Bowden 1945a	F	E: N. America
borbonia & 3 spp. Swamp Bay		24	Bringhurst 1954	—	S.E: U.S.A.

UMBELLULARIA $x = 12$
californica	Calif. Bay	24	Bambacioni 1941	HSp	W: N. America

LAURUS $x = 12?$
canariensis	Canary Is. L.	36	Bambacioni 1940	H	Canary Is., Azores
nobilis	Sweet Bay	⎧42 ⎨ ⎩48	Battaglia 1947c EKJ unp.	HSp	Mediterranean

SASSAFRAS $x = 12$
albidum (*officinale*)		48	Bowden 1940b	MSp	N. America

14 MYRISTICACEAE

MYRISTICA $x = 7?$
fragrans	Nutmeg	42	Simmonds 1954	MSp	E. Ind., Ceylon

Group II

RANALES
15–18
H(S)

BERBERIDALES
19–23
HS

ARISTOLOCHIALES
24–27
S

PIPERALES
28–31
HST

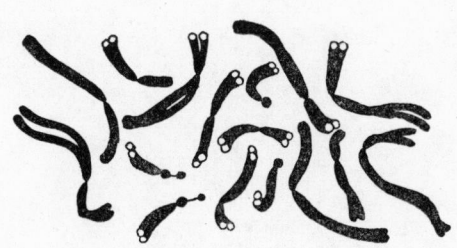

Clematis vitalba

15 RANUNCULACEAE

TRIBE I: PAEONIEAE

PAEONIA *x* = 5

anomala	10	Langlet 1927a	H	C. Asia
broteri	10	Stebbins 1938	H	Portugal
brownii	10	,, ,,	H	W: N. America
californica	10	Walters 1952	H	California
cambessedesii	10	Dark 1936	H	Balearics
clusii	10	Barber 1941a	H	Crete
delavayi	10	Dark 1936	H	China
daurica	10	Barber 1941a	H	Crimea, Cauc.
emodi	10	Dark 1936	HM	Himalayas
japonica	10	,, ,,	H	Japan
lactiflora (*albiflora*)	10	,, ,,	HMR	N.E. Asia
lutea	10	Stern 1944	H	W. China
mairei	10	La Cour 1952	—	Yunnan
mlokosewitchii	10	Barber 1941a	H	Caucasus
potanini	10	Stern 1944	H	W. China
rhodia	10	,, ,,	H	Rhodes
smouthii	10	Dark 1936	H	*cult*
suffruticosa Tree Paeony	10	Stebbins 1938	H	China, Tib., Bhut.
tenuifolia	10	,, ,,	H	Transsyl.—Cauc.
veitchii	10	Gregory 1941	H	China
mascula (*corallina*)	10, 20	Barber 1941a	HM	S. Europe
obovata	10, 20	Sinoto 1938	H	E. Asia
officinalis	{ 10 { 20	Dark 1936, Gregory 1941	HM	S. Europe
arietina	20	Langlet 1928	H	S.E. Eur., Asia M.
coriacea	20	,, 1927a	H	S. Spain, Morocco
humilis	20	Barber 1941a	H	S. Europe
mollis	20	Stern & B. 1945*	H	Siberia
peregrina	20	Dark 1936	H	S. Europe
russi	20	Barber 1941a	H	W. Med. Is.
tenuifolia hybrida	20	Dark 1936	H	*cult*
wittmanniana (*tomentosa*)	20	Stebbins 1938	H	N.W. Caucasus

TRIBE II: HELLEBOREAE

NIGELLA *x* = 6

arvensis Wild Fennel	12	Gregory 1941	MSp	Eur., S.W. Asia
ciliaris	12	Pereira 1942	—	Syria, Cyprus
damascena Love-in-a-Mist	12	Gregory 1941	HMSp	Medit.
gallica (*hispanica*)	12	Pereira 1942	H	Spain, N. Africa
garidella (*nigellastrum*)	12	Gregory 1941	—	Europe
orientalis	12	,, ,,	H	Asia Minor
sativa Black Cumin	12	,, ,,	HMSp	Medit.
viridis	12	,, ,,	—	—

KOMAROFFIA (NIGELLA)   *x* = 7

integrifolia (*N. diversifolia*)	14	Pereira 1942	M	Turkestan

ANEMOPSIS   *x* = 8

macrophylla	16	Langlet 1932	H	Japan

19

CIMICIFUGA $x = 8$

americana	American B.	16	Langlet 1932	H	E: N. America
(cordifolia)					
dahurica		16	,, ,,	H	C. Asia—Japan
foetida	Bugbane	16	Nakajima 1933	HIM	Russia—Japan
japonica (acerina)		16	Langlet 1932	H	Japan
racemosa	Black Snake Root	16	Gregory 1941	HM	E: N. America

ERANTHIS $x = 8$

cilicica		16	Langlet 1932	H	Asia M., Syria
hyemalis	Winter Aconite	16	Gregory 1941	HM	S. Europe

ACONITUM* $x = 8$

excelsum		16	S. & S. 1938	H	Russia, Siberia
lycoctonum	Wolf Bane	16	Schafer & L.C. 1934	HM	Eur., N. Asia—China
orientale	Caucasian M. and 7 spp.	16	,, ,, ,,	HM	Cauc.—Persia
septentrionale		16	Langlet 1927a	H	N. Europe
uncinatum	Climbing M.	16	Gregory 1941	H	N. America
variegatum		16	Leszczak 1950	H	E. Alps
paniculatum		{ 16	Schafer & L.C. 1934	H	S. Europe
		{ 32	Langlet 1927a		
stoerkianum		24	Schafer & L.C. 1934	HM	cult
altaicum		32	S. & S. 1938	—	Altai
anglicum		32	Schafer & L.C. 1934	M	Britain
anthora		32	,, ,, ,,	H	S. Eur. Mts., Cauc.
delavayi		32	Langlet 1927a	H	Yunnan
firmum		32	Skalinska 1950a	H	E. Europe
fischeri	and 4 spp.	32	Sakai 1933	H	Kamchatka
napellus	Monkshood	32	Gregory 1941	HM	N. Temp.
volubile		32	Schafer & L.C. 1934	H	Altai
palmatum	Bikhma	48	,, ,, ,,	M	Himalayas
wilsonii	Azure M.	64	,, ,, ,,	HM	E. China
species		96	,, ,, ,,		

ACTAEA $x = 8$

alba	White Baneberry	16	Gregory 1941	H	E: N. America
rubra	Red B.	16	Langlet 1932	H	N. America
spicata	Black B.	{ 16	,, 1927a	HM	N. Eurasia
		{ c. 32	Mattick, T. 1950		

DELPHINIUM* $x = 8$

ajacis	Rocket Larkspur & 11 spp.	16	Gregory 1941	HM	S. Europe
brachycentrum		16	Langlet 1932	—	Kamchatka
brunonianum	Musk L.	16	Lewitsky 1931b	H	Himalayas
cardinale	Scarlet L.	16 (32)	Mehlquist et al. '43	H	California
cardiopetalum		16	Lewitsky 1931b	H	Medit.
decora	& 16 spp.	16	Lewis et al. 1951	H	California
nudicaule	Orange L.	16	Lawrence 1936	HM	,,
speciosum		16	Langlet 1927a	H	Cauc., Persia
tatsiense		16	Lewitsky 1931b	H	Szechuan
zalil	& 2 spp.	16	Propach 1939	DHM	Persia

20

DELPHINIUM *(cont.)*

duhmbergii		$\begin{cases} 16 \\ 32 \end{cases}$	Propach 1939 Gregory 1941	—	S. Russia
gypsophilum		16, 32	Lewis *et al.* 1951	—	California
hanseni		16, 32	,, ,, ,,	—	,,
variegatum	Royal L.	16,32	,, ,, ,,	—	,,
staphysagria	Stavesacre Seed	$\begin{cases} 16 \\ 32 \end{cases}$	Hocquette 1922 Lewitsky 1931b	HIM	Medit.
moerheimii		24	Lawrence 1936	H	*cult*
bulleyanum	& 6 spp.	32	Gregory 1941	—	China
oxysepalum		32	Skalinska 1950a	—	E. Europe
ruysii		32	Lawrence 1936	H	*cult*
belladonna		48	Langlet 1927a	H	,,
lamartini		48	Lawrence 1936	H	,,
Garden forms		16, 24, 32, 48	Propach 1939	H	,,

TROLLIUS $x = 8$

acaulis		16	Langlet 1932	H	Himalayas
albiflorus		16	,, ,,	H	W: U.S.A.
asiaticus (& *giganteus*)		16	,, ,,	H	N. & E. Asia
europaeus	Globe Flower	16	,, ,,	H	Eur., Cauc.
japonicus		16	Lewitsky 1931b	H	Japan
ranunculinus (*caucasicus*)		16	Langlet 1932	H	Cauc., Armenia
yunnanensis		16	Gregory 1941	H	China, Yunnan
laxus (*americanus*)		32	Langlet 1932	H	N. America

CALTHA $x = 8$

cornuta	16	Leoncini 1951	—	S. Europe
laeta	$\begin{cases} 32 \\ 56\text{-}64 \end{cases}$	,, ,, ,, 1952	H	S.E. Eur.—Himal.
palustris Marsh Marigold	32, 48, 56	S. & S. '38, '41	HM	North Regions
	28	L. & L. 1948		
32, 48, 53-60 + 0-6B		Reese 1954		
	56-64	Leoncini 1952		
leptocephala	48	Langlet 1932	HM	W: N. America
radicans	48 + 0-2B	L. & L. 1948	H	Scotland
polypetala	64	Langlet 1932	M	Asia M., Persia

HELLEBORUS* $x = 8$

abschasicus		32	Gregory 1941	H	Caucasus
foetidus	& 7 spp.	32	Langlet 1927a, 1932	HM	W. & S. Europe
lividus		32	EKJ unp.	H	Balearics

TRIBE III: THALICTREAE

ANEMONELLA $x = 7$

thalictroides	Rue Anemone	$\begin{cases} 14 \\ 42 \end{cases}$	Gregory 1941 Kuhn 1928a	H	N. America

ISOPYRUM $x = 7$

fumarioides	14	Gregory 1941	—	Eur., Asia M.

KUMLIENIA $x = 7$

hystricula	14	Jakob 1949	—	N.W: N. Amer.

THALICTRUM* $x = 7$

alpinum	14	L. & L. 1944b	H	N. Temp., Arctic

21

THALICTRUM (cont.)

foetidum	14	Langlet 1927a	H	C. Europe
foliosum	14	,, ,,	—	Himalayas
montanum	14	Kuhn 1928a	—	Europe
petaloideum	14	,, ,,	H	N. Asia
yezoense	14	M. & S. 1935	—	Japan
aquilegiifolium	14, 28	Langlet 1927a	H	Eur., N. Asia
przewalski	{ 14	Kuhn 1928a	—	China
	{ 70	Langlet 1927a		
dipterocarpum	28	Kuhn 1928a	H	W. China
lucidum (angustifolium)	28	,, ,,	H	Europe
speciosissimum (glaucum)	28	,, ,,	H	Spain, Port., N.W. Africa
tuberosum & 5 spp.	28	,, ,,	H	S. W. Europe
fendleri	28, 56, c. 70	Clausen et al. 1940	H	W: N. America
flavum Yellow Meadow Rue	{ 28	Gregory 1941	H	Europe
	{ 84	Kuhn 1928a		
exaltatum (flavum)	28, 35	,, ,,	—	,,
dioicum	{ 28	Jensen 1944	H	E: N. America
	{ 42	Kuhn 1928a		
calabricum & 10 spp.	42	,, ,,	H	C. Italy
pauciflorum	42	Langlet 1927a	—	Himalayas
rubellum	42	,, ,,	—	Eur., N. Asia
dasycarpum (purpurascens)	{ 28	Gregory 1941	H	U.S.A.
	{ 42	Langlet 1927a		
minus			H	Eur., N. Afr., Asia
as majus	28	Gregory 1941		
flexuosum	42	Kuhn 1928a		
rariflorum	56, 112	Langlet 1927a		
kemense	70	,, ,,		
simplex	{ 28	Kuhn 1928a	—	Eur., N. Asia
	{ 56	Langlet 1927a		
	{ 70	Kuhn 1928a		
	{ 112	Langlet 1927a		
coriaceum	{ 70	Gregory 1941	—	N. America
	{ 140	Jensen 1944		
polygamum (corynellum)	{ 84	Jensen 1944	H	E: N. America
	{ 154	Gregory 1941		
revolutum	c. 133	,, ,,	—	N. America

AQUILEGIA*   x = 7

akitensis	14	Sakai 1935	H	Japan
alpina & 9 spp.	14	Gregory 1941	HM	Europe
caerulea	14	Winge 1925	H	W: N. America
flabellata	14	Skalinska 1931	H	Japan
formosa (truncata)	14	,, ,,	H	W: N. America
haylodgensis	14	Langlet 1927a	H	cult
nigricans (vulgaris)	14	Winge 1925	H	Eur., Persia
vulgaris Columbine	14, 28	Pereira 1948	HM	Eur., N. Afr., Temp. Asia
v. olympica	16?	S. & S. 1940	H	S.W. Asia
hirsutissima	28	Gregory 1941	H	cult

22

TRIBE IV: ANEMONEAE

ANEMONE (PULSATILLA)* x = 7, 8

x = 7

Species	Notes	No.	Author	Symbol	Region
acutiloba		14	Langlet 1932	H	E: N. America
debilis		14	Sakai 1935	—	Siberia
demissa	Drooping A.	14	Langlet 1936	H	Himalayas
flaccida		14	M. & S. 1935	H	Japan, China
narcissiflora		14	Sakai 1934	H	N. Temp.
hepatica		14	Gregory 1941	HM	Eur., Asia, E: N.
		28	Langlet 1927a		America

x = 8

Species	Notes	No.	Author	Symbol	Region
albana	& 3 spp.	16	Langlet 1932	H	Cauc., Persia
alpina	& 4 spp.	16	Rosenthal 1936	H	S. Eur., Cauc.
altaica	& 3 spp.	16	Guinochet 1935	H	Siberia
apennina		16	Bøcher 1945	H	S. Europe
caroliniana	& 5 spp.	16	Moffett 1932b	H	E: N. America
chrysantha		16	S. & S. 1940	—	Caucasus
cernua		16	M. & S. 1935	H	Japan
coronaria	Poppy A.	16	Guinochet 1935	H	Medit.—C. Asia
japonica	Japanese A. & 4 spp.	16	Gregory 1941	H	China, Japan
riparia		16	Dahl 1937	—	N. America
sieboldii		16	Miduno 1943	—	China
yunnanensis		16	„ „	—	„
blanda		16	Langlet 1927a	H	S.W. Asia
v. *rosea*		32	Moffett 1932b		
fulgens	Scarlet A.	16	„ „	H	Medit.
		32	Langlet 1932		
montana		16	Rosenthal 1936	H	S. Eur.—Cauc., Manch.
		24	Guinochet 1935		
		32, 48	Moffett 1932b		
sylvestris	Snowdrop A.	16	Gajewski 1946	H	Eur.—Turkestan
		32	Gregory 1941		
transsylvanica (*angulosa*)		28?	Gregory 1941	H	Roumania
		16	„ „		
		32	Rosenthal 1936		
decapetala		24	Moffett 1932b	H	N. & S. Amer.
baldensis		24	„ „	H	Eur., N. Amer.
		32	Gajewski 1947		
nemorosa Wood A.		24	Guinochet 1935	H	Europe
		30, 37, 45, 46	Bernström 1946		
		32	Moffett 1932b		
janczewskii (*multifida* × *sylvestris*)		24, 48 (42-47)	Gajewski 1946	H	*cult*
armena		32	Langlet 1932	H	Asia Minor
bogenhardiana		32	Zimmerman 1932	—	Europe
halleri		32	Rosenthal 1936	H	C. Europe
magellanica		32	Moffett 1932b	H	S. Chile
multifida		32	„ „	H	N. America
palmata		32	Langlet 1932	H	S.W. Europe
pulsatilla	Pasque Flower	32	Gregory 1941	H	Europe
ranunculoides		32	Bernström 1946	H	Eur., W. Asia
		(30-33)			

ANEMONE (*cont.*)

rubra (pulsatilla)	32	Rosenthal 1936	H	Eur., Siberia
rupicola	32	Moffett 1932b	H	Himalayas
slavica	32	Miduno 1943	—	Europe
trifolia	c. 30, 32	Langlet 1932	H	,,

RANUNCULUS* x = 7, 8
  x = 7

aduncus (villarsii) & 3 spp.	14	Langlet 1936	—	S. Europe
cassius	14	Gregory 1941	—	Asia M., Syria
parviflorus	14	Neves 1944	—	W. Eur., Medit.
	28	Langlet 1927a		
constantinopolitanus	14	,, 1936	—	Asia Minor
	42	Larter 1932		
californicus	28	Coonen 1939	—	California
hornemanni & 1 sp.	28	Langlet 1936	—	N. Amer.
rupestris & 3 spp.	28	Larter 1932	—	Spain
tuberosus (acris)	28	Langlet 1936	—	N. Temp.
acris Meadow	14+0-10B	Langlet 1927a	H	N. Temp., S. Afr.
Buttercup	28, 56	L. & L. 1948		

  x = 7 and 8

bulbosus	14	M. & S. 1935	H	Eur., W. Asia
	16	Neves 1944		
chius	14	Larter 1932	H	S. Eur., Asia M.
	16	Gregory 1941		
lanuginosus	14	Langlet 1927a	—	Eur., Caucasus
	28, 32	Mattick, T. 1950		
nelsoni	14	Larter 1932	—	W: N. America
	16	Gregory 1941		
platanifolius (aconitifolius)	14	Langlet 1927	H	Europe
	16	Skalinska 1950a		
polyanthemos	14	Felfoldy 1947a	—	Eur., Caucasus
	16	Reese 1953		

  x = 8

abchasicus & 1 sp.	16	S. & S. 1940, 1941	—	Caucasus
alpestris & 10 spp.	16	Langlet 1927, '32, '36	H	Eur. Alps
broteri & 3 spp.	16	Larter 1932	H	Spain, Portugal
cassubicifolius	16	Haflinger 1943	—	Europe
circinatus	16	Scheerer 1939	—	Eur., N. Amer.
cymbalaria	16	Bøcher & L. 1950	H	N. Temp.
hakkodensis & 2 spp.	16	M. & S. 1935	—	Japan
hederaceus & 2 spp.	16	Bøcher 1938b	—	W. & S. Europe
lappaceus	16	Curtis unp.	—	Australia
nemorosus	16	Gregory 1941	—	S. Europe
ophioglossifolius & 5 spp.	16	Neves 1944	—	W. Eur., Medit.
rhomboideus	16	Coonen 1939	—	N. America
asiaticus Turban B.	16	Nakajima 1936	H	S.W. Asia
	32	Larter 1932		
auricomus (Apo.) Goldilocks	16, 32	Bøcher 1938b	—	Eur., N. Asia
	32	Haflinger 1943		
breynianus (nemorosus)	16, 32	Mattick, T. 1950	H	W. Alps
confervoides	16	L. & L. 1948	—	Europe
	32	Bøcher & L. 1950		
ficaria Lesser Celandine	16, 24	Neves 1942	HM	Eur., Cauc.
(2x, 3x, 4x, 5x, 6x)	16 + 2B	Larter 1932		
	32	Bøcher 1938b		
	c. 40	Maude 1939		

24

RANUNCULUS (*cont.*)

v. *calthaefolius*		48	Rutland 1941		
glacialis		$\begin{cases}16 \\ 32\end{cases}$	Bøcher 1938b L. & L. 1948	H	Alps & Arctic
montanus		16, 24, 32	Mattick, T. 1950	H	Europe
repens	Creeping B.	$\begin{cases}16, 32 \\ 32\end{cases}$	M. & S. 1935 Neves 1944	H	N. Temp.
sardous		$\begin{cases}16 \\ 18? \\ 48\end{cases}$	Langlet 1932 Pólya 1948 Neves 1944	—	Eur., Asia M., N. Africa
alnetorum	& 11 spp.	32	Haflinger 1943	—	Europe
aquatilis	Water Crowfoot	32	Bøcher 1932	H	Temp.
flammula	Lesser Spearwort & 3 spp.	32	Neves 1944	—	Eur., Azores
hyperboreus		32	Bøcher & L. 1950	—	N. & Arctic
lenormandii	& 2 spp.	32	Larter 1932	—	W. Europe
monophyllus		32	S. & S. 1938	—	Altai
monspessulanus	& 2 spp.	32	Coonen 1939	—	Europe
reptans	& 2 spp.	32	Bøcher 1938b	—	N. & C. Europe
sceleratus	Blister B.	32	Gregory 1941	M	„ „
trachycarpus	& 1 sp.	32	Langlet 1927a	—	S.W. Asia „
septentrionalis	Swamp B.	$\begin{cases}32 \\ 64\end{cases}$	Coonen 1939 Gregory 1941	—	Arctic
falcatus		40	Langlet 1932	—	Eur., Himalayas
pulchellus		40	S. & S. 1938	—	Himal.—Sib.
stricticaulis		40	Haflinger 1943	—	Europe
nivalis		40, 48, 56	L. & L. 1948	HM	N. & Arctic
trilobus		$\begin{cases}42 \\ 48\end{cases}$	Larter 1932 Gregory 1941	—	Medit.
affinis		48	Bøcher & L. 1950	—	Arctic
allemannii		48	Haflinger 1943	—	Europe
apiifolius		48	Langlet 1932	—	Argentine
dichotomiflorus		48	Neves 1944	—	Spain
muricatus		48	„ „	—	Eur., S.W. Asia
sulphureus		$\begin{cases}c. 56 \\ 96\end{cases}$	Bøcher 1938b L. & L. 1948	M	Arctic
lingua	Great Spearwort	128	Bøcher 1938b	H	Eur., Sib.

ADONIS $x = 8$

vernalis	False Hellebore	16	Langlet 1927a	HM	Europe
dahurica (3*x*)		24	„ „	—	N. Asia
autumnalis	Pheasant-eye	32	Gregory 1941	H	S. Eur., S.W. Asia
amurensis (5*x*)		40	Sugiura 1931	HM	Manch., Japan

CALLIANTHEMUM $x = 8$

coriandraefolium		16	Langlet 1932	H	S. Europe
rutifolium (*anemonoides*)		32	„ „	H	Austria
miyabeanum		32	Sakai 1935	—	Japan

CLEMATIS* $x = 8$

addisonii	& 11 spp.	16	Gregory 1941	H	S.E. U.S.A.
campaniflora	& 8 spp.	16	Meurman & T. 1939	H	Portugal
hilarii		16	Covas & S. 1947	H	Brazil
indivisa		16	Hair 1942	H	New Zealand
integrifolia		16	Meurman & T. 1939	H	S. Europe

25

CLEMATIS (*cont.*)

jackmannii		16	Meurman & T. 1939	H		*cult*	
koreana		16	„ „	H		Korea	
lasiantha	Pipestem C.	16	„ „	H		W: N. Amer.	
ligusticifolia		16	„ „	H		„	
montana		16	„ „	H		Himalayas	
stans	& 2 spp.	16	Langlet 1927a	H		Japan	
vitalba	Traveller's Joy	16	Maude 1940	H		Eur.,N.Afr.,Cauc.	
paniculata		{ 16, 64	Greogry 1941	H		Japan	
		48	Meurman & T. 1939				
mandschurica		32	„ „	H		„	

MYOSURUS $x = 7$

minimus	Mousetail	*c.* 28	Ehrenberg 1945	H	Eur., N. Afr., S.W. Asia

KNOWLTONIA $x = 8$

vesicatoria		48	Langlet 1932	H	S. Africa

TRAUTVETTERIA $x = 8$

carolinensis	False Bugbane	16	Langlet 1932	H	N. America
japonica		16	M. & S. 1935	H	Japan

TRIBE V: COPTIDAE

COPTIS $x = 9$

japonica		18	Langlet 1932	H	Japan
trifolia		18	„ „	H	N.E. Asia, Alaska

ZANTHORRHIZA $x = 9$

apiifolia	Shrub Yellow-root	36	Langlet 1932	H	N. America

TRIBE VI: HYDRASTIDAE

GLAUCIDIUM $x = 10$

palmatum		20	M. & S. 1935	H	Japan

HYDRASTIS $x = 13$

canadensis	Golden Seal	26	Langlet 1928	HM	N. America

17 CERATOPHYLLACEAE

CERATOPHYLLUM $x = ?$

demersum	Hornwort	*c.* 24	Langlet & S. 1927	—	Cosmop.
submersum		{ 40	Wulff 1938	—	Eur., Trop. Asia
		72	Jedrychowska & S. '34		

18 NYMPHAEACEAE

NELUMBO (NELUMBIUM) $x = 8$

lutea	Amer. Lotus	16	Langlet & S. 1927	HR	N. Am., W. Indies
nucifera	Lotus	16	„ „	HVM	N. Afr., Tr. Asia
(*speciosum*)					

26

VICTORIA $x = 10, 12$
regia	Giant Water Lily	20	Langlet & S. 1927	HN	Amazon
cruziana	Santa Cruz W.L.	24	Heitz 1932	H	Bolivia, Paraguay

CABOMBA $x = 12$
caroliniana	Fish Grass	24	Nitzschke 1914	H	S.E: U.S.A.

NYMPHAEA $x = 14$
capensis	Cape Water Lily	28	Langlet & S. 1927	HR	S. & E. Afr., Mad.
stellata	Macongee Congee	28	,.	,,	HRV	S. & E. Asia
flava (mexicana)		56	,,	,,	HR	S: U.S.A.
lotus	Egyptian W.L.	56	,,	,,	HRV	O.W. Tropics
rubra	Red W.L.	56	,,	,,	HR	India
odorata	American W.L.	84	,,	,,	HMR	N. America
tuberosa	Magnolia W.L.	84	,,	,,	HR	N.E: U.S.A.
alba	Flatterdock {	84	,,	,,		
		c. 105	Ehrenberg 1945	BDH	Europe
		112	Langlet 1936		
as candida		c. 160	L. & L. 1942		
tetragona	Pygmy W.L.	112	Langlet & S. 1927	HR	Amer., Asia, Austr.
gigantea	Australian W.L.	224	Langlet 1936	HRV	Australia

NUPHAR $x = 17$
advena	Spatterdock	34	Langlet & S. 1927	H	N. America
japonica		34	,, ,,	H	Japan
lutea	Yellow W.L.	34	Y. Heslop-Harrison 1953b	HR(B)	N. Temp.
microphylla		34	Langlet & S. 1927	H	E: U.S.A.
pumila (minima)		34	Y. Heslop-Harrison 1953b	H	Eur., N. Asia
intermedia (? lutea × pumila)		34	,, ,,	—	N. & C. Europe

EURYALE $x = 29 (12 + 17)$?
ferox	Gorgon W.L.	58	Langlet & S. 1927	HMNV	India, China

19 BERBERIDACEAE

ACHLYS $x = 6$
japonica		12	M. & S. 1935	H	Japan

DIPHYLLEIA $x = 6$
cymosa		12	Langlet 1928	H	S.E: U.S.A.
grayi	Umbrella Leaf	12	M. & S. 1935	H	Japan

ACERANTHUS (EPIMEDIUM) $x = 6$
diphyllus	Maplewort	12	Suzuka 1950a	H	Japan

EPIMEDIUM $x = 6$
alpinum		12	Maude 1939	H	S. &. C. Europe
grandiflorum (macranthum)		12	Langlet 1928	H	Japan, cult
pinnatum		12	,, ,,	H	Persia
youngianum (musschianum)		12	,, ,,	H	cult

JEFFERSONIA x = 6

diphylla (binata)		12	Langlet 1928	H	E: N. America
dubia		12	,, ,,	H	E. Asia

PODOPHYLLUM x = 6

emodi	Indian P.	12	Langlet 1928	HM	Himalayas
leichtlinii?		12	,, ,,		—
peltatum	May Apple	12	,, ,,	HM	N. America
versipelle		12	Darlington 1936a	M	China

VANCOUVERIA (EPIMEDIUM) x = 6

hexandra	12	Langlet 1928	H	W. N. America

BONGARDIA x = 6

chrysogonum	14	Tören 1950	H	Syria, Persia

RANZANIA x = 7

japonica	14	Miyaji 1930	—	Japan

CAULOPHYLLUM x = 8

robustum		16	M. & S. 1935	H	Manchuria
thalictroides	Blue Cohosh	16	Langlet 1928	H	N. America

NANDINA x = 10

domestica	20	Sugiura 1936b	H	China, Japan

MAHONIA x = 14

aquifolium	Mahonia	28	Dermen 1931b	BFH	W: N. America
repens		28	,, ,,	FH	,,

BERBERIS* x = 14

canadensis	American B. & 6 spp.	28	Dermen 1931b	F	N. America
candidula		28	Vaarama 1947b	H	W. Hupeh
cretica	Parveritshia	28	Giffin 1936	D	Crete
darwinii	& 14 spp.	28	,, ,,	FH	Chile, Patag.
gagnepainii		28	Vaarama 1947b	H	W. Hupeh
julianae		28	,, ,,	H	,,
sargentiana		28	,, ,,	H	,,
stenophylla		28	,, ,,	H	cult
verruculosa		28	,, ,,	H	W. Szechuan
vulgaris	Common B.	28	Langlet 1928	DFHM	Eur., Temp. Asia
actinacantha		56	Vaarama 1947b	H	Chile
buxifolia	Magellan B.	56	,, ,,	FH	Patagonia
v. nana		?			
integerrima		56	Dermen 1931b	H	Turkestan
turcomanica		56	Tischler 1928	H	S. Asia Minor

MAHONIA × BERBERIS

M. aquifolium × B. sargentiana	28	Levan 1944b	H	cult

21 LARDIZABALACEAE

LARDIZABALA x = (7) 14

biternata	28	Langlet 1928	H	Chile

28

AKEBIA $x = (8)$ 16
quinata	Fiveleaf A.	32	Velser 1913	H	China
lobata (trifoliata)		32	Kuwada, T. 1927a	H	Japan

DECAISNEA $x = 15$
fargesi	30	Simonet & M. 1932	H	China

23 MENISPERMACEAE

TINOSPORA $x = 12, 13$?

cordifolia	$\left\{\begin{array}{l}24 \\ 26\end{array}\right.$	Joshi 1934 Abraham 1942	M	India

COCCULUS $x = 13, 19$?
laurifolius		26	Bowden 1945b	H	Himal., E. Asia
pendulus (leaeba)		26	Hagerup 1932	—	E. Tr. Asia, Trop. Africa
villosus		38	Joshi 1934	M	India, Tr. Africa
trilobus		$\left\{\begin{array}{l}50 \\ 52\end{array}\right.$	Nakajima 1937 Bowden 1945b	H	Japan, China, Philippines
carolinus	Car. Moonseed	78	,, ,,	H	E: U.S.A.

MENISPERMUM $x = 13$
canadense	52	Lindsay 1930	H	E: N. America
dahuricum	52-54	Langlet 1928	H	N. China

24 ARISTOLOCHIACEAE

ARISTOLOCHIA $x = 6, 7$
bracteata		12	Venugopalan 1949	—	India
indica		12	,, ,,	M	,,
elegans	Calico Flower	14	,, ,,	H	Brazil
clematitis	Birthwort	14	Samuelsson 1914	HM	Eur., Cauc., Asia M.
fimbriata		14	Täckholm & S. 1918	HM	Brazil
macrophylla (sipho, durior)	Dutchman's Pipe	28	,, ,,	H	E: N. America

ASARUM $x = $?
dilatatum as dimidiatum	Snakeroot	24	Tanaka 1935	Sp	Japan
europaeum	Asarabacca	$\left\{\begin{array}{l}c.\ 24 \\ 40\end{array}\right.$	Täckholm & S. 1928 Ehrenberg 1945	M	Eur., W. Asia

HETEROTROPA (ASARUM)* $x = 12$
costata	& 21 spp.	24	Tanaka 1935	H	Japan
serpens		36	,, ,,	H	cult
megacalyx		48	,, ,,	H	Japan

25 CYTINACEAE (RAFFLESIACEAE)

MITRASTEMON $x = 20$
kawa-sasakii	40	Watanabe 1935	Par	Japan
yamamotoi	40	,, 1934	Par	,,

4   29

28 PIPERACEAE

PEPEROMIA $x = 8, 11, 12$

sintenisii		16	Brown 1908	—	W. Indies
sandersii (arifolia)		24	Sugiura 1936a	H	Brazil
metallica		24	Abele 1923	—	Peru
pellucida		c. 24	Johnson 1914	HM	E. Indies
resediflora		24	Häuser 1916	—	Peru
verschaffeltii		24	Abele 1923	—	Brazil
maculosa		44	Martinoli 1948	H	Trop. America

PIPER $x = 12, 14, 16$

chaba		24	EKJ*	DM	India, Malaya
longum	Long Pepper	24	Tjio 1948	SpM	,, ,,
subpeltatum (umbellatum)		24	Johansen 1931b	Sp	S.E. Asia
geniculatum		28	Maugini 1950	—	W. Indies
unguiculatum		28	,, ,,	—	Peru
medium		28	Maugini 1953	—	Mexico
betle	Betel	32	Johnson 1910, EKJ*	Sp	India
nigrum	Pepper	c. 128	EKJ*	Sp	,,

29 SAURURACEAE

SAURURUS $x = 11$

cernuus	Lizard's Tail	22	Baldwin & S. 1949a	H	E: N. America
chinensis (loureiri)		22	Suzuka 1950a	H	China, Japan

HOUTTUYNIA $x = ?$ (Apomixis)

cordata		c. 96	Okabe 1934	H	Himalaya—Japan

30 CHLORANTHACEAE

CHLORANTHUS $x = 15$

glaber	Chloranth	30	M. & S. 1935	BHM	Ind., Mal., China
serratus		30	,, ,,	HM	Japan
japonicus		30	,, ,,	M	China, Jap.
spicatus		30	Sugiura 1936a	M	Japan

Group III

RHOEADALES
32, 33
H

LOASALES
34, 35
H

CAPPARIDALES
36–38
HST

CRUCIALES
39
H

VIOLALES
40, 41

POLYGALALES
42–44

HS

HST

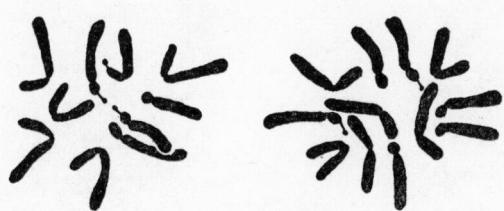

Chelidonium majus

32 PAPAVERACEAE

CHELIDONIUM $x = 5, 6$
majus   Greater Celandine

	races:	Japan	10	Nagao & M. 1943	HM	Eur., Asia M.
		U.S.A.	12	Bowden 1940a		
		Hungary	12	Felfoldy 1947a		
		England	12	Nagao & M. 1943		

DICRANOSTIGMA (CHELIDONIUM) $x = 6, 8$

franchetiana	{ 12?	Sugiura 1940	M	China
	{ 16	Smith, T. 1937		

GLAUCIUM $x = 6$

corniculatum Horned P.	12	Sugiura 1936b	H	Eur., Med.
flavum (seuperi)	12	,, ,,	H	,, ,,

HYLOMECON (STYLOPHORUM) $x = 6$

japonicum	12	Sugiura 1937b	H	Japan

PLATYSTEMON $x = 6$

californicum	12	Sugiura 1937b	H	W: N. Amer.

ESCHSCHOLTZIA $x = 6, 7$

caespitosa		12	Smith, T. 1937	H	California
californica	Calif. Poppy	12	Lawrence 1930	H	W: N. Amer.
parishii		12	Lewis & S. 1951	—	California
pulchella		12	Sugiura 1940	H	,,
minutiflora		36	Lewis & S. 1951	—	,,
glyptosperma		14	,, ,,	—	,,

ROEMERIA $x = 6, 7, 9, 11$

violacea	12	Sugiura 1937b	H	Eur., N. Afr.
rhodifolia	14	,, ,,	—	Persia
refracta	{ 14	,, 1940	H	Asia Minor
	{ 18	,, 1937b		
speciosa	18	,, ,,	H	,,
hybrida	22	,, 1940	H	S. Europe

HYPECOUM $x = 6, 8?$

procumbens	{ 12	Smith, T. 1937	H	Medit., Arabia
	{ 16?	Sugiura 1937b		

PAPAVER* $x = 6, 7, 11$
  $x = 6 (7)$

apulum		12	Sugiura 1936a	H	Italy
caucasicum		12	,, 1937b	H	Caucasus
pavoninum	Peacock P.	12	,, 1936a	H	Afgh., Turkest.
atlanticum (rupifragum)	12, 14	,, 1940	H	Morocco
argemone	{ 12	Beale, M. 1939	H	Eur., N. Afr.
	{ 42	Sugiura 1940		

  $x = 7$

alpinum (burseri)	Alpine P.	14	Fabergé 1944	H	Alps, Arctic
bracteatum	Gr. Scarlet P.	14	Yasui 1936a	H	Med., Pers.
commutatum		14	Philp 1933b	—	Eur., Med.
glaucum	Tulip P. & 12 spp.	14	Sugiura 1931, 1937b, 1940, 1944	H	Syria

PAPAVER (cont.)

lateritium		14	Yasui 1941	H	Armenia
rhoeas	Field Poppy	14	Lawrence 1930	HMSp	Eur., Cauc.
rupifragum		14	Snoad 1952	H	Spain
nudicaule	Iceland P.	{ 14 28	Fabergé 1944 Horn 1938	HMSp	Alps, Arctic
radicatum	42, 56, {	14 70 70	Sugiura 1940 Fabergé 1944 Horn 1938, L & L '48	H	Arctic, Scand.
macounii		28	,, ,,	—	N. Amer.
pinnatifidum		28	Sugiura 1940	H	Italy, Sard.
triniaefolium		28	,, ,,	H	Asia Minor
dubium		{ 28 42	Ljungdahl 1922 L. & L. 1944b	H	Europe
orientale	Oriental Poppy	{ 28 42	Snoad 1952 R. Yamazaki 1936	HMOSp	Persia, Asia M.
pygmaeum		42	Fabergé 1944	—	N. America
laestadianum		56	Horn 1938	—	Arctic, Scand.
lapponicum		56	,, ,,	—	,, ,,
dahlianum		70	,, ,,	—	,, ,,
relictum		70	,, ,,	—	Alps, Arctic

$x = 11$

somniferum	Opium P.	22 (44)	Furusato 1940	HMO	Balk., Pers.
setigerum		{ 22 44	Sugiura 1940 Kuzmina 1935	HMO	,, ,,

ARGEMONE $x = 7$

barclayana		28	Sugiura 1940	—	Mexico
grandiflora	Prickly Poppy	56	,, ,,	H	S.W. Mexico
mexicana	Mexican P.	28	,, 1936b	HMO	Mexico

DENDROMECON $x = 7$

rhamnoides		56	Lenz 1950	—	California

HUNNEMANNIA $x = 7$

fumariaefolia	Tulip P.	56	Sugiura 1936b	H	Mexico

MECONOPSIS $x = 7, 11$

cambrica	Welsh Poppy	{ 22 28?	Maude 1940 Sugiura 1940	H	W. Europe
nepalensis	Satin P.	28	,, ,,	H	Himalayas
robusta		28	,, 1944	H	,,

PTERIDOPHYLLUM $x = 9$

racemosum		18	Sugiura 1936b	H	Japan

BOCCONIA (MACLEAYA) $x = 10$

frutescens		20	Sugiura 1937b	H	Mex., Peru
microcarpa		20	,, ,,	H	China

MACLEAYA $x = 10 (9?)$

cordata	Plume Poppy	{ 18? 20 20	Negodi 1937 Sugiura 1937b Bowden 1945b	H	China, Japan

ROMNEYA $x = 19$
coulteri Matilija P. 38 Bilquez, D. 1951 H California

33 FUMARIACEAE

CORYDALIS $x = 6, 8$ $x_2 = 14$

cheilanthifolia		12	Negodi 1940	H	China
ophiocarpa		12	„ „	H	Himalayas
sibirica		12	„ „	H	Siberia, Himal.
sempervirens	Roman Wormwood	⎰12? 16 16	„ „ Bowden 1945a Ownbey 1951a	—	„ N. America
aurea		16	„ „	H	„
cava		16	Lawrence 1930	—	Europe
fabacea		16	Hagerup, L. & L. '48	—	„
intermedia		16	Ryberg 1950	—	„
micrantha		16	Ownbey 1951a	H	E: N. Amer.
pumila		16	Ryberg 1950	—	Europe
laxa		16, 24	„ „	—	„
solida (bulbosa)	Fume Wort	⎰16, 32 24	„ „ Maude 1940	R	„ „
claviculata		32	Reese 1952a	—	„
vesicaria (Cisticapnos)		28	Negodi 1940	H	S. Africa
lutea	Yellow Fumitory	⎰28 56?	„ „ Kellet, T. 1937	H	Europe

FUMARIA $x = 7, 8?$

rostellata	14	Negodi 1951	—	Medit.
micrantha	28	„ 1936a	H	W. Eur., Med.— Pers.
muralis	28	„ 1951	—	N. & W. Europe
parviflora	28	„ 1936a	H	Temp.
spicata	28	„ 1951	—	W. Medit.
agraria	56	„ 1936a	H	Medit.
capreolata	56	„ „	H	Med., C. & W. Eur.
flabellata	56	„ 1951	—	S. Italy, Algeria
major	56	„ „	—	W. Europe
officinalis	Fumitory ⎰14 28 32	Sugiura 1937b Negodi 1951 Vaarama 1949	HM	Europe, Persia

DICENTRA $x = 8$

eximia		16	Bowden 1945a	H	E: N. Amer.
pusilla		16	Sakai 1934	H	Japan
spectabilis	Bleeding Heart	16	Negodi 1940	H	E. Asia
formosa		24	Kellet, T. 1937	H	W: N. Amer.

ADLUMIA $x = (8)\ 16$
cirrhosa Allegheny Vine 32 Negodi 1940 H N. America

35 LOASACEAE

CAIOPHORA (LOASA) $x = 8$

lateritia as L. aurantiaca	Ch. Nettle	16 24?	Hamel 1938 Sugiura 1936a	H	Chile

35

MENTZELIA (BARTONIA) $x = 9, 11, 13$

humilis		18	Hamel 1938	—	N. America
albescens		22	Covas & S. 1946	H	Mex.—Argentine
decapetala		22	Hamel 1938	H	S. U.S.A.
lindleyi		$\begin{cases} 26 \\ 36 \end{cases}$	,, ,, Sugiura 1936a	H	California

BLUMENBACHIA (LOASA) $x = 12$

hieronymi	Sting Lily	24	Hamel 1938	H	Argentine
insignis		24	,, ,,	H	S. America

LOASA $x = 14, 15?$

triphylla	28	Hamel 1938	H	Peru
vulcanica	28	Sugiura 1937b	H	Ecuador
ferruginea	$\begin{cases} 28 \\ 30 \end{cases}$	Hamel 1938 Sugiura 1940	—	Peru
urens (*hispida*)	30	,, 1936a	—	,,
erinus	40	,, 1940	—	S. America

GRONOVIA $x = ?$

scandens	67	Hamel 1938	—	S. America

36 CAPPARIDACEAE

ATAMISQUEA $x = 8$

emarginata	16	Covas & S. 1946	—	Chile, Arg.

CAPPARIS $x = 9, 10, x_2 = 19$

cynophallophora		18	Kuhn 1928b	—	S. America
saligna		30	,, ,,	—	,,
rothii		40	Hagerup 1932	V	Trop. Afr.
sepiaria	Indian Capers	40	Raghavan 1938	V	India
zeylanica		40	Raghavan & V '41a	V	,,
spinosa	Caper Bush	38	Taylor 1925c	HV	Med.
acutifolia		*c.* 84	Kuhn 1928b	—	China

CLEOME $x = 9, 10, 11$, etc.

violacea		18	Sugiura 1944	—	N. America
viscosa		20	Janaki Ammal 1933	M	O.W. Tropics
spinosa	Spider Fl.	$\begin{cases} 20 \\ 24 \end{cases}$	Ufer 1937 Sugiura 1936a, b	H	S. America
as *gigantea*		$\begin{cases} 20 \\ 70, 140 \end{cases}$	Lewitsky 1931a Ufer 1927		,,
graveolens		22	Sugiura 1936a, b	—	N. America
monophylla		22	,, ,,	—	India, Trop. Afr.
candelabrum		32	,, 1936	H	—
lutea		32	Rollins 1939b	H	N. America
serrulata		32	,, ,,	H	,,
paradoxa		32	T. 1922	—	Abyssinia
chelidonii		34	Raghavan & V. 1941a	—	India, Java

MAERUA $x = 10$

arenaria	Earth-Sugar Plant	20	Raghavan & V. 1941a	M	India

POLANISIA (CLEOME) $x=10$				
trachysperma	20	Raghavan 1938	H	N. America

CRATAEVA $x=13$				
adansoni	26	Raghavan & V. 1939a	W	Trop. Afr.
religiosa Sacred Barna	26	,,　　,,	HMSp	Tropics

GYNANDROPSIS $x=?$				
pentaphylla Cat's Whiskers $\begin{cases} 30 \\ 32 \\ 34 \end{cases}$		Sugiura 1937b / V. S. Rao 1936b / Raghavan 1938	HOV	Trop. Afr., Asia

DACTYLAENA $x=16$				
micrantha	32	Sugiura 1936a, b	—	Brazil

ISOMERIS $x=17?$				
arborea	34?	Billings 1937	H	California

37 MORINGACEAE

MORINGA $x=7$				
pterygosperma (*oleifera*)				
Drumstick Tree	28	Patel & N. 1937	VO	N.W. India

39 CRUCIFERAE

Order of the Tribes with their Basic Numbers

I Lepidieae: 4–12	X Hesperideae: 7, 8, 10, 12, 13
II Stenopetaleae: 5	XI Brassiceae: 7–12
III Drabeae: 5–9	XII Schizopetaleae: 9
IV Sisymbrieae: 5–11	XIII Heliophileae: 10, 11
V Matthioleae: 6, 7, 8	XIV Cremolobeae: 11
VI Alysseae: 6, 7, 8	XV Pringleeae: 12
VII Arabideae: 6, 7, 8, 11, 15	XVI Stanleyeae: 12
VIII Lunarieae: 7	XVII Streptantheae: 12
IX Euclidieae: 7, 12	

TRIBE I: LEPIDIEAE

PHYSARIA $x=4$				
geyeri	8	Jakowska 1949	H	N.W: U.S.A.
vitulifera	16	Weber & B. 1950	—	,,

HORNUNGIA (HUTCHINSIA) $x=6$				
petraea	12	Jaretzky 1929	H	Eur., Asia M., N. Africa

HUTCHINSIA $x=6$				
procumbens	12, 24	Manton 1932	H	N. Temp.

AETHIONEMA * $x=6$				
coridifolium & 4 spp.	24	Manton 1932	H	Asia M., Lebanon
persicum	36	,,　　,,	H	S.W. Asia
thomasianum	36	,,　　,,	H	Aosta

AETHIONEMA *(cont.)*
grandiflorum & 5 spp	48	Manton 1932	H	Lebanon
ovalifolium	48	Jaretzky 1932	H	S. Eur., S.W. Asia
cordatum	60	Manton 1932	H	Lebanon

COCHLEARIA $x = 6, 7.$ $x_2 = 19$
officinalis Scurvy Grass	24+0-4B	L. & L. 1948	MSpVit	N. & Arctic Eur.
micacea Scottish S.G.	34–36	Crane & G. 1923	—	Mts., Br. Is., Norway
polonica	36	Skalinska 1950a	—	E. Europe
anglica	{ 48+2B	L. & L. 1948	MSp	N.W. Europe
	{ 37–50	Crane & G. 1923		
arctica	14	L. & L. 1948	—	North Reg.
oblongifolia	14	M. & S. 1935	V	,,
scotica (groenlandica)	14	Maude 1939	Sp	Brit. Isles
alpina Mtn. Scurvy Grass	28	Crane & G., 1923	Sp	North Reg.
danica Danish S.G.	42	,, ,,	V	,,
tatrae	42	Skalinska 1950a	—	E. Europe
glastifolia	38	Manton 1932	—	N.W. Europe

BISCUTELLA* $x = 6, 8, 9$
microcarpa (didyma)	12	Manton 1937	—	S. Spain
apula & 4 spp.	16	,, ,,	—	,, Algeria
arvernensis	18	,, ,,	—	Medit.
laevigata 18, 27, 36, 45,	54	,, ,,	H	C. & S. Europe
species	81	,, ,,	—	Spain

COLUTEOCARPUS $x = 7$
reticulatus	14	Manton 1932	—	Asia Minor

PETROCALLIS $x = 7$
pyrenaica	14	Favarger 1953	—	S. Eur. Mtns.

EUNOMIA $x = 7$
oppositifolia Stone Cress	14	Manton 1932	H	Greece
iberidea	28	,, ,,	H	S.W. Asia

ISATIS $x = 7$
tinctoria Woad	28	Manton 1932	D	C. & S. Europe

THLASPI* $x = 7$
arvense Penny Cress & 11 spp.	14	Manton 1932	—	Eur., N. Asia, N. Africa
cilicicum	14, 28	,, ,,	—	Asia Minor
montanum	c. 28	,, ,,	—	Europe
perfoliatum	c. 70	Jaretzky 1932	—	Eur., N. Africa, Nr. East

IBERIS* $x = 7, 8, 11$
gibraltarica & 5 spp.	14	Manton 1932	H	Spain, Mor.
amara Wild Candytuft	14, 16	Jaretzky 1932	H	W. & S. Eur., N. Africa
umbellata Candytuft	{ 14	Manton 1932	H	S. Europe
	{ 16	P. T. Thomas 1945*		
jordani & 2 spp.	22	Manton 1932	H	Anatolia
saxatilis	22+2B	,, ,,	H	S.W. Europe
semperflorens	22+0-1B, 44	,, ,,	H	Italy, Sicily
sempervirens	22, 44	Simonet 1932c	H	S. Eur., Asia M.

IBERIS (*cont.*)
correaefolia		44	Manton 1932	H	S. Europe
corifolia		*c.* 50	,, ,,	H	Spain

CAPSELLA $x = 8$
bursa-pastoris	Shepherd's Purse	32	Vaarama 1943	—	Cosmop.

LEPIDIUM* $x = 8$
armoracium & 5 spp.		16	Manton 1932	V	Abyssinia
campestre	Pepperwort	16	Wulff 1939b	—	Eur., As. M., Cauc.
sativum	Common Cress $\{$	16	Reese 1950	OV	S.W. Asia
		32	Vaarama 1951		
vesicarium		16, 32	Manton 1932	—	Cauc., Persia
latifolium (3*x*)	Dittander	24	Heiser & W. 1948	V	Eur., N. Africa, S.W. Asia
densiflorum	Pepperweed & 3 spp.	32	Manton 1932	—	N. America
apetalum		32	F. H. Smith 1938	—	,,
cartilagineum (5*x*)		40	Manton 1932	—	Siberia

CARDARIA (LEPIDIUM) $x = 8$
draba	Hairy Cress	64	Manton 1932	SpV	E. Med., W. Asia

CORONOPUS $x = 8$
didymus	Lesser Swine Cress	32	Manton 1932	H	S. America
squamatus (*procumbens*) Wart Cress		32	,, ,,	—	Eur., Med., Canaries

BIVONAEA $x = 8$
saviana		32	Corti 1930b	—	Italy

TEESDALIA $x = 9$
nudicaulis		36	Manton 1932	—	Eur., N. Africa

IONOPSIDIUM $x = 11, 12$
prolongoi		22	Chiarugi 1945	—	Spain
acaule	Diamond Fl.	24	Corti 1930b	H	Portugal

TRIBE II: STENOPETALEAE

STENOPETALUM $x = 5$
lineare		10	Manton 1932	—	Australia
sphaerocarpum		10	,, ,,	—	,,

TRIBE III: DRABEAE

LESQUERELLA $x = 5, 6, 8, 9$
alpina		10	Rollins 1939a	—	W: N. America
argentea	Bladder Pod	10	Manton 1932	H	C: U.S.A.
montana		10	Rollins 1939a	—	W: N. Amer.
ludoviciana		10, 30	,, ,,	—	,,
calcicola		*c.* 20	,, ,,	—	,,
mendocina		*c.* 50	Manton 1932	—	Chile
arctica		60	Bøcher & L. 1950	—	N. & Arctic Amer.
fendleri		12	Rollins 1939a	—	N. Mexico

39

LESQUERELLA (*cont.*)

gracilis		12	Manton 1932	—	W: N. Amer.
intermedia		16	Rollins 1939a	—	"
grandiflora		18	Manton 1932	—	Texas

EROPHILA (DRABA) $x = 7$
verna Whitlow Grass 14, 24,
30, 32, 34, 36, } Winge 1940   H   Eur., Asia, N. Afr.
40, 52, 58, 64

RHIZOBOTRYA $x = 7$
alpina   14   Chiarugi 1933   —   S. Tyrol

DRABA* $x = 8$

fladnizensis		16	L. & L. 1948	—	N. & Arctic
incana		32	Heilborn 1927	—	"
muralis		c. 32	Reese 1952a	—	Eur., W. Asia, N.W. Africa
crassifolia (5x)		40	Heilborn 1941	—	N. America
rupestris	& 2 spp.	48	" "	—	N. & Arctic
aurea		64	Bøcher 1938a	—	"
dahurica (*hirta*)	& 2 spp.	64	Heilborn 1941	—	Arctic
sachalinensis		64	R. Yamazaki 1936	—	"
magellanica		48, 64, 80	Heilborn 1927	—	Magellan
arctica		80	Flovik 1940	—	Arctic
alpina		{ 80	Heilborn 1941	—	N. & Arctic
		{ 112	L. & L. 1948		
arabisans		96	F. H. Smith 1938	H	E: N. Amer.

KERNERA $x = 8$
saxatilis   16   Chiarugi 1933   H   Europe

SCHIVERECKIA $x = 8$

doerfleri (*bornmuelleri*)	16	Manton 1932	—	S.E. Eur., Asia M.
podolica	16	" "	—	E. Europe

ARMORACIA $x = 8$
rusticana (*lapathifolia*)
Horse Radish   32   Manton 1932   SpVit   S.E. Eur., W. Asia

LITHODRABA (XERODRABA) $x = 8$
mendocinensis   64   Boelcke 1951   —   Argentine

TRIBE IV: SISYMBRIEAE

ARABIDOPSIS $x = 5$?

thaliana	Common Wall Cress 10	Jaretzky 1928a	—	Eur., Temp. Asia, N. Africa
suecica	c. 28	Manton 1932	—	N. Europe
pumila	32	" "	—	S.W. Asia

DESCURAINIA $x = 7$

pinnata	14, 28, 42	Baldwin & C. 1940	—	E: N. Amer.
richardsonii (*canescens*)	14, 28, 42	" "	—	Rocky Mts.
obtusa	14, 42	" "	—	S: U.S.A., Mex.
sophia Flixweed	{ 20	Baez-Major 1934	—	Temp. O.W.
	{ 28, 56	Manton 1932		

EUTREMA $x = 7$

wasabi		28	Sugiura 1936b	—	E. Sib., Japan
edwardsii		{ 28	Bøcher & L. 1950	—	Arctic, Urals
		42	S. & S. 1941		

SISYMBRIUM $x = 7, 8$

altissimum	Tall Rocket	14	F. H. Smith 1938	—	E. Eur., Nr. East
corniculatum		14	Baez-Major 1934	V	Spain
loeselii		14	Jaretzky 1932	—	S.E. Eur., W. Asia
officinale Hedge Mustard	{ 14	Wulff 1937b	V	Eur., N. Africa,
	14+4B	Baez-Major 1934		Near East
irio	London Rocket { 14	Jaretzky 1932	—	Medit.
	16	Baez-Major 1932		
supinum		42	„ „	—	Eur., Medit.
hirsutum		56	„ „	V?	Turkestan
dentatum		16	Favarger 1949b	—	Europe

CAMELINA $x = 7, 20$

		{ 28	Baez-Major 1934		
sativa	Gold of Pleasure	{ 40	Ibarra & P. 1947a	OT	E. Eur., W. Asia
		42	Jaretzky 1928a		
microcarpa		40	Manton 1932	—	C. & S. Europe, W. Asia
parodii		40	Ibarra & P. 1947a	—	Argentine
alyssum		{ 40	Manton 1932	—	S. & C. Europe
		42	Jaretzky 1928a		

BRAYA $x = 8$

alpina	32	Manton 1932	—	Alps, Arctic, Tibet
linearis	{ 42	Bøcher & L. 1950	—	Scand., Greenland
	64	L. & L. 1948		
purpurascens	64	„ „	—	Alps, Arctic
humilis	40, 56, 64	Rollins 1953	—	Alaska—Colo.

ONURIS $x = 9$

graminifolia	18	Manton 1932	—	Chile

ALLIARIA $x = 9$?

petiolata (*officinalis*)	Garlic Wort	36	Baez-Major 1934	V	Eur., N. Africa, Cauc.—Himal.

XERODRABA $x = 11$

pycnophylloides	22	Manton 1932	—	Patagonia

TRIBE V: MATTHIOLEAE

MATTHIOLA $x = 6, 7$

odoratissima		12	Manton 1932	H	S. Cauc.
tatarica		12	„ „	—	E. Eur., Asia M.
thessala		12	Jaretzky 1929	—	Medit.
tristis		12	„ „	H	„
vallesiaca		12	Manton 1932	H	Italy, Greece
bicornis	Evening Stock	14	„ „	H	Greece, Asia M.
fenestralis		14	„ „	H	Crete
parviflora		14	„ „	—	Medit.
sinuata	Sea Stock	14	„ „	—	W. Eur. & Medit.

MATTHIOLA (*cont.*)

tricuspidata		14	Jaretzky, T. 1937	H	Medit.
incana	Brompton Stock,	14	Straub 1937	H	,,
	Gilliflower	14+1B	Frost 1931		

CHORISPORA $x = 7$

tenella	14	Manton 1932	H	Cauc., N. China

AUBRIETIA $x = 8$

columnae	16	Jaretkzy 1928a	H	Italy
deltoidea	16	Sakai 1935	H	Balkans, Asia M.
edentula	16	Jaretzky 1928a	—	Kurdistan
libanotica	16	,, ,,	H	Lebanon

TRIBE VI: ALYSSEAE

FARSETIA $x = 6, 7, 8$

ramosissima	12	Hagerup 1932	—	Trop. Africa
eriocarpa	14, 16	Manton 1932	—	Asia M., Syria
clypeata	16	,, ,,	—	S. Eur., Asia M.

ALYSSUM* $x = 8$

corymbosum		16	Jaretzky 1928a	H	Balkans
saxatile Golden A. & 13 spp.		16	Manton 1932	H	C. Europe
alyssoides (*calycinum*) Small Alison		32	,, ,,	—	Eur., W. Asia
pyrenaicum		32	,, ,,	H	Pyrenees
repens		32	,, ,,	H	Eur., Asia M.
wulfenianum & 2 spp.		32	,, ,,	H	Asia Minor

LOBULARIA (ALYSSUM) $x = 8$

maritima (3x) Sweet Alison	24	Manton 1932	H	Medit. *cult*

BERTEROA $x = 8$

incana	16	Wulff 1939b	H	Eur., W. Asia
mutabilis	16	Manton 1932	—	,, ,,

CLYPEOLA $x = 8$

ionthlaspii	32	Jaretzky 1928a	H	Medit., W. & C. Asia

VESICARIA $x = 8$

graeca	16	Manton 1932	H	S. Europe
utriculata	16	,, ,,	H	S. Eur., Asia M.

TRIBE VII: ARABIDEAE

ARABIS $x = 6, 7, 8$

dentata		12	F. H. Smith 1938	—	N. America
laevigata		14	,, ,,	—	,,
lyrata		16	,, ,,	—	,,
alpina	Rock Cress	16	Sakai 1935	H	Arctic & Alpine
coerulea		16	Favarger 1953	—	Alps—Tatra
turrita		16	Mattick, T. 1950	—	C. & S. Europe, Asia Minor

42

ARABIS (*cont.*)

iwatensis	32	M. & S. 1935	—	Japan
hirsuta	32	Jaretzky 1928a	—	N. Temp.
serrata	40	Sakai 1935	H	Japan
holboellii (Apo.)	14, 21+0-1B, 28, 35, 42	Bøcher 1951, '54	—	North Region

CARDAMINE * x = 7, 8, 15

asarifolia		{14 16	Lawrence 1931 Manton 1932	—	Europe
amara	Bitter Cress & 7 spp.	16	,, ,,	V	Eur., Asia M., Alt.
bellidifolia		16	L. & L. 1948	—	North & Arctic
parviflora		16	F. H. Smith 1938	—	Temp. Europe & America
pratensis	Lady's Smock	{16, 30, 40 30–76 30–78	Guinochet 1946 Lövkvist 1947 Banach 1950	HV	N. Temp.
californica		32	Manton 1932	—	N. America
pinnata & 2 spp.		48	Schwarzenbach 1922	—	S. Eur. Mts.
chenopodiifolia		64	Manton 1932	—	S. America
pennsylvanica		64	F. H. Smith 1938	—	E: U.S.A.

BARBAREA * x = 8

hondoensis & 1 sp.		16	M. & S. 1935	—	Japan
intermedia & 2 spp.		16	Manton 1932	—	W. Eur. & Medit.
verna (praecox)	Amer. Cress	16	Jaretzky 1932	OV	W. Medit.
vulgaris	Winter Cress	16	Manton 1932	V	Eur., Asia, N. Afr.

CARDAMINOPSIS x = 8

halleri	16	Jaretzky 1928a	H	Eur. Mts.
petraea	16	L. & L. 1948	—	Arctic & Alpine

DENTARIA x = 8

macrophylla		16	Morinaga & F. 1931a	—	Sib., Him., W. Ch.
glandulosa		48	Banach-Pogan 1954	—	E. Eur., C. Asia
integrifolia		44–56	Crampton 1950	—	W. N. Amer.
enneaphyllos		80	Banach-Pogan 1954	—	E. Europe
bulbifera	Coral-wort	96	,, ,, ,,	—	Eur., Asia M., Cauc.

NASTURTIUM x = 8

officinale	Green Water Cress	32	Howard & M. 1946	V	Eur., W. Asia, N. Africa
microphyllum (uniseriatum)		64	,, ,,	—	Eur., W. Asia
off. × micr.	Brown W. Cress	48	,, ,,	V	W. Europe, cult

RORIPPA x = 8

austriaca		16	Howard 1947	—	E. Eur., W. Asia
pyrenaica		16	Manton 1932	—	W. & S. Europe
amphibia		{16 32	Howard 1947 L. & L. 1942	—	Eur., Sib., N. Afr.
islandica		{16 32	Jaretzky 1932 Howard 1947	—	Cosmop.
sylvestris		48	,, ,,	—	Eur., N. Africa

SISYMBRELLA x = 8

aspera	16	Manton 1932	—	S. Europe
dentata	32	,, ,,	—	S. Italy, Balearics

43

TURRITIS $x = 8$

glabra	Tower Mustard	$\begin{cases} 16 \\ 32 \end{cases}$	Manton 1932 Jaretzky 1928a	—	Temp. O.W.

LEAVENWORTHIA $x = 11, 15$

aurea	22	Baldwin 1945	—	S.E: U.S.A.
stylosa	30	,, ,,	—	,,
torulosa	30	,, ,,	—	,,
uniflora (*michauxii*)	30	,, ,,	—	E: U.S.A.

TRIBE VIII: LUNARIEAE

LUNARIA $x = 7$

annua	Honesty	28+2B	Manton 1932	H	S.E. Europe
rediviva		28+2B?	,, ,,	—	S. Eur., W. Sib.

PELTARIA $x = 7$

turkmena		14	Manton 1932	—	C. Asia
alliacea	Shieldwort	28, 58	,, ,,	HV	S.E. Europe

RICOTIA $x = 7$

lunaria	28	Manton 1932	H	Syria, Egypt

THYSANOCARPUS $x = 7$

curvipes	28	Manton 1932	—	W: N. America

TRIBE IX: EUCLIDIEAE

BUNIAS $x = 7$

erucago	14	Melinossi 1937	RV	Medit.
orientalis	$\begin{cases} 14 \\ 42 \end{cases}$	Resende 1937 Jaretzky 1928a	FoV	E. Eur., W. Asia

EUCLIDIUM $x = 7$

syriacum	14	Jaretzky 1932	—	E. Eur., W. Asia
tenuissimum (*tataricum*)	14	Manton 1932	—	C. Asia

MYAGRUM $x = 7$

perfoliatum	14	Jaretzky 1932	—	Medit., Nr. East

NESLIA (VOGELIA) $x = 7$

paniculata	14	Manton 1932	—	Nr. East

TAUSCHERIA $x = 7$

lasiocarpa	14	Manton 1932	—	C. Asia

HYMENOPHYSA $x = 12$

pubescens	24	Manton 1932	—	Siberia

TRIBE X: HESPERIDEAE

CHEIRANTHUS $x = 7$

cheiri	Wallflower	14	Sakai 1935	H	S. Europe
cinereus		28	Manton 1932	—	Canary Is.
menziesii		28	,, ,,	H	W: N. Amer.

44

CHEIRANTHUS (*cont.*)

tenuifolius	28	Manton 1932	—	Madeira
allionii (*Erysimum*)				
Siberian W.	42	Jaretzky 1932	H	*cult*

ERYSIMUM $x = 7, 8$

linifolium	14	Manton 1932	H	Spain
cheiranthoides Treacle Mustard	16	,, ,,	—	Eur., N. Amer., N. Asia
cuspidatum	16	,, ,,	—	Greece—Persia
perowskianum	32–36	,, ,,	H	Cauc., Afghan.
purpureum	*c.* 40	,, ,,	H	Armenia, Syria
helveticum	48	Jaretzky 1928a	—	Eur., Alps
rupestre	*c.* 56	Manton 1932	—	Asia Minor
canescens	72	,, ,,	—	S. Eur., Cauc.

GOLDBACHIA $x = 7$

laevigata	28	Manton 1932	H	Asia M., Persia— Himalayas

MALCOLMIA $x = 7, 8, 10$?

maritima Virginian Stock	14	Jaretzky 1928a	H	S. Europe
	14–16	Manton 1932		
africana	14	Jaretzky 1928a	—	S. Eur., C. Asia
	28	Manton 1932		
flexuosa	16	Jaretzky 1932	—	Greece
chia	32	Manton 1932	H	Medit.
littorea	20	,, ,,	H	W. Medit.

HESPERIS $x = 7, 12, 13$

bicuspidata	14	Manton 1932	—	Asia Minor
steveniana	14	,, ,,	—	Greece, Asia M.
runcinata	24	,, ,,	—	C. Europe
matronalis Dame's Violet	24	,, ,,	H	Eur.,W.&C.Asia
	28	Jaretzky 1928a		
sylvestris	26	Manton 1932	—	,, ,,
lutea	28	,, ,,	—	Japan

TRIBE XI: BRASSICEAE

CALEPINA $x = 7$

irregularis (*corvini*)	14	Manton 1932	—	Medit., Nr. East
	42	Jaretzky 1932		

CONRINGIA $x = 7$

orientalis	14	Jaretzky 1929	—	E. Medit.

COSSONIA (RAFFENALDIA) $x = 7$

africana	14	Manton 1932	H	Algeria, Morocco

HIRSCHFELDIA (SINAPIS) $x = 7$

incana	14	Heiser & W. 1948	—	Medit., Nr. East

MORISIA $x = 7$

monantha (*hypogaea*)	14	Manton 1932	H	Sard., Corsica

5

45

MORICANDIA $x = 7$

arvensis		28	Manton 1932	H	W. Medit.

DIPLOTAXIS $x = 7, 9, 11$

erucoides	White Wall Rocket	14	Manton 1932	—	Medit.
tenuifolia		$\left\{ \begin{array}{l} 14 \\ 20+2B \\ 22 \end{array} \right.$	Jaretzky 1932 Baez-Major 1934 Ibarra & P. 1947b	—	S. & C. Eur.
catholica		18	Manton 1932	—	S. Eur., N. Africa
muralis	Wall Mustard	$\left\{ \begin{array}{l} 18+2B \\ 22 \\ 42 \\ 44 \end{array} \right.$	Baez-Major 1934 Jaretzky 1932 Ibarra & P. 1947b Lubbert 1951	—	S. & C. Europe

CARRICHTERA $x = 8$

annua	16, 32	Manton 1932	—	Medit.—Persia

RAPISTRUM $x = 8$

hispanicum	16	Ibarra & P. 1948	—	Medit.
rugosum	16	Baez-Major 1934	—	,,

REBOUDIA $x = 8$

erucarioides	16	Manton 1932	—	Algeria, Morocco

SUCCOWIA $x = 8, 9$

balearica	$\left\{ \begin{array}{l} 32 \\ 36 \end{array} \right.$	Jaretzky 1929 Manton 1932	—	W. Medit.

ERUCASTRUM $x = 8, 15$

obtusangulum	16	Coutinho & L. 1948	—	Europe
abyssinicum	32	Manton 1932	—	Abyssinia
nasturtiifolium	32	,, ,,	—	S.W. & C. Eur.
elatum	30	,, ,,	—	Morocco
gallicum	30	,, ,,	—	W. & C. Europe

BRASSICA $x = 8, 9, 10, 11$. $x_2 = 17, 18, 19$

$x = 8$

nigra (*Sinapis*)	Black Mustard	16	Nagai & S. 1930	SpO	*cult*

$x = 9$

alboglabra		18	Karpechenko 1924a	V	S.W. Asia
balearica		18	Manton 1932	V	Balearics
insularis		18	,, ,,	—	Sardinia
rupestris		18	,, ,,	—	Sicily
sylvestris (*oleracea*)		18	Griesinger 1937	V	*cult*
oleracea	Kale (2x),	18 (36)	Howard 1939	V	*cult*
	Cabbage, etc.	18	Karpechenko 1924a	V	
		(36)	Pirschle 1942		
		(36, 72)	Schtschavinskaja 1937a		

$x = 10$

chinensis	Shantung C.	20	Richharia 1937b	V	E. Asia
japonica	Curled M.	20	Shimotomai 1925	V	Japan
narinosa		20	Nagai & S. 1930	V	China
pamirica (*campestris*)		20	Karpechenko 1924a	O	Afghanistan
pekinensis	Pet-sai	20	Richharia 1937b	V	China
tournefortii		20	Sikka 1940	V?	Medit., S.W. Asia, India
trilocularis		20	Alam 1936	—	Himalayas

BRASSICA (cont.)

campestris	Rape (2x)	20	Karpechenko 1924a	OV	cult
v. toria		20, (30)	Ramanujam 1940		
rapa	Turnip	20	Morinaga 1929	R	cult
		(40)	Schlösser 1936		

$x = 11$

elongata		22	Manton 1932	V	S.E. Eur., Nr. East

$x_2 = (8 + 9), (8 + 10), (9 + 10).$ $x_3 = (8 + 9 + 10)$

carinata	Abyssinian C.	34	Karpechenko 1930	V	Abyssinia
juncea	Rai, Indian M.	36	Alam 1936	OSp	S. Asia
campestris × nigra		18, (36)	Ramanujam & S. '43	—	expt.
napus	Rape (4x)	38	Nagai & S. 1930	OV	cult
napobrassica	Swede,	38	Howard 1938	R	cult
	Rutabaga	38, (57, 76)	Morinaga & K. '37		
rugosa	Chinese M.	38	Sikka 1940	SpV	E. Asia
rapo-oleracea	Kale (4x)	38	Crane & T. 1942	V	cult
chinensis-carinata		(54)	Howard 1942	V	expt.
napo-campestris		(56, 58?)	Frandsen & W. 1932	V	expt.

RAPHANO-BRASSICA $x = 9$

sativus-oleraceus		(18, 36)	Karpechenko 1927	V	expt.

RAPHANUS $x = 9$

caudatus	Rat-tailed Radish	18	Manton 1932	V	cult
landra	Landra	18	,, ,,	V	Italy
maritimus	Sea Radish	18	,, ,,	V	W. Eur., Medit.
raphanistroides	Jap. R.	18	Sisa 1929	V	Korea
raphanistrum	White Charlock	18	Karpechenko 1928	Sp	Cosmop.
sativus	Radish	18	,, 1924a	V	cult
		(36)	Simonet 1938		

CAKILE $x = 9$

maritima	Sea Rocket	18	Wulff 1937b	V	Eur., N. Africa, S.W. Asia
edentula		{ 18	Kruckeberg 1948	—	N. Amer., Iceland
		{ 36	L. & L. 1947		

SINAPIS $x = 9, 12$

arvensis	Charlock	18	Sikka 1940	—	Eur., N. Africa, S.W. Asia
alba	White Mustard	24	Karpechenko 1924a	MaOSp	Europe—India

ERUCA $x = 11$

cappadocica		22	Manton 1932	—	Asia Minor
orthosepala		22	Jaretzky 1932	—	Spain
sativa	Rocket Salad	22	U et al. 1937	OV	Medit., W. Asia

ORYCHOPHRAGMUS $x = 12$

violaceus		24	Manton 1932	—	Temp. E. Asia

RHYNCHOSINAPIS $x = 12$

monensis	Isle-of-Man C.	24	Sikka 1940	V	W: Br. Isles
wrightii	Lundy Cabbage	24	,, ,,	V	Lundy Is.
erucastrum (Brassica					
cheiranthos)		48	Wright 1936	—	S. & C. Europe

CRAMBE $x = 15$

filiformis		30	Manton 1932	—	S. Spain, N.W. Afr.
fruticosa		30, 60	„ „	—	Madeira
maritima	Sea Kale	$\begin{cases} 30 \\ 60 \end{cases}$	L. & L. 1948 Litardière & D. 1942	V	W. Eur., Black Sea
orientalis					Asia M., Persia
v. *koktebelica*		30	Manton 1932	VSp	
v. *juncea*		*c.* 120	„ „		
hispanica	Spanish Colewort	60	„ „	HV	Morocco—S. Per.
tatarica	Tartar Bread Pl.	60, 120	„ „	RV	E. Eur., N. Asia
abyssinica		90	„ „	—	Abyssinia
cordifolia	Colewort	*c.* 120	„ „	HV	Persia, Cauc.
grandifolia		*c.* 120	„ „	V?	Asia M., Cauc.

TRIBE XII: SCHIZOPETALEAE

SCHIZOPETALON $x = 9$

walkeri	18	Manton 1932	H	Chile

TRIBE XIII: HELIOPHILEAE

HELIOPHILA $x = 10, 11$

linearifolia	20	Manton 1932	—	S. Africa
integrifolia (*pilosa*)	20	„ „	H	„
amplexicaulis	20–22	„ „	—	„
crithmifolia	$\begin{cases} 20 \\ 22 \end{cases}$	„ „ Jaretzky 1932	—	„

TRIBE XIV: CREMOLOBEAE

MENONVILLEA $x = 11$

gayi	22	Manton 1932	—	Chile

TRIBE XV: PRINGLEEAE

PRINGLEA $x = 12$

antiscorbutica	Kerg. Cabbage	24	Hamel 1951a	VVit	Kerguelen Is.

TRIBE XVI: STANLEYEAE

STANLEYA * $x = 12$

pinnata & 2 spp.	24	Rollins 1939b	—	W: N. Amer.
v. *integrifolia*	24, 48	„ „		„

TRIBE XVII: STREPTANTHEAE

CAULANTHUS $x = 12$

crassicaulis	24	Rollins 1939b	—	W: N. Amer.

STREPTANTHUS $x = 12$

cordatus	24	Rollins 1939b	—	W: N. Amer.

40 VIOLACEAE

VIOLA * $x = 6,,10, 11, 13.$ $x_2 = 17.$ $x_3 = 27$

$x = 6$

alliariaefolia	12	Miyaji 1929	—	Japan
biflora	12	„ „	H	N. Temp.
hastata & 8 spp.	12	Gershoy 1934	H	N. Amer.
canadensis Canada V.	24	„ „	H	N. America
chaerophylloides & 23 spp.	24	Miyaji 1929	H	Japan
lanceolata & 8 spp	24	Gershoy 1934	H	E: N. Amer.
epipsila	24	J. Clausen 1926	H	N. Temp.
palustris Marsh V.	48	„ 1931c	—	„
sempervirens (sarmentosa)	{ 24	„ 1929		
	48	Gershoy 1934	H	W: N. Amer.
praemorsa Canary V.	36	„ „	H	„
lutea	48	Fothergill 1944	H	Europe
munbyana Algerian V.	48	Griesinger 1937	H	Algeria
nana	48	Fothergill 1944	—	S. Eur., S.W. Asia, N. Africa
nuttallii	48	J. Clausen, T. '36	H	W: N. Amer.
pinnata	48	Gershoy 1934	H	Eur., N. Asia
hallii Oregon V.	60–72	„ „	H	W: N. Amer.
albescens (mandschurica)	72	Miyaji 1930	H	N.E. Asia
kitaibeliana Iberian V.	14, 16 24, 36, 48 }	J. Clausen 1931d	H	S. Europe

$x = 10$

adunca (canina) Hook V. & 5 spp.	20	Gershoy 1934	H	N: U.S.A.
elegantula Bosnian V.	20	J. Clausen 1931d	H	Balkans
odorata Sweet Violet & 3 spp.	20	„ 1931c	HP	O.W. Temp.
orbelica & 2 spp.	20	Griesinger 1937	—	S. Europe
reichenbachiana (sylvestris)	20	Valentine 1950	H	Eur., Cauc., Kashmir, N. Afr.
sachalinensis & 2 spp.	20	Miyaji 1929	—	N. Temp.
striata Striped V.	{ 20 20+1B	Gershoy 1934 J. Clausen 1929	H	N. America
uliginosa	20	„ „	—	Europe
riviniana	35, 40, 46, 47	Valentine 1949	H	Eur., Morocco
bertolonii	40	Griesinger 1937	H	Corsica
calcarata Spurred V.	40	„ „	H	Eur. Alps
canina Dog V.	{ 40 40–47	Bruun 1932a J. Clausen 1931b	H	N. Temp.
contempta	40	Fothergill 1944	—	N.W. Europe
elatior Tall V.	40	Gershoy 1934	H	Temp. Eurasia
pumila (pratensis)	40	„ „	H	Europe
zoysii (calcarata)	40	Griesinger 1937	H	Balkans
howellii	c. 80	Gershoy 1934	—	Oregon
orphanidis	20, 21, 22	J. Clausen 1931d	—	Macedonia

$x = 13$

declinata (dacica)	26	Griesinger 1937	H	Hungary
diffusa	26	Miyaji 1929	—	Himal., China
saxatilis (alpestris)	26	J. Clausen 1931d	H	E. Eur. Alps
tricolor Pansy, Heartsease	26	„ 1931c	H	N. Temp.
4 vars.	26	Fothergill 1944		
tricolor × lutea	26–53	„ 1938	H	nat. pop. (Eur.)

49

VIOLA (cont.)
  x = 11

cornuta	Horned V.	22	J. Clausen 1931d	H	Pyrenees
orthoceras		22	„ 1927	—	Caucasus
blanda	Sweet White V.	44	Gershoy 1934	H	E: N. Amer.
incognita		44	„ „	H	N. America

  $x_2 = 17 (6 + 11)$

arvensis	Field Pansy	34	J. Clausen 1937c	H	Europe
deseglisei		34	Fothergill 1944	—	„
obtusifolia		34	„ „	—	„
ruralis		34	„ „	—	„
rafinesquii		c. 34	Gershoy 1934	—	N. America
hispida (*rothomagensis*)		34	J. Clausen 1931c	H	N.E. France

  $x_3 = 27 (6 + 10 + 11), 28$

affinis	Leconte V. & 20 spp.	54	Gershoy 1934	H	N. America
pedata	Birdsfoot V.	56	„ „	H	„

HYBANTHUS (IONIDIUM) x = 12

parviflorus	24	Heilborn 1926	M	S. America

41 RESEDACEAE

RESEDA x = 6, 7, 10. $x_2 = (6 + 7)$

odorata	Mignonette	12	Oksijuk 1929, 1935	HP	N. Africa
phyteuma		12	Eigsti 1936	—	Medit., A. Minor
alba		20	„ „	H	Eur., S.W. Asia
lanceolata		24	„ „	—	Spain
luteola	Dyer's Green-Weed	{ 24, 26 / 28	„ „ / L. & L. 1944b	D	Eur., S.W. Asia
virgata		28	Eigsti 1936	—	Spain & Portugal
complicata		28, 30	„ „	—	Spain
lutea		48	„ „	—	Eur., S.W. Asia
stricta		48	„ „	—	Algeria

ASTROCARPUS x = 10

sesamoides	20	Oksijuk 1935	H	Spain

42 POLYGALACEAE

BREDEMEYERA x = 7

colletioides	14	Covas & S. 1946	—	S. America

POLYGALA x = ?

triflora (*erioptera*)	38	Hagerup 1932	—	Asia, Trop. Afr.
japonica	42	Suzuka 1950a	—	Temp. & Trop. Asia
vulgaris Milkwort	{ 28, 32, c. 56 / 48, 56 / c. 70	Mattick, T. 1950 / Wulff 1938 / L. & L. 1944b	—	Eur., Asia M., N. Africa

Group IV

SAXIFRAGALES
45–47
H

SARRACENIALES
48, 49
H

PODOSTEMONALES
50, 51
H

CARYOPHYLLALES
52–56
HS

POLYGONALES
57, 58
HST

CHENOPODIALES
59–64
HST

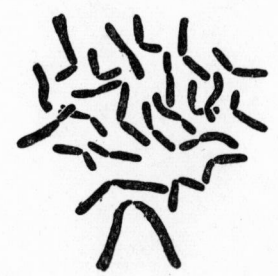

Melandrium album

45 CRASSULACEAE

SEDUM* $x = 4, 5, 6, 7$, etc.

Species		2n	Reference	H/HM	Distribution
pusillum		8	Baldwin 1940	—	N. America
stellatum		10	„ „	H	S. Europe
gracile		12	„ 1937	H	„
nevii		12	Clausen & U. 1943	H	W: N. Amer.
dumulosum		14	Uhl 1952	—	China
rhodanthum		14	„ „	—	W: N. Amer.
hispanicum		14, 28, 30, 40	Baldwin 1939	H	S. Eur., Asia M.
debile		14–18	Clausen & U. 1943	—	W: N. Amer.
alpestre		16	Favarger 1953	—	Eur. Mtns.
acre	Wall-pepper	16, 48	Wulff 1937b	HM	Eur., N. Asia
stenopetalum		16, 48	Clausen & U. 1943	—	W: N. Amer.
ternatum		16, 24, 32, 48	Baldwin 1942b	H	„
nuttallianum		20	„ 1940	—	N. America
tatarinowii		20	„ 1937	H	China
annuum & 2 spp.		22	„ 1937, 1940	—	Eur., W. Asia
verticillatum		22	Soeda 1944	—	Kamchatka
yezoense		22	„ „	—	Japan
rosea (*rhodiola*) Roseroot		22, 36	Uhl 1952	HM	North & Arctic
pulchellum		22, 44, 66 (64, 72)	Baldwin 1943	H	N. America
oreganum		24	Clausen & U. 1944	H	W: N. Amer.
sordidum		24	Soeda 1944	—	Japan
taquetii		24	Baldwin 1937	—	Korea
telephioides		24	„ „	—	E: N. Amer.
maximum		24, 48	„ 1939	H	Eur., Cauc.
wrightii		24, 72	Clausen & U. 1943	—	W: N. Amer.
coeruleum		28	Sugiura 1936a	H	Medit.
divergens & 2 spp.		28	Baldwin 1935	H	W: N. Amer.
beyrichianum		28, 56	Clausen & U. 1943	—	„
griffithsii		28, 58	„ „	—	N. Amer.
dasyphyllum		28, 42, 56	Baldwin 1939	H	Europe
glanduliferum & 2 spp.		30	Hollingshead 1942	—	W: N. Amer.
spathulifolium & 3 spp.		30	Clausen & U. 1944	H	„
cockerellii & 2 spp.		32	„ 1943	—	N. America
album		32, 64	Baldwin 1939	H	Arabia
kamtschaticum		32, 48, 64	Soeda 1944	H	E. Asia
reflexum		{ 34, 68	Baldwin 1935	H	Europe
		{ c. 112	Soeda 1944		
mexicanum		36	Skovsted 1934b	—	Mexico
telephium	Orpine, Livelong	{ 36	Baldwin 1937	H	Eur., N. Asia
		{ 48	L. & L. 1948		
stelliferum (*topsenti*)		42–44	Clausen & U. 1944	—	W: N. Amer.
oryzifolium		47	Soeda 1944	—	Japan?
cauticolum		48	„ „	H	„
alboroseum		{ 48	Baldwin 1937	H	China, Japan
		{ 50	Soeda 1944		
anglicum Stonecrop		48, 144	Baldwin 1939	H	W. Europe
anacampseros		{ 36	Favarger 1953	H	C. Europe
		{ c. 50	Baldwin 1937		
sieboldii		50	Soeda 1944	H	China, Japan

SEDUM (*cont.*)

spectabile	{ 50 { 51	Baldwin 1937 Soeda 1944	H	China, Japan
pachyphyllum	64	W.-Lindschau, T. '38	H	Mexico
palmeri	68	,,	H	,,
diffusum	*c.* 72	Clausen & U. 1943	—	Calif.
oregonense	90	,, 1944	—	W: N. Amer.
aizoon	128	Soeda 1944	H	Sib., Japan

ROCHEA   *x* = 7

coccinea	14	Baldwin 1936b	H	S. Africa

CRASSULA (incl. TILLAEA)*   *x* = 7, 8

x = 7

barbata & 10 spp.	14	Baldwin 1936b	H	S. Africa
orbicularis & 4 spp.	14	Uhl 1948	H	,,
sarcocaulis	28	Baldwin 1936b	H	,,
trachysantha	28	Uhl 1948	H	,,
aquatica	42	Hagerup 1941b	—	N. Temp.
arborescens	42	Baldwin 1936b	H	S. Africa
argentea & 2 spp.	42	Uhl 1948	H	,,
nodulosa	56	Baldwin 1936b	H	,,

x = 8

corallina & 2 spp.	16	,, ,,	H	,,
remotifolia	16	W.-Lindschau, T. '38	H	S. Africa
tetragona	48	Baldwin 1936b	H	,,
" *nana* "	34	,, ,,	H	?
nemorosa	44–46	Skovsted 1934b	H	S. Africa
sarmentosa	*c.* 60	Baldwin 1936b	H	,,
multicava	*c.* 112	,, ,,	H	,,
spathulata	*c.* 148	,, ,,	H	,,

ADROMISCHUS   *x* = 9

cooperi	18	Uhl 1948	H	S. Africa
poellnitzianus	18	,, ,,	H	,,
triflorus	18	,, ,,	H	,,
mammillaris	36	,, 1953	H	,,

COTYLEDON *   *x* = 9

decussata & 4 spp.	18	Uhl 1948	H	S. Africa
macrantha	18	Megata 1941	H	,,

DIAMORPHA   *x* = 9

cymosa	18	Baldwin 1940	—	N. America

SEDELLA (SEDUM) *   *x* = 9

congdoni & 2 spp.	18	Baldwin 1940	—	California

MUCIZONIA   *x* = 12

hispida	24	Uhl 1948	—	Europe

OROSTACHYS *   *x* = 12

malacophyllus & 1 sp.	24	Soeda 1944	—	E. Asia

UMBILICUS *   *x* = 12

horizontalis & 2 spp.	48	Uhl 1948	—	Eur., N. Africa

AICHRYSON (SEMPERVIVUM) $x = 15$

dichotomum	30	Skovsted 1934b	H	Canaries
tortuosum	30	„ „	H	„

AEONIUM (SEMPERVIVUM) $x = 15, 18$

ciliatum?	36	Skovsted 1934b	—	Canaries
tabulaeforme (berthelotianum)	36	„ „	H	Teneriffe
undulatum	72–74	„ „	H	Canaries
arboreum	60	„ „	H	Medit.

SEMPERVIVUM $x = 15, 18$

montanum	42	Favarger 1953	—	S. Eur. Mtns.
arachnoideum	60	Skovsted 1934b	H	S. Europe
tectorum Houseleek	72	Rutland 1941	H	Europe, *cult*

KITCHINGIA (BRYOPHYLLUM) $x = 17$

peltata	34	Baldwin 1938	H	Madagascar

KALANCHOË* $x = 17, 18$

aegyptiaca	34	Skovsted 1934b	H	Africa
aromatica & 1 sp.	34	Baldwin 1938	H	Madagascar
blossfeldiana & 7 spp.	34	Uhl 1948	H	„
globulifera	34	Sugiura 1936	H	„
laciniata	34, 68	Baldwin 1938	H	Tropics
spathulata	34, 68	„ „	H	Africa
varians	68	„ „	H	Tropics
crenata	102	„ „	H	Trop. Africa
faustii	170	Uhl 1948	H	Eritrea
beharensis	36	Baldwin 1938	H	Madagascar
bracteata	36	Uhl 1948	H	„
hildebrandtii	36	Baldwin 1938	H	„
orygalis	c. 72	Uhl 1948	H	„
synsepala	72	Baldwin 1938	H	„
sp.	c. 170	„ „	—	—
sp.	c. 500!	„ „	—	—

BRYOPHYLLUM (KALANCHOË)* $x = 17, 20$

aliciae	34	Skovsted 1934b	H	Madagascar
fedtschenkoi & 2 spp.	34	Uhl 1948	H	„
laxiflorum	34	Baldwin 1938	H	„
proliferum	34	Soeda 1944	HM	„
scandens	34	Baldwin 1938	H	„
gastonis-bonnieri	34+0–4B	Uhl 1948	H	„
miniatum (subpeltatum)	{ 34	Baldwin 1938	H	„
	{ 70	Uhl 1948		
verticillata	68	Baldwin 1938	H	„
pinnatum (calycinum)	40	Uhl 1948	HM	Tropics
uniflorum	40	„ „	H	Madagascar

ECHEVERIA $x = 12, 13, 15, 16, 18, 19, 21, 22$, etc. Uhl and Moran 1953

secunda	64	Rowley unp.	H	W: N. Amer.
agavoides	112	W.-Lindschau, T. '38	H	Mexico
retusa	c. 184	Rowley unp.	H	W: N. Amer.

DUDLEYA* $x = 17$

edulis & 24 spp.	34	Uhl & Moran 1953	H	W: N. Amer.
attenuata	34, 68	„ „	H	„

55

DUDLEYA (*cont.*)

ingens	34, 68	Uhl & Moran 1953	H	W: N. Amer.
pauciflora	34, 68	,,	,,	—	,,
virens	34, 68	,,	,,	—	,,
cultrata	68	,,	,,	—	,,
gatesii	68	,,	,,	—	,,
traskiae	68	,,	,,	—	,,
caespitosa	34, 102, 136	,,	,,	—	,,
greenei	68, 102	,,	,,	—	,,
lanceolata	68, 102, 136	,,	,,	H	,,
albiflora	68, 102, 136, c. 170	,,	,,	—	,,
palmeri	68, 136, ?170, 238	,,	,,	—	,,
anomala	102	,,	,,	—	,,
collomiae	136	,,	,,	—	,,
saxosa	136, 170	,,	,,	—	,,

DUDLEYA × HASSEANTHUS   *x* = 17

3 hybrids	34	Uhl & Moran 1953

HASSEANTHUS   *x* = 17

elongatus	34	Uhl & Moran 1953	—	W: N. Amer.
variegatus	34	,,	,,	—	,,
nesioticus	68	,,	,,	—	,,
blochmaniae	34, 68, 102	,,	,,	—	,,

GRAPTOPETALUM   *x* = 17, 31

amethystinum	68	Uhl & Moran 1953	H	Mexico
paraguayense	136	,,	,,	H	,,
rusbyi	62	,,	,,	H	,,

47 SAXIFRAGACEAE

VAHLIA   *x* = 6, 9

oldenlandioides	12	Skovsted 1934b	—	Trop. Asia, Afr.
viscosa	18	Raghavan & S. 1942	—	,, ,,

ASTILBE   *x* = 7

davidii	14	Hamel 1949b	H	N. China
japonica	14	Skovsted 1934b	H	Japan
rivularis	28	Hamel 1949b	H	Himalayas

HEUCHERA   *x* = 7

americana Am. Alum Root	14+4B	Skovsted 1934b	H	N. America
cylindrica	14	,,	,,	H	W: N. Amer.
hispida	14	,,	,,	H	N. America
micrantha	14	,,	,,	H	W: N. Amer.
rubescens	14	Schoennagel 1931	H	,,
sanguinea Coral Bells	14+3B	Skovsted 1934b	H	N. Mexico
villosa	14+1B	,,	,,	H	N. America

TELLIMA   *x* = 7

grandiflora Alaska Fringe-cup	14	Skovsted 1934b	—	W: N. Amer.

TOLMIEA   *x* = 7

menziesii	28	Skovsted 1934b	H	N.W: N. Amer.

TIARELLA $x = 7, 9$

cordifolia Foam-flower	14	Schoennagel 1931	H	E: N. Amer.
polyphylla	$\begin{cases} 14 \\ 18 \end{cases}$	„ „ M. & S. 1935	H	E. Himal., China, Japan

PENTHORUM $x = 8, 9$

sedoides	16	Baldwin & S. 1951e	—	China
„ Virg. Stonecrop	18	„ „	H	N.E: N. Amer.

SAXIFRAGA * $x = 8$-14

$x = 8$

androsacea	16	Hamel 1954	H	Alps
nipponica	16	Sakai 1934	—	Japan
sachalinensis	$\begin{cases} 16 \\ 40 \end{cases}$	„ „ M. & S. 1935	—	Sakhalin
flagellaris	32	Flovik 1940	H	Arctic & Subarc.
hirculus	32	L. & L. 1951	H	N. Temp.
prostii	32	Hamel 1954	H	Cevennes
bronchialis	$\begin{cases} 48 \\ 48, 49 \\ c.\ 150 \end{cases}$	Sakai 1935 Philp 1934a Skovsted 1934b	H	N. Asia, N. Amer.
granulata Meadow S.	$\begin{cases} 46\text{-}60 \\ c.\ 52 \end{cases}$	„ „ L. & L. 1951	H	Europe
hypnoides	$\begin{cases} c.\ 44 \\ 48, 64 \end{cases}$	Skovsted 1934b Webb 1950	H	„
rosacea	48, 64	„ „	H	Eur., Arctic
cernua	$\begin{cases} 50 \\ 60 \\ 64 \end{cases}$	Chiarugi, T. 1950 L. & L. 1948 „ 1951	H	N. & Arctic
foliolosa	$\begin{cases} 56 \\ 64 \end{cases}$	„ 1948 Harmsen 1939	—	Arctic
groenlandica (*caespitosa*)	$\begin{cases} 64 \\ 56\text{-}65 \\ 80 \end{cases}$	„ „ Skovsted 1934b L. & L. 1951	—	N. Temp., Arctic
hieracifolia	$\begin{cases} c.\ 80 \\ 112 \\ 120 \end{cases}$	S. & S. 1938 Flovik 1940 L. & L. 1948	—	„ „
aquatica (*petraea*)	64	Skovsted 1934b	H	S. Europe

$x = 9$

cymbalaria Ivyleaf S.	18	Skovsted 1934b	H	Asia M., Persia
stolonifera Mother of (*sarmentosa*) Thousands	$\begin{cases} 36 \\ 36, 54 \end{cases}$	„ „ Okabe 1937	H	China, Japan

$x = 10$

intricata	20	Hamel 1954	H	Pyrenees
tenuis	20	L. & L. 1951	—	North Reg.
melaleuca	40	S. & S. 1938	—	Altai
nivalis Snowball S.	60	L. & L. 1951	—	North Reg.

$x = 11$

adscendens Summer S.	22	Melchers 1935	—	N. Temp.
micranthidifolia	22	Skovsted 1934b	—	S.E: U.S.A.
mutabilis	22	M. & S. 1935	—	Japan
rotundifolia	22	Skovsted 1934b	H	N. Temp.
tridactylites Rue-leaved S.	22	Melchers 1935	—	Eur., N. Afr. S.W. Asia
ajugaefolia	44	Hamel 1954	H	Pyrenees
irrigua	44	Skovsted 1934b	H	Crimea
perdurans	66	„ „	H	Transylvania

SAXIFRAGA (*cont.*)

tenella		66	Skovsted 1934b	H	E. Alps
$x = 12$					
caesia		24	Reese 1952a	H	Alps
$x = 13$					
aizoides & 3 spp.		26	Skovsted 1934b	H	N. Temp., Arctic
aspera		26	Favarger 1949b	H	Alps
cervicornis & 2 spp.		26	Hamel 1954	H	Cors., Sard.
tricuspidata		26	Bøcher & L. 1950	H	Arctic, Subarctic
oppositifolia	Purple S.	26, 52	L. & L. 1951	H	N. Temp., Arctic
rivularis	Brook S.	26 52 56	Flovik 1940 L. & L. 1948 Bøcher 1938a	—	„ „
nathorsti (*aiz.* × *opp.*)		52	„ 1941	—	Greenland
$x = 14$					
aizoon & 7 spp.		28	Skovsted 1934b	H	N. Temp., Arctic
cuneata		28	Hamel 1954	H	Pyrenees
crustata		28	„ 1950	H	Tyrol
florulenta		28	„ „	H	Alps
mutata		28	„ „	H	E. Alps
trifurcata		28	„ 1954	H	Pyrenees
crassicarpa		56	Bøcher 1938a	—	N. America
forbesii		56	Burns 1942	—	„
pennsylvanica		56, 84, 112	„ „	H	„
exarata		c. 68	Skovsted 1934b	H	Alps—Persia

PARNASSIA $x = 9$

palustris	Grass of Parnassus	18, 27 36, 54	Erlandsson 1942c	H	N. Temp.
obtusiflora		36	S. & S. 1941	H	Arctic

BOYKINIA (SAXIFRAGA) $x = 11$

tellimoides	22	Skovsted 1934b	H	Japan

CHRYSOSPLENIUM $x = 12, 21$

flagelliferum		24	M. & S. 1935	—	E. Asia
tetrandrum		24	Flovik 1940	H	Eur., N. As., N. America
oppositifolium		42	Schoennagel 1931	H	Eur., N. As., India
alternifolium	Gold Sax.	48	Skovsted 1934b	H	Eur., N. As., N. America

FRANCOA $x = 13$

sonchifolia	52	Schoennagel 1931	H	Chile

KIRENGESHOMA $x = 13$

palmata	52	Hamel 1951b	H	Japan

RODGERSIA $x = 15$

podophylla	30	Hamel 1949b	H	Japan
pinnata	60	„ „	H	Yunnan
sambucifolia	60	„ „	H	„

ASTILBOIDES (RODGERSIA) $x = 17$

tabularis	34	Hamel 1949b	H	N. China

BERGENIA (SAXIFRAGA) $x = 17$
ciliata	34	Hamel 1948b	H	Nepal
cordifolia	34	„ „	H	Siberia
ligulata	34	„ „	H	Himalayas

PELTIPHYLLUM (SAXIFRAGA) $x = 17$
peltatum Umbrella Pl.	34	Hamel 1948a	H	Calif.

48 DROSERACEAE

DROSOPHYLLUM $x = 6$
lusitanicum	12	Behre 1929	CH	Portugal, Mor.

DROSERA $x = 10, 14$
burmanni	20	Venkatasubban 1950	C	Trop. As. & Aust.
intermedia	20	Behre 1929	CH	Eur., N. Amer.
rotundifolia Roundleaf S.	20	„ „	BCM	„ „
obovata (rot. × ang.)	30	Shimamura 1941	—	nat. hybrid
anglica English S.	40	Rohweder 1937	C	Europe
capensis Cape Sundew	40	Behre 1929	C	S. Africa
peltata	40	Venkatasubban 1950	C	Australia
cistiflora	60	Behre 1929	C	S. Africa
spathulata	80	„ „	C	Austr., N.Z.
indica	28	Venkatasubban 1950	C	O.W. Tropics

DIONAEA $x = 15, 16$
muscipula Venus' Fly-trap	⎰ 30	C. M. Smith 1929		
	⎱ 32	Behre 1929	CH	N. America

49 SARRACENIACEAE

SARRACENIA * $x = 13$
drummondii Pitcher P. & 8 spp.	26	Bell 1949, Hecht 1949	CH	E: N. America
2 hybrids	26	Tjio 1948	CH	cult

DARLINGTONIA (CHRYSAMPHORA) $x = ?$
californica Cal. Pitcher Plant	30	Bell 1949	CH	W: N. America

50 PODOSTEMONACEAE

WEDDELINA $x = 20$
squamulosa	40	Chiarugi, T. 1936	H	N. Brazil

52 ELATINACEAE

BERGIA $x = 6$
ammanoides	24	Hagerup 1932	—	S. Afr., Tr. Austr.
suffruticosa (odorata)	36	„ „	—	Tr. Afr., Persia

59

ELATINE x = ?
triandra Water Pepper *c.* 40 Frisendahl 1927 — Europe

53 CARYOPHYLLACEAE

SF1: ALSINOIDEAE

SAGINA x = 6, 11

apetala	Common Pearlwort	12	Blackburn, Wright '38	—	Eur., W. As., N. Afr., S. Amer.
ciliata		12	„ „	—	Eur., N. Afr.
glabra		18	Rohweder 1939	H	W. Alps, Scotland
subulata		{ 18	„ „	H	Europe
		{ 22	Blackburn, Wright '38		
procumbens		22	Rohweder 1939	H	N. Temp.
saginoides	Alpine P.	22	Blackburn, Wright '38	—	Alps, Subarctic
maritima	Sea P.	{ 22–24	Wulff 1937a	—	Eur., N. Afr.
		{ 28	Blackburn, T. 1938		
nodosa		{ 20–24	Wulff 1937a	—	N. Temp., Subarc.
		{ 56	Blackburn, T. 1938		
caespitosa		{ 88	Knaben, L. & L. '48	—	North & Arctic
		{ 100	L. & L. 1944b		

SPERGULA x = 9

arvensis	Corn Spurrey	18	Rohweder 1939	Fo(G)	Cosmop.
vernalis		18	„ „	—	C. Europe

SPERGULARIA x = 9

marginata		18	Castro & F. 1946	—	N. & S. Temp.
rubra	Sand Spurrey	36	L. & L. 1942	—	N. Temp.
salina		36	„ „	—	„

POLYCARPON x = 9

loeflingiae		36	Pal 1952	—	O.W. Tropics

CERASTIUM * x = 9, 19

x = 9

candidissimum		36	Rohweder 1939	—	Greece
carinthiacum	& 9 spp.	36	Söllner 1952, '53	—	Eur., Cauc.
latifolium	& 2 spp.	36	Favarger & S. 1949	—	„
semidecandrum		36	Brett 1955	—	Eur., N. Africa, W. Asia
arvense		{ 36, 72	Söllner 1952	—	N. Temp.
		{ 36, 38, 72	Brett 1955		
cerastoides		{ 36	Mattick, T. 1950		
		{ 38	Favarger & S. 1949	—	Alps, Arctic
		{ 40	L. & L. 1948		
		{ 34, 38	Bøcher & L. 1950		
tetrandrum		{ 36	Rohweder 1939	—	W. Europe
		{ 72	Brett 1955		
tomentosum	Dusty Miller	{ 38	Rohweder 1939	H	S.E. Eur., Cauc.
		{ 72	Brett 1955		
brachypetalum		{ 52	Söllner 1952	—	Eur., N. Afr., Cau.
		{ 90	Brett 1955		
tenoreanum		54	Söllner 1953	—	Eur., Medit.

CERASTIUM (*cont.*)

alpinum	54, 72	Bøcher & L. 1950	—	Arctic, Alps
{ 72, 108, *c.* 144		Brett 1952		
atlanticum & 5 spp.	72	Söllner 1952, '53	—	Spain
glomeratum & 1 sp.	72	Brett 1955	—	Cosmop.
glutinosum & 1 sp.	72	Hagerup 1944	—	Eur., N. Asia
regellii	72	Flovik 1940	—	Arctic
pumilum	90, 95	Brett 1955	—	Eur., N. Afr., W. Asia
arcticum (*edmonstonii*)	108	„ „	—	North Reg.
fontanum	*c.* 120	Mattick, T. 1950	—	N. Temp.
	c. 144	Söllner 1952		
holosteoides Mouse-ear	126	Hagerup 1944a		
Chickweed	144	Söllner 1952	—	Cosmop.
	136–152	Brett 1955		
macrocarpum	144	Söllner 1952	—	Mesopotamia
sp. aff. holosteoides	162	„ „		

x = 19

anomalum	38	Favarger & S. 1949	—	Eur., S.W. Asia
perfoliatum & 4 spp.	38	Brett 1955	—	Medit., Asia M.

DRYMARIA (CERASTIUM)   x = 19

cordifolium	38	Rohweder 1939	—	N. & S. Temp.

MOENCHIA   x = 9, 19

erecta	36	Blackburn, T. 1937	—	Europe
mantica	38	„ „	—	„

ARENARIA   x = 10, 11

marschlinsii	20	Woess 1941	—	Europe
serpyllifolia Sandwort	20, 40	„ „	—	Eur., N. Amer., Temp. As.
ciliata	40	Horn 1948	H	Europe
humifusa	40	„ „	—	„
norvegica	80	„ „	—	Scand., Scotland
gothica	100	„ „	—	Sweden, Switz., N. England
biflora	22	Favarger 1949b	H	Arctic

HOLOSTEUM   x = 10

umbellatum	20	Rohweder 1939		Eur., W. Asia, N. Africa

STELLARIA *   x = 10, 11, 12, 13.

apetala (*pallida*)	20	Negodi 1935	—	Europe
	22	Peterson 1936		
neglecta	22, 44	„ „	—	„
v. cupaniana	40	Negodi 1935		
bulbosa	33	Peterson 1936	—	„
media Common Chick-	40	Negodi 1935		
weed	42, 44	Peterson 1936	(Fo)	Cosmop.
	28	Pal 1952		
alsine (*uliginosa*)	24	Rohweder 1939	—	N. Temp.
Bog Stitchwort	26	Mattick, T. 1950		
holostea Easter Bells	26	Peterson 1936	H	Eur., N. Afr., Cauc.
& 2 spp.				
humifusa	26	Flovik	—	North & Arctic

STELLARIA (*cont.*)

nemorum	Wood C. & 1 sp.	26	Rohweder —	Eur., Cauc.
longipes		52	Bøcher & L. 1950 —	N. America
monantha		104	„ „ „ —	
palustris		*c.* 130	Peterson 1936 —	C. & N. Eur., Temp. Asia

MOEHRINGIA $x = 12$

ciliata	24	Favarger 1953 —	Alps
trinervia	24	Rohweder 1939 —	Eur., W. As., Sib.
pentandra	48	de Litardière 1948a —	Europe

MINUARTIA (ALSINE) $x = 13$

laricifolia		26	Favarger 1949b —	Europe
rubella		26	L. & L. 1948 —	North & Arctic
stricta		26	„ „ —	„ „
verna	Sandwort	78	Rohweder 1939 —	Eur., N. Amer.

MYOSOTON (STELLARIA) $x = 14$

aquaticum	Water Chickweed	28	Peterson 1936 —	Eur., N. Asia

HONKENYA $x = ?$

peploides	Sea Sandwort	{ 48, 64	Rohweder 1939	—	N. Temp. & Arctic
		66	Flovik 1940		

SF2: SILENOIDEAE $(x = 12-18)$

AGROSTEMMA (LYCHNIS) $x = 12$

githago	Corn Cockle	{ 24	Rohweder 1939	H	Europe
		48	Favarger 1946		

CUCUBALUS $x = 12$

baccifer	Berry Catchfly	24	Favarger 1946 —	C. & S. Eur., N. Asia

HELIOSPERMA $x = 12$

alpestre	24	Favarger 1946 —	E. Alps
quadrifidum	24	Rohweder 1939 H	S. Europe

LYCHNIS (PETROCOPTIS) $x = 12$

chalcedonica	Maltese Cross	24	Rohweder 1939	H	Russia, Sib.
coronaria	Rose Campion	24	„ „	H	S. Europe
flos-cuculi	Ragged Robin	24	Favarger 1946	H	Eur., N. Asia
flos-jovis		24	„ „	H	S. Europe
haageana (*arkwrightii*)		24	Blackburn 1928	H	*cult*
lagascae		24	Sugiura, T. 1938	H	Spain

MELANDRIUM (LYCHNIS)* $x = 12$

apetalum & 9 spp.		24	Blackburn 1928 —	North & Arctic
album	Evening or White Campion	♀ 22+XX ♂ 22+XY (48)	Westergaard 1946	H	Eur., N. Africa, W. Asia
rubrum (*dioicum*)	Morning or Red Campion	24, 48	L. & L. 1942 H	Eur., N. Africa, W. Asia
furcatum		48	Nygren 1949 —	North & Arctic
virginicum & 4 spp.		48	Blackburn 1928 H	N. America

MELANDRIUM *(cont.)*
triflorum		72	Bøcher & L. 1950	—	Arctic
laciniatum		96	Blackburn 1928	H	Mex., Calif.

SILENE * $x = 12$
acaulis	Moss Campion	24	L. & L. 1944b	H	Alps & Arctic
cucubalus	Bladder Campion	24	Blackburn 1928	—	Eur., Temp. Asia, N. Africa
armeria & 4 spp.		24	Favarger 1946	H	S. & C. Europe
otites	Spanish Catchfly	24	Lorenzo-Andreu 1951	—	S. & C. Eur., W. Asia
schafta & 56 spp.		24	Blackburn 1928	H	Caucasus
vallesia		$\left\{ \begin{array}{l} 24, 48 \\ 48 \end{array} \right.$	„ „ D. Löve 1942	H	Alps
fortunei		30	Heaslip 1951	—	China
ayachica		48	Favarger 1946	—	Morocco
pontica		48	D. Löve 1942	—	Rumania
campanulata & 3 spp.		48	Kruckeberg 1955	—	W : N. Amer.
stellata Starry Campion & 2 spp.		48	Heaslip 1951	H	E: N. Amer.
ciliata		$\left\{ \begin{array}{l} 24, 48, 192 \\ c.\ 120 \end{array} \right.$	Blackburn 1928 Favarger 1946	H	S. Europe
californica & 2 spp.		96	Kruckeberg 1955	—	W : N. Amer.

VISCARIA (LYCHNIS) $x = 12$
vulgaris	German Catchfly	24	D. Löve 1942	H	Eur., N. Asia
alpina	Red Alpine C.	24	Rohweder 1939	—	North & Arctic
sartorii		24	Favarger 1946	—	Balkans

SAPONARIA * $x = 14$
officinalis Soapwort & 3 spp.	28	Favarger 1946	HM	Eur., Temp. Asia
pumila & 5 spp.	28	Blackburn & B. 1930	H	Alps

VELEZIA $x = 14$
rigida	28	Favarger 1946	—	Medit.—Afghan.

DRYPIS $x = 15$
spinosa	60	Favarger 1946	H	S. Europe

KOHLRAUSCHIA $x = 15$
velutina	30	Bøcher *et al.* 1953	—	W. & C. Europe
prolifera	30, 60	„ „ „	H	„ „

TUNICA (DIANTHUS) $x = 15$
olympica		30	Blackburn, T. 1931	H	Asia Minor
saxifraga	Tunic Flower	60	„ „	H	S. Eur.—Persia

VACCARIA $x = 15$
pyramidata *(segetalis)*	30, 60	Favarger 1946	H	Eur., Asia

DIANTHUS * $x = 15$
alpinus		30	Gentscheff 1937b	H	Alps
arboreus		30	„ „	H	Greece, Crete
armeria	Deptford Pink	30	„ „	H	Eur., Cauc.
atrorubens		30	„ „	H	S. Europe
barbatus	Sweet William	30	Favarger 1946	H	S. Eur., S. Russia
capitatus		30	Gentscheff 1937b	H	E. Eur., S. Russia
cruentus		30	„ „	H	Greece

63

DIANTHUS (*cont.*)

cyri	30	Gentscheff 1937b	H	Asia M.—Afghan.
frivaldskyanus	30	„ „	H	Thrace
gracilis	30	„ „	H	Macedonia
graniticus	30	„ „	H	S. France
japonicus Japanese C.	30	Sugiura 1936a	HP	Japan, Manch.
knappii	30	Gentscheff 1937b	H	E. Balkans
liburnicus	30	„ „	H	S. Europe
microlepis	30	Rohweder 1934	H	Greece
nardiformis	30	Gentscheff 1937b	H	S.E. Europe
neglectus (*glacialis*)	30	„ „	H	S. Europe
nitidus	30	„ „	H	C. Europe
noëanus	30	„ „	H	Rumania
pancicii	30	„ „	H	Bulgaria
pelviformis	30	„ „	H	Serbia, Bulgaria
pinifolius	30	Rohweder 1934	H	Greece
pruinosus (*haematocalyx*)	30	Gentscheff 1937b	H	„
sylvestris	30	„ „	H	Alps
ramosissimus (*pallidiflorus*)	30	„ „	H	S. Russia
tergestinus	30	„ „	H	Dalmatia
viscidus (*grisebachii*) & 11 spp.	30	„ „	H	Greece
carthusianorum Cluster-head P.	30, 60	Favarger 1946	H	C. & S. Europe
as *subneglectus*	30	Gentscheff 1937b		
as *tenuifolius*	30	„ „		
as *subfastigiatus*	30	Ishii 1930		
caryophyllus Clove Pink, Carnation	30, 90	Gentscheff 1937b	HP	S. Eur., N. Africa
chinensis Rainbow Pink	30, 60	„ „	H	Eur., Temp. Asia
as *sinensis*, *collinus*, *laciniatus*	60, 90 / 30, 60	Rohweder 1934, Ishii 1930		
deltoides Maiden Pink	30	Favarger 1946	H	Eur., Temp. Asia
as *glaucus*	60	Gentscheff 1937b		
monspessulanus	30, 60, 90	Janaki Ammal & S. '52	H	S.W. Europe
plumarius Cottage Pink	30, 90	Rohweder 1930	H	S.E. Europe
as *lumnitzeri*	60	Gentscheff 1937b		
pungens	{ 30 / 90	Lorenzo-Andreu 1951 / Gentscheff 1937b	H	Spain
superbus	30, 60	Darlington 1937a	H	Eur., N. Asia
as *wimmeri*	60	Ishii 1930		
attenuatus Rosetuft Pink	60	Gentscheff 1937b	H	Spain, Morocco
brachyanthus (*subacaulis*)	60	„ „	H	Spain
furcatus	60	„ „	H	Ital. Alps
haematocalyx	60	Rohweder 1934	H	Greece
hirtus	60	„ „	H	France
hispanicus	60	„ „	H	Spain
kitaibelii (*petraeus*)	60	Gentscheff 1937b	H	S.E. Europe
latifolius	60	Shibukawa 1930	H	*cult*
leptopetalus	60	Gentscheff 1937b	H	Maced., Cauc.
orbelicus (*cruentus*)	60	Rohweder 1934	H	Greece
requieni	60	Gentscheff 1937b	H	S. Europe
sternbergii & 2 spp.	60	Rohweder 1934	H	„
strictus (*bebius*, *integer*) & 2 spp.	60	Gentscheff 1937b	H	Dalm., Greece
arenarius	60	„ „	H	N. Europe
as *praecox*	90	„ „		

64

DIANTHUS (*cont.*)

campestris	Field Carnation	60, 90	Gentscheff 1937b	H	Caucasus
gallicus		60, 90	,, ,,	H	France, Spain
gratianopolitanus	Cheddar	60, 90	,, ,,	H	W. & C. Europe
(*virgineus*)	Pink				
allwoodii		90	Shibukawa 1930	H	*cult*
anatolicus		90	Gentscheff 1937b	H	Asia Minor
angulatus		90	,, ,,	H	Himalayas
boissierii		90	,, ,,	H	S. Spain
crinitus		90	,, ,,	H	Asia M.—N.W. India
fragrans (*liboschitzianus*)		90	,, ,,	H	Caucasus
holtzeri		90	,, ,,	H	Turkestan
pubescens & 2 spp.		90	Ishii 1930	H	Greece
seguieri (*caucasicus*)		90	Gentscheff 1937b	H	S.W. Europe
squarrosus		90	,, ,,	H	Russia—Sib.
zonatus (*plumarius*?) & 5 spp.		90	,, ,,	H	Greece, Asia M.

GYPSOPHILA *x* = 17

elegans	{ ?20 (40)	Furusato 1940	H	Caucasus
	{ 34	Blackburn 1928		
altissima	34	Favarger 1946	—	E. Eur.—C. Asia
arietioides	34–36	,, ,,	H	Persia
fastigiata	34	Skalinska 1950a	H	C. Europe
muralis	34	L. & L. 1942b	H	Europe
repens	34	Favarger 1946	H	S. Europe
viscosa	34	Blackburn, T. 1931	H	Syria
arenaria	34, *c*. 51	Favarger 1946	—	Europe
arrostii	68	Blackburn, T. 1931	—	S. Eur., Asia M.
trichostoma	68	,, ,,	H	Cauc., Turkest.
pacifica	68	Favarger 1946	H	Siberia
libanotica	36	,, ,,	H	Lebanon

54 MOLLUGINACEAE

MOLLUGO *x* = 9

cerviana	18	Sugiura 1936a	V	O.W. Subtrop.
pentaphylla (*stricta*)	{ 18	,, 1944	—	Trop. Asia, Polyn.
	{ 36	Raghavan & S. 1940a		
oppositifolia	36	,, ,,	V	O.W. Trop.
racemosa	36	,, ,,	—	India
nudicaulis	54	,, ,,	—	Trop. & Subtrop.
verticillata	64	Sugiura 1936a	—	Trop. Am. & Afr.

GISEKIA *x* = 9

pharnaceoides	36	Raghavan & S. 1940a	—	India

55 FICOIDACEAE

I. Semi-succulent Group: *x* = 8

TRIANTHEMA *x* = 8

decandra		16	Raghavan & S. 1940a	—	Trop. Asia
pentandra	Horse Purslane	16	Hagerup 1932	(V)	Trop. Asia, Afr.

65

TRIANTHEMA *(cont.)*

polysperma		16	Hagerup 1932	—	India, Trop. Afr.
monogyna(portulacastrum)		26	Raghavan & S. 1940a	V	Trop. Asia
cristallina	(28)	32	Hagerup 1932	V	Trop. Asia, Africa

TETRAGONIA $x = 8$

crystallina		32	Sugiura 1940	V	Peru
echinata		32	,, 1936b	V	S. Africa
expansa	N. Zealand Spinach	32	,, ,,	HV	Australasia, Japan

SESUVIUM $x = 8$

portulacastrum	Seaside Purslane	48	Raghavan & S. 1940a	V	Tropics
as *Aizoon canariense*		32	Sugiura 1936		

II. Succulent Group: $x = 9$

All genera in this group have the same basic number ; all species are orthoploid; $2n = 18, 27, 36, 54, 72,$ and 108.

(i) Purely diploid genera

APATESIA

helianthoides	18	Rowley unp.	—	S. Africa

APTENIA

cordifolia	18	Snoad 1951	—	,,

ARGYRODERMA

ovale	18	,, ,,	H	,,
villetii	18	de Vos 1947	H	,,

ASTRIDIA

maxima	18	Snoad 1951	H	,,

BIJLIA

cana	18	,, ,,	H	,,

CARPANTHEA

pomeridiana	18	de Vos 1937	—	,,

CARPOBROTUS*

edulis & 2 spp.	18	,, ,,	FSb	,,
fourcadei	18	Snoad 1951	Sb	,,

CARRUANTHUS

caninus	18	,, ,,	H	,,

CEROCHLAMYS

pachyphylla	18	,, ,,	H	,,

CONICOSIA*

capensis & 2 spp.	18	,, ,,	H	,,

CONOPHYLLUM

herrei	18	de Vos 1947	H	,,

CORPUSCULARIA

lehmannii	18	Snoad 1951	H	,,

66

CRYOPHYTUM*
crystallinum & 1 sp.　　18　Sugiura 1936a　HV　S. Africa

CYLINDROPHYLLUM
calamiforme　　18　de Vos 1947　H　　„

DACTYLOPSIS
digitata　　18　Wulff 1940　H　　„

DIDYMAOTUS
lapidiformis　　18　„　1944　H　　„

DINTERANTHUS
microspermus　　18　Snoad 1951　H　　„

DOROTHEANTHUS
bellidiformis　　18　de Vos 1947　H　　„

ECHINUS
maximiliani　　18　Snoad 1951　H　　„

EREPSIA
inclaudens　　18　„　„　H　　„

GLOTTIPHYLLUM*
arrectum & 1 sp.　　18　de Vos 1947　H
linguiforme　　18　Takagi 1938　H　　„
uncatum & 2 spp.　　18　Sugiura 1940　H　　.

HYMENOGYNE
glabra　　18　Rowley unp.　—　　„

IMITARIA
muirii　　18　Wulff 1940　H　　„

LITHOPS*
helmuti　　18　Snoad unp.　H　　„
lesliei & 2 spp.　　18　de Vos 1947　H　　„
terricolor　　18　Snoad unp.　H　　„

MACHAIROPHYLLUM
minor　　18　de Vos 1947　H　　„

MEYEROPHYTUM
meyeri　　18　„　„　H　　„

MITROPHYLLUM*
grande & 1 sp.　　18　Wulff 1940　H　　„
mitratum　　18　de Vos 1947　H　　„

MUIRIA
hortenseae　　18　Wulff 1940　H　　„

NANANTHUS*
aloides & 1 sp.　　18　Snoad 1951　H　　„
pole-evansii　　18　Rowley unp.　H　　„
vittatus　　18　„　H　　„

67

ODONTOPHORUS				
marlothii	18	de Vos 1947	H	S. Africa

OSCULARIA				
caulescens	18	Propach 1934	H	,,
deltoides	18	Sugiura 1940	H	,,

PLEIOSPILOS*				
bolusii & 4 spp.	18	de Vos 1947	H	,,
prismaticus	18	Snoad 1951	H	,,

PRENIA				
relaxata	18	,, ,,	—	,,

PSILOCAULON				
granulicaule	18	,, ,,	—	,,

RHINEPHYLLUM				
comptonii	18	,, ,,	H	,,
macradenium	18	de Vos 1947	H	,,

SCHWANTESIA				
herrei	18	,, ,,	H	,,

SPHALMANTHUS				
canaliculatus	18	Snoad 1951	H	,,

STOMATIUM*				
conradii & 2 spp.	18	,, ,,	H	,,
fulleri	18	de Vos 1947	H	,,

TITANOPSIS				
calcarea	18	,, ,,	H	,,

(ii) Genera including polyploid species

ARIDARIA*				
tetragona	18	Snoad 1951	—	,,
viridiflora	18	de Vos 1947	—	,,
brevifolia & 5 spp.	36	,, ,,	—	,,
quaterna	c. 108	,, ,,	—	,,

BERGERANTHUS*				
multiceps & 1 sp.	18	Snoad 1951	H	,,
scapiger	{ 27 { 36	,, ,, Johansen 1933	H	,,
vespertinus	36	Snoad 1951	H	,,

CEPHALOPHYLLUM*				
aureorubrum	18	de Vos 1947	H	,,
subulatoides	18	Snoad 1951	H	,,
framesii & 3 spp.	36	de Vos 1947	H	,,
platycalyx	36	Snoad 1951	H	,,

CHEIRIDOPSIS*				
carnea & 2 spp.	18	,, ,,	H	,,
velutina	18	de Vos 1947	H	,,
inaequalis	27	Snoad 1951	H	,,

68

CHEIRIDOPSIS (*cont.*)

bibracteata & 1 sp.	36	Snoad 1951	H	S. Africa
aspera & 4 spp.	36	de Vos 1947	H	,,

CONOPHYTUM

flavum	36	,, ,,	H	,,

DELOSPERMA*

aberdeenense	18	Snoad 1951	H	,,
crassum	18	de Vos 1947	—	,,
herbeum & 2 spp.	18	Sugiura 1939	—	,,
ecklonis & 1 sp.	36	de Vos 1947	H	,,
rogersii	36	Snoad 1951	H	,,
cooperi	72	Sugiura 1944	H	,,

DISPHYMA

crassulina	18	Snoad unp.	—	,,
crassifolia	36	,, 1951	—	,,
clavellata	54	,, ,,	—	,,

DROSANTHEMUM

autumnale	36	de Vos 1947	H	,,
candens	36	Snoad 1951	H	,,
luederitzii	36	Propach 1934	H	,,

EBERLANZIA

hospitalis	72	de Vos 1947	—	,,

FAUCARIA*

bosscheana & 1 sp.	18	de Vos 1947	H	,,
lupina	18	Propach 1934	H	,,
militaris	18	Rowley unp.	H	,,
felina & 2 spp.	18	Snoad 1951	H	,,
haagei	27	,, ,,	H	,,

GIBBAEUM*

album & 12 spp.	18	de Vos 1951	H	,,
gibbosum & 1 sp.	18	Wulff 1940	H	,,
angulipes	⎰ 18	,, ,,	H	,,
	⎱ 36	de Vos 1951		
pachypodium	18, 36	,, ,,	H	,,
pubescens	⎰ 18	,, ,,	H	,,
	⎱ *c.* 54	Johansen 1933		
haagei	36	Wulff 1940	H	,,
luteoviride	36	,, 1944	H	,,
shandii & 2 spp.	36	de Vos 1947, 1951	H	,,
geminum	⎰ 36	,, 1951	H	,,
	⎱ 54	Wulff 1940		

HEREROA*

dolabriformis & 2 spp.	18	de Vos 1947	H	,,
incurva & 1 sp.	18	Snoad 1951	H	,,
crassa	36	de Vos 1947	—	,,

HYMENOCYCLUS*

luteus & 2 spp.	18	de Vos 1947	H	,,
purpureocroceus	27, 36	,, ,,	H	,,
purpureus	36	Snoad 1951	H	,,

LEIPOLDTIA*				
nelii	18	de Vos 1947	—	S. Africa
britteniae & 1 sp.	36	„ „	—	„

MESEMBRYANTHEMUM*				
aureum & 5 spp.	18	„ „	H	„
blandum & 3 spp.	18	Sugiura 1944	H	„
haworthii & 4 spp.	18	Snoad 1951	H	„
brownii	27	„ „	H	„
falciformis & 1 sp.	36	Propach 1934	—	„
glaucum	36	Snoad 1951	H	;;
reptans	36	de Vos 1947	—	„

MICROPTERUM				
sessiliflorum	36	Propach 1934	—	„

RUSCHIA*				
crassa & 4 spp.	18	de Vos 1947	—	„
perfoliata & 3 spp.	18	Snoad 1951	H	„
rigidicaulis	18	Sugiura 1944	—	.,
tenella	18	Propach 1934	—	„
karrachabensis	{ 18	de Vos 1947	—	
	{ 36	Snoad 1951		„
addita	18, *c.* 54	de Vos 1947	—	„
connata	54	„ „	—	..
kakamasensis	54	„ „	—	„
uncinata	54	Snoad 1951	H	„

TRICHODIADEMA				
barbatum	18	„ „	H	„
bulbosum	36	„ „	H	„
setuliferum	36	„ unp.	H	„

VANHEERDIA*				
primosii & 1 sp.	18	Wulff 1944	H	„
divergens	36	„ „	H	„

VANZIJLIA*				
angustipetala & 1 sp.	36	de Vos 1947	—	„

56 PORTULACACEAE

PORTULACA $x = 4, 9$				
species	8	Steiner 1944	—	Arkansas
pilosa	16	„ „	—	N. & S. Amer.
smallii	16	„ „	—	E. U.S.A.
grandiflora	{ 18, (36)	Furusato 1940	H	Brazil
	{ 18	Steiner 1944		
pusilla	18	„ „	—	Venezuela
tuberosa	18	Raghavan & A.R.S. 1941b	—	India, Java
marginata	{ 36	Steiner 1944	—	Venezuela
	{ 18, 54	Hagerup 1932		
quadrifida	48	Raghavan & A.R.S. 1941b	—	O.W. Tropics
oleracea Purslane	54	Steiner 1944	V	Trop., Subtrop.

70

CLAYTONIA $x = 6$					
asarifolia		24	Blackburn, T. 1937	—	N. As., N: N. Am.
perfoliata	Winter P.	36	Rutland 1941	V	N. America
TALINUM $x = 6$					
appalachianum		24	Steiner 1944	—	E: U.S.A.
mengesii		24	„ „	—	S.E.: U.S.A.
patens (paniculatum)		24	„ „	H(V)	Trop. Amer.
purpureum		24	Sugiura 1935	—	„
teretifolium Fame		{ 24, 48	Steiner 1944	H	E: N. Amer.
Flower		48	Bowden 1945b		
aurantiacum		48	Steiner 1944	—	Texas
parviflorum		48	„ „	—	W: N. Amer.
triangulare		{ 48	Sugiura 1940	HV	Trop. Amer.
		72	Steiner 1944		
variegatum		72	„ „	—	„ „
CALANDRINIA $x = 8, 10, 11, 12.$		$x_2 = (11 + 12)$			
grandiflora	Rock P.	{ 16	Sugiura 1936a		
		22	Blackburn, T. 1937	H	Chile
		24	Sugiura 1940		
umbellata		20	„ 1936a	H	Peru
compressa		24	„ 1937a	H	Chile
discolor		24	„ 1940	H	„
menziesii (speciosa)		24	„ 1936a	H	Calif.
procumbens		24	„ „	—	Chile
ciliata (caulescens)		{ 24	Heiser & W. 1948		
		46	Blackburn, T., 1937	H	Peru, Ecuador
		48	Sugiura 1940		
MONTIA $x = 9, 10$					
lamprosperma		18	Hagerup 1941b	—	N. Temp.
minor		18	Scheerer 1940	—	„
verna		18	Hagerup 1941b	—	„
rivularis		{ 18	„ „	—	„
		20	Scheerer 1940		

57 POLYGONACEAE

OXYRIA $x = 7$					
digyna	Mountain Sorrel	14	L. & L. 1948	(V)	Alpine
elatior		14, 42	Edman 1929	—	Arctic
KOENIGIA $x = 7$					
islandica		28	L. & L. 1948	—	Himal., Arctic
PTEROSTEGIA $x = 7$					
drymarioides		28	Sugiura 1936b	—	California
RUPRECHTIA $x = 7$					
polystachya		28	Covas & S. 1947	—	S. America
RUMEX $x = 7, 8, 9, 10$					
$x = 7$					
acetosa	Sorrel,	♀: $12 + XX$	Ono 1928,	V	N. Temp.
	Dock	♂: $12 + XY_1Y_2$	A. Löve 1944a		
		inter: 21, 22, 29	Yamamoto 1934		

RUMEX *(cont.)*

angiocarpus		♀: 12+XX	A. Löve 1944b	—	S. & C. Eur.,
		♂: 12+XY	,,		N. Africa
montanus	French	♀: 12+XX	Ono 1930a	V	Europe
	Sorrel	♂: 12+XY_1Y_2	,,		
thyrsiflorus		,, ,,	A. Löve 1944a	—	,,
tenuifolius		♀: 24+XXXX	,, 1944b	—	C. & N. Eur.,
		♂: 24+$XXXY$	,, ,,		Arctic
acetosella	Sheep's S.	42, (41, 43)	,, ,,	—	Europe
graminifolius		56	,, ,,	—	Kamchatka

$x = 8$

pallidus (salicifolius)		16	Jensen 1936	—	N. America

$x = 9$

hastatus		18	Ono 1935	—	Himalayas
papilio		18	,, ,,	—	Morocco
vesicarius		18	Datta 1952	—	Med., N. Afr., India
nepalensis		54	Sugiura 1936a	—	W. Asia—Malaya

$x = 10$

alpinus	Monk's Rhubarb	20	Takenaka 1941	MV	C. & S. Europe, Asia Minor, Cauc.
conglomeratus	Sharp Dock	20	A. Löve 1942	—	Eur., N. Africa, Asia Minor
flexuosus		20	Takenaka 1941	—	New Zealand
pulcher	Fiddle D.	20	Heiser & W. 1948	—	Eur., S.W. Asia
sanguineus	Blood Wort	20	A. Löve 1942	M	Eur., N. Afr., Cauc., C. Asia
scutatus	Garden S.	20	,, ,,	V	C. & S. Eur., N.
		(40)	Fikry 1930		Africa, W. Asia
dentatus		40	Pathak *et al.* 1949	—	Himalayas
maritimus	Golden D.	40	A. Löve 1942	—	Eur., Cauc., Am.
obtusifolius		40	,, ,,	—	Eur., Azores
palustris	Marsh D.	40	,, ,,	—	Eur., Temp. Asia
crispus	Curly Dock	60	,, ,,	M	Eur., Africa
orientalis		60	Takenaka 1941	—	Greece, Asia M.
patientia	Herb Patience	60	Kihara 1927	MV	S. Eur., S.W. Asia
domesticus		{ 60	A. Löve 1942	V	Europe
		80	Takenaka 1941		
longifolius		60, 80	Kihara & O. 1926	V	N. Temp.
cordifolius		80	Takenaka 1941	—	Eur., N. Asia
hymenosepalus	Canaigre	100	Kihara 1927	D	W: N. Amer.
britannicus		160	Jensen 1936	—	N. Amer. *(sic)*
aquaticus		c. 200	A. Löve 1942	MV	Eur., N. Asia
arcticus		c. 200	L. & L. 1948	—	Sib., Arctic
hydrolapathum	Wild Rhubarb	c. 200	A. Löve 1942	MV	Europe
maximus		c. 200	,, ,,	—	,,

FAGOPYRUM $x = 8$

cymosum	Perennial B.	16	Jaretzky 1928b	G	Himal., China
emarginatum		16	,, ,,	G	Eur., N. Asia
esculentum	Buckwheat	16	,, 1927	G	*cult*
		(32, 64)	Sinoto & S. 1940		

FAGOPYRUM (*cont.*)

tataricum	Rye B.	16 (32)	Sando 1939 ,, ,,	G	*cult*

EMEX $x = 10$

spinosa	20	Sugiura 1937b	—	Eur., N. Afr.

MUEHLENBECKIA $x = 10$

complexa	20	Jaretzky 1928b	H	New Zealand
platyclados	20	,, ,,	H	Solomons
sagittifolia	40	,, ,,	—	S. America

POLYGONUM * $x = 10, 11, 17$
$x = 10$

baldschuanicum		20	Schnack & F. 1946	H	Bokhara
equisetiforme		20	Castro & F. 1946	H	Med., S.W. Asia
foliosum		20	L. & L. 1948	—	Europe
dumetorum		20	Jaretzky 1928b	—	Eur., N. & W. Asia
maritimum	Sea Knotgrass	20	,, ,,	—	N. Temp.
hydropiper	Smartweed	{ 20 22	,, ,, S. & S. 1938	M	,,
convolvulus	Black Bindweed	{ 20 40	Jaretzky 1928b A. Löve 1942	—	,,
argyrocoleon		40	Heiser & W. 1948	—	Persia
minus		40	Wulff 1939b	—	Temp. Eur. & Asia
mite		40	,, ,,	—	Eur., Asia M.
pusillum		40	L. & L. 1948	—	Europe
aviculare	Knot Grass	40, 60	,, ,,	M	Cosmop.
tinctorium	Chinese Indigo	40	Sugiura 1936a	D	China
divaricatum		100	Jaretzky 1928b	—	Siberia

$x = 11$

lapathifolium		22	L. & L. 1948	—	N. & S. Temp.
multiflorum		22	Suzuka 1950	H	China, Japan
orientale		22	Jaretzky 1928b	H	Tropics
pamiricum		22	S. & S. 1938	—	Turkestan
tomentosum		22	L. & L. 1942	—	O.W. Tropics
viscosum & 4 spp.		22	Sugiura 1936b	—	Himalayas
nodosum		22, 44	L. & L. 1942	—	N. Temp., S. Afr.
bioritsuense		44	Sugiura 1936b	—	Formosa
flaccidum		44	,, ,,	—	India, Malaya
japonicum		44	,, ,,	—	Japan
major		44	Jaretzky 1928b	—	N. Eur. & Asia
persicaria		44	,, ,,	—	N. Temp.
bistorta	Bistort Snake-root	{ 44 46	,, ,, S. & S. 1938	HMRV	Eur., Asia M., C. Asia
polymorphum		46	,, ,,	—	S. Eur., N. Asia
amphibium	Willow Grass	*c.* 66	Jaretzky 1928b	H	N. Temp.
cuspidatum		*c.* 88	,, ,,	H	Japan
viviparum	Serpent Grass	{ *c.* 88 *c.* 100 *c.* 110 *c.* 132	S. & S. 1938 Flovik 1940 L. & L. 1948 Skalinska 1950a	R	Arctic, Alpine

$x = 17$?

sieboldii Mex. Bamboo	34	Sugiura 1936b	H	Japan

TOVARA (POLYGONUM)	$x = 11$			
filiformis	44	Sugiura 1936b	Fo	E. Asia

PLEUROPTERUS	$x = 11$			
multiflorus	22	Sugiura 1936b	—	China, Japan

TRIPLARIS	$x = 11$			
surinamensis	22	Jaretzky 1928b	H	Trop. Amer.

RHEUM $x = 11$				
collinianum	22	Edman 1929	—	China
emodi Redveined R.	22	Chin & Y. 1947	M	Himalayas
franzenbachii	22	„ „	—	Temp. Asia
palmatum Chinese R.	22	Jaretzky 1928b	HMV	Mongolia
spiciforme	22	„ „	—	Himalayas
officinale Rhubarb	{ 22	„ „	M	*cult*
	44	Suzuka 1950		
undulatum Bucharian R.	{ 22	China & Y. 1947	—	C. Asia
	44	Jaretzky 1928b		
altaicum	44	Chin & Y. 1947	—	Altai
australe	44 (66)	„ „	—	Himalayas
compactum	44	„ „	—	Mongolia
crassinervium	44	Jaretzky 1928b	—	?
rhaponticum English R.	44	„ „	MV	S. Sib., Volga
ribes Currant-fruited R.	44	Edman 1929	V	Syria, Afghan.
sanguineum Red Rhubarb	44	„ „	V	*cult*
(*macropterum*)				
tataricum	44	Chin & Y. 1947		C. Asia
webbianum	44	Edman 1929	—	Himalayas
wittrockii	44	„ „	—	Turkestan

REYNOUTRIA	$x = 11$			
japonica	44	Sugiura 1936b	—	Japan

ATRAPHAXIS	$x = 11$? (Apomixis)			
billardieri	*c.* 45	Edman 1931	—	Greece, Syria
lanceolata (*frutescens*)	*c.* 45	„ „	H	C. Asia
spinosa	*c.* 45	„ „	—	S.W. Asia

ANTIGONON	$x = 7$			
	40	Jaretzky 1928b		
leptopus Coral Vine	{ *c.* 44	Simmonds 1954	H	Mexico
	48	Edman 1929		
	48	Rao 1936a		

COCCOLOBA	$x = $?			
uvifera Sea Grape	*c.* 80	Edman 1929	FHW	S.E.: U.S.A., W.I.
diversifolia	*c.* 200	Jaretzky 1928b	H	S. Domingo

58 ILLECEBRACEAE

ILLECEBRUM	$x = 5$			
verticillatum	10	Reese 1952a	—	W. Eur., Medit.

CORRIGIOLA $x = 8, 9$

littoralis	Sergena Root	⎧16 ⎨18 ⎩32	Sugiura 1937b Blackburn, T. 1938 Rodrigues 1953	M	Eur., N. & E. Afr., W. Asia

HERNIARIA $x = 9$

fruticosa		18	Lorenzo-Andreu & G. 1950	—	W. Medit.
glabra		18	L. & L. 1944b	—	Eur., N. Asia
ciliata		72	Blackburn 1953	—	Guernsey
marginata v. ciliata		⎧108 ⎩126	„ „ Rodrigues 1953	—	Portugal

PARONYCHIA $x = ?$

argentea		⎧28 ⎨36 ⎩	Rodrigues 1953 Lorenzo-Andreu & G. 1950	—	Medit.

SCLERANTHUS $x = 11$

annuus	Knawel	⎧22 ⎩44	Rohweder 1939 Ehrenberg 1945	—	Eur., Temp. Asia
perennis		44	Blackburn, T. 1937	—	Eur., W. Asia

59 PHYTOLACCACEAE

PHYTOLACCA $x = 9$

sessilifolia		18	Sugiura 1936a	—	Mexico
acinosa	India Pokeberry	36	„ „	MV	China, Himal.
dioica	Ombù	36	Schnack & C. 1947	HFoSh	S. America
americana	Pokeberry	36	Suzuka 1950	V	S: U.S.A.
octandra	Calalu	36	Sugiura 1936b	V	C. America

PETIVERIA $x = 9$

alliacea	Guinea-henweed	72	Sugiura 1937b	M	Brazil

RIVINA $x = 9$

humilis	Rouge Plant	108	Sugiura 1936b	H	Trop. Amer.
tinctoria		108	„ 1940	D?	Peru

60 CYNOCRAMBACEAE (THELYGONACEAE)

THELYGONUM $x = 11$

japonicum	22	Sugiura 1937a	—	Japan

61 CHENOPODIACEAE

CAMPHOROSMA $x = 6$

annua	12	Pólya 1948	—	E. Europe

SPINACIA $x = 6$

oleracea	Spinach	12 (24)	Furusato 1940	V	cult, Afghan.
tetranda	Schamum	12	Lorz 1937	V	Caucasus
turkestanica		12	Dolcher 1949	—	Turkest., Pers., Afghan.

BASSIA (CHENOLEA) * $x = 9$

hirsuta & 2 spp.	18	Wulff 1936	—	Italy

CORISPERMUM $x = 9$
hyssopifolium   18   Reese 1952a   —   N. Temp.

HABLITZIA $x = 9$
tamnoides   18   Wulff 1936   —   Caucasus

CORISPERMUM $x = 9$				
hyssopifolium	18	Reese 1952a	—	N. Temp.
HABLITZIA $x = 9$				
tamnoides	18	Wulff 1936	—	Caucasus
KOCHIA $x = 9$				
arenaria	18	Wulff 1936	—	S. Eur., W. Asia
scoparia Summer Cypress	18	,, ,,	H	Eur., N. Asia
trichophylla	18	Witte 1947	—	China
MONOLEPIS $x = 9$				
chenopodiodes	18	Wulff 1936	—	W: N. Amer.
trifida	18	,, ,,	—	N. America
NITROPHILA $x = 9$				
australis	18	Covas & S. 1947	—	Argentine
ATRIPLEX* $x = 9$				
halimus	18	Castro & F. 1946	H	S. Europe
hortensis Orache	18	La Cour 1931	V	Cosmop.
littoralis Salt Bush & 3 spp.	18	Wulff 1937a	—	N. Temp.
patula	18	Witte 1947	—	Cosmop.
semibaccata	18	Kjellmark 1934	Fo	Australia
hastata Mountain O.	18, 36	Heiser & W. 1948	—	Eur., N. Asia
BETA $x = 9$				
macrocarpa	18	Wulff 1936	V	Pers., Cauc.
macrorhiza	18	Sirotina 1936	V	Eur., N. Afr., S.W. Asia
maritima Sea Beet	18	Kachidze 1935	V	Eur., N. Afr.
patula	18	Wulff 1936	—	Madeira
patellaris	18	Bleier 1930	V	Teneriffe
lomatagona	{18	Sirotina 1936	—	A. Min., Syria
	36	Müntzing 1937c		
vulgaris Beet, Mangold	18	Winge 1917	RSu	cult
18 (19, 20, 27, 36, 42, 45)		Levan 1942b		
v. cicla Spinach Beet	18 (36)	Thomas 1945*	V	cult
corolliflora	36	Zossimovich 1939	V	Persia, A. Minor
lom. × corolliflora	27, 54	Zaikovskaja 1939	—	expt.
trigyna	54	Bleier 1928	R	Balk., A. Minor
CHENOPODIUM* $x = 9$ (8?)				
botrys	16?	Kawatani & O. 1950	P	Cosmop.
hybridum Sowbane	{18	Winge 1917	—	Eur., C. Asia,
	36	G. O. Cooper, 1935		N. Africa
murale & 1 sp.	18	Winge 1917	—	N. & S. Temp.
virgatum & 1 sp.	18	Wulff 1936	V	Japan
	18	Maude 1940		
	32?	Kawatani & O. 1950		
album Fat Hen, Goosefoot	36	G. O. Cooper 1935,	(G)V	N. Temp.
	36	Witte 1947		
	54	Kjellmark 1934		
ambrosioides				
Wormseed,	16, 32, 48?	Kawatani & O. 1950	BIV	Trop. Amer.
Mexican Tea	32	Suzuka 1950		
	36	Kjellmark 1934		
	64	Suzuka & K. 1949		
v. anthelminticum	64	Kawatani & O. 1950		

76

CHENOPODIUM (*cont.*)

bonus-henricus	Good-King-Henry	{ 36 { 32?	L. & L. 1944b Kawatani & O. 1950	V	Europe
quinoa	Quinoa	{ 36 { 32?	Kjellmark 1934 Kawatani & O.1950	G	Peru, *cult*
pueblense	Cuahzontli	36	Reed 1950	Sp	Mexico

HALIMIONE (OBIONE) $x = 9$

pedunculata		18	Wulff 1936	—	Eur., N. & S.W. Asia
portulacoides	Sea Purslane	36	„ „ Castro & F. 1946	—	Eur., Syria, N. Africa

SALICORNIA $x = 9$

perennis		18	Hambler 1954	—	W. Eur., N. Afr.
ramosissima		18	„ „	—	N. & W. Eur.
stricta	Glass Wort	{ 18 { 18, 36 { 36+2B	Castro & F. 1946 König 1939 Maude 1939	V	Cosmop.
(*europaea, herbacea*)					
dolichostachya		36	Hambler 1954	—	W. Europe
arabica		c. 54	Castro & F. 1946	—	Eur., N. Afr.

SUEDA $x = 9$

splendens		18	Castro & F. 1946	—	Medit., W. Asia
fruticosa		36	Joshi 1935	M	N. Temp.
maritima	Sea Blite	36	Wulff 1937a	V	N. & S. Temp.
linearis		54	Lorz 1937	—	N. Amer., Cuba

SALSOLA $x = 9$

soda	Barilla Plant	{ 18 { 36	Castro & F. 1946 Wulff 1936	M	N. & S. Temp.
kali	Russian Thistle	36	„ 1937a	M	„ „
tragus		36	„ 1936	—	„ „

ARTHROCNEMUM $x = 9$

glaucum		36	Castro & F. 1946	—	Greece, India, Trop. Africa

BOUSSINGAULTIA $x = 9$

baselloides		36	MacKenzie, T. 1937	—	Ecuador

EUROTIA $x = 9$

ceratoides		36	Wulff 1936	H	Eur., N. Amer.

OFAISTON $x = 9$

monandrum		36	Wulff 1936	—	W. Asia

63 AMARANTHACEAE

DIGERA $x = 6$

arvensis		12	Puri & S. 1935	V	Trop. Afr. & Asia

ACHYRANTHES $x = 7$

bidentata		42	Sugiura 1936b	(G)M	Trop. Asia

7

AMARANTHUS $x = 8, 17$

albus		32	Heiser & W. 1948	—	N. America
edulis		32	Covas 1950b	G?	Argentine
graecizans		32	Heiser & W. 1948	—	N. America
hybridus	Red Cockscomb	32	Covas & S. 1946	HM	*cult*, Tropics
mangostanus		32	Takagi 1933	V	India
paniculatus	Anardana	32	,, ,,	GV	,,
retroflexus	Red Root	c. 32	Heiser & W. 1948	V	Trop. Amer.
caudatus	Love-lies-bleeding	{ 32	Takagi 1933	GHMV	Tropics
		34	Cardenas & H. 1948		
asplundii		34	,, ,, ,,	—	Bolivia
blitum	Wild Amaranth	34	Takagi 1933	V	Temp. & Trop.
gangeticus	Lal sag	34	,, ,,	HV	Tropics
spinosus	Spiny A.	34	,, ,,	V	,,
viridis	Green Calalu	34	Krishnaswamy & R. 1949	V	Temp. & Trop.

CELOSIA $x = 9$

cristata	Cockscomb	36	Grant 1954	HV	Tropics
argentea	Quail Grass	72	,, ,,	V	,,
crist. × *arg.*	51 (54, 81, 108)		,, ,,	H	*cult*

GOMPHRENA $x = 9, 10$

perennis	18	Covas & C. 1946	—	Argentine
pulchella	18	,, ,,	H	Brazil, Arg.
martiana	20	,, ,,	—	Chile
tomentosa	30	,, ,,	—·	Brazil

64 BASELLACEAE

ULLUCUS $x = 12$

tuberosus	Ulluco	24, 36	Cárdenas & H. 1948	R	Andes

BASELLA $x = 12?$

alba	Malabar Nightshade	48	MacKenzie, T. 1937	V	Tropics
rubra	Indian Spinach	{ 44	Sugiura 1936a	V	,,
		60	MacKenzie, T. 1937		

Group V

GERANIALES
65–71
HS

LYTHRALES
72–79
HST

THYMELAEALES
80–83
HST

PROTEALES
84
ST

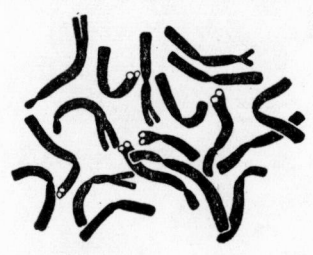

Daphne mezereum

65 LINACEAE

LINUM * $x = 8, 9, 10, 12, 14, 15, 16$
   $x = 8, 9$

viscosum		16	Ray 1944	H	S. Europe
grandiflorum	Flowering F. ⎧	16	,, ,, Masima '47	H	Algeria
	⎨	16, 17	Martzenitzina 1927		
	⎩	18	Kikuchi 1926		
hirsutum	⎧	16	Ray 1944	H	S.E. Eur., Asia M.
	⎩	18	Nagao 1941		
catharticum	⎧	16	Vilmorin & S. 1927b	M	Eur., S.W. Asia
	⎩	>57	Martzenitzina 1927		

$x = 9$

altaicum & 8 spp.		18	Ray 1944	—	Siberia
muelleri		18	Kikuchi 1929	—	Sardinia
perenne	Perennial F.	18	Ray 1944	H	Europe
punctatum		18	Martzenitzina 1927	—	Sicily
austriacum	Austrian F.	18, 27	Freiburg 1933	H	Eur.—Persia
alpinum	⎧	18	Ray 1944	H	Eur., N. Afr.
	⎩	36	Nagao 1941		
selaginoides		36	Covas 1949b	—	Argentine
suffruticosum		72	Lorenzo-A. & G. '50	—	W. Medit.
maritimum	⎧	18	Nagao 1941	H	Medit.
	⎩	20	Vilmorin & S. '27b		
campanulatum		18, 28	Ray 1944	H	S. Europe
narbonense	Narbonne F. ⎧	18	Kikuchi 1929	H	,,
	⎩	28	Ray 1944		
corymbiferum	⎧	18	Martzenitzina 1927	—	N. Africa
	⎩	30	Kikuchi 1926		

$x = 10$

gallicum		20	Ray 1944	H	C. Eur., Medit.

$x = 12, 14$

capitatum	⎧	24	Kikuchi 1926	H	S. Europe
	⎩	28	Ray 1944		
arboreum		28	,, ,,	H	E. Medit.

$x = 15, 16$

compactum		30	Ray 1944	—	N. America
medium		30	,, ,,	—	N.E.: N. Amer.
nervosum		30	Vilmorin & S. '27b	H	E. Europe
rigidum		30	Dillman 1933	—	W: N. Amer.
sulcatum		30	,, ,,	—	N. America
virginianum		30	Ray 1944	—	E: N. Amer.
africanum	⎧	30	Masima 1947	—	N. Africa
	⎩	32	Sugiura 1940		
bienne (*angustifolium*)	⎧	32	Martzenitzina 1927	—	Eur., N. Afr.
	⎩	30, (60)	Masima 1947		
flavum	Golden Flax ⎧	28	Nagao 1941	H	S. Eur., Cauc.
	⎨	30	Ray 1944		
	⎩	30–32	Martzenitzina 1927		
usitatissimum	Flax, ⎧	30	Ray 1944	MOT	S.W. Asia, *cult*
	Linseed ⎩	32	Kostoff 1940		

81

LINUM (*cont.*)

as *crepitans*		{ 30, 32 { 30 (60)	Emme & S. 1927 Masima 1947		
monogynum		86?	Kikuchi 1929	H	New Zealand

RADIOLA $x = 9$

linoides	All-seed	18	Hagerup 1941b	—	Temp. Eurasia

REINWARDTIA $x = 10$

trigyna		20	Kishore 1951	H	N. India

66 ZYGOPHYLLACEAE

BALANITES $x = 9$

aegyptica		18	Pathak *et al.* 1949	O	N. Afr., Arabia, Palestine

FAGONIA $x = 9$

cretica		18	Negodi 1939	H	W. Medit.

ZYGOPHYLLUM $x = 11$

fabago	Bean Caper	22	Warburg 1938	Sp	Spain, N. Africa W. Asia

PEGANUM $x = 12$

harmala	Turkey Red	24	Warburg 1938	D	C. Asia, Medit.

TRIBULUS $x = 12$

terrestris	Land Calthrops	{ 24 { 48	Negodi 1939 Schnack & C. 1947	M(V)	O.W. Tropics

BULNESIA $x = 13$

retamo		26	Schnack & C. 1947	—	Argentine

LARREA $x = 13$

divaricata		26	Covas & S. 1946	—	Argentine
nitida		26, 52	Covas 1949b	—	Arg., Chile
cuneifolia		52	Covas & S. 1946	—	Argentine
tridentata	Creosote Pl.	52, 104	Covas 1949b	HM	Mex., Texas

GUAIACUM $x = ?$

officinale	Lignum Vitae	*c.* 26	E.K.J.*	MReW	W. Indies, C. Am.

67 GERANIACEAE

PELARGONIUM * $x = 8, 9, 10, 11$

$x = 8$

infundibulum?		16	Gauger 1937	—	—
odoratissimum	Ger. Oil Pl.	16	Takagi 1928	HP	Trop. Africa

$x = 9$

acetosum		18	Gauger 1937	(V)	S. Africa
hortorum		18	Takagi 1928	H	*cult*
inquinans		18	„ „	H	S. Africa

82

PELARGONIUM (*cont.*)

lateripes	18	Warburg 1938	H	S. Africa
monstrum	18	Gauger 1937	—	,,
scandens	18	,, ,,	H	,,
zonale Zonal G.	17, 18, 35, 36	,, ,,	H(V)	*cult*
endlicherianum	36	Warburg 1938	—	Asia Minor
peltatum Ivy-leafed G.	36	Gauger 1937	H(V)	S. Africa
glutinosum	{ 36	,, ,,	—	,,
	{ 90	Takagi 1928		
roseum Rose G.	72 (144)	Schtschavinskaja '37b	HP	,,
radula	81	Takagi 1928	H	,,
denticulatum	90	,, ,,	H	,,
graveolens	90	,, ,,	HP	,,

x = 10, 11

roessingense	20	Gauger 1937	—	,,
violaceum	20	,, ,,	—	,,
ardens & 6 spp.	22	,, ,,	H	,,
glaucifolium	22	Warburg 1938	H	*cult*
punctatum	22	,, ,,	H	S. Africa

amabile	40, 44	Gauger 1937	—	,,
flavum	40, 44	,, ,,	—	,,
tomentosum	44	,, ,,	H	,,
quercifolium Oak-leaved G.	44, 88	,, ,,	H	,,
triste	60	,, ,,	H(R)	,,
decipiens?	88	,, ,,	—	,,
vitifolium	88	,, ,,	H	,,

ERODIUM* *x* = 9, 10

absinthoides v. *amanum*	18	Warburg 1938	H	Maced., Asia M.
ciconium	{ 18	Gauger 1937	H	Medit.
	{ 20	Warburg 1938		
corsicum	{ 18	Negodi 1937	H	Corsica, Sard.
	{ 20	Warburg 1938		
sibthorpianum	27	Gauger 1937	H	Maced., Asia M.
chrysanthum	36	Warburg 1938	H	Greece
chamaedryoides & 4 spp.	20	,, ,,	H	Corsica
glutinosum	20	Andreas 1947	—	Medit.
moschatum Musk Clover	20	Gauger 1937	FoHP	Medit., S.W. Asia
supracanum	20	,, ,,	H	Pyrenees
texanum	20	Baker unp.	—	W: N. Amer.
cheilanthifolium	{ 20	Gauger 1937	H	Spain, Morocco
	{ 40	Warburg 1938		
botrys	40	Heiser & W. 1948	—	Medit.
chium & 3 spp.	40	Warburg 1938	—	,,
cicutarium Storksbill	40	Andreas 1947	FoH(V)	Medit., C. Asia
v. *immaculatum*	40	Baker unp.		
obtusiplicatum	40	,,	—	N. Afr. (Calif., nat.)

GERANIUM* *x* = 9, 10, 11, 13, 16 x_2 = 23 (annual) *x* = 12, 14 x_2 = 25 (perennial)

columbinum	18	L. & L. 1944b	—	Eur., N. Asia
lucidum	20	Warburg 1938	H	,, ,,
dissectum	22	L. & L. 1944b	HR	S. Europe
pratense	28	Warburg 1938	H	Eur., N. Asia
sylvaticum Wood Cranesbill	28	L. & L. 1944b	DH	,, ,,

83

GERANIUM (*cont.*)

molle		26	Warburg 1938	H	Eur., N. & S.W. Asia
rotundifolium		26	,, ,,	—	Eur., N. Asia
endressii		28	,, ,,	H	Pyrenees
pyrenaicum		28	,, ,,	H	Eur., Asia M.
pusillum		26	Jackson 1951	H	Eur., Cauc., Him.
affine & 18 sp.		28	Warburg 1938	—	Altai
bohemicum		28	Dahlgren 1952	H	C. Europe
nepalense		28	Suzuka 1950	H	Asia Mtns.
platypetalum		28, 42 (3*x*)	Warburg 1938	H	Caucasus
palustre		28, 56	Gauger 1937	H	Eur., N. Asia
purpureum		32	Bøcher 1947a	—	S. Eur., N. & E. Africa
macrorrhizum		{ 46 { 87–93	Warburg 1938 Gauger 1937	H	S. Europe
lanuginosum		48	Dahlgren 1952	—	S. Africa
favosum		50	Warburg 1938	—	Abyssinia
ibericum & 2 spp.		56	,, ,,	H	Caucasus
obertianum	Herb Robert	64	Bøcher 1947a	M	N. Temp.
anemonifolium		{ 68 { 128	Warburg 1938 Jackson unp.	H	Can. Is., Madeira
sanguineum		84	Warburg 1938	H	Eur., Cauc.

SARCOCAULON   *x* = 11

burmannii	44	Gauger 1937	H	S. Africa

MONSONIA   *x* = 12

senegalensis	24	Warburg 1938	—	Trop. Africa

68 LIMNANTHACEAE

LIMNANTHES*   *x* = 10

alba	10	Mason 1952	H	California
douglasii & 6 spp.	10	,, ,,	H	,,

69 OXALIDACEAE

OXALIS*   *x* = 5, 6, 7, 9, 11

x = 5

bupleurifolia	Brazil Bush O.	10	Heitz 1927	H	Brazil
caprina		20	,, ,,	H	S. Africa
versicolor		{ 14? { 30	,, ,, Yamashita 1935	H	,,
hirta		30	,, ,,	H	,,
pentaphylla		30	,, ,,	H	,,
rhombifolia		c. 80	Heitz 1927	—	Venezuela

x = 6

corniculata	Creeping S.	24	Rutland 1941	HV	Cosmop.
stricta	Yellow O.	24	Wulff 1937b	H	N. Temp.

x = 7

deppei	Rosetta O. & 8 spp.	14	Heitz 1927	HRV	Mexico

84

OXALIS (*cont.*)

ortgiesii		14	Warburg 1938	H	Peru
brasiliensis		{ 14	Heitz 1927	H	Brazil
		28	Yamashita 1935		
asinina		28	Warburg 1938	H	S. Africa
lasiandra & 3 spp.		28	Heitz 1927	H	Mexico
violacea	Violet W. S.	28	Yamashita 1935	H(V)	U.S.A.
cernua	Bermuda Buttercup	35	,, ,,	HV	S. Africa
rubra		42	Heitz 1927	H	Brazil
truncatula		42	,, ,,	—	S. Africa

$x = 9, 11$

valdiviensis		18	Warburg 1938	H	Chile
acetosella	Wood Sorrel	22	Nakajima 1936	HMV	N. Temp.
japonica		44?	M. & S. 1935	—	Japan
tuberosa	Oka	{ 63–70	Kostoff *et al.* 1935	R	Andes
		66	Cárdenas & H. 1948		

AVERRHOA $x = 12$

carambola	Carambola	24	Krishnaswamy & R. 1949	F	India, China

70 TROPAEOLACEAE

TROPAEOLUM $x = 6, 7$

peregrinum	Canary Creeper	24	Warburg 1938	H	Peru
majus	Nasturtium	28	,, ,,	H(V)	Peru, Brazil
minus	Dwarf N.	28	,, ,,	H(V)	Peru
peltophorum		28	Sugiura 1931	H	Colombia, Ecuador
tuberosum	Per. N., Ysano	42	,, 1936a, b	HR	Peru, Bolivia

71 BALSAMINACEAE

IMPATIENS* $x = 7, 8, 9, 10$

$x = 7$

amphorata		14	Warburg 1938	H	W. Himalayas
balfourii & 2 spp.		14	Wulff, T. 1937	H	,,
balsamina	Garden Balsam	14	Warburg 1938	H	Trop. Asia
firmula		14	Heitz & R. 1936	H	Madagascar
scabrida		14	F. H. Smith 1934	H	Himalayas

$x = 8$

holstii		16	Warburg 1938	H	E. Tr. Africa
oliveri		16	Wulff 1933	H	,,
petersiana		16	,, ,,	H	W. Tr. Africa
sultani		16	Warburg 1938	H	Zanzibar

$x = 9, 10$, etc.

roylei		{ 18	F. H. Smith 1934	H	Himalayas
		18	W. Jackson unp.		
		20	Warburg 1938		
biflora	Jewel Weed	20	F. H. Smith 1934	H	N. America
noli-tangere	Touch-me-not	20	Winge 1925	H	Eur., Siberia
pallida (*aurea*)		20	F. H. Smith 1934	H	E: N. America

parviflora		$\begin{cases}20 \\ 24 \\ 26\end{cases}$ Schürhoff 1926 Wulff 1934a Heitz & R. 1936	---	Turkestan, Siberia

HYDROCERA $x = 8$
triflora (*angustifolia*)	Water Balsam	16 Schürhoff 1931	DH	Trop. Asia

72 LYTHRACEAE

PEPLIS $x = 5$
portula	Water Purslane	10 Hagerup 1941b	V	Eur., W. As.

CUPHEA $x = 6$
cyanea		12 Sugiura 1937b	—	Mexico
lanceolata		12 „ „	—	„
miniata	Cigar Flower	18 „ 1936b	H	„
platicentra		36 „ „	—	„

LYTHRUM $x = 15$
hyssopifolia		20? Tischler 1929	H	Temp.
virgatum		30 La Cour 1945*	H	Eur., N. Asia
salicaria		$\begin{cases}30 \\ 50 \\ 60\end{cases}$ Shinke 1929 L. & L. 1942 La Cour 1945*	H	N. Temp.
myrtifolium		60 „ „	—	N. America

NESAEA (LYTHRUM, DECODON) $x = 15$
triflorum	60 La Cour 1945*	H	S. America

LAGERSTROEMIA $x = 11, 25$
flos-reginae	Murata	44 Tjio 1948	HW	India
indica	Grape Myrtle	50 Bowden 1945a	H	S. Asia, N. Austr.
speciosa		50 „ „	H	Trop. Asia

75 PUNICACEAE

PUNICA $x = 8, 9$?
granatum	Pomegranate	$\begin{cases}16 \\ 18, 19 \\ 18\end{cases}$ Tjio 1948 Kostoff *et al.* 1935 Proos 1938	DFHM	*cult* (Persia)

77 ONAGRACEAE (OENOTHERACEAE)

CLARKIA (incl. GODETIA) $x = 5, 7, 8, 9.$ $x_2 = 12, 17.$ $x_3 = 26$
$x = 5$
virgata	10 Lewis 1953b	H	California

$x = 7$
amoena]	14 „ „	H	N.W.: U.S.A.
arcuata	14 „ ,,	H	California
breweri	14 „ „	H	„
concinna	14 „ ,,	H	„
lassenensis	14 „ „	H	N.W: U.S.A.

CLARKIA* *(cont.)*

mildrediae	14	Lewis 1953b	H	California
rubicunda	14	,, ,,	H	,,
gracilis (as *G. nutans*)	28+0–4B	Håkansson 1945	H	N.W: U.S.A.

$x = 8$

biloba	16	Lewis 1953a	H	California
imbricata	16	Lewis & L. 1953	H	,,
modesta	16	Lewis 1953b	—	,,

$x = 9$

bottae	18	,, ,,	H	.
cylindrica	18	,, ,,	H	.,
deflexa	18	,, ,,	H	,,
dudleyana	18	,, ,,	H	
epilobioides	18	,, ,,	—	Calif., Arizona
lingulata	18	,, 1953a	H	California
speciosa	18	,, 1953b	H	,,
unguiculata (*elegans*)	18+0–6B	,, 1951	H	,,
williamsonii	18	,, 1953b	H	,,
as *G. viminea*	18+0–3B	Håkansson 1949		
xantiana	18	Lewis 1953b	H	,,
delicata	36	,, unp.	H	,,

$x_2 = (5 + 7)$

pulchella	24	Håkansson 1931	H	N.W: U.S.A.
rhomboidea	24	Lewis 1951	H	W: N. America

$x_2 = (8 + 9)$

davyi	34	Lewis & L. 1953	—	California
similis	34	Lewis & E. 1953	—	.,
tenella	34	Hiorth 1941	H	Chile, Argentine

$x_3 = (9 + 17)$

affinis	52	Lewis & L. 1953	—	California
prostrata	52	,, ,,	H	,,
purpurea	52	,, ,,	H	W: N. America

ANOGRA (OENOTHERA) $x = 7$

pallida	14	Johansen 1931d	HW	W: U.S.A.
trichocalyx	14	,, 1929c	H	,,

OENOTHERA * $x = 7$

biennis & 24 other spp.	14	Darlington 1931b	HR	E: N. America
	14	Cleland *et al.* 1950		N. America
lamarckiana Evening Primrose	14 (21, 28)	Darlington 1931b	H	Europe
organensis	14	Emerson 1938	—	N. America
rosea	14	Schwemmle 1924	H	Texas—Peru
tetragona fraseri (*glauca*)	28	,, ,,	H	E: N. America
perennis (*pumila*)	28	Valcanover 1927	H	,, ,,

TARAXIA (OENOTHERA) $x = 7$

heteranthera	14	Johansen 1929c	H	W: U.S.A.
ovata Golden Eggs	14	,, 1931a	H	California

GAURA $x = 7, 9$

biennis	14	Bhaduri 1942	H	N. America

GAURA (*cont*.)

coccinea	14	Johansen 1929c	H	C: N. America
lindheimeri	{ 14	Bhaduri 1941	H	Texas, Louisiana
	{ 18	Suzuka & K. 1949		

JUSSIEUA *x* = 8

repens Primrose Willow	16	Sinoto 1928b	DM	Tropics

CIRCAEA * *x* = 11

alpina	22	L. & L. 1944b	—	N. Temp.
lutetiana & 1 sp. Enchanter's Nightshade	22	Uddling 1929	—	Europe

GAYOPHYTUM *x* = 11

ramosissimum	22	Johansen 1933a	—	W: N. America

LOPEZIA *x* = 11

coronata	22	Täckholm 1914	H	Mexico

FUCHSIA *x* = 11

arborescens	22	Haque 1952	H	Mexico
boliviana	22	Warth 1925	H	Bolivia
colensoi	22	,, ,,	H	New Zealand
cordifolia	22	Haque 1952	H	Mexico
corymbiflora	22	Warth 1925	H	Peru
fulgens	22	,, ,,	H	Mexico
microphylla	22	Haque 1952	H	,,
procumbens	22	Johansen 1929c	H	New Zealand
serratifolia	22	Warth 1925	H	Peru
splendens	22	,, ,,	H	Mexico
magellanica (*macrostemma*)	22, 44	Johansen 1929c	H	Peru, Chile
v. *gracilis*	44	Haque 1952		
triphylla (3*x*)	33	Warth 1925	H	W. Indies
coccinea	44	,, ,,	H	Brazil
lycioides (*rosea*)	44	,, ,,	H	Chile
Garden forms 22, 55, 66, 77		Haque 1952	H	*cult*

ZAUSCHNERIA *x* = 15

cana (*microphylla*)	30	Clausen *et al*. 1940	H	California
garrettii	30	,, ,, ,,	—	,,
septentrionalis	30	,, ,, ,,	—	,,
latifolia	60	,, ,, ,,	—	,,
californica Calif. Fuchsia	60	,, ,, ,,	H	,,
v. *angustifolia* 60, *c*. 75		,, ,, ,,		

CHAMAENERION (EPILOBIUM) *x* = 18

angustifolium Rosebay Willow-herb	36	L. & L. 1948	H	N. Hemisphere
latifolium	72	,, ,,	—	Sib., N.W. Amer.

EPILOBIUM* *x* = 18

anagallidifolium (*alpinum*)	36	Bøcher & L. 1950	H	N. Hemisphere
hirsutum Codlins and Cream	36	L. & L. 1942	H	Europe
palustre Marsh W. H.	36	,, 1948	—	N. Hemisphere
pedunculare & 19 spp.	36	Hair 1942	—	New Zealand

TRAPA *x* = ?

natans Water Chestnut	*c*. 36	Palmgren 1943	N	Eur., Asia

88

78 HALORAGACEAE

MYRIOPHYLLUM $x = 7$
exalbescens		14	Löve 1954	—	N. America
alterniflorum		14	Scheerer 1939	—	Eur., Greenland
verticillatum	Water Milfoil	28	„ 1940	H	N: N. Amer., Eur., Asia
spicatum		28	Löve 1954	—	Eurasia

GUNNERA $x = ?$
chilensis		*c.* 24	Winge 1917	H	Andes

HIPPURIS $x = (8)$ 16
vulgaris	Mare's Tail	32	Winge 1917	—	N. Temp., Patag.
		32	L. & L. 1948		

79 CALLITRICHACEAE

CALLITRICHE $x = 3, 5$
autumnalis	Aut. Starwort	6	Jørgensen 1923	—	N. Eur., Iceland
(*hermaphroditica*)					
truncata		6	Dodds, T. 1937	—	W. & S. Europe
polymorpha		12	L. & L. 1948	—	N. & C. Eur., Cauc., Sib.
stagnalis		10, 20	Jørgensen 1923	—	S. Eur., N. Afr.
verna		20	Sokolovskaja 1932	—	Eur., Sib., N. Afr., N. Amer.
intermedia (*hamulata*)		38	Schotsman 1954	—	Eur., Cauc., Palest., Mor.

81 THYMELAEACEAE

DAPHNE $x = 9$
alpina	Alpine D.	18	Strasburger 1909	H	S. & C. Europe
bholua	Nepal Paper Pl.	18	Venkateswarlu 1946	T	India
(*cannabina*)					
cneorum	Garland Fl.	18	Fuchs 1938	H	S. & C. Europe
kiusana		18	Osawa 1913	H	Japan
laureola	Spurge Laurel	18	Fuchs 1938	H	C., S. & W. Eur., W. Asia
mezereum	February D.	18	Maude 1940	HM	Eur., N. Asia
yezoensis		18	M. & S. 1935	—	Japan
glomerata		18	S. & S. 1940	H	Cauc.
odora	Winter D.	{ 28	Takenaka 1931	HP	China, Japan
		{ 30	Yamaha, K. 1931		

WIKSTROEMIA $x = 9$ (Polyploids Apomictic)
canescens	Paper Bark T.	18	Venkateswarlu 1946	T	Him., China, Cey.
viridiflora	Philippine P.B.T.	{ 27	Fagerlind 1940	T	S.E. Asia
		{ 52?	Winkler 1906		

EDGEWORTHIA $x = 9$
papyrifera	Paper Bush	36	Sugiura 1936a	HT	China, Jap., Him.

PIMELEA* $x = 9$

cinerea & 10 spp.	36	Cruickshank 1953	H	Australia
humilis	72	,,	,,	H	Austr., Tasm.
lindleyana	90	,,	,,	H	Tasmania
drupacea	108	,,	,,	H	Vict., Tasm.

83 NYCTAGINACEAE

BOUGAINVILLEA $x = 17$

glabra	20	D. C. Cooper 1931	H	Brazil
garden forms	34	Wilson 1947	H	cult
spectabilis	—		H	Brazil
garden forms	34	,, ,,	H	cult

MIRABILIS $x = 29$

jalapa	58	Showalter 1935	HM	Trop. Amer.
longiflora	58	,, ,,	—	Mexico
multiflora	58	,, ,,	H	,,

OXYBAPHUS (ALLIONIA) $x = 29$

nyctagineus	58	Bowden 1945b	H	S: U.S.A.
viscosus	58	,, ,,	—	Peru

84 PROTEACEAE

PERSOONIA* $x = 7$

ferruginea	14	H. P. Lancaster unp.	H	N.S.W.
lanceolata	14	,, ,,	H	,,
linearis & 7 spp	14	,, ,,	H	,, Vict.

BANKSIA $x = 7$

ericifolia	28	H. P. Lancaster unp.	H	Australia
integrifolia	28	,, ,,	H	,,
latifolia	28	,, ,,	H	,,
serrata	28	,, ,,	H	,,
spinulosa	28	,, ,,	H	,,

BRABEIUM $x = 7$

stellatifolium	28	de Vos 1943	—	S. Africa

CENARRHENES $x = 7$

nitida	28	H. P. Lancaster unp.	—	Australia

DRYANDRA $x = 7$

floribunda	28	H. P. Lancaster unp.	H	W. Australia

LAMBERTIA $x = 7$

formosa	28	H. P. Lancaster unp.	H	W. Australia

MACADAMIA $x = 7$

ternifolia Queensland Nut	28 (56)	Urata unp.	HN	Queensland

XYLOMELUM $x = 7$

pyriforme	28	H. P. Lancaster unp.	H	N.S.W.

GREVILLEA*	$x=10$				
banksii		20	H. P. Lancaster unp.	H	Queensland
glabrata		20	,, ,,	H	W. Australia
robusta	Silky Oak	20	,, ,,	HSh	N.S.W.
& 22 spp.		20	,, ,,	H	Australia

HAKEA	$x=10$				
acicularis		20	H. P. Lancaster unp.	H	Austr., Tasm.
dactyloides		20	,, ,,	H	W. Australia

SYMPHYONEMA	$x=10$				
montanum		20	H. P. Lancaster unp.	—	Australia
paludosum		20	,, ,,	—	,,

AULAX*	$x=11$				
cneorifolia & 2 spp.		22	de Vos 1943	H	S. Africa

CONOSPERMUM	$x=11$				
ericifolium		22	H. P. Lancaster unp.	H	N.S.W.
longifolium		22	,, ,,	H	,,

LOMATIA	$x=11$				
silaifolia		22	H. P. Lancaster unp.	H	E. Australia

STENOCARPUS	$x=11$				
sinuatus		22	H. P. Lancaster unp.	H	E. Australia

TELOPEA	$x=11$				
speciosissima	Waratah	22	H. P. Lancaster unp.	H	N.S.W.

LEUCOSPERMUM*	$x=12$				
reflexum & 3 spp.		24	de Vos 1943	H	S. Africa

MIMETES	$x=12$				
lyrigera		24	de Vos 1943	—	S. Africa

PARANOMUS	$x=12$				
spicatus		24	de Vos 1943	H	S. Africa

PROTEA*	$x=12$				
grandiflora & 9 spp.		24	de Vos 1943	H	S. Africa

SERRURIA	$x=12$				
artemisiifolia		24	de Vos 1943	H	S. Africa

LEUCADENDRON	$x=13$				
plumosum		26	de Vos 1943	H	S. Africa
argenteum	Silver Tree	26–28	,, ,,	HSh	,,

ISOPOGON	$x=13$				
anethifolius		26	H. P. Lancaster unp.	—	Australia

PETROPHILA	$x=13$				
pulchella		26	H. P. Lancaster unp.	H	Australia

Group VI

DILLENIALES
85, 86
(H)ST

CORIARIALES
87
S

PITTOSPORALES
88–90
(H)ST

BIXALES
91–96
HST

TAMARICALES
97–99
HST

PASSIFLORALES
100–102
HST

CUCURBITALES
103–106
H(S)

CACTALES
107
HS

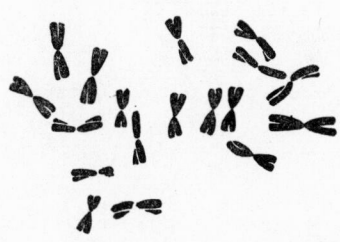

Cistus corbariensis

85 DILLENIACEAE

HIBBERTIA $x = 8$

diffusa		16	A. T. Hotchkiss unp. —	E. Australia
scandens (volubilis)		16	„ „ H	„
linearis		16, 32	„ „ —	„
amplexicaulis		32	„ „ —	W. Australia
saligna		c. 64	„ „ —	E. Australia

DILLENIA $x = 8$

ovata	32	Tixier 1953 —	Viet-Nam

WORMIA $x = 13$

suffruticosa	Marsh Simpoh	26	Paetow 1931 H	Malaya

87 CORIARIACEAE

CORIARIA $x = ?$

myrtifolia	c. 80	Bowden 1940a H	S. Eur., N.W. Afr.

88 PITTOSPORACEAE

PITTOSPORUM $x = 12$

tobira	Japanese P.	24	Schürhoff 1929a H	Jap., China

91 BIXACEAE

BIXA $x = 7, 8$

orellana	Annatto	{ 14	EKJ*	
		16	Simmonds 1954 D	S. America

93 FLACOURTIACEAE

FLACOURTIA $x = 11$

ramontchi	Uguressa	22	Bhaduri & K. 1949 FH	India, Malaya
sepiaria		{ 22	„ „ FH	„ „
		22	Tjio 1948	

IDESIA $x = 11?$

polycarpa	c. 44	Corti 1948 H	China, Japan

HYDNOCARPUS $x = 11, 12$

ilicifolia		22	EKJ* MW	Mal., Camb. Java
anthelminthica	Ch. Chaulmoogra	24	„ MW	Indo-China
laurifolia	Marotti Oil	48	Hamacher 1947 M	S. India

95 CANELLACEAE

CAPSICODENDRON $x = 13$

dinisii	26	Occhioni 1945 —	Brazil

95

96 CISTACEAE

HELIANTHEMUM* $x = 5, 11$

squamatum	10	Coutinho & L.-A. '48	—	W. Medit.
apenninum	20	Proctor 1955	H	W. & S. Europe,
as *polifolium, pulverulentum*	20	Bowden 1940a		Asia Minor
glaucum	20	,, ,,	H	Medit.
ledifolium	20	Proctor 1955	H	,,
kahiricum & 3 spp.	20	Atsmon unp.	H	N. Afr., S.W. As.
chamaecistus Rock Rose	{20	Proctor 1955	H	Eur., S.W. Asia
as *vulgare*	{32?	Bowden 1940a		
alpestre	{20	,, ,,	H	S. Eur. Mtns.,
	{22	Proctor 1955		Asia Minor
nummularium (*paniculatum*)	{20	Lorenzo-Andreu 1951	H	W. Medit.
	{22	Coutinho & L.A. '48		
canum	22	Proctor 1955	H	W. & S. Eur.,
				S.W. Asia
lunulatum	22	,, ,,	H	Italy
oelandicum	22	,, ,,	H	Arctic, N. Eng.

CROCANTHEMUM (HELIANTHEMUM) $x = (5)\ 10$

canadense	20	Bowden 1940a	H	N.E: U.S.A.

TUBERARIA (HELIANTHEMUM) $x = 6, 7$

vulgaris	14	Proctor 1955	H	W. Medit.
guttata	{36	,, ,,	H	W. Eur., Medit.
	{48	Chiarugi 1925		

FUMANA (HELIANTHEMUM) $x = 8$

arabica	32	Atsmon unp.	—	Medit., Pers.
laevipes	32	Proctor 1955	H	W. Medit.
thymifolia	2	,, ,,	—	Medit., Pers.

HALIMIUM $x = 9$

atriplicifolium	18	Chiarugi 1925	H	Spain
halimifolium	18	Proctor 1955	H	W. Medit.
lasianthum	18	Snoad unp.	H	S. Spain, Port.
libanotis	18	Rodrigues 1950	H	W. Medit.
ocymoides	18	Proctor 1955	H	Iber. Penin.
umbellatum	18	,, ,,	H	W. Eur., Medit.

CISTUS $x = 9$

albidus Rock Rose	18	Bowden 1945a	H	Medit.
crispus	18	Dansereau 1940	H	S.W. Europe
heterophyllus	18	,, ,,	—	Algeria
hirsutus	18	La Cour 1945*	H	Iber. Penin.
ladaniferus Ladanum Pl.	18	Chiarugi 1937	HMP	S.W. Europe
laurifolius	18	Bowden 1945a	H	Medit.
monspeliensis	18	La Cour 1945*	H	S. Europe
parviflorus	18	Dansereau 1940	H	E. Medit.
populifolius	18	Chiarugi 1937	M	W. Medit.
rosmarinifolius	18	La Cour 1945*	H	,,
salvifolius	18	Dansereau 1940	H	Medit.
symphitifolius	18	Chiarugi 1937	M	Teneriffe
villosus Cretan R. R.	18	,, 1925	H	Medit.
varius (*crisp.* × *monspel.*)	18	Snoad unp.	H	Algeria, France
corbariensis (*popul.* × *salv.*)	18	La Cour 1945*	H	Medit.

CISTUS (*cont.*)
florentinus (monspel. × *salv.*) 18 Snoad unp. H Medit.
purpureus (ladanif. × *vill.*) 18 ,, ,, H *cult*

HALIMIOCISTUS (HALIMIUM × CISTUS) *x* = 9
ingwersenii 18 Snoad unp. H *cult*
sahucii 18 ,, ,, H France, *cult*

97 FRANKENIACEAE

FRANKENIA *x* = 5?
pulverulenta 20 Sugiura 1937b H Med., Ind., S. Afr.
hirsuta 30 Castro & F. 1946 — Eur., S.W. Asia, S. Africa

98 TAMARICACEAE

TAMARIX* *x* = 12
aphylla (articulata) Thaia, 24 Bowden 1945b SuTW W. Asia
Athel T.
ericoides 24 Sharma 1939 T India
gallica Tamarisk & 4 spp. 24 Bowden 1940a HSbT Eur., N. Afr.

MYRICARIA *x* = 12
germanica .False Tamarisk 24 Frisendahl 1912 H N. Temp.

99 FOUQUIERACEAE

FOUQUIERA *x* = 8
burragei 16 Johansen 1936 — N. America
peninsularis 16 ,, ,, — California
splendens Ocotillo 16 ,, ,, HO S.W: U.S.A.

101 PASSIFLORACEAE

PASSIFLORA (TACSONIA) *x* = 6, 9, 10
x = 6
bryonoides 12 Bowden 1945b — Mexico
capsularis 12 ,, ,, H Trop. Amer.
pulchella 12 Storey 1950 — Venezuela
suberosa 24, 36 ,, ,, FH Trop. S. Amer.
lutea Yellow P. Fl. 84 Bowden 1945b FH W. Indies

x = 9
caerulea Blue Crown P. Fl. 18 Nakajima 1931 FH Brazil
edulis Passion Fruit 18 Storey 1950, EKJ* F Trop. S. Amer.
incarnata May Pop 18 ,, ,, FH S.E: U.S.A.
laurifolia Water Lemon 18 ,, ,, FH Trop. Amer.
ligularis Sweet Gr. 18 ,, ,, FH Peru
maliformis Sweet Calabash 18 ,, ,, FH Trop. Amer.
manicata 18 ,, ,, H Peru, Colo., Venez.

97

PASSIFLORA (*cont.*)

mixta		18	La Cour 1952	H	Andes
mollissima		18	Storey 1950	H	,,
quadrangularis	Giant Granadilla	18	,, ,, EKJ*	FH	Trop. Amer.
seemannii		18	,, ,,	—	C. America
subpeltata		18	,, ,,	H	Mex.—Venez.
vitifolia		18	,, ,,	H	C. America
allardii		18	La Cour 1951b	H	*cult*
(*caerulea* × *quadrangularis*)					

$x = 9, 10$

gracilis		⌠18 ⌡20	La Cour 1952 Bowden 1945b	H	Venezuela
foetida	Wild P. Fr.	⌠18 ⎮20 ⎨20 ⎮22	EKJ* Storey 1950 Nishiyama & K. 1942 Bowden 1945b	FHM	Trop. S. Amer. O.W. Tropics, *nat.*
v. *gossypifolia*		20	Storey 1950		

103 CUCURBITACEAE

CUCUMIS $x = 7, 12$

$x = 7$

sativus	Cucumber	14 (28)	Heimlich 1927 Shifriss 1942	(M)V	*cult*, India
trigonus	Jackal's C.	14	EKJ*	M	India, Turkest.

$x = 12$

agrestis	Wild Melon	24	Araratian 1939	F	Armenia
chinensis		24	,, ,,	F	China
microcarpus		24	,, ,,	—	Armenia
anguria	W.I. Gherkin	24	Kozhuchow 1930	V	Trop. Amer.
dipsaceus	Teasel Gourd	24	,, ,,	V	Trop. Afr., Ar.
flexuosus	Snake C.	24	,, ,,	V	Tropics
lyratus		24	,, ,,	V	Tanganyika
melo	Melon Cantaloupe	24 (48)	Yamaha & S. 1936 Shifriss 1941	NVF	*cult*, Afgh.
metuliferus	Horned C.	24	Kozhuchow 1930	V	S. Africa
myriocarpus	Gooseberry G.	24	,, ,,	V	,,
odoratissimus		24	,, ,,	F	Tropics
prophetarum	Globe Cucumber	24	,, ,,	V	Ar., Tr. Afr.
sacleuxi		24	,, ,,	V	Zanzibar

ACTINOSTEMMA $x = 8$

lobatum		16	Kurita 1939	—	Japan

CYCLANTHERA $x = 8$

explodens		32	Resende 1937	—	Ecuador
pedata		32	,, ,,	—	Mexico

ECHINOCYSTIS (MICRAMPELIS) $x = 8$

fabacea		32	McKay 1931	V	California
oregona		32	,, ,,	—	W: N. America
macrocarpa		⌠32 ⌡64	,, ,, Whitaker 1950	—	California

98

THLADIANTHA $x=9$
  dubia   18   Kozhuchow 1934   V   China

BRYONIA $x=10$
  alba   White Bryony   20   Brabec 1954   M   W. Medit.
  dioica   Red Bryony   20   ,,   ,,   M   Eur., Medit.

CITRULLUS $x=11$
  colocynthis   Colocynth   22   Whitaker 1933b   M   Africa
  vulgaris   Water Melon   22   Kozhuchow 1925   FN   Trop. Africa

GYMNOPETALUM $x=11$
  cochinchinense   22   Islam & S. 1951   —   Trop. Asia

LAGENARIA $x=11$
  vulgaris   Bottle Gourd   22   McKay 1931   V   cult, Afgh.
                or Calabash   (44) Sinnott et al. 1939

MOMORDICA $x=11, 14$
  balsamina   Balsam Apple   22   McKay 1931   MV   Tropics
  charantia   Bitter Gourd   22   Yamaha & S. 1936   VVit ,,
  dioica   28   Richharia & G. 1953 V   India

TRICHOSANTHES $x=11$
  anguina   Snake Gourd   22   McKay 1931   V   Trop. Asia
  dioica   Patol   22   Bhaduri & B. 1947   V   India
  japonica   22   Sinoto 1929   V   Trop. Asia
  multiloba   22   Kurita 1939   —   Japan
                        $(\male, 20+XY)$
  shikokiana   22   Kurita 1939   —   ,,

  cucumeroides   ⎧ 44   ,,   ,,   V   ,,
                                       ⎩ 44   Yamaha & S. 1936
  palmata   44   Rangaswami 1949   —   Trop. Asia

MELOTHRIA $x=11, 12$
  japonica   22   Nakajima 1931   V   Japan
  maderaspatana   22+0–2B Kumar & V. 1951   Trop. As. & Afr.
  leiosperma   24   ,,   ,,   India
  punctata (abyssinica)   24   McKay 1931   V   S. Africa
  scabra   24   Kozhuchow 1934   V   Mexico
  heterophylla   48   Kumar & V. 1951   Trop. Asia
  perpusilla   48   ,,   ,,   India, Malaya

CUCURBITA $x=10, 12$
  maxima   Winter or Turban   ⎧ 24   Rau 1929   OV   Peru, cult
           Squash   ⎩ 40   Pearson et al. 1951
  moschata Pumpkin,   ⎧ 24   Yamaha & S. 1936
            Cushaw or   ⎪ 40   Ruttle 1931b   V   Mexico, cul
            Toonai   ⎨ 40   Pearson et al. 1951
                             ⎩ 48   Kozhuchow 1925
  pepo   Summer Squash   ⎧ 40   Erwin & H. 1930   OMV   S.W. Asia
            or Vegetable   ⎨ 40   Castetter 1930   cult
            Marrow   ⎩ (80) EKJ*
    v. pomiformis   40   Kozhuchow 1925
    v. citrullina   42   ,,   ,,
  andreana   40   Covas & S. 1946   V   Uruguay

99

CUCURBITA (*cont.*)

digitata		40	McKay 1931	V	N. Mexico
ficifolia	Malabar Gourd	40	,, ,,	V	E. Asia
foetidissima	Calabazilla	40	,, ,,	V	Mexico
palmata		40	,, ,,	V	California

IBERVILLEA (MAXIMOWICZIA) $x = 11, 12$

lindheimeri	22	MacKay 1930	—	Texas
sp.	24	,, ,,	—	—

BENINCASA $x = 12$

hispida	Wax or White	⎧ 24	Resende 1937	MV	Trop. Asia
(*cerifera*)	Gourd	⎩ 24	Whitaker 1933b		

COCCINIA (CEPHALANDRA) $x = 12$

hirtella		24	McKay 1930	V	S. Africa
indica	Ivy Gourd	24	Chakravorti 1948	FV	Trop Asia
(*cordifolia*)		24	Kumar & V. 1952		
		($\male 22 + XY$, $\female 22 + XX$)			
(3x)		36	Kumar & V. 1952		
		($\male 33 + XXY$)			

ECBALLIUM $x = 12$

elaterium	Squirting C.	24	Mackay 1930	H	Medit.

SECHIUM $x = 12$

edule	Chayote, Chocho	24	Sugiura 1930	HVT	W. Indies

SICYOS $x = 12$

angulatus	Bur Cucumber	24	Kozhuchow 1934	HV	E: U.S.A.

CUCURBITELLA $x = 13$

asperata	26	Covas & S. 1946	—	Argentine

LUFFA $x = 13$

acutangula	Dishcloth G.	26	McKay 1930	ToV	Old World
cylindrica	Loofah	26	Yahama & S. 1936	ToTV	O.W. Trop.
v. *gigantea*		26	McKay 1930		*cult*

104 BEGONIACEAE

BEGONIA $x = ?$

picta	22	White *et al.* 1946	H	Himalayas
heracleifolia	24	Hamel 1937	H	Mexico
hirsuta	24	Matsuura & O. 1936	H	Guiana
nelumbiifolia	26	Hamel 1937	H	Mexico
haageana	48	M. & O. 1936	H	Brazil
evansiana	⎧ 24	Bowden 1945a	H	Ch., Jap., Mal.
	⎩ 26	White *et al.* 1946		
incana	⎧ 24	Hamel 1937	H	Mexico
	⎩ 28	Mereminski 1936		
socotrana	28	M. & O. 1936	H	Socotra
carminata	42	,, ,,	H	*cult*
coccinea	42	,, ,,	H	S. America
cucullata	56	Bowden 1945a	—	Brazil
maculata	56	M. & O. 1936	H	,,

100

BEGONIA (*cont.*)

gracillis	84	M. & O. 1936	H	Mexico
metallica	70	„ „	H	Brazil
schmidtiana	{ 32 { 26?	„ 1943 Pastrana 1932	H	„
dichotoma	36	Hamel 1937	H	Venezuela
longipes	36	„ „	H	Mexico
vitifolia	36	„ „	H	Brazil
albo-picta	54	M. & O. 1936	H	„
angularis	54	Hamel 1937	H	„
wilsonii	54	M. & O. 1936	H	Szechuan
dregei	26	M. & O. 1936	H	S. Africa
argenteo-guttata	52	„ „	H	*cult*
margaritae	52	„ „	H	„
ulmifolia	30	M. and O. 1943	H	Venezuela
venosa	30	Hamel 1937	H	Brazil
fuchsioides	60	M. & O. 1936	H	Mexico
kotoensis	60	„ 1943	—	Japan
semperflorens	33, 36, 60, 66	M. & O. 1943	H	Brazil, *cult*
rex	32, 33, 34 42, 43, 44	„ „	H	Himalayas, *cult*

105 DATISCACEAE

DATISCA *x* = 11

cannabina	22	Sinoto 1929	H	S.W. Asia, Him.

106 CARICACEAE

CARICA *x* = 9

candamarcensis	Mountain Papaw	18	Heilborn 1921	F	Trop. Am.
cauliflora		18	Storey 1941	—	Venezuela
chrysopetala		18	„ „	—	Ecuador
dodecaphylla		18	Kumar & S. 1944	—	Brazil
peltata		18	Storey 1941	—	Nicaragua
pentagona		18	„ „	—	Ecuador
pubescens		18	Kumar & A. 1942a	—	Guatemala
quercifolia		18	EKJ*	—	S. America
papaya	Papaya, " Papaw "	{ 18 { 36	Eichhorn 1937b Hofmeyer 1945	FM	Trop. America

107 CACTACEAE

TRIBE I: PERESKIEAE

PERESKIA *x* = 11

aculeata	Barbadoes Gooseberry	22	Katagiri 1952	F	Mexico, W.I.

101

PERESKIA (*cont.*)

saccharosa	22	Katagiri 1952	H	Argentine, Para.
tampicana	22	Remski 1954	—	Mexico

TRIBE II: OPUNTIEAE

OPUNTIA* $x = 11$ (Apomixis)

basilaris	22	Takagi 1938	—	Mexico
brasiliensis	22	Stockwell 1935	—	S. America
chlorotica	22	,, ,,	—	N. America
microdasys & 4 spp.	22	Katagiri 1952	H	Mexico
repens	22	Bowden 1945a	—	Puerto Rica
santa-rita	22	Stockwell 1935	—	S: U.S.A.
compressa (*opuntia*)	$\begin{cases} 22\,(44) \\ 44 \end{cases}$	Bowden 1945a Katagiri 1952	—	N. America
polyacantha	$\begin{cases} 22 \\ 44, c.\,66 \end{cases}$	M. & S. 1935 Stockwell 1935	—	,,
monacantha (*vulgaris*)	33	Katagiri 1952	F	S. America
leucotricha	44	,, ,,	H	Mexico
salmiana	44	,, ,,	H	S. America
tomentosa	44	,, ,,	H	Mexico
impedita	44 (88)	Bowden 1945a	—	Florida
dillenii Prickly Pear	66	Carpio 1952	FFo_1	Sub.-Trop. Amer.
discata	c. 66	Stockwell 1935	—	Arizona
fragilis	66	Bowden 1945a	—	W: U.S.A.
phaeacantha	c. 66	Stockwell 1935	—	Mex., Tex.
subulata	66	Katagiri 1952	H	Chile, Argentine
elongata	66, 88	,, ,,	—	Mexico
diademata	$\begin{cases} 22 \\ 88 \end{cases}$	Takagi 1938 Katagiri 1952	H	Argentine
ficus-indica	88	Carpio 1952	F	S. America
cylindrica	110	Katagiri 1952	H	Peru, Ecuador

PTEROCACTUS $x = 11$

tuberosus	22 (44)	Schnack & C. 1947	—	Argentine

CONSOLEA $x = 11$

rubescens	132	Katagiri 1952	H	W. Indies

TRIBE III: CEREEAE

All genera in this tribe have $x = 11$ and nearly all species have 22 or 44 chromosomes.

ACANTHOCEREUS

pentagonus	22	Beard 1937	—	Trop. America

ASTROPHYTUM*

asterias	22	Beard 1937	H	Mexico
capricorne & 2 spp.	22	Katagiri 1952	H	,,

BORZICACTUS

aurivillius	22	Katagiri 1952	H	Peru

CARNEGIEA

gigantea	22	Stockwell 1935	FW	Ariz., Calif.

CEREUS *				
peruvianus	22	Takagi 1938	H	Brazil, Argentine
tetragonus & 1 sp.	22	Katagiri 1952	—	Brazil
CORYPHANTHA				
runyonii	22	Beard 1937	H	Texas
DOLICHOTHELE				
longimamma	22	Katagiri 1952	H	Mexico
ECHINOCACTUS				
grusonii	22	Katagiri 1952	H	,,
ECHINOFOSSULOCACTUS				
crispatus	22	Katagiri 1952	H	Mexico
grandicornis	c. 22	Beard 1937	H	,,
ECHINOPSIS *				
tubiflora & 2 spp.	22	Katagiri 1952	H	Brazil, Argentine
EPIPHYLLUM				
strictum	22	Beard 1937	—	Trop. America
ESCOBARIA				
runyonii	22	Beard 1937	—	California
FEROCACTUS *				
acanthodes (rostii)	22	Stockwell 1935	H	,,
latispinus & 4 spp.	22	Katagiri 1952	H	Mexico
GYMNOCALYCIUM *				
gibbosum	22	Schnack & C. 1947	H	Argentine
platense & 2 spp.	22	Katagiri 1952	H	,,
HAMATOCACTUS *				
setispinus & 1 sp.	22	Katagiri 1952	H	Mex., Tex.
HELIOCEREUS				
amecamensis	22	Rowley unp.	H	Mexico
HOMALOCEPHALA				
texensis	22	Beard 1937	H	Mex., Tex.
HYLOCEREUS *				
undatus & 5 spp.	22	Beard 1937	H	W. Indies
LEMAIREOCEREUS *				
pruinosus & 1 sp.	22	Katagiri 1952	H	Mexico
LOPHOCEREUS				
schottii	22	Stockwell 1935	—	Calif., Ariz.
LOPHOPHORA				
williamsii	22	Beard 1937	HM	Mex., Tex.
MONVILLEA				
spegazzinii	22	Katagiri 1952	H	Argentine

NOPALXOCHIA
ackermannii   22   Beard 1937   H   Mexico

NYCTOCEREUS
serpentinus   22   Beard 1937   H   „

PHELLOSPERMA $x = 11$
tetrancistra   22   Remski 1954   H   W: N. Amer.

RHIPSALIS
mesembryanthoides   22   Beard 1937   —   Brazil

SCHLUMBERGERA
bridgesii   22   Takagi 1938   H   Trop. S. Amer.
russelliana   22   Stockwell 1935   H   Brazil

SELENICEREUS *
pteranthus & 3 spp.   22   Beard 1937   HM   Mexico

THELOCACTUS
bicolor   22   Beard 1937   H   Tex., Mex.

WERCKLEOCEREUS
glaber   22   Beard 1937   —   Guatemala

WILCOXIA
poselgeri   22   Beard 1937   H   Tex., Mex.
schmollii   22   Katagiri 1952   H   Mexico

ZYGOCACTUS
truncatus   Christmas Cactus   22   Remski 1954   H   Brazil

ECHINOCEREUS *
procumbens & 1 sp.   22   Katagiri 1952   H   Mexico
reichenbachii & 5 spp.   22   Beard 1937   H   Tex., N. Mex.
engelmannii   44   Stockwell 1935   H   N. America

MAMMILLARIA (NEOMAMMILLARIA) * $x = 11$
aureiceps & 8 spp.   22   Beard 1937   H   Mexico
bocasana & 4 spp.   22   Katagiri 1952   H   „
minuta   22   Beard 1937   H   —
  89 spp.   22   Remski 1954   H   C. America

compressa   44   „   „   H   Mexico
dioica   44   „   „   H   Calif.
morganiana   44   „   „   H   Mexico
multiceps   44   „   „   H   „
pseudocrucigera   44   „   „   H   „
ruestii   44   „   „   H   Hond., Guat.
prolifera   44, 66   „   „   H   W. Indies
parkinsonii   44, 88   „   „   H   Mexico

capensis   264!   „   „   H   Calif.

MYRTILLOCACTUS
geometrizans   22, 44   Katagiri 1952   FH   Mexico

104

TRICHOCEREUS
chiloensis	22	Katagiri 1952	—	Chile
spachianus	44	,, ,,	H	Argentine

CEPHALOCEREUS
chrysacanthus	44	Katagiri 1952	H	Mexico
royenii	44	,, ,,	H	W. Indies

MEDIOCACTUS
coccineus	44	Beard 1937	H	Brazil, Argentine

NOTOCACTUS
apricus	38?	Takagi 1938	H	Uruguay
mammulosus	44	Katagiri 1952	H	Argent., Urug.

ARIOCARPUS
fissuratus	38?	Takagi 1938	M	Tex., Mex.

Group VII

THEALES		MYRTALES

THEALES
108–117
ST

MYRTALES
118–122
ST

GUTTIFERALES
123–126
(H)ST

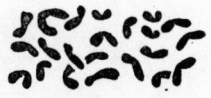

Eucalyptus rudis

108 THEACEAE (TERNSTROEMIACEAE)

CAMELLIA (THEA) $x = 15$

cuspidata		30	Janaki Ammal 1953b	H	E. & C. China
hongkongensis		30	,, ,, ,,	H	Hong Kong
kissi	Wild Tea, Letpet	30	,, ,, ,,	B	Him., Bur., China
lanceolata		30	,, ,, ,,	—	E. Indies, Philip.
maliflora		30	,, ,, ,,	H	China
salicifolia		30	,, ,, ,,	—	S.E. China, Form.
taliensis		30	,, ,, ,,	H	Yunnan
japonica	Camellia	30	,, ,, ,,	BHO	Japan, Korea
v. *grandiflora*		45	,, ,, ,,	H	*cult*
sinensis	Chinese Tea	30	,, ,, ,,	BM	Yunnan, *cult*, Chi.
v. *assamica*	Assam Tea	30	,, ,, ,,	B	Assam, S.E. Yun.
v. *macrophylla*		{45	,, ,, ,,	H	*cult*
		{60	Simura 1935		
saluenensis		30	Janaki Ammal 1953b	H	Yunnan
v. *macrophylla*		60	,, ,, ,,	H	,,
pitardi		30	,, ,, ,,	H	C. & S.W. China
v. *yunnanica*		90	,, ,, ,,	H	Yunnan
oleifera	Tea Oil Pl.	90	,, ,, ,,	O	E. China (*cult*)
reticulata		90	,, ,, ,,	H	Yunnan
sasanqua	Tea Oil Pl.	90	,, ,, ,,	HOP	Japan (*cult*)

EURYA $x = 21$

japonica		42	Nakajima 1942	H	E. Asia

TERNSTROEMIA $x = ?$

japonica		50	Morinaga & F. 1931	H	Sub.-Trop. Asia

112 ACTINIDIACEAE

ACTINIDIA $x = ?$

polygama	Silver Vine	{*c.* 58	Nakajima 1942	FH	Manch., Korea,
		{*c.* 116	Bowden 1940b		China
kolomicta		*c.* 112	Nakajima 1942	H	Jap., China, Man.
arguta	Tara Vine	*c.* 116	Bowden 1940b	H	Him., Jap., Man.
chinensis	Ch. Gooseberry	{*c.* 116	,, ,,	HFVit	China
		{*c.* 160	Rizet 1945		
fairchildii (*arguta* × *chinensis*)		*c.* 132	Bowden 1940b	F	*cult*

114 OCHNACEAE

OCHNA $x = 7$ (Apomixis)

serrulata	Natal Pear	35	Chiarugi 1930b	H	S. Africa

116 DIPTEROCARPACEAE

PENTACME $x = 6$

siamensis		12	Tixier 1953	W	S.E. Asia

9

DIPTEROCARPUS $x = 10$

alatus	20	Tixier 1953	Re	S.E. Asia
intricatus	20	„ „	ReW	Vietnam
obtusifolius	20	„ „	W	S.E. Asia

HOPEA $x = 10$

odorata Thingam	20	Tixier 1953	MReW	Burma, Siam

ANISOPTERA $x = 10$

cochinchinensis	20	Tixier 1953	W	Vietnam, Siam

118 MYRTACEAE

SF1: LEPTOSPERMOIDEAE

ACTINODIUM $x = 6$

cunninghamii	12	Smith-White 1950	—	W. Australia

DARWINIA* $x = 6, 7, 9$

(i) *citriodora* & 3 spp.	12	Smith-White 1950	H	W. Australia
diosmoides & 5 spp.	12	„ 1954a	H	„
pauciflora	18	„ „	—	„
vestita	18	„ „	—	„
(ii) *micropetala*	14	„ „	—	S. Australia

VERTICORDIA* $x = 6, 8, 9, 11$

(i) *grandiflora*	12	Smith-White 1954a	—	W. Australia
nitens & 4 spp.	16	„ „	H	„
chrysantha	32	„ „	—	„
brownii & 2 spp.	18	„ „	H	„
habrantha	36	„ „	—	„
monadelpha	*c.* 36	„ „	—	„
densiflora & 2 spp.	22	„ „	H	„
(ii) *drummondii* & 2 spp.	22	„ „	—	„
grandis	44	„ „	—	„

HOMORANTHUS* $x = 9$

darwinioides & 2 spp.	18	Smith-White 1954a	—	N.S.W.

CHAMAELAUCIUM* $x = 11$

uncinatum & 2 spp.	22	Smith-White '50, '54a	H	W. Australia

PILEANTHUS $x = 11$

peduncularis	22	Smith-White 1954a	—	W. Australia

AGONIS $x = 11$

flexuosa	22	Smith-White 1948a	H	W. Australia

ANGOPHORA $x = 11$

cordifolia	22	Smith-White 1942	H	N.S.W.
intermedia	22	„ „	H	E. Australia
lanceolata	22	„ „	H	„

BACKHOUSIA $x = 11$

citriodora Sweet Verbena T.	22	Smith-White 1942	HO	Australia
myrtifolia	22	„ 1948a	H	N.S.W.

BAECKEA* $x = 11$

crenulata		22	Smith-White 1948a	—	N.S.W.
diosmifolia & 3 spp.		22	,, ,,	H	,,

CALOTHAMNUS $x = 11$

villosus		22	Smith-White 1948a	H	W. Australia

CALYTHRIX $x = 11$

fraseri		22	Smith-White 1950	—	W. Australia
tetragona		22	,, ,,	H	E. ,,

EUCALYPTUS $x = 11$

alba		22	Krug & A. 1949	W	N. Australia
angulosa		22	Atchison 1947b	W	Australia
behriana	Mallee Box	22	Smith-White 1948a	W	N.S.W.
botryoides	Bangalay	22	Atchison 1947b	HShW	Australia
calophylla	Marri	22	,, ,,	HW	W. Australia
camaldulensis (*rostrata*) Red Gum		22	,, ,,	DMW	Australia
citriodora Lemon-scented G.		22 22	,, ,, Smith-White 1948a	HOW	E. Australia
cladocalyx (*corynocalyx*) Sugar Gum		24!	Atchison 1947b	FoHSh	Australia
diversicolor	Karri	22	,, ,,	W	W. Australia
dives Broad-leaved Peppermint		22	Smith-White 1942	HO	N.S.W.
ficifolia Red Flowering Gum		22	,, ,,	H	W. Australia
globulus Tasm. Blue Gum		22	McAulay *et al.* 1936	HOW	Tasmania
gummifera	Bloodwood	22	Smith-White 1942	OW	Australia
gunnii	Cider Gum	22	Atchison 1947b	HW	Tasmania
haemostoma	Scribbly Gum	22	Smith-White 1942	W	Australia
incrassata		22	,, ,,	OW	,,
johnstoni		22	McAulay *et al.* 1936	W	Tasmania
kirtoniana		22	Atchison 1947b	W	Australia
linearis		22	McAulay & C. 1937	H	,,
longifolia	Woolly Butt	22	Atchison 1947b	W	,,
maculata	Spotted Gum	22	,, ,,	HW	,,
obliqua	Messmate	22	McAulay & C. 1937	HW	,,
paniculata	Grey Ironbark	22	Smith-White 1942	W	,,
pauciflora	Snow Gum	22	McAulay & C. 1937	H	,,
pulverulenta		22	Atchison 1947b	H	,,
redunca v. *elata* Wandoo		24!	,, ,,	W	W. Australia
resinifera	Red Mahogany	22	,, ,,	W	Australia
rubida	Candlebark	22	,, ,,	ShW	,,
rudis Swamp Gum, Moitch		22	,, ,,	W	,,
saligna Sydney Blue Gum		22	Krug & A. 1949	W	,,
sideroxylon Red Ironbark		22	Smith-White 1942	HW	,,
staigeriana		22	,, 1950	H	N. Queensland
steedmanii		22	Atchison 1947b	W	W. Australia
stuartiana	Apple Box	22	,, ,,	W	Australia
tetraptera		22	Smith-White 1950	W	W. Australia
torquata	Coolgardie Gum	22	Atchison 1947b	H	Australia
triantha	White Mahogany	22	,, ,,	W	,,
viminalis	Manna Gum	22	,, ,,	W	,,

KUNZEA $x = 11$

ambigua (*corifolia*)		22	Smith-White 1948a	H	N.S.W.
capitata		22	,, ,,	—	,,

MELALEUCA *   x = 11

elliptica		22	Smith-White 1948a	H	W. Australia
styphelioides		22	„ „	H	N.S.W.
thymifolia & 8 spp.		22	„ „	H	„

MICROMYRTUS   x = 11

ciliata (*microphylla*)	22	Smith-White 1950	H	E. Australia

SYNCARPIA   x = 11

laurifolia	22	Smith-White 1948a	—	N.S.W.

THRYPTOMENE   x = 11

calycina (*mitchelliana*)	22	Smith-White 1950	H	E. Australia

TRISTANIA   x = 11

conferta	Brisbane Box	22	Smith-White 1942	HW	Australia
laurina		22	„ 1948a	H	N.S.W.

CALLISTEMON *   x = 11

citrinus	Bottle-Brush Tree & 9 spp.	22	Smith-White 1948a	HO	E. Australia
pinifolius	22, *c.* 30, 33		„ „	H	N.S.W.
linearis	22, 33, 44		„ „	H	„
rigidus	22, 44		„ „	H	„
viminalis	44		„ „	—	Queensland

LEPTOSPERMUM *   x = 11

stellatum & 11 spp.	22	Smith-White 1948a	H	Australia
parvifolium	44	„ „	—	„

SF2: MYRTOIDEAE

FEIJOA   x = 11

sellowiana	Feijoa, Pineapple-Guava	22	Bowden 1940a	F	Brazil

MYRTUS   x = 11

communis	Myrtle	22	Greco 1929	HPSp	Medit., S.W. Asia

PIMENTA   x = 11

acris	Lemon-scented Allspice	22	EKJ*	PSp	W. Indies

EUGENIA   x = 11

malaccensis	Malacca Apple	22	van der Pijl 1934	F	Trop. Asia
uniflora (*michelli*)	Surinam Cherry	22	Bhaduri & I. 1949	FH	Brazil
jambos	Rose Apple	28, *c.* 42	van der Pijl 1934	FH	Trop. Asia
		c. 54	„ „		
		46	Bhaduri & I. 1949		
leuhmanni		44	Smith-White 1948a	—	N.S.W.
myrtifolia		44	„ „	HW	„
smithii	Lilli-pilli	44	„ „	HW	„
cumini (*jambolana*)	Jambalam	44	Tjio 1948	ADFW	India
		44, 66	Bhaduri & I. 1949		
javanica	Jum Rool	45	„ „	F	E. Indies

112

PSIDIUM $x = 11$

guava	Guava Seedless var.	{22	Atchison 1947b, EKJ*	FVit	Trop. Amer.
		33	Kumar & R. 1952		
cattleianum	Purple or Gooseberry G.	{88	Atchison 1947b	F	Brazil
		88	Smith-White 1948a		

119 LECYTHIDACEAE

COUROUPITA $x = 18$
guianensis Cannonball T. 36 Banerji 1950a HSh Trop. America

120 MELASTOMACEAE

MEMECYLON $x = 7$
aylmeri 14 Favarger 1952a — W. Tr. Africa

SONERILA $x = 8$
wallichii 16 Subramanyam 1944 — India

GUYONIA $x = 9$
ciliata 18 Favarger 1952a — W. Tr. Africa

OSBECKIA $x = 10$

afzelii	20	Favarger 1952a	—	W. Tr. Africa
liberica	20	„ „	M	„
tubulosa	20	„ „	M	„
parvifolia (zeylanica)	20	Subramanyam 1946	H	Ceylon
rosea	40	„ „	—	Nilgiri

DISSOTIS $x = 10, 16, 17$

brazzaei	20	Favarger 1952a	—	W. Tr. Africa
rotundifolia	30	„ „	HM	„
jacquesii	32	„ „	—	„
capitata	34	„ „	BM	„

PREUSSIELLA $x = 11$
chevalieri 44 Favarger 1952a — W. Tr. Africa

DINOPHORA $x = 12$
spenneroides 24 Favarger 1952a — W. Tr. Africa

MELASTOMA $x = 14$
candidum 28 Sugiura 1936b H China

TRISTEMMA $x = 17$

hirtum	34	Favarger 1952a	—	W. Tr. Africa
incompletum	34	„ „	—	„
involucratum	34	„ „	M	„

SAKERSIA $x = ?$
africana c. 40 Favarger 1952a — W. Tr. Africa

113

CALVOA $x=$?
monticola   *c.* 44   Favarger 1952a   —   W. Tr. Africa

DICELLANDRA $x=$?
barteri   64–68   Favarger 1952a   —   W. Tr. Africa

121 COMBRETACEAE

QUISQUALIS $x=11$
indica   Rangoon Creeper   22   Rajagopalan 1949   HMN   Tr. Asia & Afr.

TERMINALIA $x=12$
catappa   Indian Almond   24   Simmonds 1954   NW   India, Malaya

123 HYPERICACEAE

HYPERICUM $x=7, 8, 9, 10, 12.$ $x_2=19$ (Apomixis)

$x=7$

rumelicum	14	Nielsen 1924	H	S.E. Europe

$x=8$

boreale (*mutilum*)	16	Hoar & H. 1932	—	N. America
elatum	16	Suzuka 1950	H	Madeira, Canar.
elodeoides	16	Sugiura 1944	—	Himal., Burma
humifusum	16	Winge 1925	H	W. & C. Eur.
montanum	16	Nielsen 1924	H	Eur., Cauc., Algeria
orientale	16	„ „	H	Asia Minor
punctatum (ring of 16)	16	Hoar 1931	—	N. America
quadrangulum (*maculatum*)	16	Noack 1939	H	Eur., W. Sib.
senanense	16	M. & S. 1935	—	Japan
tetrapterum (*acutum*)	16	Noack 1939	H	Europe, Asia M., N. Africa
tomentosum	16	Nielsen 1924	H	S. Eur., N. Africa
undulatum	32	Sugiura 1944	—	Spain
perforatum (Apo.)	32	Noack 1939	H	Eur., Himal., Sib.

$x=9$

ascyron	18	Nielsen 1924	H	N.E: N. Amer., C. & E. Asia
coris	18	„ „	H	S. Europe
frondosum (*aureum*)	18	Hoar & H. 1932	H	S.E: U.S.A.
hirsutum	18	Noack 1939	H	Eur., Cauc., Sib.
kalmianum	18	Hoar & H. 1932	H	E: N. Amer.
olympicum	18	Sugiura 1944	H	Greece, Asia M.
polyphyllum	18	„ 1936a	H	S.W. Asia Minor
prolificum	18	Hoar & H. 1932	H	E: N. Amer.
pulchrum	18	Bøcher 1940	—	Europe
rhodopeum (*origanifolium*)	18	Nielsen 1924	H	S.E. Eur., Asia M.
moserianum	36	Sugiura 1944	H	cult
patulum	36	„ 1936a	H	China

$x=10$

calycinum	St. John's Wort	20	Maude 1939	H	S.E. Europe

114

HYPERICUM (*cont.*)

androsaemum	Tutsan	40	Nielsen 1924	HM	Eur., Cauc., Asia M.
hircinum	Stinking St. J. W.	40	,, ,,	H	Medit., C. Eur.
inodorum		40	,, ,,	H	E. Eur., Cauc.

$x = 12$

gentianioides	Orange Grass	24	Hoar & H. 1932	—	N. America

$x_2 = 19$

virginicum		38	,, ,,	—	,,

CRATOXYLON $x = 7$

formosum	14	Tixier 1953	W	S.E. Asia

126 GUTTIFERAE

CALOPHYLLUM $x = 16$

inophyllum	Pinnay T.	32	Tixier 1953	MOW	O.W. Tropics

MESUA $x = 16$

ferrea	Ironwood	32	Tixier 1953	FOW	India, Ceylon

OCHROCARPUS $x = 16$

siamensis	32	Tixier 1953	FW	S.E. Asia

GARCINIA $x = ?$ (Apomixis)

hanburyi	Gamboge	44	Tixier 1953	D	Siam
indica	Kokum	*c.* 54	Krishnaswamy & R. 1949	DFMO	India
speciosa	Palawa T.	*c.* 55	,, ,,	ReW	Burma, Andaman
mangostana	Mangosteen	*c.* 76	,, ,,	F	Moluccas
cambogia	Goraka.	*c.* 58	Krishnaswamy *et al.* 1954	D Sp. ?	E. Indies
xanthochymus (*tinctoria*)		*c.* 80	,, ,,	F	India, Mal.

Group VIII

TILIALES	MALVALES
127–131	132
ST	HS(T)

MALPIGHIALES	EUPHORBIALES
133–135	136
ST	(H)ST

Gossypium arboreum

128 TILIACEAE

CORCHORUS $x = 7$

acutangulus		14	Banerji 1932	T	Tropics
capsularis	Jute	14	Nakajima 1936	T	India
fascicularis		14	Rao & D. 1953	—	O.W. Tropics
olitorius	Jew's Mallow	14	Banerji 1932	(V)T	India
tridens		14	Mukherjee 1952a	—	Tropics
trilocularis		$\begin{cases} 14 \\ 14 \end{cases}$	,, ,, Rao & D. 1953	—	O.W. Tropics
siliquosus		28	,, ,,	—	Sub-Trop. Amer

GREWIA $x = 9$

parviflora		18	Dermen 1932a	T	China
asiatica	Phalsa	36	Bhaduri & B. 1949	FT	India

CLAPPERTONIA (HONCKENYA) $x = (9)\ 18$

ficifolia	36	Baldwin & S. 1951d	H	Trop. Africa
minor	36	,, ,,	—	,,

TRIUMFETTA $x = 16$

bartramia	Champadang	32	Lay 1950	T	Tropics
as *rhomboidea*		48	Rao & R. 1952		
calderoni		32	Lay 1950	—	,,
semitriloba		32	,, ,,	T	,,

TILIA $x = 41$

cordata	Linden	82	Dermen 1932a	MW	Europe
glabra (*americana*)		82	,, ,,	W	N. America
neglecta		82	,, ,,	W	,,
oliveri		82	,, ,,	W	China
petiolaris	Weeping W. L.	82	,, ,,	H	Hungary
platyphyllos		82	,, ,,	MShW	Europe
vulgaris (*europaea*)	Lime Tree	82	,, ,,	MW	,,
amurensis	Bass Wood	164	,, ,,	TW	Siberia
insularis		164	,, ,,	W	Japan
maximowicziana		164	,, ,,	W	,,
tuan		164	,, ,,	W	China

130 STERCULIACEAE

GUAZUMA $x = 8$

tomentosa	Bastard Cedar	16	Youngman 1931	(F)TW	Tr. America

HERRANIA $x = 10$

albiflora	20	Simmonds 1954	—	Trop. Amer.
purpurea	20	,, ,,	—	,,

THEOBROMA $x = 10$

angustifolia		20	Simmonds 1954	—	Trop. Amer
bicolor	Peru Cocoa	20	,, ,,	B	,,
cacao	Cocoa	20	,, ,,	BM	,,
leiocarpa		20	Carletto 1948	—	,,

THOMASIA $x = 10$
  solanacea   20 Chatelier 1939   H   W. Australia

COLA $x = 10$
  acuminata   Kola nut   40 EKJ*   BMSp   Trop. Africa

FREMONTIA $x = 10$
  californica   40 Lenz 1950   H   California

STERCULIA (FIRMIANA) $x = 10$
  platanifolia   Parasol T.   40 Chatelier 1939   T   China, Japan
  colorata   40 Pathak *et al.* 1949 HT   India, Siam

PTEROSPERMUM $x = 19$
  aurifolium   38 Pathak *et al.* 1949 H   E. Indies

DOMBEYA $x = 23$
  spectabilis   46 Chatelier 1939   H   Trop. Africa

131 BOMBACACEAE

BOMBAX $x = ?$
  malabaricum   Silk Cotton *c.* 72 EKJ*   OTW   S.E. Asia

CEIBA (ERIODENDRON) $x = ?$
  pentandra Silk Cotton T.   72, 80 Heyn 1936   (O)T   S.E. Asia & Afr.
             Kapok T.
    indica strains   88   Tjio 1948
  occidentale   88   Heyn 1936   (O)T   Trop. Amer.
    (*pentandra* v. *caribaea*)

132 MALVACEAE

base no. (*2n*)

MODIOLASTRUM $x = 5$
  malvifolium   10 Krapovickas 1949   —   Temp. S. Am.

NOTOTRICHE $x = 5$
  caesia   10 Krapovickas 1951b   —   Temp. S. Am.
  pusilla   *diploid*   10   „   „:   —   „
  rugosa   10   „   „   —   :,
  hillii   *tetraploid* 20   „   „   —   „
  sarmentosa   20   „   „   —   :,
  copon   *hexaploid*   30   „   „   —   „
  ovata   *c.* 30   „   „   —   „

TARASA $x = 5$
  albertii   10 Krapovickas·1949   —   Chile

SPHAERALCEA* $x = 5, 17, 33$
  australis & 8 spp.   10 Krapovickas 1949   —   S. Amer.
  coccinea   Globe Mallow   10 Webber 1936   H   W: N. Amer.
               & 5 spp.
  miniata   10 Skovsted 1935   H   Trop. Amer.
  ambigua   { 10   „   1941   H   W: N. Amer.
                         { 20, 30 Webber 1936

120

SPHAERALCEA (*cont.*)

angustifolia	10, 20	Webber 1936	H	Mexico
fendleri	{ 10, 20	„ „	H	California
	{ 15	EKJ		*cult*
incana	10, 20	Webber 1936	—	W: N. Amer.
rusbyi	10, 20	„ „	—	Arizona
lobata	20	Skovsted 1941	—	N. America
patagonica	20	Covas & S. 1947	—	Patagonia
emoryi	20, 30, 50	Webber 1936	H	California
chenopodifolia	30	Krapovickas 1949	—	Argentine
mendocina	30	„ „	—	Chile
abutiloides	34	Webber 1936	H	Bahamas
umbellata	34	Skovsted 1935	H	Mexico
rivularis	66	Webber 1936	—	N. America

LECANOPHORA $x = 6$

ecristata	12	Krapovickas 1950	—	Argentine
heterophylla	12	„ „	—	„
ameghinoi	24	„ „	—	„

CALLIRHOË $x = 6, 7$

involucrata	24	Kesseler 1932	H	C: U.S.A.
v. *lineariloba*	42	Skovsted 1935	H	Mex., Texas

WISSADULA $x = 7$

contracta	14	Skovsted 1935	—	Tropics
periplocifolia	14	„ 1941	—	„

BASTARDIA $x = 7$

viscosa	28	Skovsted 1941	—	W. Indies

NAPAEA $x = 7$

dioica	28	Skovsted 1935	—	N. America

URENA $x = 7$

sinuata		28	Skovsted 1941	T	Tropics
lobata	Aramina, Congo Jute	28, 56	„ „	T	„

ALTHAEA $x = 7$

cannabina		28, 84	Skovsted 1935, 1941	T	Eur., S.W. Asia
apterocarpa		42	„ „	—	S.W. Asia
ficifolia	Antwerp H.	42	„ „	H	Siberia
officinalis	Marsh Mallow	42	„ „	HM	Eur., W. Asia, N. Africa
pallida		42	„ „	H	Hung., Balkans
pontica		42	„ 1941	H	N.E. Medit.
sulphurea		42	„ „	H	Pers., Turkestan
rosea	Hollyhock	{ 42	„ „	H	China, *cult*
		{ 56	Sugiura 1936b		
sinensis		70	Skovsted 1935	H	China
armenaica		84	„ 1941	H	E. Medit.
hohenackeri		*c.* 84	„ 1935	H	Asia M., Cauc.
kragujevacensis		*c.* 84	„ „	H	Serbia

121

PAVONIA $x = 7$

hirsuta	28	Skovsted 1941	MT	Trop. Africa
kotschyi	c. 28	,, 1935	—	Abyssinia
praemorsa	28	,, ,,	H	S. Africa
schimperiana	28	,, ,,	T	Trop. Africa
spinifex	42, 112	,, 1935, 1941	H	S. America
hastata	56	,, ,,	H	,,

MALVA $x = 7$

moschata Musk Mallow	42	Skovsted 1935	H	Eur., N. Africa
neglecta (*rotundifolia*)	42	,, ,,	—	Eur., Asia, N. Afr.
nicaeensis	42	,, ,,	—	Medit.
parviflora	42	,, 1941	—	,,
sylvestris Common Mallow	42	,, 1935	H	Europe
pusilla (*borealis*)	42, 76	,, ,, 1941	—	N. & C. Eur.
alcea	84	,, ,,	H	Europe
verticillata	c. 84	,, ,,	V	Asia
brasiliensis	c. 112	,, ,,	—	Brazil
crispa	c. 112	,, ,,	HV	Europe

TYPHALAEA $x = 7$

fruticosa	56	Skovsted 1941	—	S. America

MALACHRA $x = 7$

alceifolia	56	Skovsted 1935	T	Tropics
capitata	56	,, ,,	T	,,
fasciata	c. 112	,, ,,	—	Venezuela

MALVAVISCUS $x = 7$

" *arboreus* "	c. 84	Skovsted 1935	H	Mexico

ABUTILON* $x = 7, 8$

auritum & 2 spp.	14	Skovsted 1941	—	Ceylon
crispum	14	,, 1935	HT	Tropics
avicennae Maba	42	,, 1941	HT	*cult*, China
indicum Indian Mallow	42	,, ,,	HMT	Tropics
molle & 5 spp.	42	,, ,,	—	Peru
striatum	16	,, 1935	H	Brazil
umbellatum	16	,, 1941	—	W. Indies

SIDA $x = 7, 8, 11$

acuta	14, 28	Skovsted 1935, 1941	—	C. America
spinosa Cuba Jute	14, 28	,, ,, ,,	T	Tropics
grewioides	28	,, 1941	T	India, Trop. Afr.
triloba	28	,, ,,	—	S. Africa
veronicaefolia	14, 56	,, ,,	—	Trop. Amer.
rhombifolia Sida 14+0–1B, 28		,, ,,	MT	*cult*, India
Hemp				
v. *canariensis*	16	Nascimento 1941		
corrugata	16	Skovsted 1941	—	Queensland
subspicata	16	,, ,,	—	Australia
leprosa	32	Covas & S. 1946	—	Trop. Amer.
urens	32	Skovsted 1935	T	Tr. Afr. & Amer.
hederacea	22	Heiser & W. 1948	—	N. America

LAVATERA $x = 7, 22$

trimestris		14	Skovsted 1935	H	Medit.
arborea	Tree Mallow	{ 40	Nakajima 1936	H	W. Eur., N. Afr.
		42	Skovsted 1935		
micans		42	Davie 1935	—	Spain
olbia		42	Nakajima 1936	H	S. Europe
cachemiriana		{ 42	Skovsted 1935	H	Himalayas
		44	Davie 1935		
plebeia		43!	Skovsted 1935	—	Australia
thuringiaca		44	„ „	—	S. Europe
triloba		44	Davie 1935	—	Spain
mauretanica		c. 84	Skovsted 1935	H	N. Africa
cretica (*sylvestris*)		c. 112	„ „	—	W. Eur., Medit.

HIBISCUS $x = 7, 8, 9, 11, 12, 15, 17, 19, 20, 39$
  $x = 7, 8$

trionum	Flower-of-an-Hour	{ 28	Medvedeva 1936	H	Trop. Africa
		56	Skovsted 1935		
gossypinus (*gossypium*)		{ 28	„ „	—	S. Africa
		32	„ 1941		
ferrugineus		32	„ „	—	Madagascar
mutatus		32	„ „	—	Trop. Africa
micranthus		64	„ „	TTo	India, Trop. Afr.

  $x = 9$

cannabinus	Gamboor, Kenaf,	{ 36	Medvedeva 1936	MOTV	O.W. Tropics
	Deccan Hemp	36	Skovsted 1941		
surrattensis		36	„ „	MTV	„
abelmoschus	Moskokva	72	„ „	HMP	India
aspera		72	„ „	MT	Trop. Africa
bifurcatus		72	„ „	—	S. Amer.
radiatus		72	Tjio 1948	H	India, Malaya
sabdariffa	Javan Jute	36, 72	Skovsted 1941	BMHVT	O.W. Tropics
esculentus	Okra, Lady's	{ 72	Teshima 1933	MHVT	Abyssinia, *cult*
	Fingers	120	Purewal & R. 1947		
		130	Joshi & H. 1953		
		132	Medvedeva 1936		
tiliaceus	Mahoe	80, 96	Youngman 1931	TW	O.W. Tropics
rosa-sinensis	Shoe Flower	{ 92	Skovsted 1935	DHV	E. Asia
		144	Youngman 1927		
		168	Skovsted 1941		
diversifolius	144, c. 180		„ „	T	O.W. Tropics

  $x = 11$

cardiophyllus		22	Skovsted 1941	—	Madagascar
phoeniceus		22	„ „	—	India
pusillus		22	„ „	—	S. Africa
manihot		66	„ 1935	HT	S.E. Asia

  $x = 12$

panduraeformis		24	Skovsted 1941	—	O.W. Tropics
storkii		84	„ „	—	Fiji
waimeae		84	„ 1935	—	Hawaii

  $x = 15$

lepidospermus		30	Medvedeva 1936	—	Trop. Africa
pedunculatus		30	„ „	—	S. Africa

HIBISCUS (*cont.*)

x = 17

parkeri		34	Skovsted 1935	—	Madagascar
solandra		34	Medvedeva 1936	—	Trop. Asia, Africa
vitifolius		34+0–1**B**	Skovsted 1941	MT	Tropics

x = 19

coccineus	38	Skovsted 1935	H	S.E: U.S.A.
grandiflorus	38	„ 1941	—	N. America
lasiocarpus	38	„ „	—	?
militaris	38	Nakajima 1936	—	N. America
palustris	38	Medvedeva 1936	H	E: U.S.A.
roseus	38	Skovsted 1935, 1941	H	E: U.S.A. (*nat.* in France)

x = 20

ludwigii		40	Skovsted 1941	—	S. Africa
lunariifolius		40	„ „	—	Trop. Asia & Afr.
physaloides		40	„ „	T	E. Africa
mutabilis	Cotton Rose	{ 92 / 100	„ „ / Medvedeva 1936	HT	Burma, China
calyphyllos		80	Skovsted 1941	—	Mascarene Is.
syriacus	Rose of Sharon	80	„ „	H	E. Asia

x = 39

ficulneus	78	Skovsted 1941	—	Tr. Asia & Austr.

HIBISCADELPHUS   x = 10

species	40	Skovsted 1941	—	Hawaii

MODIOLA   x = 9

caroliniana	18	Krapovickas 1949	—	S: U.S.A.
multifida	18	Skovsted 1941	H	W: N. & S. Amer.

CIENFUGOSIA (FUGOSIA)   x = ?

heterophylla	20	Longley 1933	—	W.I., Tr. S. Amer.
hildebrandtii	{ 22 / 26	Skovsted 1941 / Youngman 1931	—	E. Trop. Africa

SIDALCEA   x = 10, 13

candida		20+1**B**	Skovsted 1935	H	Rocky Mts.
campestris		20	Ford 1938	H	W: N. Amer.
parviflora		{ 20 / 26	„ „ / Davie 1935	H	S. Calif.
malviflora	Checkerbloom	c. 60	Skovsted 1935	H	California

KITAIBELIA   x = 11

lindemuthi	44	Skovsted 1935	H	*cult*
vitifolia	44	„ „	H	E. Europe

MALOPE   x = 11

hispida	44	Skovsted 1935	—	Algeria
trifida	44, 50	„ „	H	Spain, N. Africa

MALVASTRUM *   x = 12, 15, 16, 17, 21, 22

coromandelianum	24	Skovsted 1935	—	Tropics
scoparium	24	„ „	—	Trop. Amer.
tricuspidatum	24	„ 1941	H	Australia

MALVASTRUM (*cont.*)

limense		30	Skovsted 1935	H	Peru
peruvianum		30	„ „	—	Mexico
greenmanianum		32	„ „	—	„
fasciculatum & 5 spp.		34	Webber 1936	H	California
grossulariaefolium		42	Skovsted 1935	—	S. Africa
scabrum		42	„ 1941	—	Peru
capense	False Mallow	44	„ 1935	H	S. Africa

KOKIA $x = 12$

dryarinoides		24	Skovsted 1941	H	Hawaii
rockii		24	„ „	—	„

GOSSYPIOIDES $x = 12$

brevilanatum		24	Hutchinson 1943	—	Madagascar
kirkii		24	Skovsted 1935	—	Trop. Africa

GOSSYPIUM $x = 13$

(i) Old World Wild Species

areysianum		26	Douwes 1953	—	S. Arabia
anomalum	Wild O.W. Cotton	26	Skovsted 1935	T	Tr. & S.W. Africa
somalense		26	Douwes 1951	—	E. Trop. Africa
stocksii	Wild Sind C. Arabian C.	26	Skovsted 1935	—	Sind, S.E. Arabia, Br. Somaliland
sturtii	Wild Austr. Cotton	26	„ „	H	C. & S. Australia
triphyllum		26	Douwes 1953	—	S.W. Afr., Angola

(ii) New World Wild Species

aridum	Wild N.W. Cotton	26	Skovsted 1933	—	Mexico
armorianum	Calif. Wild C.	26	„ „	—	L. Calif.
davidsonii		26	„ „	—	„
gossypioides		26	Brown & M. 1952	—	S. Mexico
harknessii		26	Webber 1934	—	L. Calif.
klotzschianum		26	Skovsted 1935	—	Galapagos
raimondii		26	Barducci & M. 1941	—	N. Peru
thurberi		26	Skovsted 1933	—	Ariz., Mexico
trilobum		26	„ 1935	—	S. Mexico

(iii) Old World Cultivated Species

arboreum	Asiatic Tree C.	26	Zaitzew 1927	T	Asia (*cult*)
		(52)	Stephens 1942		N.E. Afr., Madag.
herbaceum	Broach Kappas	26	Zaitzew 1927	MT	Asia (*cult*)
		(39)	Skovsted 1933		
		(52)	Beasley 1940		
v. *africanum*		26	Webber 1934	—	S. Africa
v. *acerifolium*		26	Nikelajewa 1923	—	India, N.E. & C. Africa

(iv) New World Cultivated Species

barbadense	Egyptian or Sea Island Cotton	52	Webber 1934	MT	Trop. S. Amer.
		(26)	Skovsted 1934a		& *cult*
		(104)	Beasley 1940		
v. *brasiliense*	Chain C.	52	Webber 1934	T	E. Tr. S. Amer.
v. *darwinii*	Galapagos C.	52	„ „	T	Galapagos
hirsutum	Upland Cotton	52	Zaitzew 1927	T	C. America
		(104)	Harland 1940		& *cult*
tomentosum	Hawaiian C.	52	Skovsted 1933	T	Hawaii

10   125

SHANTZIA $x = 13$				
garckeana		26	Longley 1933	—	Trop. Africa

THESPESIA $x = 13$					
populnea	Portia Tree	26	Youngman 1931	DShTW	O.W. Tropics
(*macrophylla*)					
rogersii		26	Skovsted 1941	—	Trop. Africa

ANODA $x = 15$				
cristata	30	Ford 1938	—	Mexico
hastata	30, 60	Skovsted 1941	H	Mex., Peru
wrightii	c. 60	„ 1935	H	New Mexico

KOSTELETZKYA $x = 17$				
hastata	34	Skovsted 1941	—	India?

133 MALPIGHIACEAE

STIGMAPHYLLON $x = 9$					
ciliatum		18	Snoad unp.	H	W. Indies

BANISTERIA $x = 10$					
caapi	Caapi	20	Baldwin 1946b	M	Brazil

135 ERYTHROXYLACEAE

ERYTHROXYLON $x = 12$					
coca	Cocaine Plant	24	Heitz 1929, EKJ*	M	Peru

136 EUPHORBIACEAE

SF1: CROTONOIDEAE

EUPHORBIA* $x = 6, 7, 8, 9, 10$ (Apomixis)

$x = 6$

capitata	12	Harrison, T. 1931	—	Tropics
cereiformis	12	„ „	H	S. Africa
	20	Perry 1943		
dulcis	12	„ „	—	Europe
	28?	Carano 1926		
nutans (*preslii*)	12	D'Amato 1947b	—	N. America
	14	Perry 1943		
welwitschii	12	Harrison, T. 1931	—	Portugal
pekinensis	24	Perry 1943	—	China

$x = 7$

bivonae	14	D'Amato 1947b	—	N. Afr., Sicily
dentata	14, 28, 56	Perry 1943	—	N. America
pubescens	14	D'Amato 1947a	—	Medit.
	16	Perry 1943		
commutata	28	„ „	—	N. America
fulgens	28	„ „	H	Mexico

126

EUPHORBIA (*cont.*)

geniculata		28	Moyer 1934	—	Trop. Amer.
graeca		28	Perry 1943	—	Greece, Asia M.
hypericifolia		28	,, ,,	—	Tropics
ipecacuanha	Ipecac Spurge	28	,, ,,	H	N. America
maculata		28	,, ,,	—	,,
corollata	Flowering Spurge	{ 28	,, ,,	—	,,
		30	Harrison, T. 1931		
pithyusa		28	Perry 1943	—	Medit.
v. *ovalifolia*		36	D'Amato 1939		
platyphyllos		{ 28	Perry 1943	—	Eur., N. Africa
		36	Harrison 1930		
pulcherrima	Poinsettia	28	Moyer 1934	H(V)	Mexico
stricta		28	Perry 1943	H	Eur., Medit., Cauc
helioscopia	Sun Spurge	42	,, ,,	—	Eur., Medit.
heterophylla	Mex. Fire Pl.	56	Moyer 1943	HM	S. America
iberica		56	Perry 1943	—	Cauc.
marginata	Snow-on-the-Mountain	56	,, ,,	H	N. America

$x = 8$

altissima		16	Perry 1943	—	Asia M., Syria
boetica		16	,, ,,	—	Spain
gerardiana		{ 16	,, ,,	—	Europe
		18	Harrison, T. 1931		
lagascae		16	Perry 1943	—	Sardinia
paralias	Sea Spurge	16	,, ,,	—	W. Eur., Medit.
peplus	Petty Spurge	16	,, ,,	—	Eur., Med., Siber.
polychroma	(*epithymoides*)	16	,, ,,	H	E. Europe
portlandica	Portland Spurge	{ 16	,, ,,	—	W. Europe
		40	Covas & S. 1947		
procera (*pilosa*)		16	Perry 1943	H	Eur., N. Asia
pterococca		16	,, ,,	—	Medit.
segetalis		16	,, ,,	H	Europe
exigua	Dwarf Spurge	{ 16	Wulff 1939a	H	Eur., Medit.
		24	Rutland 1941		
		24–26	D'Amato 1947b		
		28	Perry 1943		
esula		64	Reese 1952a	—	Eur., Tem. Asia

$x = 9$

amygdaloides	Wood Spurge	18	D'Amato 1939	—	Eur., Cauc., Alg.
dendroides		18	,, 1947	—	Medit.
nicaeensis		18	Perry 1943	—	,,
pilosa	Hairy Spurge	18	,, ,,	—	W. Eur., Algeria
pinea		18	Harrison, T. 1931	—	Medit.
rothiana		18	Perry 1943	—	India
terracina		18	D'Amato 1947b	—	Medit.
verrucosa		18	Harrison 1930	—	Europe
falcata		36	D'Amato 1939	—	Med., Temp. Asia
splendens	Crown of Thorns	{ 36	Sugiura 1936a	H	Madagascar
		40	Harrison, T. 1931		

$x = 10$

aphylla		20	Perry 1943	H	Canary Is.
biglandulosa		20	,, ,,	H	Greece, Asia M.
bulbalina		20	,, ,,	—	S. Africa

EUPHORBIA (*cont.*)

caput-medusae	Medusa's Head	20	Perry 1943	H	S. Africa
characias		20	,, ,,	—	Europe
cereiformis		20	,, ,,	—	S. Africa
clava		20	,, ,,	H	,,
cyparissias	Cypress Spurge	20, 40	Moore & L. 1953	H	Europe
glauca		20	Perry 1943	—	New Zealand
lathyrus	Caper Spurge	20	,, ,,	HV	S. Europe
melapetala		20	,, ,,	—	Sicily
meloformis	Melon Spurge	20	,, ,,	H	S. Africa
micrantha (*stricta*)		20	,, ,,	H	Eur., Medit.
monteiri		20	,, ,,	H	Trop. Africa
myrsinites		20	,, ,,	H	S. Europe
nubica		20	,, ,,	H	N. Africa
obesa		20	,, ,,	H	S. Africa
palustris		20	,, ,,	H	Europe
regis-jubae		20	,, ,,	H	Teneriffe
rigida		20	Harrison, T. 1931	—	Greece, Asia M.
schimperiana		20	Perry 1943	H	Abyssinia
tirucalli	Milk Bush	20	Tjio 1948	M(Ru)	Trop. Africa, (India, *nat.*)
royleana		30	Bhalla 1941	H	Himalayas
barnhartii (*trigona*)	Susuru	40	,, ,,	M	India, Moluc.
bojeri		40	D'Amato 1947b	H	Madagascar
granulata		40	Hagerup 1932	—	Trop. Afr. & Asia
lactea		40	Perry 1943	H	India
similis		40	,, ,,	H	S. Africa
albaspina		60	,, ,,	H	*cult*
hermentiana		60	,, ,,	H	S. Africa
echinus		*c.* 100	,, ,,	H	Morocco
ferox		*c.* 200	,, ,,	H	S. Africa

ACALYPHA $x = 7$

ostryaefolia (*caroliniana*)		14	Perry 1943	—	N. America
virginica		28	,, ,,	—	,,
wilkesiana (*tricolor*) Copper Leaf				H	S. Pacific Is.
v. *triumphans*		28	,, ,,		
v. *musaica*		*c.* 224!	,, ,,		
fallax		42	Banerji 1950b	—	Trop. Asia
hispida	Chenille Plant	*c.* 112	Perry 1943	HM	E. Indies

BALIOSPERMUM $x = 7$

axillare (*montanum*)		28	Perry 1943	M	Ind., Siam, Java

SEBASTIANA $x = 7$

ligustrina		56	Perry 1943	M	N. America

CROTON $x = 8$

glandulosus		16	Perry 1943	—	N. & Tr. Amer.
monanthogynus		16	,, ,,	—	N. America
palmeri		16	,, ,,	—	W: N. Amer.

MERCURIALIS $x = 8$

annua	Annual M.	16, 32	Ehrenberg 1945	MV	Eur., N. Africa
leiocarpa		48	Morinaga *et al.* 1929	—	Japan
perennis	Dog's Mercury	*c.* 64	Meurman 1924	M	Eur., S.W. Asia, Cauc.

DAPHNIPHYLLUM $x = 8$

macropodum		32	Sugiura 1928a	H	China, Japan

COLLIGUAJA $x = 9$

odorifera		36	Perry 1943	—	Temp. S. Amer.

HEVEA $x = 9$

pauciflora		18, 36	Baldwin 1947a	—	Brazil
brasiliensis	Para-rubber T.	36	Perry 1943	Ru	,,
		(72, 144)	Mendes 1946		
collina		36	Ramaer 1935	Ru	,,
rigidifolia		36	Baldwin 1947b	—	,,
spruceana		36	Perry 1943	—	,,
guianensis		36, 54	Baldwin 1947a	Ru	Guiana

HOMALANTHUS $x = 9$

populneus		36	Perry 1943	H	Trop. Asia

MANIHOT $x = 9$

carthaginensis		36	Tjio 1948	—	Trop. Amer.
cathartica		36	Doughty 1939	M	—
dulcis	Sweet C.	36	,, ,,	R	Brazil
dichotoma	Tiquie-Man. R.	36	,, ,,	Ru	,,
glaziovii	Ceara Rubber T.	36	,, ,,	RuR	,,
palmata		36	Bowden 1940a	R	,,
tweediana		36	Perak 1940	—	,,
utilissima	Tapioca,	36	Graner 1935	R	,,
(*esculenta*)	Cassava	(72)	,, 1942		
walkerae		36	Perry 1943	Ru	,,

PEDILANTHUS $x = 9$

tithymaloides	Redbird Cactus	36	Perry 1943	H	W. Indies

SAPIUM $x = 9$

sebiferum	Soap Tree	36	Perry 1943	MO	Tropics

STILLINGIA $x = 9$

sylvatica	Queen's Delight	36	Perry 1943	HM	N. America

MALLOTUS $x = 9$

japonicus		72	Perry 1943	DW	Japan

EREMOCARPUS $x = 10$

setigerus		20	Heiser & W. 1948	—	W: N. Amer.

RICINUS $x = 10$

communis	Castor Oil Pl.	20	Hagerup 1932	Fo_1MO	Tropics
		(40)	Sidorov & S. 1941		
gibsoni		20	Sugiura 1936b	O	,,
sanguineus	Red C.O.P.	20	,, ,,	HO	,,
zanzibariensis		20	Nemec 1910	HO	,,

ALEURITES $x = 11$

cordata	Tung (China	22	Lapin 1937b	O	China, Japan
	Wood Oil T.)				
fordii	,, ,,	22	,, ,,	O	China
montana	,, ,,	22	,, ,,	IO	Trop. Asia

129

ALEURITES (*cont.*)
trisperma		22	Stockar 1946	MO	Malaya
moluccana (*triloba*)	Candle Nut	44	,, ,,	MO	,,

CHROZOPHORA $x = 11$
plicata	Indian Turnsole	22	Bhadhuri & K. 1949	D	India

GELONIUM $x = 11$
multiflorum		22	Banerji 1951	—	Trop. Asia

JATROPHA $x = 11$
curcas	Physic Nut	22	Perry 1943	MO	Tropics
gossypiifolia	Wild Cassada	22	,, ,,	HM	Trop. Amer.
multifida	Pinhoeu Oil	22	,, ,,	HOM	,,

TREWIA $x = 11$
nudiflora		22	Bhadhuri & K. 1949	—	India, Malaya

EXOCOECARIA $x = 12$
acerifolia		24	Perry 1943	MW	O.W. Tropics

SF2: PHYLLANTHOIDEAE

PUTRANJIVA $x = 7$
roxburghii		14	Perry 1943	FoMO	Ind., Siam

BRIDELIA $x = 7$
retusa		28	Perry 1943	DFoW	Indo., Malaya

PHYLLANTHUS $x = 7$
emblica	Emblie	28	Perry 1943	DMVit	Trop. Asia
carolinensis		28	,, ,,	—	N. America

BREYNIA (PHYLLANTHUS) $x = 7$
nivosa	Snow Bush	56	Perry 1943	H	Pac. Is.

FLUGGEA $x = 8$
obovata		16	Perry 1943	F	Trop. Africa

HALLIOPHYTUM (BERNARDIA) $x = 12$
fasciculatum		24	Perry 1943	—	W: N. Amer.

Group IX

CUNONIALES
137–142
ST

ROSALES
143–145
HST

LEGUMINOSAE
146–148
HST

Vicia faba

137 CUNONIACEAE

PANCHERIA $x = 12$
  sebertii   24   Hamel 1952   —   New Caledonia

BAUERA $x = 16$
  rubioides   32   Smith-White unp.   H   E. Australia

CERATOPETALUM $x = 16$
  gummiferum   Christmas Bush   32   Smith-White unp.   HW   E. Australia

139 ESCALLONIACEAE

ITEA $x = 11$
  ilicifolia   22   Bowden 1945b   H   China
  virginica   Sweet Spire   22   Schoennagel 1931   H   N. America

ESCALLONIA $x = 12$
  macrantha   24   Hamel 1949a   H   Chile
  rubra   24   „   „   H   „
  thyrsoidea   24   „   „   —   „

141 GROSSULARIACEAE

RIBES * $x = 8$ (no natural polyploids)
S. 1. CURRANTS
  alpinum   Alpine C. & 1 sp.   16   Tischler 1927b   F   Eur., N. Asia
  aureum   Golden C.   16   Zielinski 1953   H   W: N. Amer.
  bracteosum Calif. B.C.   16   „   „   F   „
  cereum   Wax Currant   16   „   „   H   „
  fasciculatum Winterberry C.   16   K. Sax 1931b   H   China, Japan
  lacustre Swamp C. & 25 spp.   16   Zielinski 1953   F   N. America
  nigrum   Black C.   16 (32)   Vaarama 1949a   DF   Eur., N. Asia, *cult*
  odoratum Clove C. & 2 spp.   16   Meurman 1928   H   N. America
  sanguineum Flowering C.   16   Zielinski 1953   H   W: N. Amer.
  saxatile Siberian C.   16   Meurman 1928   F   Siberia
  spicatum (*petraeum*)   16   Zielinski 1953   F   Eurasia
  sylvestre   Red & White C.   16   Meurman 1928   F   *cult*
    (*rubrum* v. *sativum*)

S. 2. GOOSEBERRIES
  cynosbati Prickly G. & 1 sp.   16   K. Sax 1931b   F   W: N. Amer.
  divaricatum Coast G.   16   Zielinski 1953   F
  grossularia Gooseberry   16   Darlington 1929b   F   Eur., N. Afr., *cult*
  leptanthum Trumpet G.   16   Meurman 1928   —   N. America
  niveum & 25 spp.   16   Zielinski 1953   F   N.W: U.S.A.
  oxyacanthoides Smooth G.   16   Darlington 1927   F   N. America
  setosum   Redshoot G.   16   Zielinski 1953   F   „

142 HYDRANGEACEAE

PHILADELPHUS * $x = 13$
  argyrocalyx   26   Janaki Ammal 1951a H   New Mexico
  californicus   26   „   „   „   H   California
  confusus   26   „   „   „   —   Washington

133

PHILADELPHUS (*cont.*)

coronarius Sw. Mock Orange	26	Bangham 1929	H	S. Europe
coulteri	26	Janaki Ammal 1951a	H	Mexico
delavayi	26	Bangham 1929	H	W. China— S.E. Tibet
hirsutus	26	Janaki Ammal 1951a	H	S.E: U.S.A.
incanus Grey M.O.	26	Bangham 1939	H	Hupeh
inodorus & 11 spp.	26	,, ,,	H	S.E: U.S.A.
laxus	26	Janaki Ammal 1951a	H	,,
mexicanus	26	,, ,, ,,	H	Mexico
schrenkii	26	,, ,, ,,	H	Manch.—Korea
sericanthus	26	,, ,, ,,	H	S.W. China
subcanus	26	Bangham 1929	H	W. Szechuan
v. *wilsonii*	26	Janaki Ammal 1951a	H	Hupeh
verrucosus	26	,, ,, ,,	—	Illinois
virginalis	26	Bangham 1929	H	*cult*
garden forms	26, 28, 39	Janaki Ammal 1951a	H	*cult*

DEUTZIA *x* = 13

gracilis	26	Schoennagel 1931	H	Japan
hypoglauca	26	K. Sax 1931b	H	China
purpurascens	*c.* 26	,, ,,	H	W. China
sieboldiana	26	,, ,,	H	Japan
parviflora	26	,, ,,	H	China
v. *ovatifolia*	78	,, ,,		
mollis	78	,, ,,	—	,,
discolor	104	,, ,,	—	C. China
reflexa	104	,, ,,	—	China
vilmorinae	104	,, ,,	H	,,
crenata (*scabra*)	130	Schoennagel 1931	H	Japan, China
schneideriana	130	K. Sax 1931b	H	C. China

SCHIZOPHRAGMA *x* = 14, 18

hydrangeoides	28	M. & S. 1935	H	Japan
integrifolium	72	Hamel 1951b	H	China

JAMESIA *x* = 16

americana	32	K. Sax 1931b	H	W: N. Amer.

DEINANTHE *x* = 17

coerulea	34	Hamel 1951b	H	China

HYDRANGEA * *x* = 18

arborescens & 5 spp.	36	K. Sax 1931b	H	N. America
virens	36	Sugiura 1931	H	Japan
paniculata	36	M. & S. 1935	H	,,
v. *floribunda*	72	Sugiura 1936a		
v. *praecox*	72	K. Sax 1931b		

143 ROSACEAE

SF1: ROSOIDEAE *x* = 7, 8, 9

ROSA *x* = 7

SUBGENUS 1: HULTHEMIA

persica	14	Täckholm 1922	H	Persia

134

SUBGENUS 2: PLATYRHODON					
roxburghii (*microphylla*)		14	Täckholm 1922	H	China, Japan
SUBGENUS 3: HESPERHODOS					
stellata		14	Erlanson 1932	H	Texas, Ariz.
v. *mirifica*		14	„ „	H	New Mexico
minutifolia		14	„ „	H	Calif.
SUBGENUS 4: EUROSA					
S1: PIMPINELLIFOLIAE					
ecae		14	Täckholm 1922	H	Afghanistan
hugonis		14	„ „	H	C. China
koreana		14	Wylie unp.	H	Korea
primula		14	Erlanson 1938	H	C. Asia—N. China
sericea (incl. *omeiensis*)		14	Täckholm 1922	H	W. China, Himal.
xanthina		14	Hurst 1928	H	N. China, Korea
elasmacantha		28	„ unp.	—	Caucasus
foetida (*lutea*) Austrian Briar		28	„ 1928	H	W. Asia
v. *bicolor* Austr. Copper		28	Täckholm 1922	H	*cult*
v. *persiana* Persian Yellow		28	„ „	H	*cult*
rapinii (incl. *hemisphaerica*) Sulphur R.		28	Hurst 1928	H	W. Asia
spinosissima (incl. *pimpinellifolia*) Scotch R., Burnet R		28	Täckholm 1922	H	Eur., W. Asia
v. *altaica*		28	Hurst 1928	H	Siberia
hispida	{	28	Täckholm 1922	H	*cult*
	{ 28+1B		Wylie unp.		
lutea		28	„ „	H	*cult*
luteola		28	„ „	H	*cult*
myriacantha		28	Täckholm 1922	H	Spain, S. France
S2: GALLICANAE					
centifolia Cabbage R.		28	Hurst 1928	HP	*cult* (Cauc.)
v. *muscosa* Moss R.		28	Täckholm 1922	H	*cult*
damascena Damask R.		28	„ „	HP	*cult* (Asia M.)
gallica French R.		28	„ „	HMP	Eur., Cauc.
richardii (*sancta*)		—		H	Abyssinia
S3: CINNAMOMEAE					
(i) Old World					
amblyotis		14	Flory 1940	H	Kamchatka
banksiopsis		14	Wylie unp.	H	W. China
beggeriana		14	Täckholm 1922	H	Turkes.—N. Pers.
caudata	{	14	Flory 1940	H	W. China
	{	28	„ 1950		
cinnamomea Cinnamon R.		14	Täckholm 1922	H	Eur., N. & W. Asia
corymbulosa		14	Hurst 1928	H	W. China
davurica		14	„ „	H	N. China, N.E. As.
elegantula (incl. *farreri*)		14	Täckholm 1922	H	W. China
elymaitica		14	„ „	H	N. Persia
giraldii		14	Hurst 1928	H	C. China
macrophylla		14, 28	„ „	H	Himalayas
marretii		14		H	Sakhalin
persetosa		14	Täckholm 1922	H	W. China
prattii		14	Wylie unp	H	„
rugosa		14	Täckholm 1922	FsH	N. Ch., Kor., Jap.
sertata		14	„ „	H	C. & W. China

135

ROSA (*cont.*)

webbiana	14	Hurst 1928	H	Himal.—Turkest.
willmottiae	14	Täckholm 1922	H	W. China
bella	28	,, ,,	H	N. China
davidi	28	,, ,,	H	W. China
fedtschenkoana	28	,, ,,	HVit	Turkestan
hawrana	28	Hurst 1931	H	Hungary
laxa (Retz. non hort.)	28	Täckholm 1922	H	Turkestan
multibracteata	28	,, ,,	H	W. China
pendulina (*alpina*)	28	,, ,,	H	Alps
saturata	28	Hurst 1928	H	C. China
setipoda	28	Täckholm 1922	HVit	,,
hemsleyana	42	,, ,,	HVit	,,
moyesii	42	,, ,,	HVit	W. China
v. *fargesii*	28	Hurst 1928		
v. *rosea*	28	Täckholm 1922		
sweginzowii	42	,, ,,	HVit	N.W. China

(ii) New World

blanda (*acicularioides, subblanda*)	14 (21, 28)	Erlanson 1934	FsH	N.E: N. Amer.
foliolosa	14	Hurst 1928	H	S.E: U.S.A.
gymnocarpa	14	Täckholm 1922	H	W: N. Amer.
nitida	14	,, ,,	H	N.E: N. Amer.
palustris	14	Erlanson 1929	H	E: N. Amer.
pisocarpa (incl. *ultramontana*)	14, 21	,, 1933	H	N.W: N. Amer.
woodsii (incl. *fendleri, macounii, pyrifera, salictorum*)	14+0–2**B**, 21	,, ,,	H	W: N. Amer.
arkansana (incl. *subglauca, suffulta, pratincola*)	28	,, ,,	H	C: U.S.A.
californica	28	,, ,,	H	W: U.S.A.
carolina (incl. *deamii, humilis, lucida*)	28	,, ,,	H	E: N. Amer.
durandii (incl. *muriculata, myriadenia*)	28	,, 1934	H	W: N. Amer.
rudiuscula	28	,, 1929	H	E: U.S.A.
virginiana	28	Hurst 1928	H	N.E: N. Amer.
nutkana (incl. *melina, nuttalliana, oreophila, spaldingii*)	42	Täckholm 1922	HVit	N.W: N. Amer.
manca	42	,, ,,	HVit	W: N. Amer.

(iii) Circumpolar

acicularis	42, 56	Täckholm 1922	HVit	Circumpolar
as *bourgeauiana* (*sayi*)	42	Erlanson 1929	H	N.W: N. Amer.
engelmannii	42	Hurst 1928	H	,,
lacorum	42, 56	Erlanson 1929	H	,,
baicalensis	56	Hurst	—	C. Asia
fennica (*gmelinii*)	56	Täckholm 1922	H	Sweden
tackholmii	56	,, ,,	—	,,

S4: SYNSTYLAE

anemoneflora	14	Täckholm 1922	H	E. China
arvensis Ayrshire R.	14	,, ,,	H	Europe
brunonii Himal. Musk R.	14	Hurst 1928	H	Himalayas
cerasocarpa	14	Wylie unp.	H	C. China

ROSA (*cont.*)

crocacantha		14	Wylie unp.	H	W. China
filipes		14	„ „	H	„
helenae		14	Täckholm 1922	H	C. China
longicuspis		14	Hurst 1928	H	Himal., W. China
luciae		14	„ „	H	E. Asia
maximowicziana		14	Flory 1950	FsH	Manch., Korea
moschata	Musk Rose	14	Täckholm 1922	HP	S. Eur., N. Africa
(incl. *abyssinica, leschenaultiana, nastarana, ruscinonensis*)					
mulligani		14	Wylie unp.	H	W. China
multiflora		14	Täckholm 1922	FsH	Japan, Korea
phoenicia		14	„ „	—	Asia Minor
rubus (*ernestii*)		14	„ „	H	C. & W. China
sempervirens	Evergreen R.	14	„ „	H	S. Eur., N. Africa
setigera	Prairie Rose	14	„ „	FsH	E: U.S.A.
sinowilsonii		14	Wylie unp.	H	W. China
soulieana		14	Hurst 1928	H	„
watsoniana		14	„ „	H	*cult* (Japan)
wichuraiana	Memorial R.	14	Täckholm 1922	H	E. Asia

S5: CHINENSES (INDICAE)

chinensis	China R., Bengal R.	14, 21, 28	Hurst 1928	H	China, *cult*
gigantea		14	„ „	H	S.W. China, Bur.
odorata	Tea Rose	14	„ „	FsH	*cult* (China)

S6: BANKSIANAE

banksiae	Banksian R.	14	Täckholm 1922	H	China
cymosa (*microcarpa*)		14	Hurst 1928	H	„

S7: LAEVIGATAE

laevigata	Cherokee R.	14	Hurst 1928	FsH	China (*nat.* N. Amer.)

S8: BRACTEATAE

bracteata	Macartney R.	14	Erlanson 1929	H	China
clinophylla		—		—	India

S9: CANINAE Dog Roses, with only 14 chromosomes paired (Täckholm 1922). Subsexual, $n = 7\male$; 21, 28, 35$\female$, with or without apomixis also.

rubrifolia	28	Täckholm 1922	H	S. & C. Eur.
sherardi (*omissa*)	28	Blackburn & H. 1921	Vit	N. & C. Europe
villosa (*mollis, pomifera*)	28	„ „	HVit	Eur., W. Asia
agrestis	35	Täckholm 1922	—	Eur , N. Africa
britzensis	35	„ „	—	Kurdistan
canina (s.l.) Dog Rose	35	„ „	FsHVit	Europe
as *blondeana*	42	Gustafsson & H 1942		
coriifolia (*laxa*)	35	Täckholm 1922	FsHVit	Eur., W. Asia
corymbifera (*dumetorum*)	35	Blackburn & H. 1921	Vit	„ „
dumalis (*glauca*)	35	Täckholm 1922	HVit	„ „
eglanteria Sweet Briar (*rubiginosa*)	35	„ „	FsHVit	Europe
glutinosa	35, 42	„ „	H	S E. Eur., W. Asia
horrida (*ferox*)	35	„ „	H	S.E. Eur., Cauc.
inodora (*elliptica, klukii*)	35, 42	Täckholm 1922	—	Europe
micrantha	35	Hurst 1928	Vit	„
orientalis	35	Wylie unp.	H	S.E. Eur., W. Asia

ROSA (*cont.*)

seraphinii		35	Täckholm 1922	H	Medit.
sicula		35	„ „	H	S. Eur., N. Africa
stylosa		35, 42	„ „	H	Europe
tomentella		35	„ „	Vit	„
tomentosa		35	Blackburn & H. 1921	HVit	„
chavini		42	Täckholm 1922	—	Eur., Alps
marginata (*jundzillii*)		42	„ „	—	Eur., W. Asia
pouzini		42	Hurst 1928	—	S. Eur., N. Africa

Cultivated Roses: 14, 21, 28   Wylie 1954
cf. Darlington 1955

FRAGARIA   *x* = 7

bracteata		14	Yarnell 1931a	—	W: N. Amer.
californica		14	Ichijima 1930	—	California
campestris		14	Schiemann 1951	—	Europe
maxima		14	Ichijima 1930	—	—
helleri		14	„ 1926	—	W: N. Amer.
mexicana		14	Yarnell 1931a	—	Mexico
nilgerrensis	Nilgiri S.	14	„ 1929	—	India
vesca	Wood S.	14	Ichijima 1926	F	Temp. Reg.
v. *americana*	Amer. S.	14	„ „	F	E: N. Amer.
viridis (*collina*) Eur. S.		14	Darrow 1937	—	Eur., N. Asia
nipponica	Jap. S.	{ 14	Lilienfeld 1936	F	Japan
		28	R. Yamazaki 1936		
moupinensis		28	Schiemann 1951	—	Asia
orientalis		28	Fedorova 1946	—	„
moschata (*elatior*) Hautbois S.		42	Ichijima 1926	F	Europe
chiloensis	Pine S.	56	„ „	F	Alaska—Patag.
cuneifolia Rocky Mt. Wild S.		56	„ „	F	W: N. Amer.
glauca		56	„ 1930	F	N. America
grandiflora	Garden S.	56	„ 1926	F	*cult*
ovalis		56	Powers 1944	—	W: N. Amer.
platypetala		56	Yarnell 1931a	—	„
virginiana	Scarlet S.	56	Ichijima 1926	F	E: N. Amer.

DUCHESNEA (FRAGARIA)   *x* = 7

indica	Mock S.	84	Ichijima 1926	H	Ind., China, Mala.

NEURADA   *x* = 7

procumbens	14	Hagerup 1932	—	N. Africa, India

POTENTILLA*   *x* = 7   (Polyploids Apomictic)

arguta & 2 spp.		14	Popoff 1935	H	N. America
glandulosa		14	Clausen *et al.* 1937	H	W: N. Amer.
heptaphylla		14	Rutishauser 1943	—	Europe
argentea	{ 14, 28, 35, 42	Müntzing 1941	H	N. Temp.
	56	Håkansson 1946		
fruticosa	{ 14	Sax 1931a	—	N. America
	28	Turesson 1938	—	Europe
sterilis	{ 14	Shimotomai 1929	—	„
	28	Wulff 1938		
alba & 4 spp.		28	Popoff 1935	H	Eur., Cauc.
erecta	Tormentil	28	L. & L. 1948	M	Eur., N. Asia

138

POTENTILLA (*cont.*)

pulchella	28	L., & L. 1942	—	Greenland
reptans	28	Ehrenberg 1945	—	N. Temp.
anserina Silver Weed	28, 42	Erlandsson 1942b	HM	N. & S. Temp.
crantzii (*alpestris*)	28, 42	S. & S. 1941	H	Alps, Arctic
recta	{ 28	Popoff 1935	H	Eur., N. Asia
	42	Shimotomai 1930		
egedii	28, 35, 42	Erlandsson 1942b	—	N. Arct. & Temp.
groenlandica	28, 35, 42	,, ,,	—	N. & Arctic
arenaria	28	Skalinska 1950a	—	N. Asia
× *verna* (apo. hybrids)	35, 42, 56	Rutishauser 1943		
tabernaemontani (*verna*)	{ 28	Håkansson 1946	H	Europe
	42, 84	Müntzing 1941		
	49	L. & L. 1942		
canescens	42	Rutishauser 1943	—	Switzerland
nepalensis & 15 spp.	42	Shimotomai 1930	H	Himalayas
collina	42, 70, 84	Müntzing 1931	—	Eur., Asia M.
villosa	42, 49	,, ,,	—	C. Europe
monspeliensis	56	Löve 1954	H	N. America
bifurca	56	Popoff 1935	—	Cauc., N. Asia
curdica	56	,, ,,	—	,, ,,
argyrophylla	56, 63	,, ,,	H	Himalayas
atrosanguinea	56, 63	,, ,,	H	,,
chamissonis	{ 56	Bøcher & L. 1950	—	Arctic
	77	L. & L. 1948		
gracilis	52–109	Clausen *et al.* 1940	H	W: N. Amer.
nivea	{ 56	Erlandsson, L. & L. 1942	H	Arctic & Alpine
	63	Bøcher & L. 1950		
	70	Sakai 1934		
drummondii & 4 spp.	64–108	Clausen *et al.* 1940	H	W: N. Amer.
norvegica	70	Gentcheff 1938	H	N. Eur.
sibthorpiana	98	Shimotomai 1930	—	Japan
haematochroa	112	,, ,,	H	Mexico

COMARUM (POTENTILLA) $x = 7$

palustre	Marsh Cinquefoil	28	Ehrenberg 1945	H	N. Temp.
		42–64	S. & S. 1941		

SIBBALDIA (POTENTILLA) $x = 7$

procumbens	{ 14	Bøcher 1938a	—	N. & S. Reg.
	14	S. & S. 1941		

RUBUS * $x = 7$ (Polyploids often Apomictic)

allegheniensis & 2 spp.	14	Einset 1947	F	E: N. Amer.
arcticus Arctic Bramble	14	Vaarama 1939	F	Arctic
argutus & 4 spp.	14	Longley 1924a	F	E: N. Amer.
coreanus Korean R.	14	Marks 1952	F	China, Korea
gracilis	14	,, ,,	F	Asia
hirsutus & 7 spp.	14	Jinno 1951a, b	F	Japan
kuntzeanus	14	Darrow 1937	F	Asia
lasiostylus	14	Longley & D. 1924	F	China
laudatus Kinoyer B. & 2 spp.	14	Yarnell 1931c, 1936	F	N. America
leucodermis White Bark R. & 2 spp.	14	Darrow & L. 1333	F	W: N. Amer.
neglectus Purple Cane R. & 2 spp.	14	Crane & D. 1927	F	N. America

RUBUS (*cont.*)

xanthocarpus & 3 spp.	14	Gustafsson '33, '43	F	China
stellatus & 9 spp.	14	Vaarama 1954	F	N. America
canadensis Thornless Mt. B.	14 / 21	Longley 1924a / Einset 1947	F	N. America
idaeus European Raspberry	14, 21, 28	Crane 1936	F	Eur., N. & S.W. Asia
macrothyrsus	14, 28	Maude 1939	—	Europe
strigosus Amer. Red R.	14 / 21	Longley & D. 1924 / Einset 1947	F	N. America
ulmifolius (*rusticanus*)	14, (28)	Heslop-Harrison '53	F	Europe
avipes & 5 spp.	21	Einset 1947	F	N. America
deliciosus Rocky Mt. R.	21	Longley 1924a	H	W: N. Amer.
merceri & 1 sp.	21	Christen 1950	—	Europe
nigricans	21	Longley 1924a	F	W: N. Amer.
nitidus & 4 spp.	21	Heslop-Harrison '53	H	Europe
thyrsiflorus & 2 spp.	21	Gustafsson 1939	H	,,
bellobatus	21, 28	Einset 1947	—	N. America
thyrsanthus	21 / 28	Gustafsson 1943 / Heslop-Harrison 1953	—	Europe
affinis	28	,, ,,	F	Eur., Himal.
bifrons & 2 spp.	28	Christen 1950	—	Europe
bloxamii & 3 spp.	28	Datta 1932	F	,;
lentiginosus	28	Maude 1939	F	,,
nemorosus Caucasian D.	28	Gustafsson 1933	F	,,
omeiensis & 2 spp.	28	Marks 1952	F	China
pennsylvanicus & 5 spp.	28	Einset 1947	F	N. America
procerus Him. B. & 2 spp.	28	Crane 1936	F	
sachalinensis Siberian R.	28	Rozanova 1939	F	N. Asia
salteri	28	Maude 1939	F	Europe
sieboldii	28	Jinno 1951a	F	Java
tephrodes	28	Vaarama 1954	—	E. Asia
100 spp.	28	Fabergé, M. 1939 / Gustafsson 1942 / Heslop-Harrison 1953		
ambifarius	28, 35, 42	Gustafsson 1939	—	Europe
caesius Eur. Dewberry	28, 35	Heslop-Harrison 1953	F	Eur., N. Asia
balfourianus	28, 35	,, ,,	—	Europe
bellardii	28 / 35	,, ,, / Gustafsson 1939	—	Eur.—Persia
conjungens	28, 35	Heslop-Harrison 1953	—	Europe
hartmani (*horridus*)	28 / 35	Gustafsson 1942 / Heslop-Harrison 1953	—	,,
infestus	28, 42	Maude 1939	—	,,
formidabilis	28 / 35	,, ,, / Heslop-Harrison 1953	—	,,
granulatus (*bloxamianus*)	28 / 42	,, ,, / Maude 1939	—	,,
newbridgensis	28, 35	Heslop-Harrison 1953	—	,,
nitidioides Merton Early Bl.	28 / 42	,, ,, / Maude 1939	F	England
obcuneatus (*cenomanensis*)	28 / 35	,, ,, / Heslop-Harrison 1953	—	Europe

140

RUBUS (cont.)

ostenfeldii		28, 42, *c.* 44	Gustafsson 1939	—	Europe
pyramidalis		28, (42)	Heslop-Harrison 1953	—	,,
rosanthus		28, 35	Gustafsson 1939	—	,,
magnificus (*borreri*)		{ 28	Fabergé, M. 1939	F	,,
		{ 42	Heslop-Harrison 1953		
idaeus × *caesius*		28, 35, 42	Rozanova 1940a	F	*expt.*
abactus & 3 spp.		35	Einset 1947	—	N. Amer.
corylifolius		35	Datta 1932	F	Europe
dumetorum & 5 spp.		35	Marks 1952	—	,,
vestervicensis & 4 spp.		35	Gustafsson '39. '42	F	,,
wiegandii		36	Einset 1947	—	N. America
13 spp.		35	Heslop-Harrison 1953	—	Europe
britannicus		42	,, ,,	—	,,
divergens & 3 spp.		42	Gustafsson 1933	F	,,
loganobaccus	Loganberry	42	Thomas 1940	F	*cult*
pectinellus		42	Jinno 1951a	—	Japan
meracus		49	Einset 1947	—	N. America
hispidus	Swamp Bl.	35, 56	Longley 1924a	F	,,
buergeri & 2 spp.		56	Jinno 1951a, b	—	Japan
chamaemorus	Cloudberry	56	Heslop-Harrison 1953	F	North & Arctic
ursinus Pacific D.		42, 56, 84	Gustafsson 1943	F	W: N. Amer.
flagellaris		63	Einset 1947	—	N. America
plicatifolius		63	,, ,,	—	,,
lemurum		84	S.W. Brown 1943	F	Cent. Calif.

WALDSTEINIA *x* = 7

geoides		14	Reese 1952a	H	E. Europe

AGRIMONIA *x* = 7

eupatoria	Agrimony	28	Maude 1940	M	Europe
odorata		56	Wulff 1939b	—	Europe, W. Asia, N. Africa

GEUM* *x* = 7

heterocarpum		28	Gajewski 1949	H	Medit.
montanum		28	,, ,,	H	S. Europe
rhodopeum		28	,, ,,	—	Bulgaria
coccineum & 2 spp.		42	R. Yamazaki 1936	H	Chile
macrophyllum & 5 spp.		42	Gajewski 1949	H	N. Temp.
rivale Water Avens & 7 spp.		42	Raynor 1952	—	,, ,,
urbanum Avens, Herb Bennet		42	,, ,,	—	,, ,,
quellyon		{ 42	,, ,,	—	,, ,,
		{ 70	Gajewski 1949		
pyrenaicum		56, 84	,, ,,	H	Pyrenees
magellanicum		{ 84	,, ,,	H	S: S. Amer.
		{ 84	Raynor 1952		

SANGUISORBA (POTERIUM) *x* = 7

hakusanensis		28	Sakai 1935	—	Japan
minor	Salad Burnet	28	Lindenbein 1937	Sp	N. Temp.
officinalis	Great B.	28	Nakajima 1936	H	Europe, N. Asia, N. America
albiflora		54?	M. & S. 1936	—	Japan

11   141

FILIPENDULA $x = 7, 8$

ulmaria	Meadowsweet	$\begin{cases} 14 \\ 16 \end{cases}$	Wulff 1938 Vaarama, L. & L. 1948	HM	Eur., N. Asia
vulgaris	Dropwort	$\begin{cases} 14 \\ 15! \end{cases}$	Wulff 1938 Maude 1940	MR	,,　　,,

ALCHEMILLA $x = 8$　(All species Apomictic)

glomerulans		c. 64	Bøcher 1938a	—	Europe
glabra (*vulgaris*)		$\begin{cases} c.\ 90 \\ c.\ 100 \end{cases}$	L. & L. 1942 Ehrenberg 1945	—	,,
vulgaris s.l. Lady's Mantle		91–191	Gentscheff & G. 1940	H	Eurasia
micans		c. 93	Ehrenberg 1945	—	France, Switz.
subcrenata		c. 90, c. 96	L. & L. 1948	—	Europe
acutiloba		c. 100	Ehrenberg 1945	—	Eur., W. Asia
monticola (*pastoralis*)		101	,,　　,,	—	,,　　,,
alpina		c. 120	Gentscheff & G. 1940	—	Alps, N. Europe

APHANES (ALCHEMILLA) $x = 8$

microcarpa		16	Gudjonsson 1941	—	Spain
arvensis	Parsley Piert	$\begin{cases} 48 \\ 48, 50 \end{cases}$	,,　　,, Gentscheff & G. 1940	—	N. Temp.

CERCOCARPOS $x = 9$

betuloides	Mt. Mahogany	18	Morley 1949	H	Calif.

DRYAS $x = 9$

caucasica		18	S. & S. 1940	—	Caucasus
integrifolia		18	Bøcher & L. 1950	H	N. Am., Greenld.
octopetala		18	Maude 1940	BH	North Reg.

KERRIA $x = 9$

japonica		18	Sugiura 1936b	H	C. & W. China

RHODOTYPOS $x = 9$

scandens	Jet Bead	18	Sax 1932	H	Japan

SF2: PRUNOIDEAE $x = 8$

NUTTALLIA (OSMARONIA) $x = 8$

cerasiformis	Osoberry	16	Moffett 1931b	H	W: N. Amer.

MADDENIA $x = 8$

hypoxantha	Madden Cherry	32	Sax 1931a	—	China

PRINSEPIA $x = 8$

uniflora	32	Sax 1931a	—	Mongolia

PRUNUS $x = 8$

S1: ALMONDS AND PEACHES

amygdalus	Almond	16	Darlington 1930	HNO	S.W. Asia
fenzliana		16	,,　　,,	H	Caucasus
persica	Peach, Nectarine	16	,,　　,,	FHO	W. China (*cult*)
nana (*tenella*)	Russian A.	16	Kobel 1928	HN	Eur., Siberia
triloba	Flowering A.	64	,,　　,,	H	China

S2: PLUMS

alleghaniensis	Allegeny P.	16	Sax 1931a	F	N.E: U.S.A.
americana	Goose P.	16	,,　　,,	F	,,

PRUNUS *(cont.)*

armeniaca	Apricot	16	Darlington 1928	F	Caucasus
hortulana		16	Sax 1931a	F	C: U.S.A.
maritima	Bead P.	16	„ „	F	E: U.S.A.
nigra	Canada P.	16	Kobel 1928	F	„
triflora	Jap. P.	16	Darlington 1930	F	China
as *salicina*		16	Weeks 1941		
mume	Jap. Apricot	16, 24	Okabe 1928	F	Japan
divaricata	Myrobalan,	16, 17, 24	Rybin 1936	FFs	Caucasus
(cerasifera)	Cherry P.				
caspica		16	Kovalev 1939	F	Persia
iranica		16	„ „	F	„
media		32	„ „	F	
spinosa	Sloe, Blackthorn	32	Darlington 1930	FW	Eur., N. Africa,
nat. hybrids		16, 24, 40, 48	Mather 1937		W. Asia
insititia	Damson	48	Darlington 1928	FFs	Eur., A. Minor
as *italica*		48	Kobel 1927		
domestica	European P.	48	Darlington 1930	F	*cult*
divaricata × *spinosa*		24, 48	Rybin 1936	F	Caucasus

S3: CHERRIES

cerasoides (*puddum*)		16	Okabe 1928	F	Himalayas
crassipes		16	„ „	F	Japan
glandulosa	Almond C.	16	Sax 1931a	—	W: N. Amer.
incana	Underwood C.	16	„ „	F	Caucasus
japonica		16	„ „	F	Japan, China
kurilensis	Takane C.	16	Okabe 1928		Japan
lannesiana	Jap. Flower. C.	16	Darlington 1030	H	
mahaleb	Mahaleb C.	16	„ 1928	Fs	S. Europe, S.W. Asia
mutabilis	Jap. Flower. C.	16	Okabe 1928	F	Japan
pumila	Sand C.	16	Kobel 1928	F	N: U.S.A.
sachalinensis	Sargent C.	16	Okabe 1928	F	Japan
subhirtella	Higan C.	16	„ „	F	„
tomentosa	Manchu C.	16	„ „	F	E. Asia
yedoensis	Yoshino C.	16	„ „	—	Japan
incisa	Fuji C.	16	Sax 1931a	F	„
as *itosakura*		16, 24	Okabe 1928		
paniculata	Jap. Fl. C.	16, 24	„ „	FHP	„
(serrulata)					
as *pseudocerasus*	Yung fo	32	„ „		
avium	Sweet C., Mazzard	16, 24, 32	Darlington 1928, 1933b	FHTo	Europe, S.W. Asia, *cult*
cerasus	Sour C., Morello	32	Darlington 1928	F	Eur., S.W. Asia
cantabrigiensis	Chin. Early C.	32	Crane & L. 1938	F	China
fruticosa	Ground C.	32	Darlington 1928	F	S. Eur., N. Asia

S4: BIRD CHERRIES

grayana	Jap. Choke C.	32	Okabe 1928	F	Japan
padus	Bird C., Hagberry	32	Kobel 1928	HF	Eur., N. Amer.
serotina	Capuli	32	„ 1927	FMW	N. America
ssiori	Sakhalin C.	32	Okabe 1928	F	Sakhalin
virginiana	Amer. Choke C.	32	Sax 1931a	F	N. America

S5: CHERRY LAURELS

lusitanica	Portugal L.	64	Almeida 1947a	H	Portugal
laurocerasus	Cherry Laurel	*c.* 176	Meurman 1929	HMSp	S.W. Asia

SF3: SPIRAEOIDEAE: $x = 8, 9$

EXOCHORDA $x = 8$
giraldii	Pearl Bush	16	Sax 1931a	H	China

PENTACTINA $x = 9$
rupicola		18	Sax 1931a	—	Korea

PHYSOCARPUS (SPIRAEA) $x = 9$
capitatus	Ninebark	18	Sax 1931a	H	W: N. Amer.
intermedius	,,	18	,, ,,	—	C: N. Amer.
monogynus	,,	18	,, ,,	H	N. America
stellatus	,,	18	,, ,,	—	W: N. Amer.

SIBIRAEA (SPIRAEA) $x = 9$
laevigata		18	Sax 1931a	H	Siberia

SPIRAEA $x = 9$
Old World Group
cana	18	Sax 1936	H	S. Europe
gemmata	18	,, ,,	H	China
hypericifolia	18	,, ,,	H	S.E. Eur., T. Asia
japonica	18	,, ,,	H	Him., Ch., Jap.
media	18	,, ,,	H	E. Eur.—N.E. As.
miyabei	18	,, ,,	H	Japan
mollifolia	18	,, ,,	H	China
nipponica	18	,, ,,	H	Japan
prunifolia	18	,, ,,	H	Japan, China
pubescens	18	,, ,,	H	China
thunbergii	18	,, ,,	H	China, Japan
chamaedryfolia	18, 36	,, ,,	H	N.E. Asia
salicifolia	36	,, ,,	H	Eur.—Japan
myrtilloides (*virgata*)	54	,, ,,	H	China

New World Group
corymbosa (3x)		27	,, ,,	H	E: N. Amer.
alba	White M.	36	,, ,,	H	,,
douglasii		36	,, ,,	H	W: N. Amer.
latifolia	Meadowsweet	36	,, ,,	HM	E: N. Amer.
tomentosa		36	Bowden 1945b	H	,,

SF4: POMOIDEAE: $x = 17$

CHAENOMELES (CYDONIA, PYRUS) $x = 17$
cathayensis		34	Moffett 1931a	FH	C. China
japonica		34	,, ,,	H	Japan
sinensis	Chinese Quince	34	Sax 1931a	F	China
speciosa	Jap. Quince	34	Moffett 1931a	FH	China,
(*lagenaria*)					(Japan, *cult*)

CYDONIA $x = 17$
oblonga	Quince	34	Moffett 1931a	FFsM	Turkestan,
					N. Persia *cult*

ERIOBOTRYA $x = 17$
japonica	Loquat	34	Moffett 1931a	FH	Japan, China

MESPILUS $x = 17$

germanica	Medlar	34	Moffett 1931a	F	E. Eur., S.W. Asia

OSTEOMELES $x = 17$

schwerinae	34	Moffett 1931a	H	W. China

PYRACANTHA $x = 17$

atalantioides (*gibbsii*)	34	Moffett 1931a	H	China
coccinea Fire Thorn	34	„ „	H	S. Eur., Asia M.

QUILLAJA $x = 17$

brasiliensis	34	Bowden 1945b	—	Brazil

RAPHIOLEPIS $x = 17$

delacourii		34	Moffett 1931b	H	*cult*
indica	Ind. Hawthorn	34	„ „	FHM	S. China
umbellata	Yeddo H.	34	„ „	H	Japan

STRANVAESIA $x = 17$

davidiana	34	Moffett 1931a	H	W. China

AMELANCHIER $x = 17$

asiatica		34	Sax 1931a	FH	E. Asia
humilis		34	„ „	F	N. America
oblongifolia	June Berry	34	„ „	FH	E: N. Amer.
sanguinea		34	„ „	H	N. America
stolonifera		{ 34	„ „	FH	E: N. Amer.
		{ 68	Moffett 1931a		
canadensis	Shad	68	„ „	FH	„
laevis		68	„ „	FH	„
ovalis (*rotundifolia*)	Service B.	68	„ „	F	C. & S. Europe
spicata		68	Sax 1931a	H	*cult*

ARONIA $x = 17$

hybrida		34	Moffett 1931a	H	*cult*
melanocarpa	Black Chokeberry	34	„ „	H	E: N. Amer.
arbutifolia	Red C.	{ 34	Sax 1931a	H	„
		{ 68	Moffett 1931a		

COTONEASTER* $x = 17$ (Polyploids Apomictic)

procumbens	34	Moffett 1931a	H	?
congestus (3*x*)	51	„ „	H	Himalayas
bullatus	68	„ „	H	S.E. Tib.—W. Ch.
integerrimus (*vulgaris*)	68	„ „	—	Eur., N. Asia
microphyllus	68	„ „	H	Himalayas
acutifolius & 23 spp.	34, 51, 68	H. J. Sax 1954		China

CRATAEGUS $x = 17$

chlorosarca		34	Moffett 1931a	H	Manchuria
lavallei		34	Sax 1931a	H	*cult*
oxyacantha	Hawthorn	34	Moffett 1931a	BFsW	Eur., Temp. Asia
stipulosa		34	„ „	H	Mexico
monogyna		34	„ „	—	Eur., Temp. Asia
v. *cabulica* (3*x*)		51	„ „		
douglasii (3*x*)	Michigan H.	*c.* 51	Longley 1924b	F	Mich., W: N. Am.
intricata	Thicket H.	*c.* 51	„ „	F	E: U.S.A.

145

CRATAEGUS (*cont.*)

apposita	Delaware H.	68	Moffett 1931a	—	N. America
cognata		68	,, ,,	H	,,
crus-galli	Cockspur H.	68	,, ,,	H	,,
pedicellata	Ontario H.	68	,, ,,	—	,,
pruinosa	Frosted H.	68	,, ,,	H	E: U.S.A.
phaenopyrum	Washington H.	(72)	,, ,,	H	N. America

MALUS $x = 17$

adstringens	Crab Apple	34	Sax 1931a	F	*cult*
asiatica	Oriental C.	34	Köbel 1927	F	N. Asia
baccata	Siberian C.	34	Sax 1931a	FH	Himal., N. Asia
floribunda	Flowering C.	34	Darlington & M. '30	FH	China
fusca	Oregon C.	34	Nebel 1929	—	N. America
halliana		34	,, ,,	FH	China, Japan
ioensis	Prairie C.	34	,, ,,	FH	N. America
niedzwetzkyana		34	,, ,,	FH	S.W. Sib., Cauc.
zumi	Zumi Crab	34	Rybin 1926	FH	Japan
prunifolia	Plum Leaf C.	34, 51	Nebel 1929	FH	N.E. Asia
sylvestris	Apple	34, 51	Darlington & M. '30	F	Afghan., *cult*
(*pumila*)	266 vars.	34	Einset & I. '47, '49,		
	18 vars.	51	Einset & L. '51		
	15 vars.	34/68	(chimaeras) ,,		
angustifolia	Southern C.	{34, 68}	Rybin 1926 / Sax 1931a	F	N. America
coronaria	American C.	51, 68	Dermen 1949	FH	,,
platycarpa		{51, 68}	,, ,, / Lincoln & M. 1937	FH	,,
hupehensis		51, 68	Dermen 1936c	FH	China
lancifolia		51, 68	,, 1949	FH	N. America
sargentii		34, 68	Nebel 1930	FH	Japan
glaucescens		68	Sax 1931a	FH	E: N. Amer.
sieboldii (5x)		85	Olden 1945	FH	Japan

PYRUS $x = 17$

aromatica		34	Adati 1933	F	Japan
betulifolia		34	,, ,,	FHV	China
calleryana	Callery P.	34	,, ,,	F	Japan
dimorphophylla		34	,, ,,	F	,,
eleagrifolia	Oleaster P.	34	Rybin 1927	FH	Asia Minor
fauriei	Korean P.	34	Adati 1933	F	E. Asia
hondoensis		34	,, ,,	F	Japan
nivalis	Snow P.	34	Rybin 1927	FH	N. Asia, Himal.
phaeocarpa		34	Adati 1933	FH	N. China
pyrifolia	Sand P.	34	,, 1935	FH	Java
salicifolia		34	Köbel 1927	FH	Caucasus
sohayakiensis		34	Adati 1933	F	Japan
ussuriensis	Chinese P.	34	Rybin 1927	FH	China
uyematsuana		34	Adati 1933	F	*cult*
communis	Pear	34, 51	Darlington & M. '30	F	Afghan., *cult*
		34/68	Marks 1953		

PHOTINIA $x = 17$

glabra	Jap. Medlar	34	K. 1931	H	Japan
villosa		68	Moffett 1931a	H	China, Korea, Jap.

SORBUS (PYRUS) $x = 17$ (Apomixis, obligatory in triploids)

alnifolia		34	Sax 1931a	H	Japan, Korea
americana	American M.A.	34	„ „	H	E: U.S.A.
aria	White Beam	34	Moffett 1931a	FH	C. & S. Europe
aucuparia	Rowan, Mt. Ash	34	„ „	BFH	Eur., Asia Minor, N. Africa
confusa		34	Poucques 1951	—	?
domestica	Service Tree	34	Moffett 1931a	HW	Eur., N. Africa
latifolia		34	Poucques 1951	H	Europe
torminalis	Wild Service T.	34	Moffett 1931a	FH	S. & C. Europe
bristoliensis		51	Warburg 1952	—	W. England
lancifolia		51	Liljefors 1934	—	Norway
minima		51	Moffett 1931b	—	Wales
mougeotii		51	Liljefors 1934	H	C. Europe
porrigentiformis		51, 68	Warburg 1952	—	Wales, W. Eng.
anglica		68	„ „	—	„ „
chamaemespilus		68	Liljesfors 1934	H	C. Europe
decora		68	Bøcher & L. 1950	H	E: U.S.A.
eminens		68	Warburg 1952	—	W. England
hybrida (*fennica*)		68	Liljefors 1934	H	N. Europe
intermedia (*suecica*)		68	„ „	H	N.W. Europe
leptophylla		68	Warburg 1952	—	Wales
meinichii		68	Liljefors 1934	—	N. Europe
obtusifolia (*aria* v. *norvegica*)		68	„ „	—	Scandinavia
rupicola (*salicifolia*)		68	„ „	—	W. Europe
sudetica		68	„ „	—	C. Europe

AMELASORBUS (AMELANCHIER × SORBUS) $x = 17$

jackii		34	Sax & S. 1947	H	W: N. Amer.

SORBARONIA (SORBUS × ARONIA) $x = 17$

alpina		34	Sax & S. 1947	H	*cult*
dippelii		34	„ „	H	„
jackii		34	„ „	H	„

145 CALYCANTHACEAE

CHIMONANTHUS $x = 11$

fragrans	Jap. Allspice, Winter Sweet	22	Sugiura 1931	HSp	Japan

CALYCANTHUS $x = 11$

fertilis		22	Sax 1933b	HSp	N. America
occidentalis	Cal. Allspice	22	Cave 1948a	HSp	California
floridus	Carolina All.	22	Sax 1933b	HSp	N. America
v. *ovatus*	(3*x*)	33	„ „	HSp	„

146 CAESALPINACEAE

CERCIS $x = 6, 7$

canadensis	Red Bud	12	Senn 1938	H(V)	E: N. Amer.
occidentalis		14	Atchison 1949a	H	S.W: N. Amer.
siliquastrum	Judas Tree	14	Corti 1930b	H(V)	S. Eur.—N. Persia

147

CASSIA $x = 6, 7, 8$ $x_2 = 13$

auriculata	Avarum	$\begin{cases} 14, 16 \\ 28 \end{cases}$	Jacob 1940 Pantulu 1942	DMMa	India
chamaecrista & 1 sp.		16	Senn 1938	—	S: U.S.A.
dimidiata		16	Sugiura 1931	—	Tropics
mimosoides (*leschenaultiana*)		16, 32, 48	Kawakami 1930	BMa	,.
alata	Ringworm Plant	24	Senn 1938	M(Sh)	,,
antillana		24	Atchison 1951	—	W. Indies
atomarica		c. 24	,, ,.	—	S. America
egregia		24	Covas & S. 1946	—	,,
fastuosa		24	Atchison 1951	—	Trop. America
nodosa	Jointwood	24	,, ,,	ShMW	Trop. Asia
renigera		24	,, ,,	H	Upper Burma
tomentosa		24	Sugiura 1931	Ma	Trop. America
fistula	Ind. Laburnum	$\begin{cases} 24 \\ 28 \end{cases}$	Tischler 1922 Pantulu 1946	DHM	Trop. Asia
sophera		$\begin{cases} 24 \\ 28 \end{cases}$	Kawakami 1930 Pantulu 1948	H	O.W. Tropics
obtusifolia		26	Pantulu 1942	Ma(V)	Tropics
splendida		26, 52	Covas 1949b	H	Brazil
occidentalis	Nigger Coffee	$\begin{cases} 26 \\ 28 \end{cases}$	Muto 1929 Pantulu 1940	BMaV	Tropics
tora	Tavara	$\begin{cases} 26 \\ 28 \end{cases}$	Datta 1933b Jacob 1940	DMa(V)	,,
angustifolia	Indian Senna	28	Sampath & R. 1949	M	India, Afr., Arabia
corymbosa (*floribunda*)		28	Atchison 1951	H	Argentine
didymobotrya		28	Sethi 1930	HMaSh	Abyssinia
grandis	Pink Shower	28	Atchison 1951	HM	Panama
hirsuta		$\begin{cases} 28 \\ 56 \end{cases}$	Frahm-Leliveld 1953 Sampath & R. 1949	H	Trop. America
javanica	Java Cassia	28	Ramanathan 1950	HShM	E. Indies
marginata	Red Cassia	28	Atchison 1951	DShW	Trop. Asia
moschata		28	,, ,,	—	Trop. America
obtusa		28	Ramanathan 1950	—	O.W. Tropics
siamea	Kassod Tree	28	Atchison 1951	DShVW	Mal., E. Indies
torosa		28	Nakajima	Ma	Tropics
glauca		28, 56	Pantulu 1942	H	Tr. Asia, Austral.

LYSIDICE $x = 8$

rhodostegia		16	Atchison 1951	—	S. China

SINODORA $x = 8$

supa		16	Atchison 1951	—	Philippines

TRACHYLOBIUM $x = 8$

verrucosum	Zanzibar Copal	16	Atchison 1951	Re	Trop. Africa

PTEROGYNE $x = 10$

nitens		$\begin{cases} 20 \\ 20 \end{cases}$	Atchison 1941 Covas & S. 1947	—	Brazil

AMBURANA $x = 11$

cearensis		22	Covas & S. 1947	W	Brazil

PHYLLOCARPUS $x = 11$

septentrionalis		22	Atchison 1951	H	Guatemala

CAESALPINIA $x = 11, 12$

japonica		22	Sakai 1951	H	Japan
bahamensis		24	Atchison 1951	—	W. Indies
bonduc	Nicker-Nut	24	,, ,,	DHM	,,
coriaria	Divi-divi	24	,, ,,	DHW	Dry Trop. Amer.
crista	Wood Gossip	24	,, ,,	DM	Tropics
ferrea		24	,, ,,	—	Brazil
floribunda		24	Covas & S. 1947	—	,,
gilliesii		24	,, 1946	H	Argentine
mexicana		24	Atchison 1951	H	Mexico
pauciflora		24	,, ,,	—	W. Indies
paucijuga		24	,, ,,	—	,,
pulcherrima	Peacock Flower	24	,, ,,	HM	Tropics
vesicaria		24	,, ,,	—	Cuba
rubicunda		24	Covas 1949b	—	Brazil
sappan	Sappan Wood	24	Ghose 1952	D	India, Malaya

AMHERSTIA $x = 12$

nobilis	Tree of Heaven	24	Pantulu 1943	H	Burma

BROWNEA $x = 12$

coccinea (*hybrida*)		24	Atchison 1951	HM	Venezuela

CERATONIA $x = 12$

siliqua	Carob, Locust Bean	24	Almeida 1948	DFFoSh	S. Eur., S.W. Asia

COPAIFERA $x = 12$

officinalis	Copaiba-Balsam, Maracaibo	24	Atchison 1951	ReW	Trop. S. Amer.

ERYTHROPHLOEUM $x = 12$

guineense	Red Water Tree	24	Atchison 1951	H	Fr. W. Africa

HAEMATOXYLON $x = 12$

campechianum	Logwood	24	Atchison 1951	DW	Trop. America

HOFFMANSEGGIA $x = 12$

andina		24	Covas & S. 1946	—	Chile
falcaria		24	,, ,,	—	Chile, Peru

HYMENAEA $x = 12$

courbaril	Locust Tree Anime Resin	24	Atchison 1951	HReW	Tr. Amer., W. Ind.

INTSIA $x = 12$

africana		24	Atchison 1951	—	Trop. Africa
bijuga		24	,, ,,	MW	Pacific Is.

SARACA $x = 12$

declinata		24	Atchison 1951	H	Sumatra
indica	Ashoka	24	,, ,,	DHM	India, Burm., Cey.
thaipingensis		24	,, ,,	—	Malaya

TAMARINDUS $x = 12$

indica	Tamarind	24	Atchison 1951	FMW	Trop. Asia, Africa

BAUHINIA $x = 14$

acuminata		28	Atchison 1951	HM	India, China, Mal.
galpini		28	,, ,,	H	Trop. & S. Africa
godefroyi		28	,, ,,	—	Cambodia
hookeri		28	,, ,,	—	Australia
macrostachya		28	,, ,,	—	Guiana
mollicella		28	,, ,,	—	Venezuela
purpurea		28	,, ,,	DH(V)	India, Bur., China
rufescens		28	,, ,,	—	S. Africa
saigonensis		28	,, ,,	—	Cochin China
tomentosa	St. Thomas T.	28	,, ,,	H	India
variegata	Mountain Ebony	28	,, ,,	DHT(V)	India, China
monandra		42	Poucques 1945	—	Burma

COLVILLEA $x = 14$

racemosa	28	Atchison 1951	H	Madagascar

DELONIX (POINCIANA) $x = 14$

		⎧24?	Poucques 1945		
regia	Flamboyante	⎨28	Jacob 1940,	HShW	Madagascar
		⎩28	Atchison 1951		

DIALIUM $x = 14$

guineense	28	Atchison 1951	W	W. Africa

DIMORPHANDRA $x = 14$

mollis	28	Covas 1949b	—	Brazil

GLEDITSIA $x = 14$

amorphoides		28	Atchison 1949a	—	Argentine
aquatica		28	,, ,,	H	S: N. Amer.
fera		28	,, 1951	—	China
heterophylla		28	,, 1949a	H	,,
horrida		28	,, ,,	H	,, Japan
sinensis		28	,, ,,	H	,,
triacanthos	Honey Locust	28	,, 1947a	AH(Su)	E: N. Amer.

GYMNOCLADUS $x = 14$

dioica	Kentucky Coffee T.	28	Atchison 1949a	HN	N. America

PARKINSONIA $x = 14$

aculeata	Jerusalem Thorn,	⎧28	Pantulu 1942	HT	Trop. America
	Cina-Cina	⎩28	Atchison 1951		

PELTOPHORUM $x = 14$

inerme (ferrugineum)	28	Atchison 1951	ShWH	Austr., Philip., Ceylon, Malaya

147 MIMOSACEAE

CALLIANDRA $x = 8$

hematocephala	16	Atchison 1951	H	Brazil
inaequilatera	16	,, 1949a	—	Bolivia

ENTADA $x = 8?$

sudanica	c. 16	Atchison 1951	FoMT	Trop. Africa

SCHRANKIA $x=8$

angustata	16	Atchison 1949a	—	E: N. Amer.
occidentalis	24	Turner & B. 1953	—	America

ENTEROLOBIUM $x=13$

contortisiliquum	{ 26	Covas 1950c	—	Brazil
	{ 26	Atchison 1951		
cyclocarpum	26	„ „	—	Jamaica
timbouva	26	Tjio 1948	DW	Brazil

LYSILOMA $x=13$

bahamensis	26	Atchison 1951	—	Bahamas, Cuba
divaricata	26	„ „	—	Mexico
latisiliqua	26	„ „	W	Cuba
tergemina	26	„ „	—	S. Mexico

PARKIA $x=13$

biglandulosa	26	Sampath & R. 1949	H	Malaya

PIPTADENIA $x=13$

macrocarpa	26	Atchison 1951	H	Brazil, Bolivia

SIDEROCARPUS $x=13$

flexicaulis	26	Atchison 1951	—	Texas, Mexico

ACACIA $x=13$
(i) American Group

aroma	26	Atchison 1948	—	S. America
bonariensis	26	„ „	—	Argentine
cavenia	26	„ „	—	Chile
chloriophylla	26	„ „	—	Bahamas
curvifructa	26	Covas 1950c	—	S. America
furcata	26	Covas & S. 1946	—	„
macracantha	26	Atchison 1948	—	„
moniliformis	26	„ „	—	Argentine
tenuifolia	26	„ „	—	W. I., S. Amer.
tortuosa	26	„ „	—	S. Amer., Galap.
villosa	26	„ „	—	Jamaica
visco	26	Covas & S. 1947	—	Argentine

(ii) Australian & Pacific Island Group

alata	26	Covas & S. 1946	—	W. Australia
armata Kangaroo Thorn	26	„ „	Sb	Australia
auriculaeformis	26	Atchison 1948	—	„
baileyana Cootamundra Wattle	26	„ „	HW	N.S.W.
calamifolia	26	Chevalier 1945	—	Australia
cultriformis	26	„ „	H	N.S.W.
cyanophylla	26	Atchison 1948	DW	W. Australia
confusa	26	„ „	—	Philippines
dealbata Silver Wattle	26	„ „	DHW	Australia
decurrens Black Wattle	26	„ „	DW	„
dermatophylla	26	„ „	—	„
falcata	26	Tjio 1948	W	„
glaucoptera	26	„ „	—	„
graveolens	26	„ „	—	„
longifolia Sydney Golden W.	26	Atchison 1948	H	„
melanoxylon Austr. Blackwood	26	„ „	HW	„
mollissima Green Wattle	26	„ „	DW	„

151

ACACIA (cont.)

penninervis	Mt. Hickory W.	26	Tjio 1948	H	Australia
podalyrifolia	Q'land Silver W.	26	Atchison 1948	H	,,
retinodes		26	Tjio 1948	—	,,
richii		26	Atchison 1948	—	Fiji Is.
rubida		26	Chevalier 1945	—	Australia
saligna		26	Atchison 1948	—	W. Australia
verticillata		26	Tjio 1948	—	Australia
xylocarpa		26	,, ,,	—	N. Australia
koa		{ 52	Atchison 1948	W	Hawaii
		52	Tjio 1948		

(iii) Asiatic & African Group

albida	Winter Thorn	26	Atchison 1948	DFoMW	N. Africa
catechu	Catechu	26	,, ,,	DMW	India, E. Indies
detinens		26	,, ,,	—	S. Africa
mellifera		26	Khan 1951	T	India
modesta		26	,, ,,	—	,,
senegal	Gum Arabic	26	,, ,,	FoTM	Trop. Africa
suma	Cutch	26	Atchison 1948	DMW	S.E. Asia
sundra		26	,, ,,	—	,,
senegal × *mellifera*		39	Khan 1951	—	*nat. hybrid*
arabica	Babul, Gum Arabic	52	Atchison 1948	FoDMW	Trop. Afr. & Asia
eburnea	Ivory Acacia	52	,, ,,	W	India
horrida	All Thorn	52	,, ,,	DW	Trop. & S. Africa
laeta		52	,, ,,	—	Arabia, N. Africa
nilotica		52	,, ,,	MWH	Trop. Afr. & Asia
scorpioides		52	,, ,,	—	,, ,, ,,
seyal		52	,, ,,	FoM	Egypt
spirocarpa		52	,, ,,	—	Trop. Africa
xanthophloea		52	,, ,,	—	E. Trop. Africa

(iv) Cosmopolitan

farnesiana	Cassie	52	Atchison 1948	DHPW	Trop. & Sub-Trop.

ALBIZZIA $x = 13$

gamblei		26	Atchison 1951	—	India
lebbekoides		26	,, ,,	—	Philippines
lophantha	Plum Acacia	26	Covas & S. 1946	FoSh	Australia
neumannia		26	,, ,,	—	,,
odoratissima	Black Siris	26	Atchison 1951	HW	India, Bur., Cey.
procera	White Siris	26	Covas & S. 1946	W	Trop. Asia & Aus.
julibrissin		{ 26	Sakai 1951	(B)HSh	Sub-Tr. Asia, Afr.
		52	R. Yamazaki 1936		
polyphylla		104	Covas & S. 1946	—	Madagascar

ARTHROSAMANEA $x = 13$

polycephala		26	Burkart 1949b	—	Argentine
polyantha		*c.* 52	,, ,,	—	,,

PITHECELLOBIUM (PITHECOLOBIUM $x = 13$

brevifolium		26	Atchison 1951	—	Mexico
dulce	Madras Thorn	26	Sampath & R. 1949	DFoH	Trop. America
guadelupensis		26	Atchison 1951	—	W. Indies
saman	Rain Tree	{ 26	,, ,,	FoSh	Trop. America
		26	Simmonds 1954		

152

PITHECELLOBIUM (*cont.*)

scalare	$\begin{cases} 26 \\ 26 \end{cases}$	Covas 1950c Atchison 1951	—	Argentine
polycephalum	52	,, ,,	—	Trop. America

LEUCAENA *x* = 13

glauca	$\begin{cases} 104 \\ 104 \end{cases}$	Tjio 1948 Sampath & R. 1949	BDFoMaVW	Trop. America

MIMOSA *x* = 13, 14

bimucronata	26	Covas & S. 1947	—	Brazil
invisa	$\begin{cases} 24 \\ 26 \end{cases}$	Frahm-Leliveld 1953 Tjio 1948	—	,,
biuncifera	52	,, ,,	—	Mexico
pudica Sensitive Plant	52	,, ,,	FoHM	Brazil
ephedroides	28	Covas & S. 1946	—	Chile
hamata	40?	Dnyansagar 1951	—	India

PROSOPIS *x* = 13?, 14

juliflora Mesquite	$\begin{cases} 26 \\ 52 \\ 56 \end{cases}$	Ramanathan 1950 Sampath & R. 1949 Atchison 1951	AFoRe	Trop. America
alba	28	Covas & S. 1947	FW	Argentine
alpataco	28	,, ,,	—	Chile
argentina	28	,, 1946	—	Argentine
campestris	28	,, 1947	—	,,
chilensis Algarrabo	28	,, ,,	Re	S. America
ferox	28	,, ,,	—	Argentine
ruizleali	28	,, ,,	—	,,
ruscifolia	28	Covas 1950c	FoM	,,
strombulifera	28	Schnack & C. 1947	—	S. America
striata	28, 56, *c.* 112	Castronovo 1945	—	Pagatonia

DESMANTHUS * *x* = 14

acuminatus & 4 spp.	28	Turner & B. 1953	—	S: U.S.A.

NEPTUNIA *x* = (9) 18

triquetra	36	Dnyansagar 1952	—	India
plena	*c.* 72	Frahm-Leliveld 1953	H	N. & S. America, Trop. As., Aust.

DICHROSTACHYS *x* = 14

glomerata	56	Atchison 1951	FoHMTToW	Trop. Africa

148 PAPILIONACEAE

Order of the Tribes with their Basic Numbers

I	Vicieae: 5, 6, 7, 8		VI	Podalyrieae: 7, 8, 9
II	Hedysareae: 5, 6, 7, 8, 9, 11		VII	Genisteae: 7, 8, 9, 10, 11, 12
III	Loteae: 6, 7, 8		VIII	Sophoreae: 7, 8, 9, 10, 13
IV	Trifolieae: 6, 7, 8, 9		IX	Phaseoleae: 8, 10, 11, 12
V	Galegeae: 6, 7, 8, 9, 10, 11		X	Dalbergieae: 8, 10, 11, 12, 13

VICIA x = 5, 6, 7
  x = 5 or 6

Species	Common name	No.	Reference	Code	Region
amphicarpa		10	Sweschnikova '30, '40	—	Eur., W. As.
		12	Coutinho 1940		N. Africa
lathyroides	Spring Vetch	10	Sweschnikova 1927a	—	Eur., Asia Minor
		12	Heitz 1931a		N. Africa
macrocarpa		10	,, ,,	—	S. Europe
		12	Coutinho 1940		

x = 6

Species	Common name	No.	Reference	Code	Region
ambigua		12	Coutinho 1945	—	Eur., S.W. Asia, N. Africa
angustifolia	Narrowleaf Vetch	12	Sweschnikova 1927a	Fo	,, ,,
ferruginea		12	Coutinho 1945	—	?
grandiflora		12	,, ,,	—	S. Eur., S.W. Asia
hybrida		12	Heitz 1931b	—	Eur., Med.
hyrcanica		12	,, ,,	—	Caucasus
michauxii		12	Coutinho 1945		Syria, Persia
orobus	Upright V.	12	Heitz 1931b	—	Europe
pannonica	Hungarian V.	12	,, ,,	Fo	S. Eur., Asia
peregrina		12	,, ,,	—	Medit., India
pisiformis	Pea Vetch	12	,, ,,	V	Europe
amoena		12	Moriya & K. 1949b	—	Siberia
		24	Sweschnikova 1927a		
unijuga	Pair Vetch	12	Heitz 1931b	—	E. Asia
		24	Sakamura, I. 1916		
		36	Kawakami 1930		
tenuifolia	Marrachero	24	Heitz 1931b	FoV	Eur., S.W. & N. Asia
		24	Ryka 1954		

x = 6 or 7

Species	Common name	No.	Reference	Code	Region
calcarata		12	Senn 1938	—	Medit., Persia
		14	Heitz 1931b		
faba	Broad, Horse or Field Bean	12	McLeish 1953	FoV	Medit., *cult*
		(24)	Rybin 1939		
		12	Hirayoshi & M. 1952		Eur. strains
		14	,, ,, ,,		Jap. strains
sativa	Common V. or Tare	12	Sweschnikova 1940	GFo	Eur., N. Africa, W. Asia
		12	Sakai 1951		
		12, 14	Moriya & K. 1949b		
		12, 14	Coutinho 1940, '45		
cracca	Cow Vetch	12, 14, 28	Sweschnikova 1927b	FoG	Eur., W. Asia, N. America
		14	Moriya & K. 1949b		S. Poland
		14, 28	Ryka 1954		

x = 7

Species	Common name	No.	Reference	Code	Region
articulata (*monantha*)		14	Heitz 1931b	MaFo	Medit.
atropurpurea	Purple Vetch	14	,, ,,	FoMa	Algeria
aurantia		14	,, ,,	—	Asia Minor
bithynica		14	,, ,,	—	Medit.
calcarata		14	,, ,,	—	Medit., Persia
cassubica		14	Wulff 1939b	—	Europe
dasycarpa	Woolly Pod V.	14	Sweschnikova 1927a	Fo	,,
disperma		14	Heitz 1931b	—	S. France
dumetorum	German Vetch	14	,, ,,	—	Europe, Siberia
erviformis		14	,, ,,	—	W. Medit.

154

VICIA (*cont.*)

ervilia	Bitter Vetch	14	Heitz 1931b	FoV	Eur., N. Africa Asia Minor
gracilis		14	Sweschnikova 1927a	—	Eur., Syria
grandiflora		14	Heitz 1931b	—	S. Eur., A. Minor
hirsuta	Hairy Tare	14	,, ,,	FoV	Eur., N. Afr., Asia
lutea	Yellow Vetch	14	,, ,,	—	Med., Pers., A.M.
monantha	Bard Vetch	14	,, ,,	FoG	Medit.
musquinez		14	,, ,,	—	Europe
narbonensis	French Vetch	14	,, ,,	FoV	Med., W. Asia
picta		14	Sweschnikova 1927a	—	Armenia
pseudo-orobus		14	Heitz 1931b	—	N. China
pseudo-cracca		14	Sweschnikova 1927a	—	Italy
pyrenaica	Pyrenees V.	14	Heitz 1931b	—	Pyrenees
sepium	Bush Vetch	14	,, ,,	V	Eur., N. As., Him.
serratifolia		14	Senjaninova 1932	—	Med., S.W. Asia
sicula		14	Heitz 1931	—	Sicily
sylvatica	Wood Vetch	14	Sweschnikova 1927a	—	Europe
tetrasperma	Sparrow V.	14	,, ,,	—	Eur., Medit.
varia		14	Senn 1938	—	Eur., W. Asia, N. Africa
villosa	Russian V.	14	,, ,,	VFo	Russia
alpestris		28	Heitz 1931b	—	Cauc., A. Minor

LENS $x = 7$

esculenta	Lentil	14	Heitz, T. 1927	G	*cult*
v. *microsperma*		14	Miranda 1931, EKJ		
v. *macrosperma*		14	,, ,, ,,		

PISUM $x = 7$

abyssinicum		14	Fedotov 1935	VG	Abyssinia
elatius		14	,, ,,	VG	Med., S.W. Asia
fulvum		14	,, ,,	—	A. Minor, Syria
sativum	Garden Pea	14	Sansome 1933	FoVG	*cult*, S.W. Asia

LATHYRUS* $x = 7$

angulatus		14	Simonet 1932c	—	Europe
annuus		14	,, ,,	—	Medit., S.W. Asia
aphaca	Yellow Vetchling	14	,, ,,	G	Medit., W. Asia
articulatus		14	Senn 1938	—	W. Medit.
cicera	Lesser Chick P.	14	,, ,,	G	Eur., S.W. Asia
cirrhosus		14	,, ,,	—	Pyrenees
clymenum		14	,, ,,	—	Medit.
grandiflorus	Everlasting P.	14	,, ,,	H	Italy, Greece
ensifolius		14	,, ,,	—	Europe
heterophyllus		14	,, ,,	—	,,
latifolius	Perennial P.	14	,, ,,	H	,,
magellanicus	Cape Horn P.	14	Melderis & V. 1931	G	Magellan
montanus	Heath P.	14	Scheerer 1940	—	Europe
maritimus	Sea Pea	14	Kawakami 1930	G	Eur., N. Asia
(*japonicus*)		14	Sakai 1951		
niger	Black Vetchling	14	Corti 1931b	—	Europe
nissolia	Grass Vetchling	14	Simonet 1932c	—	Eur., S.W. Asia
numidicus		14	,, ,,	—	Algeria
ochrus		14	,, ,,	FoRG	Medit.
pannonicus		14	Melderis & V. 1931	—	S. Eur., Asia M.
pisiformis		14	Marks 1952	—	Europe
pubescens		14	Simonet 1932c	—	Chile

155

LATHYRUS (*cont.*)

roseus		14	Marks 1952	—	Europe
rotundifolius		14	Simonet 1932c	—	E. Eur., S.W. Asia
sativus	Grass Pea	14	Bhattacharjee 1955	FoG	N. Afr., W. Asia
sessilifolius	& 10 Spp.	14	Senn 1938	—	C: S. America
sylvestris	Flat Pea	14	Simonet 1932c	—	Europe
sphaericus		14	,, ,,	—	S. Europe
tingitanus	Tangier P.	14	,, ,,	Fo	W. Medit.
tuberosus	Earthnut P.	14	Fisk 1931	R	Europe, Asia
vernus	Spring Bitter V.	14	Melderis & V. 1931	—	Europe
hirsutus	Winter Vetch	14	Senn 1938	Fo	Eur., S.W. Asia
		(28)	Marks 1950		
odoratus	Sweet Pea	14	Simonet 1932c	HP	Sicily, *cult*
		(28)	Fabergé 1935		
		14	Melderis & V. 1931	Fo	Eur., Asia, N. Afr.
pratensis		28	Marks 1950		(England)
		14, 28	Larsen 1953		
palustris	Marsh Pea	14	Senn 1938	—	N. Hemis.
		42	Scheerer 1940		
venosus		28	Senn 1938	Fo	N. America

CICER $x = 7, 8$

soongaricum		14	Iyengar 1939	G	N.W. Him.
arietinum	Chick Pea	16	Thomas & R. 1946	GFoV	India, W. Asia
		16, (32)	Milovidov 1932		
as *kabulicum*	Kabuli Gram	16	Iyengar 1936		
pinnatifidum		16	Tschechow, T. 1938	G	Mesop., Asia M.

TRIBE II : HEDYSAREAE

ADESMIA $x = 5$

sp. aff. *trijuga*		10	Covas & S. 1946	—	Chile
coronilloides		20	,, ,,	—	,,
fernandezii		20	,, ,,	—	,,
capricornu		20	Covas 1949b	—	,,
trijuga		20	,, ,,	—	,,
uspallatensis		20	,, ,,	H	,,
bicolor		20	Castronovo 1945	—	Argentine
sp. aff. *glanduligera*		20, 40	Covas 1949b	—	Chile
remyana		20	Krapovickas & K. '51	—	Argentine
subterranea		20	,, ,,	—	,,

CORONILLA $x = 6$

glauca var. *pygmaea*		12	La Cour 1952	H	S. Europe
glauca		24	Atchison 1949a	—	
varia	Crown Vetch	24	Romanenko 1937	FoH	Europe

HIPPOCREPIS $x = 7$

multisiliquosa		14	Lorenzo-Andreu & G. 1950	H	Medit.
comosa	Horseshoe V.	28	Maude 1940	FoH	,,

SCORPIURUS $x = 7$

vermiculatus		14	Senn 1938	H	Medit.
sulcatus		14, 28	,, ,,	H	,,
		28	Coutinho & R. 1945		

SCORPIURUS (*cont.*)

muricatus		28	Coutinho & R. 1945	—	Medit.
subvillosus		28	,, ,,	—	,,

HEDYSARUM *x* = 7, 8

elongatum	Sweet Vetch	14	Sakai 1934	Fo	Russia
obscurum		14	Reese 1952a	H	Europe, N. Asia
coronarium	Sulla S.V.	16	Lewitsky, T. 1937	FoH	S. Europe
hedysaroides		14	Favarger 1953	—	Arctic, Alps, Altai

ORNITHOPUS *x* = 7

compressus		14	Griesinger & K. 1939	—	Europe
isthmocarpus		14	,, ,,	—	W. Medit.
macrorhynchus		14	,, ,,	—	Europe
perpusillus	Birdsfoot	{ 14	Milovidov 1941	Fo	,,
		14	Maude 1940		
sativus	Serradella	{ 14	Romanenko 1937		
		14	Griesinger & K. 1939	Fo	E. Europe
		16?	Kawakami 1930		
		(56)	Klinkowski & G. 1939		

ONOBRYCHIS *x* = 7, 8

arenaria		14	Favarger 1953	—	Alps
caput-galli		14	Senn 1938	Fo	Medit.
crista-galli		{ 14	Corti 1931a		
		16	Senn 1938	Fo	S.E. Medit.
pulchella		16	,, ,,	Fo	Manchuria
viciifolia (*sativa*)	Sainfoin	{ 14	Romanenko 1937		
		28	Maude 1939	Fo	*cult*
montana		28	Favarger 1953	—	S. Eur. Mtns.

LESPEDEZA *x* = 9, 10, 11

homoloba		18	Kawakami 1930	Fo	Japan
sericea		18	Cooper 1936	Fo	Himalaya
sieboldii		18	Kawakami 1930	FoH	Japan, Him.
frutescens		18, 20	Young 1940	—	N. America
pilosa		{ 18	Sakai 1951		
		20	Pierce 1939	—	Japan
variegata		{ 18	Cooper 1936		
		20	Pierce 1939	—	Himal., N. Asia
bicolor		{ 18	Kawakami 1930		
		22	Pierce 1939	FoH	Japan, China
cyrtobotrya		{ 18	Kawakami 1930		
		22	Pierce 1939	Fo	Japan, Korea
daurica		{ 36	Cooper 1936		
		c. 44	Pierce 1939	—	Siberia
capitata		20	Young 1940	—	N. America
hirta (*villosa*)		20	,, ,,	—	
inschanica		20	,, ,,	—	China?
procumbens (*repens*)	Bush C.	20	,, ,,	—	N. America
repens		20	,, ,,	—	,,
simulata		20	,, ,,	—	,,
stipulacea (*striata*)		20	Hanson 1953	—	Japan
stuevei		20	Young 1940	—	N. America

LESPEDEZA *(cont.)*

tomentosa (*villosa*)		20	Cooper 1936 —	N. America
virginica (*sessiliflora*)		20	Young 1940 —	,,
floribunda		22	Pierce 1939 —	China
japonica		22	,, ,, —	Japan
striata	Japan C.	22	Young 1940	FoMa	,,
thunbergii		22	,, ,, —	,,
virgata		22	Pierce 1939 —	,,

STYLOSANTHES $x = 10$

guianensis	20	Kishore 1951 —	Guiana
riparia	20	Atchison 1949a —	E: N. America

ZORNIA $x = 10$

bracteata	20	Atchison 1949a —	S.E: N. Amer.

ARACHIS $x = 10$

diogoi		20	Mendes 1947 —	Brazil
marginata		20	,, ,, —	,,
villosa		20	Krapovickas & R. '51 —	,,
villosulicarpa		20	Mendes 1947 —	,,
prostrata		$\begin{cases} 20 \\ 40 \end{cases}$	,, ,, / Husted 1933	O	,,
hypogaea	Groundnut	40	Frahm-Leliveld 1953	FoNO	,, *cult*
nambiquarae		40	Husted 1933	O	,,
rasteiro		40+0–1B	,, ,,	O	,,
pusilla		40 (80)	Krapovickas & R. '51 —	,,

DESMODIUM * $x = 11$

bracteosum & 9 spp.		22	Young 1940	Fo	N. America
discolor		22	,, ,,	Fo	Brazil
glabellum		22	,, ,,	Fo	N. America
grandiflorum		22	,, ,,	Fo	India
gyrans		22	,, ,,	Fo	Trop. Asia
gyroides		22	,, ,,	MMa	S.E. Asia
incanum		22	,, ,,	Fo	W. Indies
strictum		22	,, ,,	Fo	Japan
tortuosum	Beggarweed	22	,, ,,	FoH	N. Amer., W. Ind.
triquetrum		22	,, ,,	MMa	Trop. Asia
leiocarpum		22	Frahm-Leliveld 1953 —	Argentine

KUMMEROWIA $x = 11$

striata	22	Sakai 1951 —	Japan

ORMOCARPUM $x = 12$

trichocarpum	24	Atchison 1951 —	E. Africa

AESCHYNOMENE $x = 20$

indica	Pith Plant	40	Kawakami 1930	T	Tropics

TRIBE III: LOTEAE

SECURIGERA $x = 6$

coronilla	Hatchet Vetch	12	Tschechow & K. '32a	H	S. Europe

ANTHYLLIS $x = 6, 7, 8$

alpestris	12	Tschechow & K. '32a —	C. Europe

158

ANTHYLLIS (*cont.*)

maritima		12	Tschechow & K. '32a	—	N. Europe
vulneraria	Kidney Vetch	12	Corti 1931a	FoH	Eur., W. As., Aby.
barba jovis		14	Tschechow & K. '32a	FoH	Medit.
gerardii		16	„ „ „	Fo	W. Medit.

LOTUS $x = 6, 7$

angustissimus		12, 24	Tschechow & K. '32a	Fo	Eur., N. Asia
corniculatus	Bird's Foot T.	24	Milovidov 1941	FoH	Temp. Eur. & As.
v. *tenuifolius*		12	Guinochet 1945		
v. *arvensis*		24	„ „		
v. *hirsutus*		24	„ „		
uliginosus		{ 12	Dawson 1941	Fo	Eur., Medit.
		{ 24	Milovidov 1941		
hispidus	Hairy Deer V.	24	Tschechow & K. '32a	Fo	Eur., N. Africa
cytisoides		14	„ „ „	Fo	Medit.
edulis		14	Senn 1938	Fo	„
ornithopodioides		14	Tschechow & K. '32a	Fo	„
creticus		28	„ „ „	Fo	„

TETRAGONOLOBUS (LOTUS) $x = 7$

maritimus (*L. siliquosus*)		14	Tarnavschi 1938	—	Med., C. Europe
purpureus	Winged Pea	14	Tschechow & K. '32a	FoHV	Medit.

DORYCNIUM $x = 7$

herbaceum	14	Tschechow & K. '32a	H	S. Eur., Asia M.
hirsutum	14	„ „ „	H	Medit.
rectum	14	„ „ „	H	„
suffruticosum	14	„ „ „	H	C. & S. Europe

HYMENOCARPUS $x = 8$

circinnatus	16	Tschechow & K. '32a	—	Med.—Persia

TRIBE IV: TRIFOLIEAE

TRIFOLIUM $x = 6, 7, 8, 9$
    $x = 6, 8$

subterraneum	Subterranean C.	{ 12	Brock 1953	Fo	Israel
		{ 16	„ „	Fo	Medit.

    $x = 7$

angustifolium	Fineleaf C.	14	Karpechenko 1925	Fo	Eur., N. Africa
arvense	Rabbit Foot C.	14	„ „	Fo	O.W. Temp.
aureum	Hop Clover	14	Wulff 1939b	Fo	Eur., Med.
(*agrarium*)					
badium		14	Bleier 1925	Fo	„
campestre	Mignonette C.	14	Karpechenko 1925	Fo	„
(*procumbens*)					
filiforme	Slender C.	14	„ „	Fo	Eur., Cauc.
(*micranthum*)					
incarnatum	Crimson C.	14	„ „	Fo	S.W. Eur., Alg.
pratense	Red Clover	14 (28)	Levan 1942a	Fo	Eur., W. As., Alg.
spadiceum		14	Karpechenko 1925	Fo	C. Eur., W. Asia
squarrosum		14	„ „	Fo	Med., W. Asia
striatum	Knotted C.	14	Wulff 1939a	Fo	S. Eur., A. Minor
dubium (*minus*)	Suckling C.	{ 14	Karpechenko 1925	Fo	Europe
		{ 28	Bleier 1925		
		{ 16	Noda 1946		

TRIFOLIUM (*cont.*)

$x = 8$

albopurpureum		16	Wexelsen 1928	—	W: N. Amer.
alexandrinum	Beerseem	16	„ „	Fo	N. Africa
alpinum		16	Favarger 1953	—	S.W. Eur. Mtns.
alpestre	Purple Globe C.	16	Karpechenko 1925	Fo	S. Eur., N. Asia
fragiferum	Strawberry C.	16	„ „	Fo	Med., Abyssinia
fucatum	Puff Clover	16	Wexelsen 1928	Fo	W. : N. America
glomeratum	Cluster C.	16	„ „	Fo	Med., W. Eur.
hybridum	Alsike C.	16	Kawakami 1930	Fo	S. Europe
lappaceum	Burdock C.	16	Karpechenko 1925	Fo	Med., S.W. Asia
maritimum		16	„ „	Fo	„ „
microcephalum		16	Wexelsen 1928	Fo	W: N. Amer.
montanum	Mountain C.	16	Karpechenko 1925	Fo	S. Eur., N. Asia
obtusiflorum	Soursalt C.	16	Wexelsen 1928	Fo	W: N. Amer.
ochroleucon		16	Bleier 1925	Fo	Eur., A. Minor
reflexum	Buffalo C.	16	Wexelsen 1928	Fo	N. America
resupinatum	Persian C.	16	Karpechenko 1925	Fo	Afghanistan
rubens		16	„ „	Fo	C. & S. Europe
scabrum	Rough C.	16	„ „	Fo	Med., W. Europe
variegatum	White Tip C.	16	Wexelsen 1928	Fo	W: N. Amer.
thalii		16	Bleier 1925	Fo	S., C. & W. Eur.
tumens		16	Karpechenko 1925	Fo	Cauc., Pers., Afgh.
dichotomum		32	Wexelsen 1928	Fo	N. America
repens White or Dutch C.		32, 32, 48 (64)	Atwood & H. 1940, Moriya & K. 1949b, Levan 1942a	Fo	Temp. O.W.
lupinaster		48	Karpechenko 1925	Fo	Japan, Korea
wormskoeldii	Sierra Clover	c. 48	Wexelsen 1928	Fo	W: N. Amer.
medium Zigzag Clover		c. 84, c. 98, c. 126, c. 130	Levan, L. & L. 1942, Bleier 1925, L. & L. 1944b, Wexelsen 1928	Fo	Eur., N. Amer.
pannonicum Hungarian C.		c. 130, c. 180	Noda 1946, Tschechow 1930	Fo	Eur., S.W. Asia

MEDICAGO $x = 7, 8$

hispida	Tooth M., Bur C.	14	Fryer 1930	FoMa	S. Europe
as *denticulata*		16	Ghimpu 1930		
rigidula	Tifton Bur C.	14, 16	Fryer 1930, Ghimpu 1930	—	Europe
arabica (*maculata*) Spotted Medick		16	„ 1928	FoMa	W. & S. Europe
carstiensis		16	Fryer 1930	—	Europe
ciliaris		16	Ghimpu 1929b	Fo	Medit.
disciformis		16	„ 1928	—	S. Eur., A. Minor
echinus		16	„ „	—	Medit.
gerardi		16	„ 1929b	—	Europe
helix		16	„ „	—	Medit.
intertexta		16	Fryer 1930	—	S. Europe
laciniata		16	„ „	—	Medit.
littoralis		16	„ „	—	„
marina		16	Ghimpu 1929b	—	„
minima	Woolly Bur M.	16	„ „	Fo	E. Europe
murex		16	Fryer 1930	—	Europe
muricata		16	„ „	—	„
nigra		16	Ghimpu 1929b	—	N. Temp.
oliviformis (*turbinata*)		16	Tschechow 1933	Fo	Medit.

MEDICAGO (*cont.*)

orbicularis	Button C.	16	Fryer 1930	Fo	Medit., Abys.
pentacycla		16	Ghimpu 1929b	—	N. Temp.
platycarpa		16	Fryer 1930	Fo	Turkestan
ruthenica		16	„ „	Fo	Siberia
soleirolii		16	„ „	Fo	Italy
sphaerocarpa		16	Ghimpu 1928	Fo	Medit.
tenoreana		16	„ „	Fo	Italy
truncatula (*tribuloides*)		16	„ „	Fo	Europe
tuberculata		16	Tschechow 1933	Fo	Medit.
turbinata		16	„ „	Fo	„
lupulina	Black M.	16, 32	„ „	FoMa	N. Temp.
falcata	Yellow Lucerne	16, 32	Ledingham 1940	Fo	„
arborea	Tree Alfalfa	32	Ghimpu 1929b	Fo	Medit.
hemicycla		32	D. C. Cooper 1935b	Fo	Transcauc.
media	Sand Lucerne	32	Fryer 1930	Fo	Temp.
ovalis		32	Tschechow 1933	Fo	Spain
rugosa		32	Fryer 1930	Fo	Europe
		16	Bolton & G. 1950		
sativa	Lucerne, Alfalfa {	32	Fryer 1930	FoMa	Persia, *cult*
		32, 64	Tomé 1947		
scutellata	Snail Clover	32	Fryer 1930	Fo	Medit.

TRIGONELLA $x = 8, 9, 11, 14$

balansae		16	Tschechow 1933	Fo	Gr., Asia Minor
besseriana		16	Gardé 1948	—	E. Eur., A. Minor
brachycarpa		16	Tschechow 1933	—	Asia
calliceras		16	„ „	—	Cauc.
coerulea	Curd Herb	16	Fryer 1930	SpV	W. Eur., Cauc.
cretica		16	Tschechow 1933	—	Medit.
corniculata	Piring Sak	16	„ „	V	S.W. Asia
foenum-graecum	Fenugreek	16	Fryer 1930	GSpV	„
gladiata		16	Coutinho & S. 1943	—	Medit.
glomerata		16	Tschechow 1933	—	S.W. Asia
lipskyi		16	Gardé 1948	—	Bokhara
monspeliaca		16	„ „	—	Medit.
radiata		16	Tschechow 1933	V	Asia M., Persia
striata		16	Gardé 1948	—	Asia. M., Turkest.
hamosa		16, 44!	„ „	—	Egypt
ornithopodioides		18	Rutland 1941	—	Europe
polycerata		28, 30, 32	Gardé 1948	Fo	Medit., S.W. Asia
geminiflora		44	„ „	—	Asia Minor, Persia
grandiflora		44	„ „	—	Turkestan

MELILOTUS $x = 8$

alba	Bokhara C.	16, 24 (32)	Atwood 1936	Fo	Eur., Asia
altissima		16	Scheerer 1939	Fo	„ „
dentata		16	Tschechow 1933	Fo	Eur., E. Asia
indica	Sour C.	16	„ „	FoMa	Medit.—India
italica		16	Clarke 1932	FoMa	Medit.
messanensis		16	„ „	Fo	„
neapolitana		16	Tschechow 1933	Fo	Medit., Asia M.
officinalis	Sweet C.	16	„ „	Fo	Eur., N. Asia
segetalis		16	Clarke 1932	Fo	Medit.
speciosa		16	„ 1934	—	Algeria

MELILOTUS (*cont.*)

suaveolens		16	Tschechow 1933	Fo	N. China
sulcata		16	,, ,,	Fo	Medit.
taurica		16	,, ,,	Fo	,,
wolgica		16	,, ,,	Fo	Russia

PAROCHETUS *x* = 8

communis	Shamrock Pea	16	Clarke 1934	H	Trop. Asia

ONONIS *x* = (8), 15, 16

tridentata		30	Lorenzo-Andreu '51	—	Spain
spinosa	Rest Harrow	{ 32	Tschechow 1933	V	Eur., Medit.
		60	Senn 1938		
alopecuroides		{ 30	,, ,,	—	Medit.
		32	Tschechow 1933		
biflora		32	,, ,,	—	Algeria
fruticosa		32	,, ,,	—	Europe
natrix		32	,, ,,	H	S. Europe
ornithopodioides		32	,, ,,	—	Medit.
rotundifolia		32	,, ,,	—	C. Europe
viscosa		32	,, ,,	Fo	S. Europe
repens (*arvensis*)		32	Reese 1952a	—	Eur., Siberia
reclinata		{ 60	Senn 1938	Fo	Medit.,
		64	Tschechow 1933		Abyssinia

TRIBE V: GALEGEAE

SESBANIA *x* = 6

aegyptiaca	Sesban	{ 12	Rao 1946	HMMa	Egypt
		12	Haque 1946		
macrocarpa		12	Atchison 1949a	—	S.E: N. Amer.
punctata		12	Frahm-Leliveld 1953	Ma	O.W. Tropics
punicea		12	Covas & S. 1947	—	Argentine
speciosa		12	Simmonds 1954	—	E. Trop. Africa
tetraptera		12	Senn 1938	Ma	Trop. Africa
aculeata	Dhencha	{ 12	Rao 1946	FoMaT	Tropics
(*bispinosa*)		24	Haque 1946		
grandiflora	Agathi	{ 24	Jacob 1941	DHM	Trop. Asia
Vegetable Humming Bird		24	Tjio 1948	MaShV	
sericea		24	Frahm-Leliveld 1953	Ma	W. Indies

INDIGOFERA *x* = 6, 7, 8

anil	Indigo	12	Senn 1938	D	S. Trop. Asia
parviflora		14	Hagerup 1932	Ma	Tropics
arrecta	" Java I. "	16	Frahm-Leliveld 1953	DMa	Trop. Africa
aspera		16	Hagerup 1932	—	,,
diphylla		16	,, ,,	—	,,
dosua		16	Sampath & A. 1949	—	Himal.
hirsuta		16	Frahm-Leliveld 1953	(D)Ma	Tropics
kirilowi		16	Kawakami 1930	Ma	China, Korea
pseudotinctoria		16	,, ,,	DMa	Japan
sumatrana		16	Frahm-Leliveld 1953	—	Tropics
tinctoria	Ceylon I.	16	Ramanathan 1950	D	India, Ceylon
viscosa		16	Hagerup 1932	Ma	Trop. Africa, Ind.
endecaphylla		{ 32	Frahm-Leliveld 1953	FoMa	O.W. Tropics
		32	Simmonds 1954		
		36	Kishore 1951		
sessiliflora		32	Hagerup 1932	—	Trop. Africa

INDIGOFERA (*cont.*)
suffruticosa	Am. Indigo	32	Kawakami 1930	DMa	S. America
teysmannii		32	Atchison 1951	—	Trop. E. Asia
decora		48	Tschechow 1930	—	China
gerardiana		48	Kreuter 1930	D	Himalayas

CYAMOPSIS $x=7$
psoralioides	Cluster Bean	14	Frahm-Leliveld 1953	FoV	India

DALEA $x=7$
alopecuroides	14	Atchison 1949a		E: N. Amer.
occidentalis	14	,, ,,		C. America

GUELDENSTAEDTIA $x=7$
monophylla	14	Tschechow 1935	—	Sib., Altai

BISERRULA $x=8$
pelecinus	16	Kreuter 1930	—	Med., Canaries

CALOPHACA $x=8$
wolgarica	16	Kreuter 1930	H	S. Russia, Turkest.

CLIANTHUS $x=8$
puniceus	Parrot's Bill	16	Tschechow 1935	H	New Zealand

COLUTEA $x=8$
arborescens	Bladder Senna	16	Tschechow 1930	H	Med., Asia Minor

CRACCA $x=8$
species	16	Wood 1949	—	N. America

DIPHYSA $x=8$
robinioides	16	Atchison 1951	—	C. America

GALEGA* $x=8$
officinalis	Goat's Rue & 3 spp.	16	Gardé & G. 1953	FoH	Eur., W. Asia

GLYCYRRHIZA $x=8$
aspera		16	Tschechow 1930	M	E. Eur., C. Asia
astragalina		16	Covas & S. 1946	—	Chile
echinata	Chinese L.	16	Senn 1938	M	E. Med., S. Rus.
glabra	Liquorice Root	16	Tschechow 1935	M	Medit., Asia
lepidota		16	Heiser & W. 1948	—	N. America
uralensis	Chinese L.	16	Tschechow 1930	MSu	Siberia

HALIMODENDRON $x=8$
argenteum	16	Atchison 1949a	H	E. Asia

PHACA (ASTRAGALUS) $x=8$
alpina	16	Favarger 1949b	—	N. & Arctic

SABINEA $x=8$
carinalis	16	Atchison 1951	—	Dominica

SPHINCTOSPERMUM $x=8$
constrictum	16	Wood 1949	—	N. America

163

WISTARIA (MILLETTIA) $x = 8$

floribunda	Japanese W.	{ 16	Moriya & K. 1949b	H	Japan
		24 (3x)	Matsuura 1937		
frutescens		16	Kawakami 1930	H	S.E: U.S.A.
macrostachya		16	Roscoe 1927	H	C: U.S.A.
sinensis	Chinese W.	16	,, ,,	H	China
venusta	Silky W.	16	,, ,,	H	Japan

CARAGANA $x = 8$

arborescens	Pea Tree	16	Tschechow 1930	H	Siberia, China
frutex		32	,, ,,	H	S. Russia, Siberia

CARMICHAELIA $x = (8)$ 16

kirkii	32	Slade 1953	H	New Zealand
monroi	32	,, ,,	H	,,
petriei	32	,, ,,	H	,,
williamsii	32	,, ,,	H	,,

CHORDOSPARTIUM $x = (8)$ 16

stevensoni	32	Slade 1953	H	New Zealand

CORALLOSPARTIUM $x = (8)$ 16

crassicaule	32	Slade 1953	H	New Zealand

NOTOSPARTIUM $x = (8)$ 16

carmichaeliae	32	Slade 1953	H	New Zealand

SWAINSONA $x = (8)$ 16

coronillaefolia	32	Cooper 1936	H	Australia

OXYTROPIS $x = 8, 9$

montana	16	Favarger 1953	—	Eur. Mtns.
halleri (uralensis)	16	Tschechow 1930	H	C. & E. Europe
vaginata	16	,, ,,	—	Siberia
lapponica	48	,, 1935	—	Eur., N. Asia
campestris	36	Jalas, L. & L. 1948	—	N. Temp. & Arct.
rishiriensis	c. 53	Sakai 1934	—	Japan

MILLETTIA $x = 8, 10$

dasyphylla	16	Toxopeus 1952	—	E. Indies
thonningii	16	Atchison 1951	Sh	Trop. Africa
ovalifolia	20	,, ,,	—	Burma

ASTRAGALUS * $x = 8, 11, 12$
$x = 8$

alopecuroides		16	Kreuter 1930	H	Siberia
alopecuros & 24 spp.		16	Tschechow 1935	—	C. Asia
candidissimus		16	,, ,,	—	Siberia, N. Amer.
chinensis		16	,, ,,	H	China
carolinianus (canadensis)		16	,, ,,	FoH	N. America
danicus (hypoglottis)		16	,, ,,	FoH	Europe
glycyphyllos		16	,, ,,	FoH	C. Eur., W. Asia
incanus		16	Lorenzo–A. & G. '50	H	S. France
frigidus		16	L. & L. 1944b	H	N. America
sinicus		16	Sugiura 1936b	H	China
boeticus	Swedish Coffee	16, 30	Tschechow 1935	BH	Medit.
edulis		28?	Kreuter 1930	Fo	Algeria

164

ASTRAGALUS (*cont.*)

adsurgens	32	Sakai 1935	FoH	E. Siberia, Japan
bubaloceras	32	Tschechow 1935	—	Morocco
campylotrichus	32	,, ,,	—	Temp. Asia
campylorhynchus	36	,, ,,	—	Asia M., Turkest.
asper	48	,, ,,	—	S. Eur., Caucasus
cornutus (*vimineus*)	48	,, ,,	—	E. Siberia
hamosus	48	,, ,,	H(V)	Medit., N. Africa
scorpioides	48	,, ,,	—	Spain
alpinus	*c.* 56	,, ,,	—	N. Arct. & Temp.
cicer	64	,, ,,	FoH	S. Europe
echinus	64	,, ,,	H	Asia Minor
mexicanus?	64	,, ,,	HV	Ill., Texas
onobrychis	64, 72	,, ,,	H	Eur., W. Asia
verus	64	,, ,,	—	Persia
brachylobus	96	,, ,,	—	Caspian

$x = 11, 12, 13$ (New World)

gambellianus	22	James 1951	—	W: U.S.A.
crassicarpus & 12 spp.	22	Vilkommerson 1943	—	N. America
grayi	44	,, ,,	—	W: N. America
beathii & 9 spp.	24	,, ,,	—	N. America
didymocarpus	24	James 1951	—	California
sp.	26	Schnack & C. 1947	—	S. America
garbancillo	26	Krapovickas & K. '51	—	Argentine
aff. *joergensenii*	26	,, ,,	—	,,
dispermus	26	James 1951	—	S.W: U.S.A.

HEBESTIGMA $x = 10$

cubense	20	Atchison 1951	—	W. Indies

MUNDULEA $x = 10, 11$

suberosa	{ 20	Atchison 1951	Ma	India, Ceylon
	{ 22	Frahm-Leliveld 1953		

PSORALEA $x = 10$

bituminosa		20	Kreuter 1930	H	Canaries
glandulosa	Jesuits' Tea	20	,, ,,	B	Chile, Peru
macrostachya	Leather Root	20	,, ,,	R	N. America

ROBINIA $x = 10$

fertilis		20	Whitaker 1934c	H	S.E: U.S.A.
hartwigii		20	,, ,,		,,
kelseyi		20	,, ,,	H	N. Carolina
luxurians		20	,, ,,	H	S.W: U.S.A.
viscosa		20	,, ,,	H	S.E: U.S.A.
pseudacacia	Black Locust	20	Kreuter 1930	H	E: U.S.A.
boyntonii (3*x*)		30	Whitaker 1934c	H	S.E: U.S.A.
hispida (3*x*)	Rose Acacia	30	,, ,,	H	,,

AMORPHA $x = 10$

californica		20	Kreuter 1930	H	California
canescens	Lead Plant	20	Tschechow 1935	H	N. America

AMORPHA (*cont.*)
microphylla (*nana*)		20	Tschechow 1935	H	C. & N. America
fruticosa	Bastard Indigo	40	,, 1930	DH	N. America

GLIRICIDIA $x = 10, 11$

sepium	Madre	$\begin{cases} 20 \\ 22 \end{cases}$	Atchison 1951 Simmonds 1954	HSh	Trop. Amer., *cult*
as *maculata*		20	Sampath & R. 1949		

TEPHROSIA * $x = 11$ (12, 16?)

candida	Boga Medola	22	Simmonds 1954	HMa	Trop. Asia
grandiflora		22	Woods 1949	H	S. Africa
noctiflora (*hookeriana*)		22	Frahm-Leliveld 1953	Ma	Trop. Africa
vestita		22	,, ,,	—	China, Sumatra
villosa		22	,, ,,	—	Trop. Asia & Afr.
virginiana		22	Woods 1949	H	N. America
vogelii	Igun	22	,, ,,	IMa	Trop. Africa
conzattii		22+0–2B	,, ,,	—	N. America
23 species		22	,, ,,		
purpurea		24	Ramanathan 1950	DMa	Trop. Africa
hookeriana		32	Kawakami 1930	Ma	E. Indies
toxicaria	Yarro Conalli	—		Ma	Trop. Amer.

TRIBE VI: PODALYRIEAE

PULTENAEA $x = 7, 8, 9$

gunnii	14	Curtis 1952	H	Australia
daphnoides	16	,, ,,	H	,,
stricta	16	,, ,,	H	,,
tenuifolia	16	,, ,,	H	,,
juniperina	18, 27, 36	,, ,,	H	,,

BAPTISIA $x = 9$

australis	Blue False Indigo	18	Tschechow 1931	H	S.E: U.S.A.
leucantha		18	Atchison 1949a	H	,,
sulphurea	Yellow False I.	18	Tschechow 1931	—	E: N. America
tinctoria	False Indigo	18	,, ,,	DHV	,,

PIPTANTHUS $x = 9$

laburnifolius (*nepalensis*)	18	Tschechow 1931	H	Himalayas

PODALYRIA $x = 9$

australis	18	Atchison 1949a	—	S. Africa

THERMOPSIS $x = 9$

alterniflora	18	Tschechow 1931	—	Turkestan
montana	18	,, ,,	H	W: N. America

TRIBE VII: GENISTEAE

ROTHIA $x = 7$

trifoliata	14	Rao 1950a	—	O.W. Tropics

CROTALARIA * $x = 7, 8$

incana	Shack-Shack	14	Atchison 1950	Ma	Trop. America
alata		16	Kawakami 1930	Ma	Trop. Asia

CROTALARIA (*cont.*)

anagyroides	16	Kawakami 1930	Ma	Venezuela
arenaria	16	Hagerup 1932	Ma	Senegambia
argyrea	16	Senn 1938	—	Trop. Africa
dilloniana & 7 spp.	16	Atchison 1950	—	,,
fulva	16	Eichhorn 1937a	Ma	Trop. Asia
juncea Sunn Hemp & 2 spp.	16	Ramanujam *et al.* '33	FoMaT	Trop. Asia, Austr.
laburnifolia Rattlebox	16	,, ,,	Ma	India, Phil.
lanceolata	16	Raghavan & V. '43	Ma	Trop. E. Africa
medicaginea & 3 spp.	16	Rao 1950a	Ma	Tropics
mucronata (*striata*)	16	Senn '38, Rao '50a	Ma	W. Indies
obovata	16	Hagerup 1932	—	Trop. Africa
quinquefolia & 9 spp.	16	Rao 1943	Ma	Trop. Asia
spinosa	16	Eichhorn 1937a	—	Abyssinia
usaramoensis	16	Kawakami 1930	Ma	E. Trop. Africa
valetonii	16	,, ,,	Ma	E. Indies
pilosa	32	Atchison 1950	—	C. & S. Am., W. I.
pumila	32	,, ,,	—	S: U.S.A., W.I.

HEYLANDIA $x = 8$

latebrosa	16	Rao 1950a	—	S. India, Ceylon

ULEX $x = (8)\ 16$

micranthus	32	de Castro 1945a	—	Spain
minor (*nanus*) Dwarf Gorse	32	,, 1941	—	W. Europe
	64	Tschechow 1931		
parviflorus (*calycotomoides*) 32, 64, 96		de Castro 1943	—	W. Medit.
densus	64	,, 1941	—	Europe
erinaceus	64	,, ,,	—	,,
ianthocladus	64	,, 1943	—	S.W. Spain
europaeus Gorse, Furze	64	,, 1941	FoH	W. Europe
	96	Tschechow 1931		
gallii Dwarf Furze	80	de Castro 1943	H	,,
argenteus	96	,, ,,	—	Portugal

STAURACANTHUS (ULEX) $x = 8$

aphyllus	48	de Castro 1943	—	Portugal, S.W. Sp.
spectabilis	48	,, ,,	—	,, Morocco
vicentinus	48	,, 1945a	—	,,

NEPA (ULEX) $x = (8)$

boivini	*c.* 128	de Castro 1943	—	W. Medit.

ARGYROLOBIUM $x = (8)$

linnaeanum	48	Lorenzo-Andreu 1951	—	Medit.

LUPINUS $x = 12$

hirsutus European Blue L.	24	de Zeeuw 1936	FoGH	Medit.
v. *micranthus*	50?	Tuschnjakowa 1935		
tassilicus	36	Eichhorn 1949	—	Sahara
consentini	32	Malheiros 1942	—	Egypt
subcarnosus Texas Lupin	36	Tuschnjakowa 1935	FoH	Calif., Texas
	48	Savchenko 1935		

167

LUPINUS (*cont.*)

albus	Wolf Bean, White L.	⎰30	Olszewska 1954		
		{ 40	Savchenko 1935	FoV	S. Eur., W. Asia
		⎱50	Malheiros 1942		
as *varius*		48	Savchenko 1935		
angustifolius	Blue L.	⎰40	Malheiros 1942	Fo	Medit.
		⎱48	Kawakami 1930		
arboreus	Tree L.	40	Savchenko 1935	FoH	California
pilosus		⎰40	„ „	FoH	Levant
		⎱42	Tuschnjakowa 1935		
luteus	Eur. Yellow L.	⎛46	de Zeeuw 1936		
		⎜48	Kawakami 1930	GFoV	Medit.
		⎨52	Malheiros 1942		
		⎝52	Olszewska 1954		
densiflorus	Gully L.	48	Tuschnjakowa 1935	—	California
douglasii		48	„ „	—	„
elegans		48	Savchenko 1935	—	Mexico
micranthus	Field L.	48	Tuschnjakowa 1935	—	W: N. Amer.
mutabilis	S. Amer. L.	48	Malheiros 1942	FoH	S. America
nanus	Sky Lupin	48	Tuschnjakowa 1935	H	California
nootkatensis		48	Maude 1940	—	N.W: N. Amer., N.E. Asia
ornatus		48	Tuschnjakowa 1935	Fo	N.W: N. Amer.
polyphyllus	Washington L.	48	Cooper 1936	H	W: U.S.A.
pubescens	Rusty L.	48	Savchenko 1935	H	Mexico, Guat.
hartwegii		48–50	Tuschnjakowa 1935	H	Mexico
barkeri		50	„ „	—	„
rothmaleri		52	Malheiros 1942	—	Medit.

CYTISUS $x = 11, 12\ (13)$ $x_2 = 23, 25$

procumbens		22	de Castro 1949	H	S.E. Europe
fontanesii		24	„ „	—	W. Medit.
albus		⎰24	Santos 1945	H	S.W. Europe
as *lusitanicus*		⎱48	de Castro 1949		
as *multiflorus*		*c.* 48, *c.* 96	„ „		
grandiflorus		48	„ „	H	Iber. Penin.
leiocarpus		48	„ „	—	Hungary
maderensis	•	48	Santos 1945	H	Madeira
proliferus	Escabon	48	de Castro 1949	H	Canary Is.
purgans		*c.* 48	„ „	H	W. Medit.
purpureus		48	Senn 1938	H	S. Austria
austriacus		48, 96	de Castro 1949	H	Eur., Cauc.
nigricans		48, 96	„ „	H	S. Europe
supinus (*capitatus*)		*c.* 48, 96	„ „	H	C. & S. Europe
rochelii		96	„ „	H	C. Europe
patens		*c.* 46	„ „	—	Portugal
praecox		46	„ „	H	*cult*
reverchonii		*c.* 46	„ „	—	Medit.
canariensis	Genista	⎰46	„ „	H	Canary Is.
		⎱48	Santos 1945		
monspessulanus	Montpelier B.	*c.* 46	de Castro 1949	H	S. Eur., Medit.
as *candicans*		48	„ „		
hirsutus		*c.* 46, *c.* 48, 96	„ „	H	S. Eur., Asia M.

CYTISUS (cont.)

battandieri		50	de Castro 1949	H	N.W. Africa
ruthenicus		50	,, ,,	—	S.E. Europe
sessilifolius		52	Tschechow 1931	H	S. Europe, N. Afr.

GENISTA $x = 12$

pilosa	Hairy Greenweed	24	Tschechow 1931	—	W. & S. Europe
falcata		36	Santos 1945	H	Spain, Port.
scorpius		40	Lorenzo-Andreu & G. 1950	H	,, ,, Bal. Is.
umbellata		42	Santos 1945	—	N. Africa, Corsica
germanica		46–48	Reese 1952a	H	C. & W. Europe
sagittalis		c. 44 c. 46, 48	Tschechow 1931 Santos 1945	H	Eur., W. Asia
anglica	Petty Whin	42 48	Maude 1939 Santos 1945	H	W. Europe
dorycnifolia		48	,, ,,	—	Balearics
ferox		48	Tschechow 1931	—	N. Africa
florida		48	Santos 1945	H	Spain
monosperma		48	,, ,,	H	,, N. Africa
radiata		48	,, ,,	H	S. Europe
tinctoria	Dyer's Greenweed	48	Tschechow 1931	DHV	Eur., Cauc.
triangularis		48–50	,, ,,	—	S.E. Europe

ECHINOSPARTON $x = 11, 13$

boissieri		44	de Castro 1945	—	S.E. Spain
horridum		44	,, ,,	—	Pyren., S. France
barnadesii		c. 52	,, ,,	—	Spain
lusitanicum		c. 52	,, ,,	—	C. Port. & Spain

SAROTHAMNUS (CYTISUS) $x = 12$

scoparius	Scotch Broom	24, 48 46 48	Morton 1955 Maude 1940 de Castro 1949	BHMSp	C. Europe

LABURNUM $x = 12$

alpinum	Scotch L.	48	Tschechow 1931	H	S. Europe
anagyroides	Common L.	48	Ishikawa 1916	H	,,

SPARTIUM $x = 12$?

junceum	Spanish Broom	48–52	Tschechow 1931	HMT	Medit., Can. Is.

TRIBE VIII: SOPHOREAE

ORMOSIA $x = 8$

krugii		16	Atchison 1949a	—	W. Indies
panamensis		16	,, ,,	—	C. America
dasycarpa	Necklace T.	16	,, 1951	H	W. Indies

BELAIRIA $x = 9$

ternata		18	Atchison 1951	—	Cuba

CAMOENSIA $x = 9$

maxima		18	Atchison 1951	H	W. Trop. Africa

SWEETIA $x = 9$

dasycarpa		18	Covas 1949b	—	Brazil

169

SOPHORA $x = 9, 14$

davidii		18	Tschechow 1931	W	China
flavescens (angustifolia)		18	,, ,,	D	Siberia
microphylla		18	Atchison 1949a	H	Chile, Peru
moqrcroftiana		c. 16	Lechtova-Trnka 1931	W	Himal., China
secundiflora		18	Atchison 1949a	H	C. & S. America
tetraptera	Kowhai	18	,, ,,	H	New Zealand
tomentosa		18	,, 1951	—	Tropics
chinensis	Ch. Pagoda T.	28	Kawakami 1930	M	China
japonica	Japanese P. T.	28	Tschechow 1931	DHM	China, Japan

ATELEIA $x = 10$

gummifera		40	Atchison 1951	—	W. Indies

GOURLIEA $x = 10$

spinosa		20	Covas & S. 1947	V	Chile

CASTANOSPERMUM $x = 13$

australe	Austr. Chestnut	26	Sampath & R. 1949	N	N. Australia

CLADRASTIS $x = 14$

lutea	Yellow Wood	28	Atchison 1949a	H	U.S.A.

MYROXYLON $x = 14$

pereirae	Balsam of Peru	28	Atchison 1951	MRe	C. America

TRIBE IX: PHASEOLEAE

CLITORIA $x = 8$

ternata	Butterfly Pea	16	Frahm-Leliveld 1953	DHM(V)	Tropics
cordobensis		24	Krapovickas & K. '51	—	Argentine

AMPHICARPA $x = 10$

monoica	Hog Peanut	20	Cooper 1936	V	E: N. America

CENTROSEMA $x = 10$

pubescens		20	Frahm-Leliveld 1953	—	Brazil

GALACTIA $x = 10$

volubilis		20	Atchison 1949a	—	E: N. America

GLYCINE $x = 10$

javanica	Rhod. Kudzu Vine	20	Ramanathan 1950	Fo	O.W. Tropics
gracilis	Manch. Soya	40	Fukuda 1933	FoG	Manchuria
max	Soya Bean	{ 40 / (80)	Sakai 1951 / Tang & Loo 1940	FoG	China, cult
ussuriensis	Wild Soya	40	Tschechow & K. '32a	FoG	N.E. Asia

APIOS $x = 10$

tuberosa	Wild Bean	c. 40	Atchison 1949a	R	E: N. America

VIGNA $x = 10, 11, 12$

ambacensis		20	Dusseau & M. '41b	—	Trop. Africa
capensis	Cow Pea	22	Tschechow et al. '32a	V	,, cult
glabra	Clay Pea	22	,, ,,	V	,,
lanceolata		22	Karpechenko 1925	—	Australia

170

VIGNA (*cont.*)

luteola		22	Schnack & C. 1947	—	Tropics
owahuensis		22	Tschechow & K. '32a	V	Hawaii
unguiculata	Cow Pea	{ 22	Karpechenko 1925	FoMV	Trop. Afr., *cult*
as *sinensis*		{ 24	„ „		
sesquipedalis	Asparagus B.	24	Kawakami 1930	FoV	Trop. & Sub-trop Asia

ABRUS $x = 11$

precatorius	Ind. Liquorice, Rosary Pea	{ 22 { 22	Senn 1938, Poucques 1945	MTo	Trop. Asia

ATYLOSIA (DOLICHOS) $x = 11$

barbata (*ornatus*)		22	Tschechow & K. '32a	Ma	India, Malaya

ERIOSEMA $x = 11$

psoralioides (*cajanoides*)		22	Frahm-Leliveld '53	—	Trop. Africa

HARDENBERGIA $x = 11$

monophylla		22	Smith-White unp.	H	Australia

KENNEDYA $x = 11$

rubicunda		22	Smith-White unp.	H	Australia

MUCUNA $x = 11$

pruriens	Cowage	22	Frahm-Leliveld '53	FoMa	Tropics

STIZOLOBIUM (MUCUNA) $x = 11$

deeringianum	Florida Velvet B.	22	Schnack & F. 1946	V	S. Asia

PACHYRRHIZUS $x = 11$

erosus	Yam Bean	22	Roy 1933	IRV	Tropics
tuberosus	Potato B., Jicama	22	Senn 1938	RV	W. Indies

RHYNCHOSIA $x = 11$

erecta		22	Atchison 1949a	—	E: N. America
minima		22	Senn 1938	—	Tropics
phaseoloides		22	Tschechow & K. '32a	H	„
senna		22	Schnack & C. 1947	—	Argentine
volubilis		22	Sakai 1951	—	China, Japan

VOANDZEIA $x = 11$

subterranea	Bambarra, Gnd. N.	22	Frahm-Leliveld '53	NV	Madagascar

CANAVALIA $x = 11$

ensiformis	Jack Bean	22	Kawakami 1930	MaV	W. Indies
plagiosperma		22	Simmonds 1954	V	Cuba
gladiata	Sword Bean	22, 44	Covas 1949b	V	O.W. Tropics

CAJANUS $x = 11$

cajan (*indicus*)	Pigeon Pea	22, 44, 66	Pathak & Y. '51	Fo_1GV	India, *cult*

DOLICHOS $x = 11, 12$

lablab	Lablab, Bonavist	{ 22 { 24	Frahm-Leliveld '53 Ayyangar & K. 1935	FoG	Abyss., *cult*
lubia		22	Tschechow & K. '32a	V	Egypt
biflorus	Horse Gram	24	Rau 1929b	FoG	India, Burma

PHASEOLUS $x = 11, 12$

aborigineus		22	Burkart & B. 1953	G	C. Amer.—Argen.
aconitifolius	Math or " Moth " B.	22	Tschechow & K. '32	FoGMaV	India, *cult*
acutifolius	Tepary Bean	22	Karpechenko 1925	V	Ariz., Mex.
angularis	Azuki B.	22	,, ,,	GV	China, *cult*
aureus	Mung or Green Gram	{ 22 (44)	Kumar & A. 1942b	FoGV	India, China, *cult*
as *radiatus*		{ 22 24	Frahm-Leliveld 1953 Karpechenko 1925		
calcaratus	Rice Bean	22	Frahm-Leliveld 1953	GMaV	India, Malaya
chrysanthos		22	Muto 1929	V	China, Japan
coccineus (*multiflorus*)	Scarlet Runner	22	Karpechenko 1925	V	Peru, *cult*
helvolus	Amberique B.	22	Senn 1938	FoGMa	N. America
lunatus	Lima Bean	22	Karpechenko 1925	V	Peru, *cult*
mungo	Urd or Black G.	{ 22 24	,, ,, Rau 1929b	GMa	Trop. Asia, *cult*
polystachys	Thicket B.	22	Allard & A. 1940	Ma	E: U.S.A.
ricciardianus	Assam B.	22	EKJ*	GV	Assam
semierectus		22	Senn 1938	FoMa	Trop. Amer.
trilobus	Jungli Math B.	22	Karpechenko 1925	Fo(G)Ma	O.W. Tropics
vulgaris	French, Kidney or Dwarf B.	22	Thomas 1945*	GV	Peru, *cult*

PUERARIA $x = 11, 12$

thunbergiana (*hirsuta*)	Kudzu Vine	{ 22 24 24	Simmonds 1954 Suzuka 1950, Sakai 1951	FoRT	China, Japan
javanica (*phaseoloides*)		{ 22 24	Hardas & J. 1954 Frahm-Leliveld 1953	MaT	Malaya

DIOCLEA $x = 12$

boykinii		24	Nemec 1910	—	N. America

CALOPOGONIUM $x = 18$

mucunoides		36	Frahm-Leliveld 1953	—	Guiana

ERYTHRINA * $x = 21$

caffra		42	Atchison 1947c	H	S. Africa
corallodendron	Coral T.	42	,, ,,	H	Trop. America
crista-galli	Ceibo	42	,, ,,	FoHMaSh	S. America
herbacea		42	,, ,,	FoH	S.E: U.S.A.
indica	Indian C. T.	{ 42 44	Rao 1945 Poucques 1945	DFoMShW	Trop. Asia, Austr.
poeppigiana	Anauca Imortelle	42	Simmonds 1954	—	Peru
velutina		42	,, ,,	—	Trop. America
vespertilia & 27 spp.		42	Atchison 1947c, 1951	H	Australia
acanthocarpa		84	,, 1947c	—	S. Africa
amazonica		84	,, ,,	—	Peru, Brazil
burtii		c. 126	,, 1951	—	Tanganyika

TRIBE X: DALBERGEAE

ANDIRA $x = 10$

inermis	Cabbage Bark T.	20	Atchison 1951	MW	Trop. Amer., W. I.

DALBERGIA x = 10

cochinchinensis		20	Atchison 1951	—	Cochin China
lanceolaria		20	,, ,,	—	India
latifolia	Rosewood T.	20	,, ,,	W	
melanoxylon	Blackwood T.	20	,, ,,	W	Trop. Africa
paniculata		20	,, ,,	—	India

INOCARPUS x = 10

edulis	Tahiti Chestnut	20	Atchison 1951	N	Pacific Is.

TIPUANA x = 10

tipu	20	Atchison 1951	—	Argentina

GEOFFRAEA x = 10

decorticans	Channar	20	Covas & S. 1947	FoMW	S. America
striata	Mandubira	60	Burkart 1949a	—	,,

PONGAMIA (GALEDUPA) x = 10, 11

pinnata (glabra)	Pongam,	{ 20	Atchison 1951	FoHO	India, Malaya,
	Indian Beech	{ 22	Patel & N. 1937	ShW	Austr., Poly.

PISCIDIA x = 11

piscipula	22	Atchison 1951	M	Fla., Mex., W. I.

LONCHOCARPUS x = 11

cyanescens	Yoruba Indigo	22	Atchison 1949b	D	W. Trop. Africa
formosianus		22	,, ,,	—	E. Asia
hintonii		22	,, ,,	—	C. America
latifolius		22	,, ,,	—	Trop. America
leucanthus		22	Covas & S. 1947	—	Uruguay
longistylis		22	Atchison 1949b	—	Mexico
neuroscapha		22	,, ,,	—	Brazil
punctatus		22	,, ,,	—	S. America
violaceus		22	,, ,,	—	W. Indies
utilis	Timbo-blanco	44	,, ,,	I	Amazon

PTEROCARPUS x = 11

macrocarpus		22	Atchison 1951	—	Burma
marsupium	Indian Kino	44	,, ,,	MW	India, Ceylon
vidalianus		44	,, ,,	—	Philippines

DERRIS x = 11, 12, 13

elegans		22	Toxopeus 1952	—	Burma
pubipetale		22	Tjio 1948	—	Java
pterocarpus		22	Atchison 1949b	—	S. America
sinuata		22	,, ,,	—	Burma, Malaya
malaccensis	M. Derris	22, 24	Toxopeus 1952	I	Malaya
uliginosa		{ 22	Tjio 1948	—	O.W. Tropics
		{ 24	Toxopeus 1952		
elliptica	Tuba Root	{ 22	Atchison 1949b	I	Malaya
		{ 22, 24, 36 (3x)	Toxopeus 1952		,, cult
heterophylla		24	,, ,,	—	E. Indies
timorensis		26	,, ,,	—	Timor, Java, N. Guinea

PLATIMISCIUM x = 16

pinnatum	32	Atchison 1951	W	Nicaragua

13   173

Group X

HAMAMELIDALES
149–155
ST

SALICALES
156
ST

GARRYALES
157
ST

LEITNERIALES
158
S

MYRICALES
159
ST

(BALANOPSIDALES)
160
ST

FAGALES
161–163
ST

CASUARINALES
164
ST

URTICALES
165–170
HST

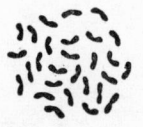

Betula verrucosa

151 HAMAMELIDACEAE

DISTYLIUM $x = 12$
racemosum		24	Sugiura 1936a	H	Japan

HAMAMELIS $x = 12$
vernalis	Witch Hazel	24	Anderson & S. 1935	HM	E: N. America
virginiana	N. Amer. W. H.	24	Whitaker 1933a	HM	„ „

PARROTIOPSIS $x = 12$
jacquemontiana	24	Anderson & S. 1935	H	Himalayas

SINOWILSONIA $x = 12$
henryi	24	Anderson & S. 1935	H	C. China

CORYLOPSIS $x = 12$
pauciflora	Winter Hazel	24	Anderson & S. 1935	H	Japan
spicata		72	„ „	H	„
veitchiana		72	„ „	H	China

FOTHERGILLA $x = 12$
monticola	48	Anderson & S. 1935	H	S.E: U.S.A.
major	72	„ „	H	„

LIQUIDAMBAR $x = 15$?
styraciflua	Sweet Gum	30	Anderson & S. 1935	HM	E: U.S.A.

152 EUCOMMIACEAE

EUCOMMIA $x = 17$
ulmoides ♂	Ch. Gutta Percha	34	EKJ*	M	China

154 BUXACEAE

BUXUS $x = (7)\ 14$
balearica	Spanish Box	28	Simonet & M. 1932	HW	W. Medit.
sempervirens	Common Box	28	„ „	HW	Eur., S.W. & C. A.

SARCOCOCCA $x = (7)\ 14$ (Apomixis)
saligna (*pruniformis*)	28	Simonet & M. 1932	H	Himalayas
humilis	56	„ „	H	China
ruscifolia	56	„ „	H	„

155 PLATANACEAE

PLATANUS $x = (7)\ 21$
acerifolia	London Plane	42	Sax 1933b	Sh	*cult*
occidentalis	Buttonwood	42	„ „	ShW	E: U.S.A.

156 SALICACEAE

POPULUS * $x = 19$
acuminata	38	E. C. Smith 1943	—	C: U.S.A.
angustifolia	38	„ „	H	S: U.S.A.

177

POPULUS (*cont.*)

cathayana		38	E. C. Smith 1943		N.W. Ch.—Korea
deltoides	Cottonwood	38	Dillewijn 1942	H	E: N. America
grandidentata		38	Smith 1943	HW	„ „
koreana		38	„ „	H	Korea
lasiocarpa	Chinese P.	38	Wettstein, T. 1937	HW	C. & W. China
laurifolia		38	Smith 1943	H	Siberia
maximowiczii		38	„ „	H	N.E. Asia, Japan
sieboldii	Japan. Aspen	38	Nakajima 1937	HW	Japan
simonii		38	Smith 1943	HW	N. China
tomentosa	Ch. White P.	38	„ „	H	„
tremuloides	Amer. Aspen	38	„ „	DW	N. America
trichocarpa	Calif. P.	38	„ „	HW	W: N. America
alba	White Poplar	38, 57	Dillewijn 1939	DHW	Eur., N. Asia
nigra	Black P.	38, 57	Suto 1944	HW	Eur., W. Asia
tremula	Eur. Aspen	37, 57 (57–76)	Johnsson 1940a „ 1942b	W	Eurasia, N. Africa
tacamahaca (*balsamifera*)	Balsam P.	{ 38 76	Smith 1943 Blackburn & H. 1924	HMW	N. America
candicans & 10 spp.	Balm of Gilead	38	Smith 1943	HM	*cult*
canescens	Grey P.	38, 57	Peto 1938	HW	„

SALIX * $x = 19, 22$
  $x = 19$

bockii & 2 spp.		38	Wilkinson 1944	—	W. China
gracilistyla		38	Håkansson 1929a	H	Japan, Korea
humboldtiana		38	Bowden 1940a	—	S. America
japonica & 2 spp		38	Sinoto 1929	H	Japan
myrtilloides & 4 spp.		38	Holmberg 1931	H	Eurasia
purpurea	Purple Osier	38	Blackburn & H. 1924	HT	Temp. O.W.
pyrolaefolia	Balsam Willow	38	L. & L. 1942	H	N.E. Asia
repens & 2 spp.		38	Nakajima 1937	H	Eur., N. Asia
reticulata		38	S. & S. 1941	H	N. & Arctic
seringeana (*salvaefolia*)		38+0–4B	Almeida 1946	H	Europe, *cult*
viminalis	Osier, Basket W.	38	Sinoto 1929	TW	Eurasia
sachalinensis		38, *c.* 48	„ „	—	Sachalin
daphnoides		{ 38 57	Blackburn & H. 1924 Wilkinson 1944	—	Eur., N. Asia
capraea	Goat W.	{ 38, 76 57	„ „ L. & L. 1942	HP	„ „
aurita		38, 76	Wilkinson 1944	—	„ „
lapponum		38, 76	„ „	—	„ „
myrsinites		{ 38, 190 152	„ „ Holmberg 1931	H	„ „
bonplandiana		42!	Bowden 1945b	—	Mexico
alba	White W.	76	Blackburn & H. 1924	W	Eur., W. Asia, N. Africa
v. *coerulea*	Cricket-bat W.	76	Wilkinson 1941		
atrocinerea		76	„ „	—	Eur., S.W. & N. Asia
babylonica	Weeping W.	76	Almeida 1946	H	China
cinerea	Grey W.	76	Harrison 1926	H	Eur., S.W. & N. Asia

SALIX (*cont.*)

eriocarpa		76	Nakajima 1942	—	Japan
lasiandra		76	Wilkinson 1944	—	W: N. America
laurina	Goat Tea W.	76	Heribert-Nilsson '28	—	Europe
lucida		76	Harrison 1926	—	N. America
medemii		76	Wilkinson 1944	—	Persia, Armenia
pentandra	Bay W.	76	Blackburn & H. 1924	H	Eur., N. Asia
polaris		76	Holmberg 1931	—	Arctic
sieboldiana		76	Wilkinson 1944	—	Japan
dasyclados		76, 114	L. & L. 1942	—	Europe
fragilis	Crack W.	{ 76	Blackburn & H. 1924	W	Eur., W. Asia
		114	L. & L. 1942		
nigricans		114	Harrison 1926	H	Eur., W. & N. As.
borealis		152	L. & L. 1942	H	„ „
superlaurina		152	Heribert-Nilsson '35	H	*cult*
dasycladioides		152	„ „ „	H	Europe

$x = 19$ or 22?

livida		{ 44	Wilkinson 1944		
as *depressa*		38	L. & L. 1948	—	Eur., N. Asia
amygdalina (*triandra*)		38, 44, 88	Wilkinson 1944	—	Eur., Temp. Asia
cordata		44	„ „	—	N. America
phylicifolia	Tea-leaf W.	{ 88	„ „		
		144	Håkansson 1333	H	Eur., N. Asia
		(38)	L. & L. 1942		
glauca	Grey-leaf W.	{ 152	Holmberg 1931	H	Eur. Alps, Asia,
		176	Wilkinson 1944		N. America

TOISUSU (SALIX) $x = 19$

cardiophylla	38	Suto 1938	—	N.E. Asia

157 GARRYACEAE (CORNACEAE)

GARRYA $x = 11$

elliptica	Silk-Tassel Bush	22	Meurman 1930	H	W: N. America

159 MYRICACEAE

MYRICA $x = 8$

carolinensis	North. Bayberry	16	Stokes 1937	HM	E: N. America
cerifera	S. Wax Myrtle	16	„ „	HM	„
pumila		16	„ „	—	„
rubra		16	Sugiura 1927	HSp	Tr. & Sub-tr. As.
gale	Sweet Gale	48	Hagerup 1941b	HSp	N. Temp.

COMPTONIA $x = 8$

peregrina	Sweet Fern	32	Stokes 1937	HM	E: N. America

161 BETULACEAE

ALNUS $x = 14$ (Apomixis)

crispa	Amer. Green A.	28	Woodworth 1931	W	N. America
incana	Speckled A.	28	„ „	W	N. Temp.

ALNUS (cont.)

maritima		28	Woodworth 1931	W	N. America
rubra	Red Alder	28	Wetzel 1929	W	W: N. America
rugosa	Hazel A.	28	Woodworth 1931	W	E: N. America
tenuifolia	Mountain A.	28	Gram *et al.* 1941		W: N. America
viridis	Eur. Green A.	28	Wetzel 1929	W	N. Temp.
cordata	Italian A.	28	Gram *et al.* 1941	W	Eur., S.W. Asia
		42	Poucques 1949b		
hirsuta	Manchurian A.	28	Gram *et al.* 1941	—	N.E. Asia
v. *sibirica*		28	Poucques 1949b		
as *tinctoria*		42	„ „		
orientalis		28	Poucques 1949b	—	E. Eur., S.W. Asia
		42	Gram *et al.* 1941		
japonica	Jap. Alder	28	Wetzel 1929	W	Japan, N.E. Asia
		42	Gram *et al.* 1941		
		56	Woodworth 1931		
subcordata	Caucasian A.	28	Wetzel 1929	W	Cauc., Persia
		42, 56	Gram *et al.* 1941		
glutinosa	Eur. Black A.	28	Wetzel 1929	MW	Eur., N. Asia
		56	Woodworth 1931		
borealis		56	Poucques 1949b	—	Japan
spaethii		56	Woodworth 1931	W	*cult*

BETULA $x = 14$

coerulea		28	Woodworth 1931	—	E: N. America
fontinalis	Water Birch	28	„ „	W	W: N. America
glandulosa		28	Poucques 1949c	—	N. America
humilis		28	Jaretzky 1930	—	Eur., N. Asia
lenta	Sweet B.	28	Woodworth 1931	MW	N. America
luminifera		28	Poucques 1949c	—	China
maximowicziana	Monarch B.	28	Woodworth 1931	W	Japan
nana	Dwarf Arctic B.	28	Flovik 1940	W	N. Region
nigra	River B.	28	„ „	W	N. America
populifolia	Grey B.	28	„ „	—	E: N. America
utilis	Himalayan B.	28	„ „	TW	Japan, Himal.
raddeana		28	Poucques 1949c	—	Caucasus
verrucosa	Silver Birch	28	Johnsson 1940b	HOW	Eur., N. Asia, N.
(*pendula, alba*)		42	„ 1944		Amer.
mandschurica	Jap. White B.	56	Woodworth 1929a	—	Jap., Manch., Kor.
v. *japonica*		28!	„ „		
papyrifera	Paper B., Canoe B.			TW	N. America
v. *occidentalis*		84	Woodworth 1931		
as *lyalliana*		28	Poucques 1949b		
v. *cordifolia*	Mtn. P. B.	56	Woodworth 1929a		
v. *subcordata*		56	„ 1931		
v. *kenaica*		70	„ „		
callosa		56	L. & L. 1948	—	Europe
celtiberica		56	de Castro 1944	—	Iber. Penin.
fruticosa		56	Poucques 1949c	—	N.E. Asia, China
pubescens (*odorata*)		56	Johnsson 1940a	H	Eur., N. Amer., N. Asia
v. *urticifolia*		56	Jaretzky 1930	—	*cult*
pumila	Low B.	56	Woodworth 1931	HW	N. America
tortuosa		56	L. & L. 1944b	—	Europe

BETULA (*cont.*)

davurica		{ 56	Poucques 1949c	W	N.E. Asia
		{ 90	Woodworth 1929a		
grossa	Jap. Cherry B.	84	,, 1931	W	Japan
lutea	Yellow B.	84	,, ,,	W	N. America

162 CORYLACEAE

CARPINUS *x* = 8

caroliniana	Bluebeech	16	Woodworth 1931	W	N. America
cordata		16	,, ,,	W	Japan
japonica	Jap. Hornbeam	16	,, ,,	W	,,
laxiflora	Loose flower H.	16	,, ,,	W	,,
orientalis	Oriental H.	16	,, ,,	W	S. Europe
tschonoskii	Yeddo H.	16	Johnsson 1942a	W	Japan
turczaninovii		16	Woodworth 1931	W	China
betulus	Eur. H.	16, 64	Johnsson 1942a	W	Europe, Persia

OSTRYA *x* = 8

carpinifolia	Eur. Hop. H.	16	Woodworth 1931	—	S. Eur., A. Minor
japonica	Jap. Hop H.	16	,, ,,	—	E. Asia
virginiana	Amer. Hop. H.	16	,, ,,	W	E: U.S.A.
davidiana		16	,, ,,	—	Asia Minor

CORYLUS *x* = 11, 14

avellana	Eur. Hazel	{ 22	Danielsson 1946	NW	Europe, W. Asia
	Cobnut	{ 28	Woodworth 1929b		
tibetica		{ 22	Poucques 1950	N	Himalayas
		{ 28	Woodworth 1929b		
americana	Amer. Hazel	28	,, ,,	N	N. America
colurna	Turkey Filbert	28	,, ,,	N	E. Eur., A. Minor, Himalayas
heterophylla	Siberian F.	28	,, ,,	N	N.E. Asia
maxima	Giant F.	28	,, ,,	N	Eur., A. Minor
pontica	Caucasian F.	28	,, ,,	N	E. Eur., A. Minor, Himalayas
rostrata	Beaked H.	28	,, ,,	N	E: N. America
sieboldiana	Japanese F.	28	,, ,,	N	Japan

163 FAGACEAE

CASTANEA *x* = 12

crenata	Jap. Chestnut	24	Almeida 1947b	NW	Japan
dentata	American Ch.	24	Jaretzky 1930	NW	E: U.S.A.
mollissima		24	Poucques 1950	NW	China
sativa	Sweet or	24	Jaretzky 1930	HNW	S. Eur., W. Asia,
(*vesca*)	Spanish Ch.				N. Africa

FAGUS *x* = 12

sylvatica	Eur. Beech	24	Jaretzky 1930	NOW	Europe

QUERCUS * *x* = 12

acutissima	Sawtooth Oak	24	R. Yamazaki 1936	W	China
alba	White O.	24	Sugiura 1931	W	N. America

QUERCUS (*cont.*)

chrysolepis	Canyon Live O.	24	Duffield 1940	—	California
coccifera	Kermes Oak	24	Ghimpu 1929b	Fo_1W	Medit.
dalechampii (*aurea*)		24	Jaretzky 1930	—	Eur., W. Asia
fruticosa (*humilis*)		24	Natividade 1937	NW	Medit.
glandulifera		24	Jaretzky 1930	—	Japan
ilex	Holm Oak	24	Natividade 1937	HW	Medit., S.W. Asia
imbricaria	Shingle O.	24	H. J. Sax 1930	W	N. America
incana		24	Vignoli 1933	W	Himalayas
libani	Lebanon Oak	24	Jaretzky 1930	W	Syria
lusitanica	Portuguese O.	24	Natividade 1937	W	Med., S.W. Asia
macrocarpa	Bur Oak	24	H. J. Sax 1930	W	N. America
marilandica	Blackjack O.	24	Friesner 1930	W	,,
mongolica	Mongolian O.	24	H. J. Sax 1930	Fo_1W	N.E. Asia
muhlenbergii	Chinkapin O	24	,, ,,	W	N. America
nigra	Water O.	24	Jaretzky 1930		,,
palustris	Pin O.	24	Ghimpu 1929b	W	,,
polymorpha		24	Vignoli 1933	W	Mexico
pontica		24	Jaretzky 1930	W	Asia Minor
prinoides	Dwarf Chinkapin O.	24	Friesner 1930	W	N. America
prinus	Swamp Ch. O.	24	,, ,,	W	,,
pubescens (*lanuginosa*)		24	Vignoli 1933	W	S.E. Eur., W. Asia
pyrenaica (*toza*)		24	,, ,,	W	S. Europe
petraea	Durmast O.	24	Natividade 1937	W	Eur., W. Asia
robur & 19 spp.		24	Duffield 1940	DNW	Eur., N. America
tomentosa		24	Vignoli 1933	W	Mexico
dentata	Jap Silk Worm O.	48	H. J. Sax 1930	Fo_1W	Jap., Kor., Ch.

164 CASUARINACEAE

CASUARINA $x = 11, 12, 13$

distyla		22, 44	Purcell 1953	HW	Aust., Tasm.
equisetifolia	Horsetail Tree	24	Wetzel 1929	HShW	N. Austr., *cult*
montana		24	,, ,,	W	Malaya
nana	Dwarf She-Oak	36	Purcell 1953	H	New South Wales
suberosa	Erect Beefwood	48	,, ,,	HW	Austr., Tasm.
stricta	Coast Cas.	26	,, ,,	HShW	,, ,,
torulosa	She-Oak	26	,, ,,	HW	E. Australia
paludosa		c. 52	,, ,,	—	Austr., Tasm.

165 ULMACEAE

CELTIS $x = 10, 11, 14$

laevigata		20	Bowden 1945b	H	S.E: U.S.A.
sinensis		20	,, ,,	H	Ch., Kor., Jap.
australis	Hackberry	40	,, ,,	FoH	S. Eur., N. Africa, W. Asia
occidentalis	Sugar-berry	$\begin{cases} 20 \\ 28 \end{cases}$	,, ,, Sax 1933a	FH	E: N. America
spinosa		22	Covas & S. 1947	—	Brazil

HOLOPTELEA (ULMUS) $x \doteq 14$

integrifolia		28	Capoor 1937	W	India

ZELKOVIA $x = 14$

serrata	Keaki	28	Sax 1933a	W	Japan

ULMUS $x = 14$

carpinifolia	Smooth-leaf Elm	28	Sax 1933a	W	Eur., S.W. Asia
hollandica	Dutch E.	28	„ „	—	*cult*
fulva	Slippery Elm	28	„ „	MW	N. America
japonica	Japanese E.	28	„ „	W	E. Asia
laciniata	Manchurian E.	28	„ „	W	„
laevis	Russian E.	28	„ „	W	Eur., Cauc.
procera	English Elm	28	„ „	W	Eur., N. Asia
pumila	Siberian E.	28	Leliveld 1933	W	N. Asia
racemosa	Rock Elm	28	Sax 1933a	W	N. America
wilsoniana		28	Krijthe 1939	W	China
americana	White Elm	{ 28	Krause 1930	W	N. America
		56	Sax 1933a		
glabra	Scotch Elm 28, (42, 56)		Ehrenberg 1949	HW	Eur., N. Asia
v. *montana*		28	Leliveld 1933		
v. *scabra*		28	Sax 1933a		

167 MORACEAE

DORSTENIA $x = 12, 13, 14$, etc.

barteri		24	Krause 1930	—	Trop. Africa
convexa		24	„ „	—	„
yambuyaensis		24	„ „	—	„
plumeriaefolia		26	„ „	—	Brazil
erecta		28	„ „	HM	„
contrajerva	Contrayerva	30	„ „	HM	Trop. America
argentata	Brazilian C.	32	„ „	M	Brazil
scabra		40	„ „	—	Trop. Africa
mannii		48	„ „	—	„

BROSIMUM $x = 13$

alicastrum	Breadnut	26	Krause 1930	(V)W	Trop. America

BROUSSONETIA $x = 13$

papyrifera	Paper Mulberry	26	Bowden 1940a	T	China, Japan
kazinoki		26, 39	Seki 1950	T	Japan, Korea

FICUS $x = 13$

altissima		26	Krause 1931	—	Trop. Asia
asperrima	Sandpaper F.	26	Condit 1933	ToW	India
benghalensis	Banyan Tree	26	„ „	FoShW	India, Trop. Afr.
benjamina		26	„ „	FoSh	Trop. Asia
calophylloides		26	„ „	—	Philippines
carica	Fig	26	„ 1928	FM	Med., *cult*
cumingii		26	„ 1933	—	Philippines
diversifolia	Mistletoe Fig	26	„ „	Fo	Malaya
erecta		26	„ 1928	H	India, Ch., Jap.
eugenioides	Eugenia F.	26	„ 1933	—	Australia
elastica	India-rubber T.	26	Sugiura 1936	HRu	Trop. Asia
glabella	Smooth F.	26	Condit 1933	Ru(V)	Himal., Burma, Malaya
glomerata	Cluster Fig	26	„ 1928	F	India, Burma
henneana		26	„ 1933	—	Australia
hirsuta (panduraefolia)		26	Krause 1930	—	Brazil

183

FICUS (*cont.*)

indica	Indian Fig	26	Condit 1933	Fo₁W	Trop. Asia, Mal.
macrophylla	Moreton Bay F.	26	„ 1928	—	Australia
mitrophora		26	„ „	Sh	W. Indies
mysorensis	Mysore F.	26	„ „	Sh	India
palauanensis		26	„ „	T	Philippines
palmata		26	„ „	—	N.W. Ind., Abyss., Arabia
pandurata	Riddle-leaf F.	26	„ „	—	China
papaya		26	„ „	—	Malaya
parcelli		26	Krause 1931	—	Pacific Is.
platypoda		26	Condit 1928	—	Australia
populnea (*brevifolia*)		26	„ „	—	S. America
pseudocarica	Abyss. F.	26	„ „	—	Abyssinia
pseudopalma		26	„ 1933	—	Philippines
pumila	Ok-gue	26	„ 1928	FH	China, Japan
quercifolia		26	„ 1930	—	Burma, Malaya
religiosa	Peepel Tree	26	„ 1933	Fo₁H	India
retusa	India Laurel	26	„ „	MRu	India, Malaya
rubiginosa		26	„ 1928	—	Australia
scabra	Rough Fig	26	„ 1933	T	New Hebrides
schlechteri		26	Krause 1930	—	S. Ind., New Cal.
subscabrida		26	Condit 1933	—	W. Indies
ulmifolia	Elm Leaf F.	26	„ „	—	Malaya
vogelii	Abba Tree	26	„ „	Ru	Trop. Africa
watkinsiana		26	„ „	—	Australia

CASTILLOA $x = 14$

elastica	Panama Rubber	28	EKJ*	Ru	Mex. T. Amer.

CECROPIA $x = 14$

palmata	Silverleaf S.	28	Krause 1931	—	Brazil
peltata	Indian S.	28	„ „	(V)W	Trop. America
leucocoma		28	Bouharmont 1954	—	S. America

ARTOCARPUS $x = 14$

cannoni		28	Krause 1931	H	S. Sea Is.
integra	Jack Fruit	56	EKJ*	FFoN ReW	India, Malaya
lakoocha		56	Banerji & H. 1954	—	India, Malaya
communis	Bread Fruit	⎧ 56	EKJ*	FoMTVW	Malaya, Pacific
(*incisa*)		⎨ 54	Nishiyama & K. '42		
	(seedless)	⎩ *c*. 81 (3*x*)	„ „		

MUSANGA $x = 14$

cecropioides		28	Bouharmont 1954	—	Congo

MORUS $x = 14$

acidosa		28	Osawa 1920	F	Jap., Ch., Korea
atropurpurea		28	„ „	F	Temp. Asia
bombycis		28	Sinoto 1929	FFo₁	„
cordatifolia		28	Ishida 1951	—	Japan
indica	Silk Mulberry	28	Tahara 1910	FFo₁	Trop. Asia
kagayamae		28	Osawa 1920	Fo₁	Japan
laevigata		28	Janaki Ammal 1948	—	W. Himalayas
microphylla		28	„ „ „	F	Texas, Mexico
multicaulis	Downing M.	28	Osawa 1920	F	N. America

184

MORUS (*cont.*)

rubra	Red Mulberry	28	Janaki Ammal 1948	F	E: U.S.A.
serrata		28	„ „ „	—	W. Himalayas
alba	White M.	28	Osawa 1920	FFo$_1$TV	Temp. Asia
v. *makado* (3x)		42	„ „		
(*atropurpurea* × *alba*)					
cathayana		56, 84, 112	Janaki Ammal 1948	—	Hupeh, Szechuan
nigra	Black M.	308!	P. T. Thomas, D. & L. C. 1942	FFo$_1$W	Persia, *cult*

CUDRANIA $x = 14$

tricuspidata (*triloba*)	Silkworm T.	56	Sinoto 1929	FFo$_1$D	Jap., Ch., Korea

169 URTICACEAE

PARIETARIA $x = 7, 13$

ramiflora	Pellitory	14	Krause 1930	M(V)	S. Eur., S.W. Asia
judaica		26	„ „	—	Greece

BOEHMERIA (URTICA) $x = 7, 13$

biloba		28	Krause 1930	—	Japan
nivea	Rhea Fibre, Ramie	28	„ „	T	Trop. Asia
argentea		52	„ „	T	Mexico

URTICA $x = 11, 12, 13$

membranacea		22	Fothergill 1936	—	Medit.
		24	Negodi 1930		
urens	Dog Nettle	24, 26, 52	L. & L. 1942a	T	N. Temp.
atrovirens		26	Fothergill 1936	T	S. Europe
grandidendata		26	„ „	T	Java
pilulifera	Roman N.	26	Krause 1931	T	Med.—Ind.
dioica	Common Sting. N.	52	Fothergill 1936	VMT	N. Temp.
		48	Meurman 1925		
		48	L. & L. 1942a		
cannabina		52	Fothergill 1936	T	A. Minor, Persia

PILEA $x = 12$

cadierei		48	Hamel 1939	—	Indo-China

170 CANNABINACEAE

HUMULUS $x = 8, 10$

japonicus	♀ : $14 + XX$		Kihara & H. 1932	T	Japan, China
	♂ : $14 + XY_1Y_2$				
lupulus	Hop ♀ : $16 + X_1X_1X_2X_2$		Kihara 1929	B	Eurasia
	♂ : $16 + X_1X_2Y_1Y_2$		Ono 1937		

CANNABIS $x = 10$

sativa L	Hemp	20	Medvedeva 1935	MTO	C. Asia, Him.
	Ganja	(40)	Furusato 1940		

Group XI

CELASTRALES
171–181
ST

(OLACALES)
182, 183
ST

SANTALALES
184–189
HST

RHAMNALES
190–193
ST

RUTALES
194–196
(H)ST

MELIALES
197
ST

SAPINDALES
198–206
ST

JUGLANDALES
207, 208
T

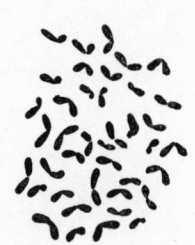 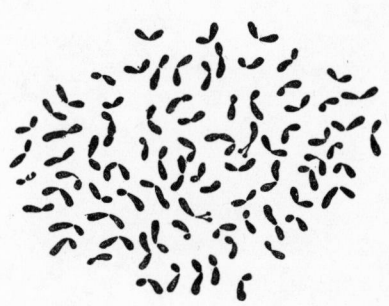

Aesculus hippocastanum & Ae. carnea

171 AQUIFOLIACEAE

ILEX $x = 9, 10$

opaca	Amer. Holly	36	Jensen 1944	H	N. America
verticillata	Winterberry	36	,, ,,	M	,,
aquifolium	Holly	40	Maude 1940	HMW	Eur., W. Asia
dumosa		40	Andres & S. 1945	—	Brazil
paraguariensis	Maté,	⎰ 40	,, ,,	B	,,
	Paraguay Tea	⎱ 40	E.K.J.*		
serrata		40	Nakajima 1942		Japan
theezans		40	Andres & S. 1945		Brazil
vomitoria	Yapon Tea	40	Jensen 1944	B	S.E: U.S.A.
decidua	Possum-Haw	40	,, ,,	H	S: U.S.A.
monticola (montana)		40	,, ,,	H	E: U.S.A.

172 EMPETRACEAE

EMPETRUM $x = 13$

nigrum ♂♀	Crowberry	⎰ 26	Wanscher 1933b	F	Eur., N. Asia
		⎱ 26	Hagerup 1927		
v. hermaphroditum		52	,, ,,	H	Arctic

173 CELASTRACEAE

PACHYSTIMA $x = 8$

canbyi		32	Bowden 1940a	H	Virginia

EUONYMUS $x = 8$

fortunei (radicans)		32	Bowden 1940a	H	China, Japan
japonicus	Jap. Sp. Tree	32	Sugiura 1931	HV	,, ,,
europaeus	Spindle Tree	64	Wulff 1937b	HRu	Eur., Asia Minor
americanus	Strawberry Bush	64	Bowden 1940a	H	S.E: U.S.A.

CELASTRUS $x = 23$

orbiculatus		46	Bowden 1945a	H	Japan, China
scandens	Waxwork	46	,, 1940a	H	E: N. America

MAYTENUS $x = 40$

vitis-idaea		80	Covas & S. 1947	—	Peru

181 STACKHOUSIACEAE

STACKHOUSIA $x = 10$

monogyna	20	W. D. Jackson unp.	H	Australia

185 LORANTHACEAE

STRUTHANTHUS $x = 8$

angustifolius	16	Covas 1949b	Par	Trop. Amer.

PHRYGILANTHUS $x = 8$

flagellaris	16	Schnack & C. 1947	Par	Brazil
verticillatus (3x?)	24	,, ,,	Par	Chile

14 189

LORANTHUS (SCURRULA, DENDROPHTHORA) $x = 8, 9$
atropurpureus		16	Rauch 1936	Par	India, Malaya
pentandrus		16	„ „	Par	Java
longiflorus		18	Kumar & A. 1942c	Par	Mal.—Australia
rubromarginatus		18	Pienaar 1952	Par	S. Africa

PSITTACANTHUS $x = 10$
cuneifolius		20	Schnack & C. 1947	Par	Peru

VISCUM $x = 10, 12$
album	Mistletoe	20	Steindl 1935	MPar	Eur., Trop. As.
articulatum		24	„ „	Par	Trop. Australia

186 SANTALACEAE

SANTALUM $x = 10$
album	Ind. Sandalwood	20	G. S. Iyengar 1937	ParMPW	Ind., Malaya

THESIUM $x = 10, 12$
wightianum		20	L. N. Rao 1942	ParW	India
montanum		24	Schulle 1933	Par	Europe

BUCKLEYA $x = 15$
joan		30	Nakajima 1937	Par	Japan

OSYRIS $x = 10, 15$
arborea	Bischar Tea	30	L. N. Rao 1942	BM	India
alba		40	Schaeppi & S. 1937	Par	Medit.

PYRULARIA $x = 19$
pubera		38	Jensen 1939	Par	N. America

IODINA $x = (12) 36$
rhombifolia		72	Schnack & C. 1947	Par	Brazil

189 BALANOPHORACEAE

CYNOMORIUM $x = 12$
coccineum		24	Juel, T. 1927	ParM	Medit.

HELOSIS $x = 18$
guyannensis (cayennensis)		36	Fagerlind 1938	Par	Trop. America

THONNINGIA $x = 18$
sanguinea		36	Mangenot 1947	Par	Trop. Africa

BALANOPHORA $x = ?$ (Apomixis)
dioica		c. 18	Panje 1934	Par	India, Burma
japonica		94–112	Kuwada 1928	Par	Japan

190 RHAMNACEAE

RHAMNUS $x = 10, 12, 13$
frangula	Alder Buckthorn	{ 20	Rutland 1941	HMW	Eur., N. Asia,
		26	Wulff 1937b		N. Africa

190

RHAMNUS (cont.)

californicus	Coffee Berry	24	Bowden 1945b	—	California
catharticus	Purging B.	24	Wulff 1939a	DHM	Eur., N.As.,N.Afr.
utilis		24	Bowden 1945b	D	China

ZIZYPHUS $x = 10, 12, 13$

oenoplia	·	⎧ 20 ⎨ ⎩ 48	Srinivasachar 1940 Srinivasan 1952	—	Tr. Asia, Austr.
sativa as *vulgaris*	Chinese Jujube	⎧ 24 ⎨ ⎩ 26	Morinaga et al. 1929 Chiarugi 1930b	F	Medit., China
iujuba	Indian J.	⎧ 24 ⎨ 40 ⎩48, 72, 96	Morinaga et al. 1929 Srinivasachar 1940 Srinivasan 1952	FFo$_1$W	India, Malaya
mauritiana		48	„ „	F	Trop. Asia
rotundifolia		72	„ „	—	„

COLLETIA $x = 11$

cruciata	Anchor Pl.	22	Dolcher 1947	H	S. Brazil, Uruguay
spinosa		22	„ „	HM	S. America

CEANOTHUS * $x = 12$

americanus	New Jersey Tea	24	Bowden 1940a	B	E: U.S.A.
arboreus		24	„ 1945b	H	Calif.
thyrsiflorus	Blue Blossom	24	Nobs 1942	H	„
20 spp.		24	„ 1942	H	W: N. America

HOVENIA $x = 12$

dulcis	Raisin Tree	24	Sugiura 1936b	F W	Himal.—Japan

PALIURUS $x = 12$

spina-christi (*aculeatus*)	Jerusalem Thorn	24	Dolcher 1947	H	S. Eur.—N. China

SAGERETIA $x = 12$

theezans		24	Bowden 1945b	BF	Burma, China

191 ELAEAGNACEAE

ELAEAGNUS $x = 14$

angustifolia	Oleaster, Trebizond Date	28	Fyfe 1945*	BFH	S. Eur., W. Asia
commutata (*argentea*)	Silverberry	28	„ „	FH	S. & C. U.S.A.
pungens		28	„ „	FH	Japan
umbellata		28	„ „	FH	China, Him., Jap.

HIPPOPHAE $x = 6$

rhamnoides	Sea Hawthorn	12, 24	Darmer 1947	H	Eur., Temp. Asia

SHEPHERDIA $x = 11, 13$

canadensis	Buffalo-berry	22	Cooper 1932	BFHN	N. America
argentea	Silver B.	26	Fyfe 1945*	FH	„

193 AMPELIDACEAE (VITACEAE)

TETRASTIGMA $x = 11, 13$

sulcatum		22	Krishnaswamy *et al.* 1954	—	S.E. Asia
lanceolarium		44	,, ,,	—	,,
rumiscispermum		52	Eichhorn 1938	—	Trop. Asia
voinerianum		52	,, ,,	H	,,

CISSUS $x = 12, 13, 14, 16$

repens (glauca)		24	Krishnaswamy *et al.* 1954	—	S.E. Asia
javana (discolor)		24	,, ,,	—	,,
repanda (pallida)		26	,, ,,	—	Ceylon, Siam, E. Ind.
heyneana		28	,, ,,	—	E. Indies
gongyloides		32	Langlet 1927b	H	Brazil, Peru
quadrangularis		c. 45	Ghimpu 1929b	VMVit	Asia, Trop. Africa

VITIS $x = 19, 20$

amurensis	Amur Grape Vine	38	Nebel 1929	F	E. Asia
arizonica	Canyon G. V.	38	Christoff 1929	F	Ariz., Mexico
berlandieri	Winter G. V.	38	Sax 1929	F	Texas, N. Mexico
bicolor	Blue G. V.	38	,, ,,	F	E. & C. U.S.A.
californica	Calif. G. V.	38	Kobel 1929a	F	California
candicans	Mustang G. V.	38	Sax 1929	F	N. America
cinerea	Sweet Winter G. V.	38	Kobel 1929a	F	E: N. America
coignetiae	Glory G. V.	38	Nebel 1929	H	Japan
doniana		38	,, ,,	—	N. America
labrusca	Fox G. V.	38	,, ,,	FO	E: N. America
lincecumii	Post-Oak G. V.	38	Christoff 1929	—	S.C: U.S.A.
longii	Bush G. V.	38	Sax 1929	—	,,
monticola	Sweet Mtn. G. V.	38	Christoff 1929	F	Texas
riparia	Riverbank G. V.	38	,, ,,	FO	E: N. America
rubra	Red G. V.	38	,, ,,	—	C: U.S.A.
rupestris	Sand G. V.	38	,, ,,	Fs	S.E. & C. U.S.A.
treleasei		38	Sax 1929	—	N. America
vulpina	Frost G. V.	38	Nebel 1929	Fs	,,
vinifera	Grape Vine	38, 57, 76	Olmo 1937	ABFO	S.W. Asia (*cult*)
rotundifolia	Muscadine	40	Branas 1932	FO	S. & C. U.S.A.
riparia × *monticola*		40	de Lattin 1951	—	*exp.*
vinifera × *rotund.*		39	Patel & O. 1955	—	*exp.*

AMPELOPSIS $x = 20$

cordata		40	Sax 1929	H	N. America
heterophylla		40	Mitsukuri & H. '51	H	E. Asia
vitifolia		40	Christoff 1929	—	Persia, Afghan.

PARTHENOCISSUS $x = 20$

quinquefolia	Virginia Creeper	40	Sax 1929	H	E: N. America
tricuspidata	Boston Ivy	40	,, ,,	H	China, Japan

CAYRATIA (COLUMELLA) $x = ?$

japonica		c. 60	Mitsukuri & H. '51	H	E. Asia

194 RUTACEAE

SF1: AURANTIOIDEAE

AEGLOPSIS $x = 9$
chevalieri 18 Longley 1925 — Guinea

AFRAEGLE $x = 9$
gabonensis 18 Krug 1943 — Congo

ATALANTIA $x = 9$
citroides 18 Krug 1943 HFs Indo-China

CLAUSENA (COOKIA) $x = 9$
lansium Wampee 18 Krug 1943 F China

FERONIA $x = 9$
limonia Wood Apple 18 Toxopeus 1933 FReW Ind., Bur., Cey.

MICROCITRUS (CITRUS) $x = 9$
australasica 18 Krug 1943 F Australia

MURRAYA $x = 9$
exotica Boxwood 18 Pathak *et al.* '49 HW Polynesia As., Austr.
koenigii Curryleaf 18 EKJ* Sp E. Indies
paniculata Jasmine Orange 18 Toxopeus 1933 PSp Tr. Asia, Austr.

CITRUS* $x = 9$ (Apomixis)
aurantium Seville Orange 18 Sugiura 1931 FFsP Trop. Asia
bergamia Bergamot 18 Nakamura 1934 FP „
celebica 18 Krug 1943 — E. Indies
hystrix Sattora 18 „ „ P India, Malaya
ichangensis 18 „ „ H China, Assam
limetta Sweet Lime 18 Nakamura 1934 FsP Trop. Asia
" *limonia* " Jap. Citron 18 „ „ FP „
macroptera 18 Krug 1943 — N. Caled.
medica Citron 18 Longley 1925 FMPV Trop. Asia
medioglobosa 18 Nakamura 1934 — Japan, *cult*
mitis Calamondin 18 Longley 1925 F *cult*
nobilis Tangerine, Mandarin O. 18 Nakamura 1934 FPVit China, *cult*
" *obovata* " 18 „ „ F *cult*
pyriformis Ponderosa Lemon 18 „ „ F Java
tachibana (*leiocarpa*) 18 „ „ F Japan, Korea
tamurana 18 „ „ F Japan
webberi 18 Krug 1943 — Philip. Is.
  25 other species 18 Nakamura 1934, 1942 — E. Asia

aurantifolia Acid Lime, { 18 Longley 1925 FP Trop. Asia
  Tahiti { 19–21, 27 Krug & B. 1943
  Lime { 27 Bacchi 1940
natsudaidai 18, 27, 36 Lapin 1937a F Japan
paradisi Grape Fruit 18, 27, 36 „ „ F E. Asia
sinensis Sweet O. { 18, 27, 36 „ „ FVit China, *cult*
  { 45 Krug 1943
grandis Pummelo 18, 36 Frost, Krug 1943 F Java
limon Lemon 18, 36 Krug 1943 FVit *cult*
madurensis 18, 36 Nakamura 1942 — China, Japan

CITRUS *(cont.)*

maxima	Shaddock	18, 36	Lapin 1937a	F	Trop. Asia
microcarpa	(japonica)	18, 36	Nakamura 1934	F	Japan
reticulata	Dancy Tang.	18, 36	Frost, Krug 1943	F	cult
unshiu	Satsuma O.	18, 36	Lapin 1937a	FP	Japan

FORTUNELLA $x = 9$

crassifolia	Cumquat	18	Longley 1925	F	China
japonica	Round C.	18	„ „	F	Japan, China
margarita	Oval C.	18	Lapin 1937a	F	„ „
obovata		18	Nakamura 1941	F	China
hindsii	Cumquat	18, 36	Longley 1925	F	„

PONCIRUS $x = 9$

trifoliata	Trifoliate O.	{ 18 18, 36	Longley 1925 Lapin 1937a	FP	Japan

TRIPHASIA $x = 9$

trifolia	Chinese Lime	{ 18 36	Longley 1925 Krug 1943	F	Trop. Asia

AEGLE $x = 9$

marmelos	Bael T.	36	EKJ*	DFM	India

SF2: RUTOIDEAE

BORONIA* $x = 7, 8, 9, 11$

$x = 7$

megastigma	14	Smith-White 1954b	H	W. Australia
pulchella	14	„ „	H	„

$x = 8$

elatior	16	„ „	H	„
gracilipes	16	„ „	H	„
fraseri	32	„ „	H	N.S.W.
ledifolia	32	„ „	—	„
mollis	32	„ „	—	„
triphylla	32	„ „	—	„

$x = 9$

barkeriana	18	„ „	—	„
fastigiata	18	„ „	H	W. Australia
nematophylla	18	„ „	—	„
parviflora	18	„ „	—	N.S.W.
purdieana	18	„ „	—	W. Australia
tenuis	18	„ „	—	„
viminea & 2 spp.	18	„ „	H	„
crenulata	18, 36	„ „	H	„
crassifolia	18, 36	„ „	—	„
anemonifolia	36	„ „	H	N.S.W.
polygalifolia	36	„ „	H	„
ramosa	36	„ „	—	W. Australia
rigens	36	„ „	—	N.S.W.
coerulescens	36, 72	„ „	—	S. Australia

$x = 11$

floribunda	22	„ „	—	N.S.W.

194

BORONIA (*cont.*)

microphylla	22	Smith-White 1954b	—	N.S.W.
pilosa	22	,, ,,	H	,,
pinnata	22	,, ,,	H	,,
serrulata	22	,, ,,	H	,,
thujona	22	,, ,,	—	,,

CHORILAENA $x = 7$

hirsuta	28	Smith-White 1954b	—	W. Australia
quercifolia	28	,, ,,	—	,,

GELEZNOWIA $x = 7$

verrucosa	28	Smith-White 1954b	—	W. Australia

PHILOTHECA $x = 7$

australis	28	Smith-White 1954b	H	N.S.W.
miniata	28	,, ,,	—	W. Australia
reichenbachiana	28	,, ,,	—	N.S.W.

ASTEROLASIA $x = 7, 13$

dielsii	26	Smith-White 1954b	—	W. Australia
correifolia	28	,, ,,	—	N.S.W.

ERIOSTEMON $x = 7, 17$

buxifolius	28	Smith-White 1954b	H	N.S.W.
hispidulus	28	,, ,,	—	,,
myoporoides	28	,, ,,	H	,,
scaber	28	,, ,,	H	,,
brevifolius	56	,, ,,	—	S. Australia
obovalis	56	,, ,,	H	N.S.W.
spicatus	56	,, ,,	—	W. Australia
lanceolatus	34	,, ,,	—	N.S.W.

CORREA $x = 8$

alba	32	Smith-White 1954b	H	N.S.W.
lawrenciana	32	,, ,,	H	,,
speciosa	32	,, ,,	H	,,

PHEBALIUM* $x = 8$

dentatum	& 2 spp.	32	Smith-White 1954b	H	N.S.W.
ralstoni		32	,, ,,	—	,,
squameum		32	,, ,,	—	Tasmania
squamulosum		32	,, ,,	H	N.S.W.
ozothamnoides		64	,, ,,	—	,,
drummondii		64	,, ,,	—	W. Australia
microphyllum		64	,, ,,	—	,,

BOENNINGHAUSENIA $x = 9$

albiflora	China Rue	18	Sugiura 1936a	M	Himal., Japan

RUTA $x = 9$

patavina		18	Negodi 1939	HM	S. Europe
chalepensis		36	,, ,,	H	Medit.
montana		36	,, ,,	—	Medit., Cauc.
graveolens	Rue	$\begin{cases} 72 \\ 81 \end{cases}$	,, ,, Revell 1945*	HMP	S. Europe

ZIERIA $x = 9$

pilosa		36	Smith-White 1954b	H	N.S.W.
smithii		36, 72	,, ,,	H	,,
aspalathoides		72	,, ,,	—	,,
cytisoides		72	,, ,,	—	,,
laevigata		72	,, ,,	H	,,

DICTAMNUS $x = 9$?

albus	Dittany, Burning Bush	{ 30, 36 }	Negodi 1939, Bowden 1945b	HP	S. Eur.—N. China

EVODIA $x = 9$

micrococca	36	Smith-White 1954b	—	N.S.W.
daniellii	72	Bowden 1945b	H	N. China, Korea
fraxinifolia	72	,, ,,	H	Himal., Malaya
hupehensis	72	,, ,,	H	C. China

COLEONEMA $x = 9$

pulchrum	36	Smith-White 1954b	H	S. Africa

CALODENDRUM $x = 9$

capense	54	Smith-White 1954b	H	S. Africa

GEIGERA $x = 9$

parviflora	108	Smith-White 1954b	H	N.S.W.

DIPLOLAENA $x = 13$

grandiflora	26	Smith-White 1954b	H	W. Australia

CROWEA $x = 19$

dentata	38	Smith-White 1954b	—	W. Australia
saligna	38	,, ,,	H	N.S.W.

ZANTHOXYLUM (XANTHOXYLUM) $x = $?

americanum	Prickly Ash	68	Walker 1942	W	E: N. America
piperitum	Jap. Pepper T.	70	Nakajima 1937b	OSp	N. China, Japan
clava-herculis		c. 72	Bowden 1940a	W	S.E. U.S.A.

SF3 : TODDALIOIDEAE

ACRONYCHIA $x = 9$

laevis	36	Smith-White 1954b	H	E. Aust., N. Caled.

195 SIMARUBACEAE

QUASSIA $x = 9$?

amara	Surinam Quassia	36	EKJ*	M	Guiana

PICRASMA $x = $?

quassioides		50	Nakajima 1942	M	Himalayas
excelsa	Jamaica Q.	c. 60	EKJ*	M	W. Indies

AILANTHUS $x = $?

excelsa	62	Pathak *et al.* 1949	—	India

196 BURSERACEAE

COMMIPHORA $x = 13$
berryi   Mullu kiluvai   26   Krishnaswamy & R.   H   Trop. Ind. & Afr.
1949

197 MELIACEAE

MELIA $x = 14$
azedarach   Persian Lilac   28   Bowden 1945a   MOW   Himalayas
(of India)
azadirachta   Margosa, Neem   28   Pathak *et al.* 1949   DMOW   India

FLINDERSIA $x = 18$
bourjotiana   36   Smith-White 1954b   W   Australia
oxleyana   Yellow wood   36   ,,   ,,   W   ,,
pubescens   36   ,,   ,,   —   ,,
schottiana   36   ,,   ,,   —   ,,
australis   Native Teak   108   ,,   ,,   W   E. Australia

SWIETENIA $x = ?$
mahogoni   Mahogany   46–48   Krishnaswamy & R.   W   C. America
1949

CEDRELA $x = ?$
odorata   W.I. Cedar   50–52   Simmonds 1954   W   Trop. Amer., W.I.
toona   Toona   56   Singh 1951   W   India, Burma

DYSOXYLUM $x = ?$
ramiflorum   *c.* 72   Paetow 1931   W   Java

198 SAPINDACEAE

CARDIOSPERMUM $x = 11$
halicacabum   Heart Seed   22   Kadry 1951   H(V)   Tropics

KOELREUTERIA $x = 11$
formosana   22   Bowden 1945b   H   Formosa
paniculata   Golden Rain T.   { 22   ,,   ,,   HNV   Ch., Kor., Japan
                                      { 30?   Eichhorn & F. 1936

LITCHI $x = ?$
chinensis   Lichi   { 28   Chaudhuri 1940   F   China
                         { 30   EKJ*

EUPHORIA (NEPHELIUM) $x = 15$
longana   Longyen   30   Bhadhuri & B. 1949   FH   India

MELICOCCA $x = 16$
bijuga   Mamoncillo, Genip   32   Simmonds 1954   F   Trop. America

AESCULUS $x = 20$
parviflora   Common B.   40   Dobronz 1935   HN   S.E: U.S.A.
flava (octandra)   Yellow Buckeye   40   Upcott 1936b   HSh   E: U.S.A.
hippocastanum   Horse Chestnut   40   ,,   ,,   Sh   Balkans
pavia   Red B.   40   ,,   ,,   H   S.E: U.S.A.

197

AESCULUS (*cont.*)
plantierensis (*carnea* × *hippo*)   60   Upcott 1936b   HSh   *cult*
carnea (*pavia* × *hippo*)   80   ,,   ,,   H   ,,

200 ACERACEAE

ACER   *x* = 13

argutum		26	Takizawa 1952	H	Japan
campestre	Hedge Maple	26	Foster 1933	HW	Eur., W. Asia
circinatum	Vine M.	26	,, ,,	HW	W: N. America
cissifolium		26	Takizawa 1952	H	Japan
crataegifolium		26	,, ,,	H	,,
diabolicum		26	,, ,,	H	,,
ginnala		26	,, ,,	H	Ch., Manch., Jap.
griseum	Paper Bark M.	26	Foster 1933	HW	W. China
japonicum		26	Takizawa 1952	H	Japan
mandschuricum	Manch. M.	26	Foster 1933	HW	Manch., Korea
miyabei		26	,, ,,	HW	Japan
mono (*pictum*)	Painted M.	26	Takizawa 1952	H	China—Manch.
negundo	Box Elder	26	Foster 1933	HW	E: N. America
nikoense	Nikko M.	26	,, ,,	H	Japan, C. China
palmatum (*ornatum*) Jap. M.		26	Takizawa 1952	HW	China, Korea
pseudosieboldianum		26	Foster 1933	HW	Manch., Korea
rufinerve	Red-vein M.	26	,, ,,	HW	Japan
saccharum	Sugar M.	26	Taylor 1920	SuW	E: N. America
tschonoskii		26	Foster 1933	HW	Japan
platanoides	Norway M.	26, 39	Meurman 1933	Su	Eur., S.W. Asia
carpinifolium	Hornbeam M.	*c.* 52	Taylor 1920	HW	Japan
pseudoplatanus	Sycamore	52	Foster 1933	(ASu)W	Eur., S.W. Asia
saccharinum	Silver M.	52	Taylor 1920	HSu	E: N. America
rubrum	Red M.	*c.* 78, *c.* 104	Duffield 1943	H	,, ,,

201 SABIACEAE

SABIA   *x* = 12
japonica   24   Sugiura 1936a, b   H   Japan

MELIOSOMA   *x* = 16
wightii   32   Raju 1952   —   India

204 STAPHYLEACEAE

STAPHYLEA   *x* = 13

bumalda	Bladder Nut	26	Foster 1933	H	Japan
pinnata	,, ,,	26	,, ,,	H	Eur., W. Asia
colchica	,, ,,	52	,, ,,	H	Caucasus
trifolia	,, ,,	78	,, ,,	H	N. America

205 ANACARDIACEAE

PISTACIA   *x* = 12, 14, 15

lentiscus	Mastic	24	Haran, Zohary 1953	MPRe	Medit.
atlantica v. *latifolia*		28	,, ,, ,,	Re	S.W. As., N. Afr.

198

PISTACIA (*cont.*)
vera	Pistachio Nut	30	Haran, Zohary 1953	N	Turkest., *cult*

SCHINUS $x = 14$
molle	Peruvian Mastic T.	28	Schnack & C. 1947	HRe	Trop. Amer.
polygamus		28	„ „	—	Argentine

ASTRONIUM $x = 15$
urundeuva		30	Covas & S. 1947	—	Brazil

RHUS $x = 15$
succedanea	Jap. Veget. Wax	30	Sugiura 1936b	Re	Jap., Ch., Himal.
toxicodendron	Poison Oak	30	Grimm 1912	M	N. America

SPONDIAS $x = 16$
mangifera	Hog Plum	32	Banerji 1936	FV	Trop. Asia
purpurea (*mombin*)	Spanish P.	32	Simmonds 1954	F	Trop. America

MANGIFERA $x = 10$ (Apomixis)
caloneura		40	Mukherjee 1950	—	Burma
sylvatica		40	„ „	—	Himalayas
indica	Mango	40	„ „	FVitW	India, Malaya

SEMECARPUS $x = 15$?
anacardium	Marking Nut T.	60	EKJ*	D	Tr. Asia & Austr.

ANACARDIUM $x = $?
occidentale	Cashew Nut T.	42	EKJ*	AFNVit	Trop. America

207 JUGLANDACEAE

CARYA $x = 16$
cordiformis	Bitternut	32	Woodworth 1930c	H	N. America
laneyi		32	„ „	W	„
laciniosa	King Nut	32	„ „	N	„
ovata	Shagbark Hick.	32	„ „	W	„
alba	Mokernut	64	„ „	WN	„
glabra	Pignut	64	„ „	DW	„
ovalis	False Shagbark	64	„ „	W	„
tomentosa	Hickory	64	„ „	N	„

JUGLANS $x = 16, 17$?
cinerea	Butternut	32	Woodworth 1930c	NWVit	E.N. America
intermedia		32	McKay & M. 1941	N	W. Asia, Himal.
insularis		32	Bowden 1945a	—	Cuba
mandschurica	Manch. W.	32	Woodworth 1930c	W	Manchuria
nigra	Black W.	32	„ „	WNVit	N. America
regia	English W.	32	„ „	NOWVit	S.E. Eur.—China
rupestris	Texas Black W.	32	„ „	W	W: N. America
sieboldiana	Giant W.	32	„ „	NW	Japan
californica	Cal. Black W.	34?	Babcock 1915	W	California
notha		32	Woodworth 1930c	HW	*cult*

PTEROCARYA $x = 16$
fraxinifolia		c. 32	Woodworth 1930c	HW	Cauc.—Persia
stenoptera		c. 32	„ „	HW	China
rehderiana (*fraxinifolia* × *sten*)		32	„ „	HW	*cult*

Group XII

UMBELLIFLORAE
209–213
HST

Silaum silaus

209 CORNACEAE

AUCUBA $x = 8$

chinensis		16	Kihara & Y. 1935	H	China
japonica		32	Meurman 1929a	H	Him.—Japan
		32+2**B**	Yamamoto 1937		
dentata		32	Meurman unp.	H	cult
longifolia		32	,, ,,	H	,,

COROKIA* $x = 9$

cotoneaster & 1 sp.		18	Hamel 1953	H	New Zealand

GRISELINIA $x = 9$

littoralis		36	Wanscher 1933a	H	New Zealand

MACROCARPIUM (CORNUS) $x = 9$

officinale		18	Sugiura 1936b	H	China, Japan
mas	Cornelian Cherry	18, 27	D'Amato 1946	HW	Balk., S.W. Asia

CORNUS * $x = 10, 11$

alternifolia	Pagoda Dogwood	20	Dermen 1932b	H	N. America
controversa		20	,, ,,	H	Him.—Japan
alba	Tartarian D.	22	,, ,,	H	N. Asia
amomum	Silky D. & 7 spp.	22	,, ,,	H	N. America
arnoldiana		22	,, ,,	H	cult
bretschneideri		22	,, ,,	H	,,
coreana		22	,, ,,	H	Korea
paucinervis		22	,, ,,	H	C. China
sanguinea	Blood Twig D.	22	,, ,,	HW	Eur., N.W. Asia

CYNOXYLON (CORNUS) $x = 11$

floridum	Flowering D.	22	Dermen 1932b	HMW	E: U.S.A.

DENDROBENTHAMIA (CORNUS) $x = 11$

capitata		22	Wanscher 1933b	H	Him., China
japonica (kousa)	Kousa	22	Dermen 1932b	H	China, Japan

CHAMAEPERICLYMENUM (CORNUS) $x = 11$

suecicum		22	Wulff 1939b	H	Arctic
canadense	Bunch Berry	44	Dermen 1932b	H	N.E. Asia, N. Amer.

HELWINGIA $x = ?$

japonica		120	Nakajima 1944	H	Japan
(rusciflora)		c. 72, 144	Wanscher 1933a		

210 ALANGIACEAE

ALANGIUM (MARLEA) $x = 8, 11$

lamarckii		16	Gopinath 1945	—	O.W. Tropics
begonifolium		22	Wanscher 1933a	H	India—Japan

211 NYSSACEAE

DAVIDIA $x = ?$

involucrata	Handkerchief T.	c. 40	Dermen 1932b	H	China

NYSSA *x* = 11
  sylvatica   Black Tupelo   44   Dermen 1932b   H   S.E: U.S.A.

212 ARALIACEAE

PANAX *x* = 11, 12
  fruticosa   Ginseng   ⎰ 22   Gopinath 1944   H   Trop. Asia
                           ⎱ 24   Wanscher 1933a
  japonicum   Jap. G.   24   M. & S. 1935   HM   Japan
  ginsing   Chinese G.   44   Sugiura 1936a   HM   Manch., Korea

FATSIA (TETRAPANAX) *x* = 12
  japonica   Rice-paper Plant   24   Sugiura 1931   HT   Japan, Formosa

ARALIA *x* = 12
  filicifolia   24   Wanscher 1933a   HM   Pacific Is.
  nudicaulis   Virg. Sarsaparilla 24   Bowden 1945a   HM   N. America
  spinosa   24   „   „   —   „
  californica   48   „   „   —   California
  cachemirica   48   Wanscher 1933a   HM   Himal.

HEDERA *x* = 12
  australiana   24   Gopinath 1944   —   Australia
  helix   Ivy   48   Jacobsen 1954   HM   Eur., Asia Minor
    v. *hibernica*   96   „   „   Ireland
  canariensis   96   „   „   —   Medit., Canaries
  colchica   192   „   „   H   Cauc.—Persia

NOTHOPANAX *x* = ?
  sp.   40   Nishiyama & K. 1942

ACANTHOPANAX (KALOPANAX) *x* = ?
  aculeatus   *c.* 54   Wanscher 1933a   H   E. Asia
  sessiliflorus   *c.* 54   „   „   H   N. China
  leucorrhizus   *c.* 127   „   „   H   E. Asia

213 UMBELLIFERAE

Order of the Tribes with their Basic Numbers

    I   Ammieae: 6, 7, 8, 9, 10, 11, 12   VI   Laserpitieae: 7, 8, 9, 11
   II   Scandiceae: 6, 7, 8, 9, 10, 11   VII   Smyrnieae: 9, 11
  III   Saniculeae: 7, 8   VIII   Coriandreae: 11
   IV   Hydrocotyleae: 8, 9, 10, 11   IX   Peucedaneae: 6, 10, 11
    V   Dauceae: 8, 9, 10, 11

TRIBE I: AMMIEAE

PTYCHOTIS *x* = 6
  ammoides   12   Gardé & G. 1949   —   Medit.

CICLOSPERMUM *x* = 7
  ammi   14   Gardé & G. 1951   —   Medit.

204

BUPLEURUM $x = 7, 8$

fruticosum	Shrub Thorowax	14	Gardé & G. 1951	M?	Medit.
paniculatum		14	,, 1949	—	W. Medit.
falcatum		28	Suzuka 1950	—	Eurasia
aureum		16	Håkansson 1953	—	W. Europe
candollii		16	Wanscher 1932	—	Himalayas
gerardi		16	Gardé & G. 1951	—	Eur., N. Africa
longifolium		16	Wanscher 1931	—	Europe
rotundifolium	Thorowax	{ 16	Tamamschjan 1933	Sp	,,
		{ 22?	Melderis 1930		
tenuissimum		16	Gardé & G. 1949	—	Portugal, Moroc.

BERULA $x = 9$

erecta		18	Scheerer 1940	—	N. Temp.

TRINIA $x = 9$

glauca	Honewort	18	Gardé & G. 1949	—	W. Europe

CARUM $x = 9, 10, 11$

copticum		18	Shah 1953	Sp	N. Afr., N. Asia
roxburghianum		18	Sharma & G. 1954	Sp	India
carvi	Caraway	20	Gardé & G. 1949	Sp	Eur., N. & S.W. A.
verticillatum		20		—	Europe
bulbocastanum		22	Schulz-Gaebel 1930	—	Eur., N. Asia
rigidulum		22	,, ,,	—	Italy

PIMPINELLA $x = 9, 10$

major		18	Håkansson 1953	—	Eur., Cauc.
peregrina		18	Schulz-Gaebel 1930	—	S. Eur., Asia M.
rotundifolia		18	Håkansson 1953	—	Caucasus
tragium		18	Gardé & G. 1949	—	S. Eur.—India
villosa		18	,, ,,	—	W. Medit.
saxifraga	Burnet Saxifrage	18, 36	Håkansson 1953	M	Eur., N. Asia
anisum	Anise	{ 18	Schulz-Gaebel 1930	MSp	Greece, Egypt
		{ 20	Tamamschjan 1933		
aromatica		20	,, ,,	—	Caucasus
adscendens		22	Shah 1953	—	India

SESELI * $x = 9, 10, 11$

bocconi & 4 spp.		18	Gardé & G. 1949	—	Sicily
libanotis		{ 18	,, ,,	—	Eur., S.W. Asia
		{ 22	Wanscher 1932		
gummiferum		20	Gardé & G. 1949	—	Asia Minor
annuum		22	Håkansson 1953	—	Eur., W. Asia
montanum		22	Favarger 1953	—	S. Europe
tortuosum		22	Gardé & G. 1949	—	S. Eur.—Cauc.

PETROSELINUM $x = 9, 11$

segetum	Corn Caraway	18	Gardé & G. 1951	—	Eur., Asia M., N. Afr.
crispum	Parsley	22	Rutland 1941	Sp	Eur., W. Asia, *cult*
as *sativum*		23	Tamamschjan 1933		

AETHUSA $x = 10$

cynapium	Fool's Parsley	20	Håkansson 1953	—	Eur., S.W. Asia

15

AMMI $x = 10, 11$

visnaga		{ 20	Gardé & G. 1951	—	S. America
		{ 22	Covas & S. 1947		
majus		22	Gardé & G. 1951	—	Medit., Abyss.

CRITHMUM $x = 10, 11$

maritimum	Samphire	{ 20	Gardé & G. 1951	Sp	Europe
		{ 22	Wanscher 1932		

SIUM $x = 10, 11$

latifolium	Water Parsnip	20	Håkansson 1953	(V)	Eur., N. Amer.
sisarum	Skirret	22	„ „	R	W. Asia

ACIPHYLLA $x = 11$

squarrosa		22	Wanscher 1933a	—	New Zealand
traversii		22	„ „	—	„

ANETHUM (PEUCEDANUM) $x = 11$

graveolens	Dill	22	Tamamschjan 1933	Sp	Medit., S.W. Asia

APIUM (HELOSCIADIUM) $x = 11$

graveolens	Celery	22	Shah 1953	SpV	Eur.—N. India
inundatum		22	Scheerer 1939	—	Europe
nodiflorum		22	Wulff 1939b	—	„
prostratum	Australian C.	22	Whitaker 1941	V	Australia
prostratum × *graveolens* (3x)		33	„ „	—	*exp.*

ATHAMANTHA $x = 11$

matthioli		22	Wanscher 1931	—	Medit.

CICUTA $x = 11$

virosa	Cowbane	22 (44)	Melderis 1930	—	N. Eurasia

CONOPODIUM $x = 11$

capillifolium		22	Gardé & G. 1949	—	Portugal

CORTIA $x = 11$

hookeri		22	Wanscher 1933a	—	Himalayas

CRYPTOTAENIA $x = 11$

canadensis		22	Kihara *et al.* 1931	—	N. America

FALCARIA $x = 11$

vulgaris		22	L. & L. 1942	—	Eur., W. Asia

FOENICULUM $x = 11$

piperitum		22	Gardé & G. 1949	—	S. Europe
vulgare	Fennel	22	„ „	MSp	Medit.

KUNDMANNIA $x = 11$

sicula		22	Gardé & G. 1949	—	Medit.

LIGUSTICUM $x = 11$

scoticum	Scotch Lovage	22	Wanscher 1932	M	N. W. Europe
japonicum		22	M. & S. 1935	H	Japan
mucronatum		22	Håkansson 1953	—	Siberia

MEUM $x = 11$
   athamanticum Spignel   22   Håkansson 1953   —   Europe

OENANTHE $x = 10, 11$

benghalensis		20	Sharma & G. 1954	—	India
aquatica		22	Wulff 1937a	M	Eur., N. Asia
crocata		22	Gardé & G. 1949	—	W. Europe
fistulosa	Water Dropwort	22	Wulff 1939a	M	Eur., S.W. Asia
lachenalii		22	„ 1937a	M	Eur., Cauc., Alg.
pimpinelloides		22	Håkansson 1953	—	Eur., Asia M.

RIDOLFIA $x = 11$
   segetum   22   Gardé & G. 1951   —   Medit.

SELINUM $x = 11$
   carvifolia   22   Schulz-Gaebel 1930   —   Eur., W.Asia

SILAUM $x = 11$
   silaus   Pepper Saxifrage   22   Maude 1939   —   Eur., Sib.

TROCHISCANTHES $x = 11$
   nodiflorus   22   Wanscher 1931   —   S. Europe

AEGOPODIUM $x = 11$

podagraria   Gout Weed   { 22   Gardé & G. 1951   M   Eur., N. Asia
                        { 44   Håkansson 1953

CNIDIUM $x = 12$
   ajanense   24   M. & S. 1935   —   N. Asia

TRIBE II: SCANDICEAE

TORILIS $x = 6, 8, 11$

neglecta		12	Gardé & G. 1949	—	S. Europe
japonica	Hedge Parsley	16	Melderis 1930	—	N. Temp.
nodosa		22	Gardé & G. 1949	—	Eur., W. Asia

CAUCALIS $x = 6, 10$

leptophylla		12	Wanscher 1932	—	Eur., Medit.
lappula (*daucoides*)		20	„ „	—	Eurasia
latifolia	Bur Parsley	c. 32	„ „	—	„

PETAGNIA $x = 7$
   saniculifolia   42   Wanscher 1933a   —   Sicily

ANTHRISCUS $x = 7, 8, 9$

tenerrimus		14	Wanscher 1933a	—	Greece, Asia M.
sylvestris	Cow Parsley	{ 16	Wanscher 1931	—	Eur., N. Asia
		{ 18	Tamamschjan 1933		
fumarioides		{ 16	Wanscher 1931	—	Europe
		{ 18	Schulz-Gaebel 1930		
cerefolium	Chervil	18	Wanscher 1931	Sp	Eur., S.W. & N. Asia
neglecta	Bur Chervil	18	Wanscher 1931	—	Eur., W. Asia

207

SCANDIX* $x = 8$

pecten-veneris	Shepherd's Needle	16	Wanscher 1931	—	Eur., S.W. Asia
pinnatifida	& 2 spp.	16	Gardé & G. 1949, '54	—	Medit., S.W. Asia
macrorrhyncha		32	„ 1954	—	Asia Minor

ASTRODAUCUS $x = 10$

orientalis	20	Wanscher 1933a	—	Cauc., Persia

ORLAYA $x = 10$

grandiflora	20	Reese 1952a	—	Eur., S.W. Asia

CHAEROPHYLLUM $x = 11$

aromaticum		22	Wanscher 1932	—	Europe
aureum		22	Håkansson 1953	—	Eur., Asia M.
bulbosum	Chervil	22	„ „	R	„ „
hirsutum		22	Wanscher 1931	—	„
temulum	Rough Chervil	22	Wulff 1939a	—	Eur., Cauc., N. Afr.

MYRRHIS $x = 11$

odorata	Myrrh	22	Wanscher 1931	Sp	S. Eur., Cauc.

OSMORHIZA $x = 11$

aristata	22	Wanscher 1932	—	N. America
longistylis	22	„ „	—	„

MOLOSPERMUM $x = 11$

peloponnesiacum	44	Håkansson 1953	—	W. Medit.

TRIBE III: SANICULEAE

ASTRANTIA $x = 7$

helleborifolia	14	Wanscher 1932	—	Caucasus
minor	14	Håkansson 1953	—	S. Europe
major	14	Wanscher 1932	H	Europe—Cauc.
v. *biebersteinii*	28	Håkansson 1953		

ERYNGIUM * $x = 7, 8$

amethystinum		14	Tamamschjan 1933	H	Europe
campestre	Eryngo	14	Håkansson 1953		
		28	Gardé & G. 1949,	M	Eur., C. Asia
		28	Reese 1953		
alpinum	& 4 spp.	16	Wanscher '32, '33a	—	Europe
dichotomum	& 4 spp.	16	Gardé & G. 1949, '51	—	Medit.
maritimum	Sea Holly	16	„ „ 1951	HR	Eur., Asia M.
pandanifolium		48	„ „ „	—	Brazil
aquaticum (*yuccaefolium*)		96	Bowden 1945b	—	E: U.S.A.

HACQUETIA $x = 8$

epipactis	16	Wanscher 1933a	H	Europe

LAGOECIA $x = 8$

cuminoides	16	Tamamschjan 1933	—	Medit.

SANICULA * $x = 8$

europaea	Sanicle	16	Wanscher 1931	M	Eur., N. Asia
arctopoides	& 12 spp.	16	Bell 1954	—	W: N. America
crassicaulis		32, 48, 64	,, ,,	—	W: N. & S. Amer.

TRIBE IV: HYDROCOTYLEAE

AZORELLA $x = 8$

pedunculata		16	Wanscher 1932	—	S. America
trifurcata		16	,, ,,	—	,,

BOWLESIA $x = 8$

tenera		16	Håkansson 1953	—	Andes

DRUSA $x = 8$

oppositifolia		16	Wanscher 1933a	—	Canaries

HYDROCOTYLE $x = 8, 9, 11$

asiatica		18	Sharma & G. 1954	—	India
moschata		{ *c.* 36	Tamamschjan 1933	—	New Zealand
		48	Wanscher 1932		
novae-zealandiae		48	,, 1933a	—	,, ,,
umbellata		48	,, 1932	—	O.W. Tropics
vulgaris	Pennywort	*c.* 96	Håkansson 1953	—	Eur., N. Afr.
bonariensis		22	Covas & S. 1946	—	Tropics

ACTINOTUS $x = 10$

helianthi	Flannel Fl.	20	Smith-White unp.	H	Australia

ASTERISCIUM $x = 10$

glaucum		20	Covas & S. 1946	—	Andes

TRACHYMENE (DIDISCUS) $x = 11$

coerulea	Blue Lace Fl.	22	Wanscher 1933a	H	Australia
pilosa		44	,, ,,	—	,,

TRIBE V: DAUCEAE

DAUCUS $x = 8, 9, 10, 11$

pumilus		16	Gardé & G. 1949	—	Medit.
muricatus?		16	Wanscher 1933a	—	,,
carota	Carrot	{ 18	Heiser & W. '48,	VVit	S.W. Asia, *cult*
		18	Gardé & G. 1951		
gingidium (*gummifer*)		18	Lindenbein 1932	—	Eur., N. Afr.
maritimus		18	Gardé & G. 1949	—	W. Europe
polygamus		18	,, ,, ,,	—	Spain, Sicily
platycarpus		18	Tamamschjan 1933	—	Eur., Temp. Asia
maximus		{ 18	Lindenbein 1932	—	Medit., S.W. Asia
		22	Wanscher 1932		
grandiflorus		20	,, 1933a	—	Algeria
pulcherrimus		20	,, ,,	—	Cauc., Pers.
crinitus		22	Gardé & G. 1949	—	Portugal
muricatus		22	,, ,, 1951	—	Medit.

TRIBE VI: LASERPITIEAE

CUMINUM $x = 7$
cyminum	Cumin	14	Sharma & G. 1954	MSp	Medit.

SILER $x = 8, 9, 11$
divaricatum	16	Suzuka & K. 1949	—	Siberia
trilobum	⎰ 18	Håkansson 1953	—	Eur., Asia M.,
	⎱ 22	Wanscher 1932		Cauc.

LASERPITIUM $x = 11$
halleri	22	Favarger 1953	—	Alps
latifolium	22	Håkansson 1953	—	Europe
prutenicum	22	Gardé & G. 1949	—	,,

MARGOTIA $x = 11$
gummifera	22	Gardé & G. 1949	—	Spain

THAPSIA $x = 11$
decipiens	22	Wanscher 1933a	—	W. Medit.
garganica	22	Gardé & G. 1949	—	Medit.

TRIBE VII: SMYRNIEAE

NOTHOSMYRNIUM $x = 9$
japonicum	18	Suzuka & K. 1949	—	Japan

CONIUM $x = 11$
maculatum	Hemlock	22	Gardé & G. 1949	M	Eur., S.W. Asia

HIPPOMARATHRUM $x = 11$
pterochloenum	22	Gardé & G. 1949	—	Medit.

SMYRNIUM $x = 11$
perfoliatum	22	Wanscher 1932	M	S. Eur., Cauc.
olusatrum	Alexanders	22	Rutland 1941	V	Eur., Med.

TRIBE VIII: CORIANDREAE

BIFORA $x = 11$
radians	22	Wanscher 1933a	—	S. Eur., Asia M.

CORIANDRUM $x = 11$
sativum	Coriander	22	Gardé & G. 1949	Sp	S. Eur., S.W. Asia

TRIBE IX: PEUCEDANEAE

ANGELICA $x = 11$
archangelica	Angelica	22	Gardé & G. 1949	M	Eur., Sib., Himal.
glabra	22	Suzuka 1950	—	Japan
pachycarpa	22	Vaarama 1947a	—	Spain
ursina	22	,, ,,	—	Kamchatka
pubescens	22	Ogawa 1929	—	Japan
sylvestris	22	,, ,,	—	Eur., N. & S.W. Asia
sp.	66	,, ,,	—	—

210

FERULA $x = 11$

assafoetida	Asafoetida	22	Håkansson 1953	MSp	Pers., Afghan.
communis		22	Gardé & G. 1949	—	Medit.
glauca		22	„ „	—	S. Europe
longifolia		22	„ „	—	Russia

HERACLEUM $x = 11$

sphondylium	Cow Parsnip	22	Maude 1939	—	Temp. O.W.

LEVISTICUM $x = 11$

officinalis	Lovage	22	Melderis 1930	H	S. Europe

LOPHOSCIADIUM $x = 11$

meifolium		22	Håkansson 1953	H	S. Europe

OPOPANAX $x = 11$

chironium		22	Gardé & G. 1949	P	Medit.

PASTINACA $x = 11$

sativa	Parsnip	22	Ogawa 1929	R	Eur., N. Amer.
urens		22	Vazart 1950	—	France

TORDYLIUM $x = 10, 11$

cordatum		20	Gardé & G. 1954	—	Cyprus, Mesop.
syriacum		20	„ „	—	Syria, Asia M.
maximum		22	Tamamschjan 1933	—	S. Eur., S.W. Asia

PEUCEDANUM $x = 6, 11$

angustifolium		12	Gardé & G. 1954	—	Italy
decursivum		22	Ogawa 1929	M	Japan
japonicum		22	„ „	—	„
graveolens	Dill	22	Schulz-Gaebel 1930	MSp	Medit.
hispanicum		22	Gardé & G. 1949	—	Spain
oreoselinum		22	Håkansson 1953	—	S. & C. Europe
palustre	Hog's Fennel	22	„ „	M	Europe
verticillare		22	Gardé & G. 1949	—	S. Europe
officinale		c. 66	Reese 1952a	M	C. Eur., W. Asia

CAPNOPHYLLUM $x = 10$

peregrinum		20	Gardé & G. 1954	—	Medit.

Group XIII

ERICALES
214–220
(H)S(T)

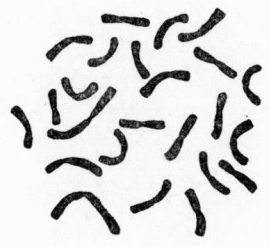

Daboecia cantabrica

214 CLETHRACEAE

CLETHRA $x = 8$

arborea		16	Hagerup 1928	—	Madeira
alnifolia	Sweet Pepperbush	32	,, ,,	H	S: U.S.A.

215 ERICACEAE

CALLUNA $x = 8$

vulgaris	Heather, Ling	16	Hagerup 1928	FoBDH	Eur., N. Amer.

BRUCKENTHALIA $x = 9$?

spiculifolia	Spike Heath	36	Callan 1941	H	E. Eur., A. Minor

PERNETTYA $x = 11$

tasmanica	22	Callan 1941	H	Tasmania
buxifolia	44	,, ,,	H	Mexico
ciliata (*ciliaris*)	44	,, ,,	H	,,
pentlandii	44	,, ,,	H	Andes
prostrata	44	,, ,,	H	Magellan
furens	66	,, ,,	HM	Chile
mucronata	66	,, ,,	H	Magellan

GAULTHETTYA $x = 11$

wisleyensis	77	Callan 1941	H	*cult*
(*G. shallon* × *P. mucronata*)				

GAULTHERIA $x = 11, 12, 13$

antipoda		22	Callan 1941	H	Tasm., New Zeal.
cuneata		22	,, ,,	H	W. China
glomerata		22	,, ,,	H	S. America
hispida	Snowberry	22	,, ,,	H	Austr., N.Z.
cumingiana		44	,, ,,	H	Philip. Is.
griffithiana		44	,, ,,	H	Himalaya
shallon	Salal	88	,, ,,	HF	W: N. Amer.
procumbens	Checkerberry	24	Newcomer 1941	FH	N. America
itoana		26	Callan 1941	H	Japan

KALMIA $x = 11, 12$

latifolia	Calico Bush	24	Hagerup 1928	H	E: N. Amer.
glauca		48	,, ,,	H	W: N. Amer.
polifolia	Bog K.	44	Callan 1941	H	,,

DABOECIA $x = 12$

cantabrica	Irish Heath	24	Maude 1940	H	W. Europe

ERICA $x = 12$

arborea	Tree Heath	24	Hagerup 1928	W	Medit., Cauc.
carnea		24	,, ,,	H	C. & S. Eur.
cinerea		24	,, ,,	H	W. Europe
curvirostris		24	Callan 1941	—	S. Africa
hiemalis		24	Hagerup 1928	—	*cult*
sessilifolia (*spicata*)		24	Callan 1941	—	S. Africa
tetralix		24	Hagerup 1928	H	N. & W. Europe
vagans	Cornish H.	24	Maude 1939	H	W. Europe
wilmoreana		24	Callan 1941	H	*cult*

215

LEIOPHYLLUM $x = 12$
buxifolium Sand Myrtle 24 Hagerup 1928 H S.E.: U.S.A.

LEUCOTHOË $x = 12$
populifolia (acuminata) 24 Callan 1941 H S.E.: U.S.A.

LOISELEURIA $x = 12$
procumbens Apline Azalea 24 Hagerup 1928 H North Reg.

LYONIA (PIERIS) $x = 12$
lucida Fetterbush 24 Callan 1941 H S.E: U.S.A.
mariana Staggerbush 24 „ „ H E: U.S.A.

OXYDENDRON $x = 12$
arboreum Sourwood 24 Baldwin 1942a W E: U.S.A.

PIERIS $x = 12$
japonica 24 Callan 1941 H Japan

PHYLLODOCE $x = 12$
coerulea 24 Wanscher 1933b H North Reg.

ANDROMEDA $x = 12$
polifolia Bog Rosemary 48 Callan 1941 H North Reg.

ENKIANTHUS $x = 12$
campanulatus 60 Hagerup 1941a H Japan

ARBUTUS $x = 13$
andrachne 26 Hagerup 1928 FHW E. Medit.
canariensis 26 „ „ FH Canary Is.
andrachnoides 26 Callan 1941 H *cult*
xalapensis 26 „ „ H Mexico
unedo Strawberry Tree 26 Sealy & W. 1950 FH Medit.

ARCTOUS (ARCTOSTAPHYLOS) $x = 13$
alpina Black Bearberry 26 L. & L. 1948 — North Reg.

CASSIOPE $x = 13$
tetragona 26 L. & L. 1948 H Circumpolar
hypnoides c. 48 Hagerup 1928 H Arctic

CHIMAPHILA * $x = 13$
umbellata & 1 sp. c. 26 Hagerup 1941a H Eurasia

MONESES (PYROLA) $x = 13$
uniflora Shinleaf 26 Hagerup 1941a H North Reg.

ARCTOSTAPHYLOS $x = 13$
bicolor 26 Callan 1941 H Calif.
pungens 26 „ „ H Calif., Mex.
uva-ursi 52 Hagerup 1928 HM North Temp.

LEDUM $x = 13$
latifolium Labrador Tea 26 Hagerup 1928 BHM Arctic
columbianum 26 Callan 1941 H N. America
palustre Crystal Tea 52 Hagerup 1941a H N. Eur., N. Asia

216

RHODODENDRON * $x = 13$ (374 species counted)

S. 1. GLABRATAE (AZALEA)

Series Azalea				
39 species	26	Janaki-Ammal *et al.* '50	H	North Temp.
calendulaceum	52	,, ,,	H	N.E: N. Amer.
canadense	52	,, ,,	H	,, ,,
3 Series: 3 spp.	26	,, ,,	H	Colo., E. Asia

S. 2. NON-LEPIDOTAE

Series Fortunei				
15 species	26	,, ,,	H	S.W. China
diaprepes	26, 39	,, ,,	H	S.W. Yunnan, Bur.
14 Series: 134 spp.	26	,, ,,	H	S.E. Asia etc.

S. 3. LEPIDOTAE

Series Glaucum				
9 species	26	,, ,,	H	Sikkim, S.E. Tib.,
pemakoense	26, 52	,, ,,	H	N. Bur., Yunnan
tsangpoense	52	,, ,,	H	
Series Lepidotum				Himal., S. Tibet
3 species	26	,, ,,	H	
baileyi	52	,, ,,	H	
patulum	52	,, ,,	H	
				N.E. Bur., S.E.
Series Saluenense				Tibet, Yunnan
7 species	26	Janaki-Ammal *et al.* 1950	H	
cosmetum	26, 52	,, ,,	H	
riparium	26, 52	,, ,,	H	
saluenense	26, 52	,, ,,	H	
prostratum	52	,, ,,	H	
Series Lapponicum				Yunnan, Szechuan
17 species	26	,, ,,	H	
fastigiatum	26, 52	,, ,,	H	
intricatum	26, 52	,, ,,	H	
lapponicum	26, 52	,, ,,	H	(Lapland)
lysolepis	26, 52	,, ,,	H	
rupicola	26, 52	,, ,,	H	
idoneum	26, 52	,, ,,	H	
flavidum	26, 52	,, ,,	H	
russatum	39, 52	,, ,,	H	
capitatum	52	,, ,,	H	
dasypetalum	52	,, ,,	H	
edgarianum	52	,, ,,	H	
drumonium	52	,, ,,	H	
ramosissimum	52	,, ,,	H	
violaceum	52	,, ,,	H	
yungingense	52	,, ,,	H	
ravum	52, 78	,, ,,	H	
complexum	78	,, ,,	H	
cuneatum	78	,, ,,	H	
tapetiforme	78	,, ,,	H	
Series Triflorum				Yunnan, Szechuan
8 species	26	,, ,,	H	
aechmophyllum	52	,, ,,	H	
ambiguum	52	,, ,,	H	

217

RHODODENDRON (*cont.*)

amesiae	52	Janaki-Ammal *et al.* 1950	H	
augustinii	52	,, ,,	H	
charianthum	52	,, ,,	H	
chasmanthum	52	,, ,,	H	
concinnum	52	,, ,,	H	
exquisitum	52	,, ,,	H	
pseudovanthinum	52	,, ,,	H	
searsiae	52	,, ,,	H	
zaleucum	52	,, ,,	H	
artosquamatum	78	,, ,,	H	
davidsonianum	78	,, ,,	H	
oreotrephis	78	,, ,,	H	
siderophyllum	78	,, ,,	H	
timeteum	78	,, ,,	H	
xanthocodon	78	,, ,,	H	
yunnanense	78	,, ,,	H	
Series Maddenii				Sikkim—W. Yun-
23 species	26	,, ,,	H	nan & Burma
crassum	52, 78	,, ,,	H	
maddenii	52, 78	,, ,,	H	
polyandrum	78	,, ,,	H	
manipurense	78, 156	,, ,,	H	
Series Heliolepis				N. Bur.—Kansu
aporinum	52	Janaki-Ammal *et al.* 1950	H	
brevistylum	52	,, ,,	H	
desquamatum	52	,, ,,	H	
rubiginosum	52, 78	,, ,,	H	
heliolepis	78	,, ,,	H	
pholidotum	104	,, ,,	H	
Series Cinnabarinum				Sikkim, Bhutan
cinnabarinum	78	,, ,,	H	
concatenans	78	,, ,,	H	
keysii	78	,, ,,	H	

15 series: 47 spp.	26	,, ,,	H	⎧ 1 S.E: U.S.A. ⎨ 1 N.E. Asia ⎪ 44 Himalaya ⎩ 1 Eur. Alps

RAMISCHIA (PYROLA) $x = 19$

secunda	38	Hagerup 1941a	—	N. Europe

PYROLA (PIROLA) $x_2 = 23 (11 + 12)$

grandiflora		46	Hagerup 1928	—	North Temp.
minor	Common Winter- green	46	,, ,,	H	,,
rotundifolia		46	,, ,,	H	Eur., N. Amer.
virens (*chlorantha*)		46	,, 1941a	H	N. America
media		92	,, ,,	H	Europe

216 VACCINIACEAE

GAYLUSSACIA $x = 12$

baccata (*resinosa*)	Huckleberry	24	Newcomer 1941	F	N. America

PENTAPTERYGIUM $x = 12$
serpens		24	Callan 1941	H	Himalayas

POLYCODIUM $x = 12$
stamineum	Deerberry	24	Longley 1927b	F	N: U.S.A.

OXYCOCCUS (VACCINIUM) $x = 12$
macrocarpus	Cranberry	24	Darrow *et al.* 1944	F	E: N. America
microcarpus		24	,, ,,	F	North Reg.
quadripetalus	Cranberry	48	,, ,,	F	,,
(*palustris*)					
as *ovalifolius*		48	,, ,,	F	,,
gigas		72	Hagerup 1940	—	N.W. Europe

VACCINIUM $x = 12$
atrococcum		24	Darrow *et al.* 1944	FH	E: U.S.A.
angustifolium	Sugarberry	24	,, ,,	F	N.E.: N. Amer.
caesariense		24	,, ,,	F	E: U.S.A.
darrowi		24	,, ,,	F	S.E: U.S.A.
elliotii	Mayberry	24	,, ,,	F	,,
crassifolium	Creeping Blue-berry	24	,, ,,	F	,,
myrtilloides	Canda. Bl.	24	,, ,,	F	N. America
myrtillus	Whortleberry	24	Rutland 1941	F	North Temp.
ovatum	Calif. Bl.	24	Darrow *et al.* 1944	F	W: N. America
parvifolium		24	,, ,,	F	N.E: N. Amer.
pallidum		24	,, ,,	F	E: U.S.A.
tenellum		24	,, ,,	F	S.E: U.S.A.
vacillans		24	,, ,,	F	U.S.A.
vitis-idaea	Red Whortle-berry	24	Newcomer 1941	F	Arctic, Subarctic
uliginosum	Moorberry, Bog Bilberry	24, 48	Hagerup 1933	F	North Temp.
australe		48	Darrow *et al.* 1944	F	E: U.S.A.
arctostaphylos	Broussa T.	48	,, ,,	B	Caucasus
brittonii		48	,, ,,	F	N.E.: N. Amer.
corymbosum	Highbush Bl.	48	,, ,,	F	E: N. America
hirsutum	Hairy Bl.	48	,, ,,	F	E: U.S.A.
lamarckii		48	,, ,,	F	,,
myrsinites	Myrtle Bl.	48	,, ,,	FH	S.E: U.S.A.
simulatum		48	,, ,,	F	E: U.S.A.
tallapusae (*alto-montanum*)		48	,, ,,	F	E: N. America
virgatum		48	,, ,,	F	E: U.S.A.
amoenum		72	,, ,,	F	,,
ashei	Rabbiteye Bl.	72	,, ,,	F	,,
constablaei		72	,, ,,	F	S: U.S.A.

217 EPACRIDACEAE

TRIBE I: STYPHELIEAE

STYPHELIA * $x = 4$
longiflora	& 4 spp.	8	Smith-White 1948b	H	E. Australia
tenuiflora		8	,, unp.	—	W. ,,

219

LEUCOPOGON * $x = 4, 6, 11$						
(i) *fraseri*	& 11 spp.	8	Smith-White	'48b & unp. (1955)	H	Aust., N.Z.
juniperinus	(3*x*)	12	,,	,,	H	E. Australia
biflorus		16	,,	unp.	—	,,
ericoides	& 5 spp.	12	,,	'48b & unp.	H	Australia
(ii) *richei*	& 2 spp.	12	,,	,,	H	W. Australia
amplexicaulis		24	,,	,,	H	N.S.W.
australis		24	,,	unp.	H	W. Australia
lanceolatus		48	,,	'48b	H	E. ,,
revolutus	$22 + 0 - 3\mathbf{B}$		,,	unp.	—	W. ,,
glabellus	& 3 spp.	22	,,	unp.	—	W. ,,
oldfieldii	$22 + 0 - 2\mathbf{B}$, *c.* 66		,,	,,	—	,, ,,
cuculatus	*c.* 44		,,	,,	—	,, ,,
ASTROLOMA * $x = 4, 7$						
ciliatum	& 8 spp.	8	Smith-White	unp.	—	W. Australia
microdonta		16	,,	,,	—	,, ,,
humifusum		24	,,	'48b	H	Aust., Tasm.
stomarrhena		32	,,	unp.	—	W. Australia
conostephioides		14	,,	,,	—	S. ,,
pinifolium		14	,,	'48b	H	E. ,,
LISSANTHE $x = 7$						
sapida		14	Smith-White	'48b	H	E. Australia
strigosa		14	,,	,,	H	,,
montana		28, 42	,,	unp.	—	,,
BRACHYLOMA $x = 7, 9$						
preissii	$14 + 0 - 1\mathbf{B}$		Smith-White	unp.	—	W. Australia
daphnoides		18	,,	'48b	H	E. ,,
scortechinii		18	,,	unp.	—	,, ,,
MELICHRUS $x = 8$						
rotatus		16	Smith-White	'48b	H	E. Australia
urceolatus		16	,,	,,	H	,, ,,
ACROTRICHE $x = 9$						
divaricata		18	Smith-White	'48b	H	E. Australia
fasciculiflora		18	,,	unp.	—	S. ,,
ovalifolia		18	,,	,,	H	W. ,,
serrulata		18	,,	'48b	—	E. ,,
TROCHOCARPA $x = 10$						
laurina		20	Smith-White	'48b	—	E. Australia
MONOTOCA $x = 12$						
elliptica		24	Smith-White	'48b	H	E. Australia
scoparia		24	,,	,,	H	,,

TRIBE II: EPACRIDEAE

SPHENOTOMA $x = 6, 7$						
dracophylloides		12	Smith-White	unp.	—	W. Australia
drummondii		14	,,	,,	—	,,

SPRENGELIA $x = 6$
 incarnata   24 Smith-White '48b   H   E. Aust., Tasm.

ANDERSONIA $x_2 = 13 \, (6 + 7)$
 coerulea   26 Smith-White unp.   H   W. Australia
 sprengelioides   26   „   „   H   „

COSMELIA $x_2 = 13$
 rubra   26 Smith-White unp.   H   W. Australia

DRACOPHYLLUM $x_2 = 13$
 secundum   26 Smith-White '48b   H   E. Australia

LYSINEMA $x = 6$
 ciliatum   24 Smith-White unp.   H   W. Australia
 conspicuum   24   „   „   H   „

RICHEA * $x_2 = 13$
 gunnii   26 Smith-White unp.   —   E. Australia
 scoparia   & 3 spp.   26   „   „   H   Tasmania

WOOLLSIA $x_2 = 13$
 pungens   26 Smith-White '48b   H   E. Australia

EPACRIS * $x_2 = 13$
 longiflora   & 8 spp.   26 Smith-White '48b & H   E. Australia
                                           unp.
 serpyllifolia   26, 52   „   unp.   H   N.S.W., Tasm.

218 MONOTROPACEAE

MONOTROPA $x = 8$
 hypophegea   16 L. & L. 1944b   —   North Temp.
 hypopithys   Y. Bird's Nest   48   „   —   „

219 DIAPENSIACEAE

DIAPENSIA $x = 6$
 lapponica   12 Hagerup 1928   H   North Temp.
   as *obovata*   12 Sugiura 1937b

PYXIDANTHERA $x = 6$
 barbulata   12 Baldwin 1939   H   E: N. America

SHORTIA $x = 6$
 galacifolia   12 Baldwin 1939   H   S.E: U.S.A.

SCHIZOCODON $x = 6$
 soldanelloides   12 Baldwin 1939   H   Japan

GALAX $x = 6$
 aphylla   12, 24 Baldwin 1941a   H   E: N. America

16   221

Group XIV

EBENALES
221, 222
ST

MYRSINALES
223
ST

STYRACALES
224–227
ST

LOGANIALES
228, 229
ST

APOCYNALES
230, 231
HST

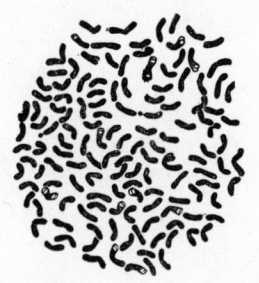

Fraxinus chinensis

221 EBENACEAE

DIOSPYROS $x=15$

discolor	Velvet Apple	30	Namikawa & H. 1928	F	Philippines
embryopteris	Gaub	30	Pathak et al. 1949	F	India, Malaya
lotus	Date Plum, Lotus	30	Namikawa & H. 1928	F	Temp. Asia
texana	Black Pers.	30	Baldwin & C. 1941		Mexico
virginiana	Persimmon	60, 90	,, ,,	F	N. America
kaki	Japanese Pers.	90	Namikawa & H. 1928	F	Ind.—Japan

222 SAPOTACEAE

BUMELIA $x=12$

lanuginosa	Chittamwood	24	Brown & C. 1940	H	S.E: U.S.A.

MADHUCA (BASSIA) $x=12$

latifolia	Mahwah	24	Singh 1951	AOW	India

PALAQUIUM $x=12$

gutta	Gutta-percha	24	EKJ*	Ru	India, Malaya

CHRYSOPHYLLUM $x=12, 13$

cainito	Star Apple	24	Krishnaswamy & R. 1949	F	W. Ind., Trop. Amer.
		26	Tjio 1948		
oliviforme	Satin Leaf	52	,, ,,	H	Fla., Trop. Amer.

ACHRAS $x=13$

zapota	Sapodilla	26	EKJ*	RuFW	W. Indies, C. Amer.

223 MYRSINACEAE

ARDISIA (ICACOREA) $x=12, 13$

crispa (crenata)	24	La Cour 1945*	H	China, Malaya
	46	Sugiura 1936b		

224 STYRACACEAE

STYRAX $x=8$

obassia	Fragrant Styrax	16	Manshard 1936	HM	Japan
japonica		40	,, ,,	M	,,

HALESIA $x=12$

diptera		24	Simonet & M. 1932	—	S.E: U.S.A.
carolina (tetraptera)	Wild Olive, Snowdrop T.	24	Manshard 1936	FH	,,

PTEROSTYRAX $x=12$

corymbosa		24	Manshard 1936	HM	Japan

228 LOGANIACEAE

FAGRAEA $x=6$

fragrans	12	Mohrbutter 1936	—	Burma, Malaya
litoralis	12	,, ,,	—	Java

225

DESFONTAINIA $x=7$
spinosa   14   Moore 1947   H   Chile, Peru

GELSEMIUM $x=8$
sempervirens False Jasmine   16   Moore 1947   HM   S.E: N. Amer.

POLYPREMUM $x=11$
procumbens   22   Moore 1947   —   S.E: N. Amer.

STRYCHNOS $x=12$

laurina		24	Mohrbutter 1936	M	E. Ind., Malaya
nux-vomica	Nux-vomica	24	EKJ*	M	India, Burma
sansibariensis	Zanz. Poison Nut	24	Mohrbutter 1936	M	Trop. Africa

SPIGELIA $x=(12)\ 24$
marilandica   Indian Pink Root 48   Moore 1947   H   S.E: N. Amer.

CHILIANTHUS $x_2=19\ (7+12)$
oleaceus   38   Moore 1947   H   S. Africa

NICODEMIA $x_2=19\ (7+12)$
madagascariensis   38   Moore 1947   —   Mascarene Is.

BUDDLEIA $x_2=19\ (7+12)$

alternifolia		38	Moore 1947	H	Kansu
asiatica		38	,,	H	Trop. Asia, Mal.
brasiliensis		38	,,	H	Brazil
globosa	Panil	38	,,	H	Chile, Peru
japonica		38	,,	H	Japan
lindleyana		38	,,	H	China
salviifolia		38	,,	H	S. Africa
scordioides		38	,,	—	Texas, Mexico
tibetica v. farreri		38	,,	H	Kansu
americana		76	,,	—	Mexico, C. Amer.
davidii	Summer Lilac	76	,,	H	C. China, Tibet
(17 garden forms)		76	,,	H	*cult*
fallowiana		76	,,	H	Yunnan
albiflora		c. 114	,,	H	Hupeh, Shensi
forrestii		c. 114	,,	H	Yunnan
limitanea		c. 114	,,	—	China, Burma
nivea		c. 114	,,	H	Szechuan
stenostachya		c. 114	,,	H	,,
colvilei		c. 300	,,	H	Himalayas

229 OLEACEAE

MENODORA $x=11$

longiflora	22	Taylor 1945	—	Texas
scoparia	22	Bowden 1945b	—	W: N. Amer.
scabra	44	Taylor 1945	—	New Mexico

JASMINUM $x=(12),\ 13$

mesneyi	$\begin{cases} 24 \\ 26 \end{cases}$	Bowden 1945b Taylor 1945	H	China

JASMINUM (*cont.*)

affine		26	Bowden 1940a	P	Malaya
auriculatum		26	Krishnaswamy & R. 1948a	P	India, Ceylon
beesianum		26	Bowden 1945b	H	W. China
calophyllum		26	Krishnaswamy & R. 1949	P	India
flexile		26, 52	Raman 1955	P	,,
floridum		26	Bowden 1940a	—	China
fruticans		26	Sax & A. 1932	—	Med., S.W. Asia
gracillimum		26	Taylor 1945	H	N. Borneo
humile	Italian Jasmine	26	Bowden 1940a	P	Afghan., Persia
malabaricum		26	Krishnaswamy & R. 1949	—	India
odoratissimum		26	Bowden 1945b	H	Madeira
officinale (*grandiflorum*)	White J.	26	Krishnaswamy & R. 1948a	HP	Persia—China
parkeri		26	Bowden 1945b	H	Himalayas
pubigerum		26	Taylor 1945	H	,,
rigidum		26	Krishnaswamy & R. 1949	H	India
simplicifolium (*lucidum*)		26	Taylor 1945	—	Aust., Pacific
tortuosum		26	,, ,,	—	S. Africa
wallichianum		26	Bowden 1940a	P	Nepal
multiflorum (*pubescens*)		26, 39	Dutt 1952b	H	India, China
nitidum		26, 39	Taylor 1945	H	S. Pacific
sambac	Mohle, Arabian J.	26 26, 39 39	Bowden 1945b Krishnaswamy & R. '48a Tjio '48, Taylor '45	HP	Trop. Asia
primulinum (3*x*)		39	Krishnaswamy & R. '48a	H	China, *cult*
angustifolium		52	,, ,, '49	—	India
dichotomum	Gold Coast J.	52	Taylor 1945	—	Trop. W. Africa
nudiflorum	Winter J.	52	Bowden 1940a	HP	China
calophyllum as *calcyphytum?*		52	Dutt 1952b		

FONTANESIA *x* = 13

fortunei	26	Taylor 1945	H	China
phillyraeoides	26	,,	H	Sicily, A. Minor, Syria

ABELIOPHYLLUM *x* = 14

distichum	28	Taylor 1945	H	Korea

FORSYTHIA *x* = 14

europaea	28	Sax & A. 1932	H	Albania
ovata	28	,, ,,	H	Korea
suspensa	28	,, ,,	H	China
viridissima	28	,, ,,	H	,,

CHIONANTHUS *x* = 23

virginicus	Fringe Tree	46	Sax & A. 1932	H	E: U.S.A.

FORESTIERA *x* = 23

acuminata	46	Sax & A. 1932	H	Texas
neo-mexicana	46	Taylor 1945	H	S.W: U.S.A.

FRAXINUS $x = 23$

angustifolia		46	Taylor 1945	H	S. Eur., N. Afr.
berlanderiana		46	,, ,,	H	Texas, Mex.
biltmoreana		46	,, ,,	H	E: U.S.A.
bungeana		46	,, ,,	H	N. China
excelsior	European Ash	46	Sax & A. 1932	VW	Eur., Asia Minor
floribunda	Himalaya A.	46	Bowden 1940a	W	Himalayas
griffithii		46	Taylor 1945	—	China, Philip., Malaya
holotricha		46	,, ,,	H	E. Balkans
oregona	Oregon Ash	46	Sax & A. 1932	W	N.W: U.S.A.
ornus	Manna Ash	46	Taylor 1945	HM	Medit., A. Minor
pennsylvanica	Red Ash	46	Sax & A. 1932	W	E: N. America
sogdiana		46	Taylor 1945	H	Turkestan
xanthoxyloides		46	,, ,,	H	Himal., Afghan
velutina		46, 92	,, ,,	H	S.W: U.S.A.
americana	White Ash	46, 92, 138	Wright 1944	HW	E: N. America
chinensis	Chinese Ash	138	Taylor 1945	Fo_1W	E. Asia

LIGUSTRUM $x = 23$

acuminatum		46	Taylor 1945	H	Japan
acutissimum		46	,, ,,	—	C. China
amurense		46	Sax & A. 1932	H	N. China
delavayanum		46	Taylor 1945	H	China
ibota		46	,, ,,	H	China, Japan
insulare		46	,, ,,	H	(unknown)
japonicum		46	,, ,,	H	Japan, Korea
lucidum	Glossy Privet	46	,, ,,	Fo_1H	China—Japan
obtusifolium		46	,, ,,	H	Japan
quihoui		46	,, ,,	H	China
vulgare	Common Privet	46	,, ,,	H	Eur., N. Africa
yezoense		46	M. & S. 1935	H	Japan

OLEA $x = 23$

europaea	Olive	46	Breviglieri & B. 1955	FOW	Med., S.W: Asia
laurifolia	Bl. Ironwood	*c.* 48	Andersson 1931	W	S. Africa

OSMANTHUS $x = 23$

armatus		46	Taylor 1945	H	China
fragrans		46	,, ,,	H	Himal.—Japan
ilicifolius		46	,, ,,	H	Japan
americanus	Devil Wood	138	,, ,,	H	S.W: U.S.A.

OSMAREA $x = 23$

burkwoodii (*Siphonosmanthus delayavi* × *Phillyrea decora*)		46	Taylor 1945	H	*cult*

PHILLYREA $x = 23$

decora		46	Taylor 1945	H	W. Asia

SYRINGA $x = 22, 23, 24$

emodi	Himalayan Lilac	44	Tischler 1930	H	Himalayas
persica	Persian L.	44	Sax & A. 1932	H	Pers.—N.W: Ch.
amurensis	Amur L.	46	,, ,,	H	W. China, Manch.
oblata		46	Taylor 1945	H	N. China
potanini		46	,, ,,	H	W. China

SYRINGA (cont.)

reflexa		46	Taylor 1945	H	C. China
sweginzowii		46	,, ,,	H	N.W. China
velutina	Manchurian L.	46	Sax & A. 1932	H	N. China, Korea
wolfi		46	Sax 1930b	H	Manch., Korea
josikaea	Hungarian L.	46-48	Sax & A. 1932	H	Hungary, Galicia
komarovii		46-48	,, ,,	H	W. China
meyeri		46-48	,, ,,	H	N. China
tomentella		46-48	,, ,,	H	W. China
villosa	Late L.	46-48	,, ,,	H	China
vulgaris	Common L.	46, 47, 48	Taylor 1945	HP	S.E: Eur., cult
microphylla		48	,, ,,	H	N. China
pinnatifolia	Pinnate L.	48	Sax & A. 1932	H	W. China ·
pubescens	Hairy L.	48	,, ,,	H	N. China
yunnanensis		48	Sax 1930b	H	W. China

230 APOCYNACEAE

LOCHNERA $x = 8$

rosea	16	Sugiura 1936b	M	Tropics

ALLAMANDA $x = 9$

cathartica v. grandiflora	18	Pathak et al. 1949	H	Guiana
williamsii	18	Sugiura 1936a	H	cult

THEVETIA $x = 9, 10$

peruviana	Yellow	{ 18	Pathak et al. 1949	HM ·	Trop. Amer.
(nereifolia)	Oleander	{ 20	Hardas & J. 1954		

PLUMERIA $x = (9), 18$

alba	White Fr.	36	Singh 1951	H	W. Indies
rubra	Frangipani	36	,, ,,	H	Mex.—Ecuador
v. acutifolia	Pagoda T.	36	,, ,,	HM	Mexico

STROPHANTHUS * $x = 10$

arnoldianus		20	Witkus 1951	H	Congo
grandiflorus		20	,, ,,	H	Trop. S. Africa
gratus		20	,, ,,	H	W. Africa
hispidus		{ 20	,, ,,	HM	,,
		{ 20	Delay 1951		
kombe		20	Witkus 1951	M	,,
preussi		20	,, ,,	H	,,
sarmentosus		{ 20	,, ,,	H	,,
		{ 18	Snoad 1952		
speciosus	& 9 spp.	20	Witkus 1951	H	Trop. S. Africa

TRACHELOSPERMUM $x = 10$

jasminoides	Star Jasmine	20	Sugiura 1936a	H	Japan

VALLARIS $x = 10$

heynei	20	Rau 1941	H	Him.—Burma, Ceylon

CERBERA $x = 10, 11$

odallum		40	Rau 1941	M	India
tanghin	Tanghin Poison T.	44	EKJ*	M	Madagascar

APOCYNUM $x = 11$

androsaemifolium	Dogbane	16?	Schürhoff *et al.* 1937	—	N. America
cannabinum	Indian Hemp	{ 16?	„ „ „	MT	„
		22	Breslawetz *et al.* 1934		
venetum		{ 16?	Schürhoff *et al.* 1937	T	Medit., Asia
		22	Medvedeva 1937		

CARISSA $x = 11$

carandas	Karaunda	22	Singh 1951	DFHW	India
edulis		22	Tjio 1948	FH	Egypt
spinarum		22	Singh 1951	H	India, Ceylon

MASCARENHASIA $x = 11$

elastica	Madagascar Rubber	22	EKJ*	Ru	Trop. Africa

NERIUM $x = 11$

odorum	Scented O.	22	Tjio 1948	HM	Persia, Ind., Japan
oleander	Oleander	22	„ „	H	Medit.

TABERNAEMONTANA (ERVATAMIA) $x = 11$

coronaria	Grape Jasmine	22	Pathak *et al.* 1949	H	India

ODONTADENA $x = 12$

speciosa		24	Andersson 1931	H	Brazil, Guiana

VINCA (CATHARANTHUS) $x = (8), 23$

rosea		16, (32)	Furusato 1940	H	Tropics
difformis		46	Bowden 1945a	—	Spain
herbacea		46	Finn 1928	H	E. Eur., A. Minor
minor	Periwinkle	46	Rutland 1941	HM	Europe
major		92	„ „	HM	Medit.

231 ASCLEPIADACEAE

ARAUJIA $x = 10$

sericifera		20	Schnack & C. 1947	H	S. Brazil

PHILIBERTIA $x = 10$

gilliesii		20	Covas & S. 1946	—	S. America

ASCLEPIAS $x = 11$

curassavica	Blood Flower	22	Moore 1946	HTM	Trop. Amer.
incarnata	Milk Weed	22	„ „	HTRu	N. America
latifolia	Broad Leaf M.	22	Moyer 1936	—	„
salicifolia		22	„ „	—	Mexico
speciosa		22	Moore 1946	H	W: N. America
sullivantii		22	„ „	H	N. America
syriaca	Silk Weed	22	„ „	RuV	„
tuberosa	Butterfly M.	22	„ „	H	„

GOMPHOCARPUS $x = 11$

fruticosus		22	Pardi 1934	—	Medit.
physocarpus		22	„ „	—	S. Australia

HOYA $x = 11$

carnosa	Wax Plant	22	Pardi 1934	HM	Tr. Austr. & Asia

STAPELIA * $x = 11$ Carrion Fl.
gigantea	& 2 spp.	22	Pardi 1934	—	S. Africa
variegata	& 4 spp.	44	,, ,,	H	,,

STEPHANOTIS $x = 11$
floribunda	22	Pardi 1934	H	Madagascar

VINCETOXICUM (CYNANCHUM) $x = 11$
officinale	Tame Poison	22	Pardi 1934	HM	Eur., Cauc.
nigrum		44	,, ,,	H	S. Eur., A. Minor

CEROPEGIA $x = 11$
debilis	44	Pardi 1934	H	Trop. Africa
woodii	44	,, ,,	H	S. Africa

PERIPLOCA $x = 11, 12$
sepium		22	Sax & H. 1936	H	China
graeca	Silk Vine	⌈ 22	Bowden 1940a		
		{ 24	Pardi 1934	H	S. Eur., S.W. Asia
		⌊ 24	Lopane 1951		

CRYPTOSTEGIA $x = 12$
grandiflora	24	Pardi 1934	H(Ru)	Madag., India

DAEMIA $x = 12$
extensa	24	Nirula 1945	H	India, Mal., Tr. Africa

Group XV

RUBIALES
232, 233
HST

ASTERALES
234–238
HS(T)

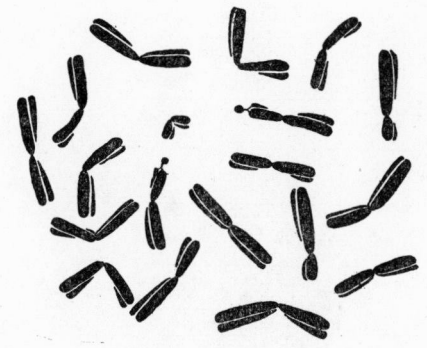

Chrysanthemum millefoliatum

232 RUBIACEAE

OLDENLANDIA $x=9$

crystallina		18	Raghavan & R. '41	—	India, Malaya
senegalensis		18	Hagerup 1932	—	Trop. Africa
alata		36	Raghavan & R. '41	—	India
aspera		36	,, ,,	—	India, Trop. Afr.
capensis		36	Hagerup 1932	—	Trop. & S. Afr.
corymbosa	Parpata	36	Raghavan & R. '41	M	India
umbellata	Chay	36	,, ,,	D	Abyss., E. Indies
paniculata		72	,, ,,		Tropics

VAILLANTIA $x=9$

hispida	18	Fagerlind 1937	—	Medit.
muralis	18	,, ,,	—	S. Europe

BOUVARDIA $x=9$

corymbosa (humboldti)	36	Fagerlind 1937	H	cult
hybrida	36	,, ,,	H	,,
coccinea	c. 72	,, ,,	H	Guiana
leiantha	c. 72	,, ,,	H	Mexico

DENTELLA $x=(9), 18$

repens	36	Raghavan & R. '41	—	Tr. Asia & Austr.

HOUSTONIA $x=9$

caerulea	36	Fagerlind 1937	—	N. America

MANETTIA (LYGISTUM) $x=9?, 11$

coccinea	c. 36	Fagerlind 1937	H	Mex.—Colombia
inflata	c. 36	,, ,,	H	Parag., Urug.
bicolor	22	Poucques 1949a	H	Brazil

PENTAS $x=10$

carnea (lanceolata)	20	Fagerlind 1937	H	Trop. Afr., Arab.
coccinea	20	,, ,,	—	Trop. Africa
oncostipula	20	,, ,,		,,

ASPERULA (GALIUM) * $x=10, 11$

molluginoides		20	Fagerlind 1937	—	Caucasus
arcadiensis		22	,, ,,	H	Greece
taurina	Pink Woodruff	22	,, ,,	—	S. Europe
6 species		22	,, ,,		
galioides (glauca)		22, 44	,, ,,	H	Eur., Cauc.
cynanchica	Squinancywort	44	,, ,,	H	Eur., Asia Minor
hexaphylla		44	,, ,,	H	S. Europe
odorata	Sweet Woodruff	44	,, ,,	HMSp	Eur., S.W. Asia
tinctoria	Dyer's W.	44	,, ,,	D	Europe
5 species		44	,, ,,		

PHUOPSIS (CRUCIANELLA) $x=10, 11$

stylosa	Crosswort	{ 20 { 22	Fagerlind 1937 Homeyer 1935	H	Caucasus

RONDELETIA $x=10, 11$

amoena	c. 40	Fagerlind 1937	H	Guatemala
cordata	c. 40	,, ,,	H	,,
erythroneura	c. 40	,, ,,	H	Trop. America

235

RONDELETIA (*cont.*)

latifolia		44	Fagerlind 1937	H	Guatemala
odorata (*speciosa*)		44	,, ,,	H	Cuba

GALIUM * $x = 10, 11, 12$

vaillantii		20	Fagerlind 1937	—	N. Temp.
spurium		{ 20	,, ,,	—	Eur., S.W. Asia
		{ 44	Homeyer 1935		
cruciata	Crosswort	22	Fagerlind 1934, 1937	M	Eur., N. Africa
	& 14 spp.				
tricorne	& 11 spp.	44	,, ,,	—	Medit.
austriacum		22, 44	Ehrendorfer 1949	—	Europe
flavicans		22, 44	Fagerlind 1937	—	Hungary
corrudaefolium (*lucidum*)		22, 44	,, ,,	—	S. Europe
setaceum		22, 44	,, 1934	—	Medit., Temp. As.
uliginosum		44	,, 1937	—	Eur., N. Asia
verum	Lady's	22, 44, (66)	,, ,,	BM	North Temp.
	Bedstraw				
mollugo	White	22, 44, 55, 66	,, ,,	H	Europe
	Bedstraw				
parisiense		22, 44, 66	,, ,,	—	Eur., S.W. Asia
aparine	Cleavers	{ 22, 44	Poucques 1949a	M	North Temp.
		{ *c.* 66, *c.* 88	Fagerlind 1934		
anisophyllum		44, 66	Ehrendorfer 1949	—	Europe
boreale		44	Löve & L. 1954	H	N. Eurasia
septentrionale (*boreale*)		66	,, ,,	H	N: N. Amer., N. Asia
pumilum		{ 44	Fagerlind 1937	—	Europe
		{ 88	Ehrendorfer 1949		
aristatum (*laevigatum*)		44, 66, 88	Fagerlind 1937	—	,,
helveticum	& 2 spp.	66	,, ,,	—	,,
rubioides		{ 66	Homeyer 1935	—	Eur., N. Asia
		{ *c.* 132	Fagerlind 1934		
trifidum		24	,, 1937	—	North Temp.
palustre		24, 48, 96	Hancock 1942	—	Eur., N. Asia

CALLIPELTIS $x = 11$

cucullaria		22	Fagerlind 1934	—	Caucasus

CHOMELIA $x = 11$

asiatica		22	Raghavan & R. 1941	—	India

EXOSTEMMA $x = 11$

subcordata		22	Fagerlind 1937	—	W. Indies

GARDENIA $x = 11$

jasminoides	Cape Jasmine	22	Fagerlind 1937	HP	China, Japan
intermedia		22	,, ,,	H	*cult*
spatulifolia		22	,, ,,	—	Trop. Africa
thunbergia		22	,, ,,	H	S. Africa

MACROSPHYRA $x = 11$

longistyla, as *G. longistella*		22	Raghavan & R. 1941	—	Trop. Afr.

HYMENODICTYON $x=11$				
excelsum		22	Fagerlind 1937 —	Ind., Malaya
IXORA * $x=11$				
chinensis	& 14 spp.	22	Fagerlind 1937 H	S.E. Asia
finlaysoniana		22	Raghavan & R. 1941 —	Siam
LEPTACTINIA $x=11$				
mannii		22	Fagerlind 1937 —	Trop. Africa
MERICARPAEA $x=11$				
vaillantoides		22	Fagerlind 1937 —	W. Asia
MITCHELLA $x=11$				
repens	Partridge Berry	22	Atchison 1947a HM	N. Amer., Japan
MITRIOSTIGMA $x=11$				
axillare		22	Snoad 1952 H	S. Africa
MORINDA $x=11$				
tinctoria		22	Raghavan & R. 1941 D	India, Malaya
OPHIORRHIZA $x=11$				
brunonis		22	Raghavan & R. 1941 —	India
PHYLLIS $x=11$				
nobla		22	Fagerlind 1934 —	Canaries, Madeira
PORTLANDIA $x=11$				
grandiflora		c. 22	Fagerlind 1937 H	W. Indies
PUTORIA $x=11$				
calabrica		22	Fagerlind 1937 H	Medit.
RANDIA $x=11$				
dumetorum		22	Fagerlind 1937 D	Trop. Asia
longiflora		22	,, ,, —	Ind., Malaya
maculata		22	,, ,, —	Trop. Africa
SERISSA $x=11$				
foetida (japonica)		22	Fagerlind 1937 —	China, Japan
SHERARDIA $x=11$				
arvensis	Field Madder	22	Fagerlind 1937 —	Eur., T. Asia
WARBURGINA $x=11$				
factorovskyi		22	Fagerlind 1937 —	Palest., Syria
CEPHAELIS (URAGOGA) $x=11$				
peduncularis		22	Fagerlind 1937 H	Sierra Leone
ipecacuanha	Ipecacuanha	{ 22 / 44	,, ,, / E.K.J.* M	Brazil
COFFEA $x = 11$				
bengalensis		22	Fagerlind 1937 —	Ind., Malaya
canephora	Quillow Coffee	22	Doughty 1939 B	Trop. Africa
dewevrei		22	Krug 1937 —	,,

17　　　　　　237

COFFEA (cont.)

dybowskii		22	Krug 1937	—	Trop. Africa
eugenoides	E. African C.	22	Doughty 1939	B	E. Africa
excelsa	Senoussi C.	22	Heyn 1936	B	W. Africa
robusta	Congo C.	22	,, ,,	B	Trop. Africa
semiexserta		22	Homeyer 1935	—	E. Indies
stenophylla	Sierra Leone C.	22	Fagerlind 1937	B	Abyssinia
ugandae		22	Krug 1936	—	Trop. Africa
abeokutae		{ 22	Heyn 1936	B	,,
		44	Fagerlind 1937		
congensis		{ 22	Krug 1934	B	Congo
		44	Fagerlind 1937		
liberica	Liberian C.	{ 22	,, ,,	B	Trop. Africa
		44	Heyn 1936		
arabica	Mocha C.	44	Mendes 1945	B	,,
v. nacional etc.		44	Krug 1936		
v. bullata		44, 66, 88	,, 1936, 1937		

COPROSMA x = 11

baueri		{ 22	Poucques 1949a	H	New Zealand
		44	Fagerlind 1937		
robusta		{ 22	Poucques 1949a	H	,,
		44	Fagerlind 1937		
acerosa		44	,, ,,	H	,,
cunninghamii		44	,, ,,	H	,,
lucida		44	,, ,,	H	,,

CRUCIANELLA * x = 11

angustifolia		22	Poucques 1949a	H	C. Eur., Medit.
glauca	& 9 spp.	22	Fagerlind 1937	H	Persia
latifolia		{ 22	Poucques 1949a	H	Medit.
		44	Fagerlind 1937		

LEPTODERMIS x = 11

lanceolata		{ 22	Poucques 1949a	—	Himalayas
		c. 66	Fagerlind 1937		
pilosa		44	,, ,,	—	China

MUSSAENDA * x = 11

corymbosa		22	Raghavan & R. 1941	—	India
erythrophylla	& 3 spp.	22	Fagerlind 1937	H	Trop. Africa
stenocarpa		c. 70	,, ,,	—	,,

PAVETTA * x = 11

indica	& 2 spp.	22	Fagerlind 1937	MMa	Tr. Asia & Aust.
gardeniifolia		44	,, ,,	—	Abyssinia

PSYCHOTRIA x = 11

bacteriophila	C. Is. Wild Coffee	22	Fagerlind 1937	Ma	Comoro Is.
brasiliensis		22	,, ,,	—	Brazil
emetica		22	,, ,,	M	Peru
hirtella		22	,, ,,	—	Tr. E. Africa
undulata	Seminole Wild C.	22	,, ,,	Ma	W. Indies
africana		44	,, ,,	—	Africa

RUBIA x = 11

cordifolia	Indian M.	22	Homeyer 1935	D	Tr. Asia and Afr.

238

RUBIA (*cont.*)

tinctorum	Madder	{ 22, 44 44	Poucques 1949a Fagerlind 1937	D	S.E. Eur., S.W. Asia
oliverii		44	,, 1934	—	E. Europe
cordata		44	,, 1937	D	Tr. Asia & Amer.
peregrina	Levant M.	{ 66 *c.* 132	Poucques 1949a Fagerlind 1937	D	Eur., Medit.

CEPHALANTHUS $x = 11$
occidentalis	Button Bush	44	Fagerlind 1937	H	N. America

GUETTARDA $x = (11), 22$
speciosa	44	Raghavan & R. 1941		Trop. Asia

LUCULIA $x = 11$
pinceana	44	Fagerlind 1937	—	Himalaya

MYRMECODIA $x = (11), 22$
platyrea	44	Homeyer 1935	—	S.E. Asia
echinata	{ 44 88	Fagerlind 1937 Homeyer 1935	—	,,

NERTERA $x = 11$
depressa	Bead Plant	44	Fagerlind 1937	H	S. Am., N.Z., Tas.

HYDNOPHYTUM $x = (11), 22$
formicarum	44	Fagerlind 1937	—	E. Indies

PLECTRONIA $x = (11), 22$
parviflora	44	Raghavan & R. 1941	—	Burma, Malaya

SARCOCEPHALUS $x = (11), 22$
diderrichii		44	Fagerlind 1937	—	Trop. Africa
esculentus	Negro Peach	44	,, ,,	DFM	,,

VANGUERIA $x = (11), 22$
edulis	Voa Vanga	44	Fagerlind 1937	F	Trop. Africa
acutiloba		44	,, ,,	F	E. Africa

CATESBAEA $x = 12$
latifolia	24	Fagerlind 1937	—	W. Indies

HAMELIA $x = 12$
patens (erecta)	24	Fagerlind 1937	H	Trop. Amer.

HOFFMANNIA $x = 12$
discolor	48	Fagerlind 1937	H	Mexico
ghiesbreghtii	48	,, ,,	H	,,
refulgens	48	,, ,,	H	,,
roezlii	48	,, ,,	H	*cult*
regalis	48	Homeyer 1935	H	Mexico

RICHARDIA (RICHARDSONIA) $x = 14$
pilosa		28	Fagerlind 1937		Trop. America
scabra	Mex. Clover	28	,, ,,	H	,,

239

SPERMACOCE x = 14

tenuior		28	Fagerlind 1937 —	Trop. America
hispida		56	Raghavan & A. R. S. — 1941	O.W. Tropics
stricta		56	Raghavan & R. 1941 —	„ „

CINCHONA x = 17

calisaya	Yellow C.	34, (68)	Dawson 1948	M	Bolivia
ledgeriana		34, (68)	„ „	M	„
succirubra	Red C.	34, (68)	„ „	M	Ecuador

POSOQUERIA x = 17

cookii		34	Fagerlind 1937	H	*cult*
longiflora		34	„ „	H	Guiana

233 CAPRIFOLIACEAE

KOLKWITZIA x = (8), 16

amabilis		32	Sax & K. 1930	H	C. China

LINNAEA x = (8), 16

americana		32	L. & L. 1944b	H	Eur., N. Amer.
borealis		32	Ehrenberg 1945	H	„ „

VIBURNUM x = 8, 9, 10
x = 8

bitchiuense		16	Janaki Ammal 1953a	H	W. Japan
foetens		16	„ „	H	N.W. Himal., Kashmir
foetidum		16	„ „	H	W. China
grandiflorum		16	„ „	H	Himal., Bhutan
mongolicum		16	„ „	—	E. Sib., Kansu
suspensum		⎰16	„ „	H	Liukiu Is.
as *sandankwa*		⎱18	Poucques 1949a		
wrightii		16	Janaki Ammal 1953a	H	Japan
fragrans		16	„ „	H	Kansu
v. *alba*		32	„ „	H	„ *cult*
erubescens		48	„ „	H	Szechuan, Hupeh, Nilgris, Himal.
henryi		48	„ „	H	Hupeh, Szech., Yunnan

x = 9

acerifolium	Dockmackie	18	„ „	H	N. America
alnifolium	Hobble Bush	18	„ „	H	„
betulifolium		18	„ „	H	C. & W. China
cinnamomifolium		18	„ „	H	W. China
cotinifolium		18	Poucques 1949a	H	Himalayas
davidi		18	Janaki Ammal 1953a	H	W. China
furcatum		18	„ „	H	Japan
harryanum		18	Poucques 1949a	H	W. China
lantana	Wayfaring Tree	18	Janaki Ammal 1953a	H	Eur., W. Asia
lentago	Nannyberry	18	„ „	FH	W: N. Amer.
nudum		18	„ „	H	„ „
opulus	Guelder Rose	18	„ „	HM	Eur., N. Asia, N. Africa
ovalifolium		18	„ „	—	W. China

240

VIBURNUM (cont.)

propinquum		18	Poucques 1949a	H	C. & W. China
prunifolium	Black Haw	18	Janaki Ammal 1953a	FHM	W: N. America
rhytidophyllum		18	,, ,,	H	C. & W. China
sargentii		18	Sax & K. 1930	H	N.E. Asia
tomentosum		18	Janaki Ammal 1953a	H	China, Japan
trilobum	Am. Cranberry Bush	18	,, ,,	F	N. America
utile		18	,, ,,	H	C. China
carlesii		{ 18	Poucques 1949a,	H	Korea
		{ 20	Janaki Ammal 1953a		
lobophyllum		{ 18	Sax & K. 1930	H	C. & W. China
		{ 20, 22	Janaki Ammal 1953a		
tinus	Laurustinus	36	,, ,,	H	S.E. Europe
dentatum		54	,, ,,	H	N. America
x = 10					
buddleifolium		20	,, ,,	H	C. China
odoratissimum	Sweet V.	40	,, ,,	H	India, China

ABELIA   x = (8), 16, 18

engleriana	32	Sax & K. 1930	H	C. & W. China
uniflora	36	Poucques 1949a	H	E. China

DIERVILLA   x = 9

lonicera	18	Poucques 1949a	H	E: N. America
rivularis	36	Sax & K. 1930	H	S.E: U.S.A.
sessilifolia	36	,, ,,	H	,,
splendens	36	Poucques 1949a	H	cult

WEIGELA (DIERVILLA)   x = 9

japonica	18	Poucques 1949a	H	Japan
florida (candida)	36	,, ,,	H	N. China
hortensis	36	Sax & K. 1930	H	Japan
praecox	36	,, ,,	H	Korea

LONICERA   x = 9

altmanni	18	Jan. Ammal & S. '52	—	Turkestan
bella	18	Poucques 1949a	H	cult
biflora	18	Jan. Ammal & S. '52	—	S.W. Eur., N. Afr.
canadensis (ciliata)	18	,, ,,	(F)H	E: N. America
caprifolium	18	Poucques 1949a	H	Eur., W. Asia
chaetocarpa	18	Jan. Ammal & S. '52	H	W. China
chrysantha	18	,, ,,	H	N.E. Asia, Japan
deflexicalyx	18	,, ,,	H	W. China, Tibet
discolor	18	,, ,,	—	Kashmir–Afghan.
etrusca	18	,, ,,	H	Medit.
ferdinandii	18	Poucques 1949a	H	N. China
fragrantissima	18	,, ,,	H	E. China
hildebrandtii	18	Jan. Ammal & S. '52	H	Burma
hispida	18	Poucques 1949a	H	Turkestan—W. China
implexa	18	Jan. Ammal & S. '52	H	Medit.
involucrata	18	,, ,,	(F)H	Can., Rocky Mts.
japonica	18	,, ,,	H	E. Asia
koehneana	18	,, ,,	—	W. China
korolkowii	18	,, ,,	H	Turkestan
ledebourii	18	,, ,,	H	California
maackii	18	Poucques 1949a	H	Manch., Korea

LONICERA (*cont.*)

maximowiczii		18	Jan. Ammal & S. '52	H	Manch., Korea
minutiflora		18	Poucques 1949a	H	*cult*
morrowii		18	Jan. Ammal & S. '52	H	Japan
myrtilloides		18	Poucques 1949a	H	Himalayas
nervosa		18	Jan. Ammal & S. '52	H	N.W. China
nigra		18	Poucques 1949a	H	Eur., Korea
nitida		18	,, ,,	H	W. China
orientalis	Buckthorn H.	18	Sax & K. 1930	H	Asia M., Cauc.
pileata		18	Poucques 1949a	H	S. & W. China
prolifera		18	Jan. Ammal & S. '52	H	U.S.A.
pyrenaica		18	Poucques 1949a	H	Pyrenees
quinquelocularis		18	,, ,,	H	Himalayas
rupicola		18	Jan. Ammal & S. '52	H	,,
ruprechtiana		18	Poucques 1949a	H	Manch., N. China
splendida		18	Jan. Ammal & S. '52	H	Spain
stabiana		18	Vilmorin & S. 1927b	—	Italy
standishii (*sinensis*)		18	Poucques 1949a	H	China
syringantha		18	Jan. Ammal & S. '52	H	N.W. China
tatarica	Tartarian H.	18	,, ,,	H	S. Russ., Alt., Turkestan
tatsienensis		18	Poucques 1949a	H	W. China
tomentella		18	Jan. Ammal & S. '52	H	Sikkim
trichosantha		18	,, ,,	H	W. China, Tibet
vesicaria		18	,, ,,	—	Korea
xylosteum	Eur. Fly Honey-suckle	18	Poucques 1949a	H	Eur.—Altai
yunnanensis		18	Jan. Ammal & S. '52	H	S.W. China
alpigena		{ 18 36	Poucques 1949a Jan. Ammal & S. '52	H	C. Europe
coerulea		18, 36	Sax & K. 1930	H	N. Eurasia
glehnii		{ 18 36	Poucques 1949a Jan. Ammal & S. '52	—	Japan, Sakhalin
myrtillus		18	,, ,,	H	Afghan., Himal.
v. *depressa*		36	,, ,,	H	Alpine Himal.
periclymenum	Woodbine	18, 36	,, ,,	H	Eur., Medit.
sempervirens	Trumpet H.	{ 18 36	Poucques 1949a Jan. Ammal & S. '52	H	E. & C. U.S.A.
tenuipes		{ 18 36	,, ,, M. & S. 1935	H	Japan
thibetica		18, 36	Sax & K. 1930	H	Tibet, W. Szech.
alseuosmoides		36	,, ,,	H	W. China
microphylla		36	Jan. Ammal & S. '52	H	C. Asia
henryi		54	,, ,,	H	Assam, S.W. Ch.
v. *coriacea*		54	,, ,,	H	W. Szechuan
tragophylla		54	,, ,,	H	S.W. China

SYMPHORICARPOS *x* = 9

orbiculatus	Indian Currant	18	Sax & K. 1930	(F)H	E: N. America
albus	Snowberry	*c.* 54	,, ,,	(F)H	N. America

SAMBUCUS *x* = (9), 18, 19

ebulus	Dwarf Elder	{ 32 36	Battaglia 1946 Poucques 1949a	H	Eur., N. Afr., Asia
canadensis	Sweet Elder	36	Sax & K. 1930	A(F)M	E: N. America

SAMBUCUS (*cont.*)

chinensis		36	Suzuka 1950a	—	Trop. Asia
javanica		36	Bowden 1940a	—	,,
nigra	European El.	36	Poucques 1949a	AB(F)	Eur., N. Afr., W. Asia
pubens	Red-berried E.	36	Bowden 1940a	H	E: N. America
racemosa	Eur. Red E.	36	Sax & K. 1930	AB(F)	Eur., W. Asia
buergeriana		38	M. & S. 1935	—	Japan

234 ADOXACEAE

ADOXA *x* = 9

moschatellina	Moschatel	⎧ 36 ⎨ 36 ⎩ 54 ⎩ 56	Geitler 1940, Poucques 1949a Oikawa 1942 M. & S. 1935	H	North Reg.

235 VALERIANACEAE

KENTRANTHUS (CENTRANTHUS) *x* = 7

angustifolius		14	Poucques 1949a	H	S. Europe
gilloti		14	,, ,,	—	France
ruber	Red Valerian	14	,, ,,	H	Eur., S.W. Asia

VALERIANA *x* = 7, 8
x = 7

baltica		14	Runquist 1937	—	Scandinavia
exaltata		14, 18	Skalinska 1950b	—	Europe
officinalis	Valerian, All-heal	⎰ 14 ⎱ 28, 56	Poucques 1949a Skalinska 1946	HM	Eur., N. Asia
tenuifolia		28	,, 1950b	—	C. Europe
wallichii		28	Kishore 1951	M	India
capitata		56	S. & S. 1941	—	Arctic, Alp.
sambucifolia		56	Skalinska 1950b	H	Europe
as *excelsa*		14, 56	Runquist 1937		
salina		56	,, ,,	—	Scandinavia

x = 8

dioica	Marsh V.	16	Meurman 1925	—	Europe
flaccidissima		16	M. & S. 1935	—	Japan
simplicifolia		16	Skalinska 1950a	—	Europe
tripteris		16	,, ,,	—	,,

VALERIANELLA * *x* = 7, 8, 9

dentata		14	Elvers 1932b	—	Eur., W. As., N. Africa
eriocarpa	Ital. Corn Salad	14	Poucques 1949a	V	Medit., N. Africa
locusta	Lamb's Lettuce	14	,, ,,	V	Eur., W. As., N. Africa
rimosa	& 4 spp.	14	Elvers 1932b	—	Eur., N. Africa
echinata	Prickly Corn Salad	⎰ 14 ⎱ 16	Poucques 1949a Elvers 1932b	H	S. Eur., Asia M.
diodon		32	,, ,,	—	Asia Minor
stenaphodon		32	,, ,,	—	Algeria
szovitziana		c. 32	,, ,,	—	Ar., Syr., Persia
uncinata		16	,, ,,	—	Cauc., Persia

VALERIANELLA (*cont.*)

carinata	18	Elvers 1932b	—	Eur., S.W. Asia
turgida	18	„ „	—	Medit.

FEDIA (MITROPHORA) $x = (8), 16$

cornucopiae	Afr. V.	32	Poucques 1949a	V	Medit.

PATRINIA $x = 11$

scabiosaefolia	22	Sugiura 1936b	—	N. China

236 DIPSACACEAE

CEPHALARIA $x = 5, 9$

syriaca	10	Kachidze 1929	HO	Medit., S.W. Asia
ambrosioides	18	„ „	—	Greece
caucasica	18	„ „	—	Caucasus
graeca	18	„ „	—	Greece
leucantha	18	„ „	H	S.W. Europe
media	18	„ „	—	Transcaucasia
rigida	18	„ „	H	S. Africa
transsylvanica	18, 36	Poucques 1949a	H	S.E. Eur., S.W. Asia
uralensis (corniculata)	18	Kachidze 1929	—	Banat
as laevigata	36	„ „		
alpina	Yellow C.	36	„ „	H	Europe
tatarica	36	„ „	H	N. & W. As., Russ.
tchihatchewi	36	„ „	H	Armenia

CALLISTEMMA $x = 7$

brachiatum	14	Kachidze 1929	H	E. Medit.

DIPSACUS $x = 8, 9$

laciniatus	{ 16	Poucques 1949a	H	Eur., S.W. Asia
	18	Kachidze 1929		
sylvestris Wild T.	{ 16	Poucques 1949a	H	Eur., S.W. Asia, N. Africa
	18	Kachidze 1929		
azureus	18	„ „	H	Siberia
ferox	18	„ „	—	Corsica
fullonum Fuller's Teasel	18	„ „	HTo	Eur., Cauc.
as sativus	18	„ „		
inermis Spineless T.	18	„ „	H	Himalayas
japonicus	18	Suzuka 1950	—	China, Japan
pilosus	18	Kachidze 1929	H	Eur., Cauc.
torsus?	18	„ „	—	
chinensis China T.	36	„ „	H	China

SCABIOSA * $x = 8, 9$
$x = 8$

atropurpurea Sweet Scabious	16	Braun, T. 1937	H	Medit., Canaries
caerulea	16	Risse 1928	—	E. Europe
canescens	16	L. & L. 1944b	H	Cent. Europe
columbaria Small S. & 7 spp.	16	Kachidze 1929	H	Old World
daucoides	16	Risse 1928	—	Algeria
lucida	16	Poucques 1949a	H	Cent. Europe
purpurea	16	Poddubnaja 1933b	—	Caucasus
suaveolens	16	Poucques 1949a	H	C. Eur., Asia M.

SCABIOSA (*cont.*)
$x = 9$

cretica	& 5 spp.	18	Kachidze 1929	—	Crete, Sicily
prolifera	Carmel Daisy	18	,, ,,	H	Syr.-Cyp.
stellata		36	,, ,,	—	W. Medit.
caucasica		36, 54	,, ,,	H	Cauc., C. Asia

KNAUTIA (SCABIOSA) $x = 8, 10$
$x = 8$

magnifica		16	Chiarugi 1927b	—	Macedonia
orientalis		{ 16	Kachidze 1929,	—	S.W. Asia
		{ 16	Poucques 1949a		
sylvatica		16	Risse 1928	H	Caucasus
v. *dipsacifolia*		48	Chiarugi 1927c		
		⌐16?	Poucques 1949a		
arvensis	Field S.	{ 20	Wulff 1938	H	Eur., Caucasus
		{ 40	Kachidze 1929,		
		⌊40	L. & L. 1944b		

$x = 10$

hybrida (*integrifolia*)		20	Kachidze 1929	H	Gr., Asia M.
purpurea		20	,, ,,	—	Caucasus

SUCCISA (SCABIOSA) $x = 8, 10$

inflexa		16	Poucques 1949a	—	Europe
australis		20	Kachidze 1929	H	S. Europe
pratensis	Devil's Bit Sc.	20	,, ,,	H	Europe

PTEROCEPHALUS (SCABIOSA) $x = 9$

parnassi (*S. pterocephala*)		18	Kachidze 1929	H	Greece
plumosus		18	,, ,,	—	Asia Minor

MORINA $x = 17$

longifolia	Whorl Fl.	{ 34	Kachidze 1929	H	Himalayas
		{ 34	Poucques 1949a		
persica		34	Kachidze 1929	—	Himal., S.W. As.

238 COMPOSITAE

Order of the Tribes with their Basic Numbers

I	Cichorieae: 3–9	VIII	Arctotideae: 5, 7, 8, 9
II	Heliantheae: 4–19	IX	Calenduleae: 7, 8, 9, 10
III	Astereae: 4, 5, 6, 9	X	Anthemideae: 8, 9, 10, 17
IV	Inuleae: 5, 7, 8, 9, 10, 11 13	XI	Vernonieae: 9, 11
V	Cynareae: 6–18	XII	Eupatorieae: 10, 17, 19
VI	Senecioneae: 5, 9, 11, 12, 23, 26, 29	XIII	Mutisieae: 18, 23, 24, 25, 27
VII	Helenieae: 7–17		

TRIBE I: CICHORIEAE

CREPIS (115 species counted) *
A. RHIZOMATOUS $x = 4, 5, 6, 8$

chrysantha	& 5 spp.	8	Babcock 1947	—	C. & N.E. Asia
aurea	& 2 spp.	10	,, ,,	—	C. & E. Europe
pygmaea	& 13 spp.	12	,, ,,	—	Eur. Alps
polytricha		16	,, ,,	—	C. Asia

CREPIS (*cont.*)

B. PRIMITIVE TAP-ROOTED $x = 4, 5, 7, 8,$ $x_2 = 11$ (High Polyploids Apomictic)

tectorum	& 17 spp.	8	Babcock 1947	—	Eur., Temp. Asia
albida	& 10 spp.	10	,, ,, , '51	—	S. Eur., N. Afr.
flexuosa	& 2 spp.	14	,, ,,	—	C. Asia
crocea	& 1 sp.	16	,, ,,	—	C. & E. Asia
runcinata		22	,, ,,	—	W: N. Amer.
bakeri		22–55	,, ,,	—	,,
acuminata	& 5 spp.	22–88	,, ,,	—	,,
intermedia		33–88	,, ,,	—	,,
barbigera		44–88	,, ,,	—	,,
biennis		40	,, ,,	—	Eur., W. Asia
ciliata		40	,, ,,	—	S. Caucasus
taygetica		40	,, ,,	—	S. Greece

C. ADVANCED TAP-ROOTED $x = 3, 4, 5$

capillaris		6	Babcock 1947	—	Europe
fuliginosa		6	,, ,,	—	E. Medit.
zacintha		6	,, ,,	—	Medit.
neglecta		8	,, ,,	—	S. Eur., Asia M.
setosa	& 31 spp.	8	,, ,,	—	,, ,,
vesicaria		8, 16	,, ,,	—	Medit.
foetida		10	,, ,,	—	Eur., As. M., Pers.
rubra	& 4 spp.	10	,, ,,	—	S.E. Eur., Asia M.
syriaca		10 + 0–8**B**	,, ,,	—	Syria, Palestine

HYPOCHAERIS (HYPOCHOERIS)* $x = 3, 4, 5$

cretensis		6	Stebbins *et al.* 1953	—	Crete
pinnatifida		6	,, ,,	—	Corsica
aetnensis		12	,, ,,	—	Europe
brasiliensis	& 2 spp.	8	,, ,,	—	Urug., Argent.
elata		8	Krapovickas 1951a	—	S. America
halophila		8	Schnack & C. 1947	—	,,
radicata	Cat's Ear	8	Stebbins *et al.* 1953	—	Eur., N. Africa
tweediei	& 3 spp.	8	Saez 1949a	—	S. America
stenocephala		16	Stebbins *et al.* 1953	—	Andes
maculata	& 2 spp.	10	,, ,,	—	Eur., W. Asia
uniflora		10	Szwabowicz 1954	—	Europe
glabra		{ 10	Stebbins *et al.* 1953	—	,,
		{ 12	Negodi 1935		

ROBERTIA $x = 4$

taraxacoides		8	Martinoli 1953	—	Medit.

HEDYPNOIS (RHAGADIOLUS) $x = 4$

cretica		8	Stebbins *et al.* 1953	—	Medit.
globulifera		16	Negodi 1936b	—	,,
tubaeformis		16	Stebbins *et al.* 1953	—	,,

LEONTODON $x = 4, 5, 6, 7$ (Apomictic)

asperrimus		8	Stebbins *et al.* 1953	—	S. Eur., S.W. Asia
graecum		8	,, ,,	—	Greece
nudicaulis		{ 8	,, ,,	—	Europe
as *Thrincia hirta*		{ 10	Wulff 1937b		
helveticus		12	Favarger 1953	—	S. Eur. mtns.
montanus		12	,, ,,	—	,, ,,
autumnalis		{ 12	Bergman 1935c	—	Europe
		{ 24	L. & L. 1948		
crispus		14	Bergman 1935c	—	S. Europe

246

LEONTODON (cont.)

hispidus	$\left\{\begin{array}{l} 14 \\ 14 + \mathbf{B} \end{array}\right.$	Elliot 1950 Bergman 1935c	—	Eur., S.W. Asia
villarsii	14	Stebbins et al. 1953	—	Europe

GARHADIOLUS $x = 5$

hedypnois	10	Stebbins et al. 1953	—	S.W. Asia

PICRIS $x = 5$

echioides	10	Schnack & C. 1947	H	Medit., N. Afr.
hieracioides	10	Bergman 1932	—	Eur., Temp. Asia

RHAGADIOLUS $x = 5$

edulis	10	Stebbins et al. 1953	—	Medit., Asia M.
stellatus	10	,, ,,	—	Medit.

WILLEMETIA $x = 5$

stipitata	10	Stebbins et al. 1953	—	Alps

CHONDRILLA $x = 5$ (Apomixis) *

ambigua (pauciflora)		10	Poddubnaja 1933a	—	Russia, Siberia
chondrilloides		10	Bergman 1952	—	E. Eur. mtns.
juncea		15	Battaglia 1949	—	Eur., C. Asia
leiosperma	& 5 spp.	15	Poddubnaja 1933a	—	,, ,,
ornata	& 1 sp.	20	,, ,,	—	Russia, C. Asia

KRIGIA $x = 5$

virginica	10	Stebbins et al. 1953	—	E. U.S.A.
dandelion	59	,, ,,	—	,,

IXERIS (LACTUCA, CREPIDIASTRUM)* $x = 5, 6, 7, 8$ (Triploid Apomictic)

denticulata		10	Ono 1943	—	Japan
lanceolata	& 2 spp.	10	Babcock et al. 1937	—	,,
alpicola		14	Ishikawa 1921	—	,,
dentata		$\left\{\begin{array}{l} 21 \\ 24 \end{array}\right.$	Babcock et al. 1937 Ono 1941	—	,,
stolonifera	& 3 spp.	16	Babcock et al. 1937	—	,,
chinensis		32	,, ,,	—	,,
japonica	(3x)	48	Ishikawa 1921	—	,,

YOUNGIA (LACTUCA, CREPIS) * $x = 5, 8$

tenuifolia		15, 20	Babcock et al. 1937	—	Himal., N. Asia
japonica	& 2 spp.	16	,, ,,	—	Japan
paleacea		32	,, ,,	—	Yunnan

LYGODESMIA $x = 6$

rostrata	12	Stebbins et al. 1953	—	W: N. America

PYRRHOPAPPUS $x = 6$

carolinianus	12	Stebbins et al. 1953	—	E. U.S.A.
rothrockii	12	,, ,,	—	,,

LAPSANA $x = 6, 7$

communis	Nipplewort	$\left\{\begin{array}{l} 12 \\ 14 \end{array}\right.$	L. & L. 1948 Stebbins et al. 1953	—	Eur., N. & S.W. Asia

247

SCORZONERA * $x = 6, 7$

deliciosa	Sicilian Sc.	12	Telezynski, T. 1931	R	Sicily
tuberosa	& 2 spp.	12	Poddubnaja *et al.* '35	R	Turkestan
nervosa		12, 13	Krajevoy 1934b	—	Arm., Persia
acanthoclada	& 3 spp.	14	P. *et al.* 1935	—	Turkestan
cana		14	Polya 1948	—	E. Eur., Asia M.
hispanica	Black Salsify	14	P. *et al.* 1935	R	S. Europe
humilis		14	Wulff 1938	—	Europe
tau-saghys	Tau Saghyz	14	Krajevoy 1934a	Ru	N. Asia

TRAGOPOGON* $x = 6, 7$

dubius (*major*)	& 1 sp.	12	P. *et al.* 1935	R	Europe
porrifolius	Salsify	12	„ „	R	Medit.
pratensis	Goat's Beard	12	Winge 1926	HR	Eur., Cauc.—Sib.
cupani		24	P. *et al.* 1935	R	Sicily
mirus		24	Ownbey 1950	—	N.W: U.S.A.
miscellus		24	„ „	—	„
crocifolius		14	R. D. Brock unp.	H	Italy

ANISOCOMA $x = 7$

acaulis		14	Stebbins *et al.* 1953	—	Calif., Nevada

CALYCOSERIS $x = 7$

wrightii		14	Stebbins *et al.* 1953	—	S.W: U.S.A.

LAUNAEA $x = 7, 8, 9$

arborescens		14	Stebbins *et al.* 1953	—	N.W. Africa
integrifolia		16	Hagerup 1932	—	Sudan
pumila		16	Lorenzo-Andreu & G. 1950	—	Spain, Arabia
quercifolia		16	Stebbins *et al.* 1953	—	N. Africa
resedifolia		16	„ „	—	Algeria
acaulis		18	„ „	—	India
nudicaulis		18	„ „	—	Medit., S.W. Asia

MALACOTHRIX * $x = 7, 9$

californica	& 5 spp.	14	Stebbins *et al.* 1953	—	W: U.S.A.
clevelandii		14, 28	„ „	—	„
saxatilis		18	„ „	—	„

SONCHUS * $x = 7, 8, 9$

$x = 7$

tenerrimus		14	Stebbins *et al.* 1953	—	Medit.

$x = 8$

oleraceus	Sow or Milk Thistle	32	„ „	Fo(V)	Cosmop.
arvensis		64	Wulff 1937b	—	Eur., W. Asia

$x = 9$

asper	& 7 spp.	18	Stebbins *et al.* 1953	—	Cosmop.
grandifolius		36	„ „	—	New Zealand
javanicus		54	„ „	—	Java
oleraceus × *asper* (16 + 9)		25	Barber 1941b		*nat. hybrid*

APOSERIS $x = 8$
foetida   16   Stebbins *et al.* 1953   —   Alps

DUBYAEA (LACTUCA) * $x = 8$
hispida   & 1 sp.   16   Babcock *et al.* 1937   —   Asia M., Syria

HYOSERIS * $x = 8$
radiata   16   Stebbins *et al.* 1953   —   Medit.
lucida   & 2 spp.   16   Martinoli 1953   —   „

RAFINESQUIA * $x = 8$
californica   & 1 sp.   16   Stebbins *et al.* 1953   —   California

REICHARDIA (PICRIDIUM) $x = 8$
tingitana   16   Telezinsky, T. 1931   D?   Medit., S.W. Asia

STEPHANOMERIA * $x = 8$
cichoriacea   & 3 spp.   16   Stebbins *et al.* 1953   —   W: U.S.A.
virgata   16, 32   „   „   —   „

TARAXACUM * $x = 8$ (Polyploids Apomictic)
bessarabicum & 4 spp.   16   Poddubnaja & D. '34   V   Eur., N. Asia
kok-saghyz Kok-Saghyz   16 (32)   Navashin & G. 1941   Ru   Turkestan
laevigatum   Smooth D.   24   Poddubnaja & D. '34   (V)M   N. & S. Temp.
parnassicum   24   „   „   Ru   Greece
robustum   24   „   „   Ru   Japan
vulgare   Dandelion   16, 24, 48   Woess 1949   M(V)   N. & S. Temp.
         (22-26, 33, 46-48)   Sorensen & G. 1946
hybernum (*gymnanthum*)   32   Poddubnaja & D. '37   Ru   Medit.
megalorrhizon Krim-Saghyz   32   Battaglia 1948   Ru   Crimea

other apomicts   24, 32, 40, 48 $\left\{\begin{array}{l}\text{Battaglia 1948,}\\ \text{Erlandsson 1939b,}\\ \text{Gustafsson '32, '35a, b,}\\ \text{Poddubnaja & D. '37}\end{array}\right.$

PRENANTHES (CREPIS) * $x = 8, 9$
nana   & 5 spp.   16   Babcock *et al.* 1937   —   N. America
alba   32   „   „   —   „
purpurea   & 1 sp.   18   „   „   —   Europe

LACTUCA (MULGEDIUM) * $x = 8, 9$ (Old World). $x_2 = 17$ (New World)
$x = 8$
aurea   16   Babcock *et al.* 1937   —   Europe
bracteata   & 8 spp.   16   „   „   —   Himalayas
bourgaei   Bourget   16   Whitaker & J. 1939   —   Asia Minor
macrantha   & 5 spp.   16   Stebbins *et al.* 1953   —   India
$x = 9$
chondrillaeflora   18   Whitaker & J. 1939   —   S. Europe
perennis   Perennial L.   18   Thompson *et al.* '41   —   Europe
raddiana   18   „   „   —   Japan
saligna   & 3 spp.   18   „   „   —   Europe
sativa   Lettuce $\left\{\begin{array}{l}18\\ (36 + \mathbf{B})\end{array}\right.$ „   „   V   *cult*
                      Einset 1944
serriola   Prickly L.   18   Thompson *et al.* '41   V   Europe
squarrosa   18   Ono 1943   —   Japan
tatarica   18   Whitaker & J. 1939   —   India, W. Asia
viminea   18   Babcock *et al.* 1937   —   Turkey

LACTUCA (*cont.*)
virosa	Wild L.	18	Thompson *et al.* '41	M	Europe
orientalis		36	Babcock *et al.* 1937	—	Himalayas

$x_2 = 17$
campestris		34	Babcock *et al.* 1937	—	E: N. America
canadensis		34	Whitaker & J. 1939	—	,, ,,
ludoviciana		34	Stebbins *et al.* 1953	—	,, ,,
spicata	& 3 spp.	34	Thompson *et al.* '41	—	,, ,,

MYCELIS (LACTUCA) $x = 9$
muralis	Wall Lettuce	18	Thompson *et al.* '41	—	Eur., Asia M., Caucasus

CEPHALORRHYNCHUS (LACTUCA) $x = 9$
glandulosus	18	Babcock *et al.* 1937	—	Asia Minor

APARGIDIUM $x = 9$
boreale	18	Stebbins *et al.* 1953	—	N. America

ANDRYALA * $x = 9$
integrifolia	& 2 spp.	18	Stebbins *et al.* 1953	—	Medit.

ARNOSERIS $x = 9$
maxima		18	Wulff 1939b	—	Europe
minima (*pusilla*)	Lamb's Succory	18	Stebbins *et al.* 1953	—	,,

ATRICHOSERIS $x = 9$
platyphylla	18	Stebbins *et al.* 1953	—	S.W: U.S.A.

CATANANCHE $x = 9$
lutea	18	Stebbins *et al.* 1953	—	Medit.

CHAETADELPHA $x = 9$
wheeleri	18	Stebbins *et al.* 1953	—	W: U.S.A.

CICERBITA (LACTUCA, SONCHUS) $x = 9$
alpina	18	Stebbins *et al.* 1953	—	Arctic, Alpine

CICHORIUM $x = 9$
intybus	Chicory	18	Stebbins *et al.* 1953	BV	Eur., S.W. Asia, N. Africa
endivia	Endive	{ 18 / 36	Rick 1953 / Thomas 1945*	V	Eur., S.W. Asia

GLYPTOPLEURA $x = 9$
marginata	18	Stebbins *et al.* 1953	—	S.W.: U.S.A.

PHALACROSERIS $x = 9$
bolanderi	18	Stebbins *et al.* 1953	—	N. America

TOLPIS * $x = 9$
succulenta	& 3 spp.	18	Stebbins *et al.* 1953	—	Canary Is.

HIERACIUM * $x = 7?, 9$
japonicum	14	M. & S. 1935	—	Japan
sexual species	18	Bergman 1941, Böcher & L. 1950	—	N. Temp.

HIERACIUM (*cont.*)

apomicts	27, 36, 45	⎧Christoff & C. 1948, ⎪Favarger 1949b, 1953, ⎨Gentcheff & G. 1940b, ⎪Gustafsson 1935, 1947, ⎩Stebbins *et al.* 1953	—	N. Temp.

AGOSERIS* $x = 9$

grandiflora	& 1 sp.	18	Stebbins *et al.* 1953	—	W: N. America
glauca		18, 36	,,	,,	—	,,
heterophylla		18, 36	,,	,,	—	,,
apargioides		36	,,	,,	—	,,

MICROSERIS * $x = 9$

laciniata	& 7 spp.	18	Stebbins *et al.* 1953	—	W: N. America
acuminata		36	,,	,,	—	,,
lindleyi		36	,,	,,	—	,,

PINAROPAPPUS $x = 9$

roseus	18, 36	Stebbins *et al.* 1953	—	Tex., Mex.

DENDROSERIS $x = 9$

macrophylla	36	Stebbins *et al.* 1953	—	Juan Fernandez
pinnata	36	,,	,,	—	,, ,,

KOELPINIA $x = 9$

linearis	54	Stebbins *et al.* 1953	—	S.W. As., N. Afr.

SCOLYMUS $x = 10$

hispanicus	Span. Oyster Pl.	20	Stebbins *et al.* 1953	R	Medit.
maculatus		20	,,	,,	—	,,

TRIBE II: HELIANTHEAE

HOLOCARPHA $x = 4, 6$

macradenia	8	J. Clausen 1951	—	California
virgata	8	,,	,,	—	,,
heermannii	12	,,	,,	—	,,
obconica	12	,,	,,	—	,,

CALYCADENIA (HEMIZONIA) $x = 4, 6, 7$

spicata	8	J. Clausen *et al.* '34	—	California
villosa	12, 14	,,	,,	—	,,

MADIA $x = 6, 7, 8, 9$
$x = 6$

bolanderi	12	J. Clausen 1951	—	California

$x = 7$

madioides	14	,,	,,	—	,,
glomerata	28	,,	,,	H	,,

$x = 8$

citriodora	16	,,	,,	—	,,
elegans Tidy Tips	16	,,	,,	H	,,
radiata	16	,,	,,	—	,,
rammii	16	,,	,,	—	,,
subspicata	16	,,	,,	—	,,
wheeleri	16	,,	,,	—	,,
yosemitana	16	,,	,,	—	,,
capitata	32	,,	,,	—	W: N. & S. Amer.

MADIA (*cont.*)

chilensis	32	J. Clausen 1951	—	Chile
exigua	32	,, ,,	—	California
gracilis	32, 48	,, ,,	—	,,
minima	32	,, ,,	—	,,
sativa	32	,, ,,	HO	,,
x = 9				
hallii	18	,, ,,	—	,,
nutans	18	,, ,,	—	,,
citrigracilis	48	,, ,,	—	,,
(*gracilis* × *citriodora*)				

LAYIA *x* = 7, 8

x = 7

chrysanthemoides	14	J. Clausen 1951	H	California
fremontii	14	,, ,,	—	,,
jonesii	14	,, ,,	—	,,
leucopappa	14	,, ,,	—	,,
munzii	14	,, ,,	—	,,
platyglossa	14	,, ,,	H	,,
x = 8				
carnosa	16	,, ,,	—	,,
gaillardioides	16	,, ,,	—	,,
glandulosa	16	,, ,,	H	W: N. America
heterotricha	16	,, ,,	—	California
hieracioides	16	,, ,,	—	,,
pentachaeta	16	,, ,,	—	,,
septentrionalis	16	,, ,,	—	,,
paniculata	32	,, ,,	—	,,

HOLOZONIA (LAGOPHYLLA) *x* = 7

filipes	14	Johansen 1933b	—	California

LAGOPHYLLA *x* = 7

ramosissima & 2 spp,	14	Johansen 1933b	—	W: N. America

HEMIZONIA *x* = (7), 9–14

x = 9

kelloggii	18	J. Clausen 1951	—	California
pallida	18	,, ,,	—	,,
pungens	18	,, ,,	—	,,
x = 10				
angustifolia	20	,, ,,	—	,,
halliana	20	,, ,,		,,
x = 11				
lobbii	22	,, ,,	—	,,
mohavensis	22	,, ,,	—	,,
pentactis	22	,, ,,	—	,,
parryi	22, 24	,, ,,	—	,,
x = 12				
arida	24	,, ,,	—	,,
australis	24	,, ,,	—	,,
clementina	24	,, ,,	H	,,
fasciculata	24	,, ,,	H	,,
greeneana	24	,, ,,	—	,,
minthonnii	24	,, ,,	—	,,

HEMIZONIA (*cont.*)

paniculata		24	J. Clausen 1951	—	California
ramosissima		24	,, ,,	—	,,
$x = 13$					
fitchii		26	,, ,,	—	,,
floribunda		26	,, ,,	—	,,
$x = (7), 14$					
calyculata		28	,, ,,	—	,,
clevelandii		28	,, ,,	—	,,
congesta		28	,, ,,	—	,,
lutescens		28	,, ,,	—	,,
luzulaefolia		28	,, ,,	—	,,
multicaulis		28	,, ,,	—	,,
tracyi		28	,, ,,	—	,,

GALINSOGA $x = 8 (9)$

parviflora	$\begin{cases} 16 \\ 16 \end{cases}$	Covas & S. 1946 Haskell & M. 1952	—	S. Amer. (Eur)
ciliata	32	,, ,,	—	,, ,,
as *quadriradiata*	36	Reese 1952a		

HELIOPSIS $x = 8$

helianthoides (*laevis*)	32	Cooper & M. 1935	H	E: N. America

DAHLIA $x = 8, 18$

coccinea	Fire D.	32	Lawrence 1929	—	Mexico
coronata		32	,, ,,	—	,,
imperialis		32	,, ,,	—	,,
maxonii		32	,, ,,	—	Mex., Guat.
variabilis	Garden D.	64	,, 1931a	HRV	*cult*
merckii		36	,, 1931b	—	Mexico

THELESPERMA $x = 9, 11$

burridgeanum (*hybridum*)	18	Bilquez, D. 1951	H	Texas
megapotamicum	22	Schnack & C. 1947	—	Temp. S. Amer.

PARTHENIUM $x = (9) 18$ (Apomixis)

incanum	Mariola	$\begin{cases} 36 \\ 54, 72, 90 \end{cases}$	Botschanzewa 1933 Stebbins & K. 1944	—	W: N. America
argentatum Mex. Rubber Guayule		$\begin{cases} 36 + 0\text{-}2\mathbf{B} \\ 54, 72 \\ + 0\text{-}2\mathbf{B} \\ 108\text{–}111 \end{cases}$	,, ,, Catcheside 1950	Ru	Texas, Mexico

XANTHIUM * $x = (9) 18$

cavanilesii		36	Covas & S. 1946	—	N. & S. Amer.
italicum	& 2 spp.	36	Symons 1926	M	China, Japan
strumarium	Bur Weed	36	M. Ishikawa 1916	MO	Cosmop.
spinosum		$\begin{cases} 36 \\ 36 \end{cases}$	Covas & S. 1946 Heiser & W. 1948	—	,,

ECHINACEA (RUDBECKIA) $x = 11$

purpurea	Purple Cone- flower	22	Battaglia 1947a	H	S: U.S.A.

ECLIPTA $x = 11$

erecta	22	Singh 1951	—	Cosmop. Trop.

18   253

HETEROSPERMUM $x = 11$

xantii		22	Gelin 1934	—	California

LEPTOSYNE (COREOPSIS) $x = 12$

bigelowii		24	Gelin 1934	H	California
maritima	Sea Dahlia	24	„ „	H	„

ZINNIA $x = 12$

elegans	24	Ishikawa 1916	H	Mexico
pauciflora	24	Schnack & C. 1947	H	Mex., S. Amer.

COSMOS (BIDENS) $x = 12$

bipinnatus	24	Sugiura 1936b	H	Mexico
diversifolius (dahlioides)	24	Gelin 1934	H	„
sulphureus	24	Sugiura 1936b	H	„
atrosanguineus	48	Lawrence 1929	H	„

BIDENS $x = 12$

andicola		24	Covas & S. 1946	—	Ecuador
cernua	Bur Marigold	24	Lewitzky, T. 1937	—	N. Temp.
ferulaefolia		24	Gelin 1934	H	Mexico
chinensis (pilosa)		48	„ „	H	S. America
heterophylla		48	„ „	—	W: N. Amer., Mexico
radiata		48	Hagerup 1944	—	Eur., Siberia
subalternans		48	Covas & S. 1946	—	W. I., S. Amer.
tripartita		48	Lewitzky, T. 1937	—	Eur., Siberia
pilosa (leucantha)		72	Gelin 1934, Covas & S. 1946	H	W. I., S. Amer.

COREOPSIS $x = 12, 13, 14$

auriculata	24	Bilquez, D. 1951	H	S: U.S.A.
tinctoria (bicolor)	24	Gelin 1934	H	C: U.S.A.
lanceolata	24, 48	Bilquez, D. 1951	H	E: U.S.A.
cardaminifolia	{ 24 / 26	„ „ / Gelin 1934	H	S: U.S.A.
drummondii (picta)	26	„ „	H	Texas
grandiflora (floribunda)	26	„ „	H	S: U.S.A.
tripteris	26	„ „	—	U.S.A.
pubescens	28	Snoad 1952	H	S: U.S.A.

AMBROSIA $x = 12, 17, 18$

trifida	Ragweed	24	Cooper & M. 1935	—	N. America
bidentata		34	K. L. Jones 1943	—	„
artemisifolia (elatior)		36	„ „	—	„
trifida × elatior		30	„ „	—	expt.
psilostachya		100–104	Heiser & W. 1948	—	N. America

SPILANTHES $x = 13$

decumbens	26	Covas & S. 1947	—	S. America

HIDALGOA $x = 15$

werklei	Climbing Dahlia	30	Lawrence 1931b	H	Costa Rica

GUIZOTIA $x = 15$

abyssinica	Nigerseed	30	Richharia & K. '38	O	Trop. Africa

RUDBECKIA	$x = 16, 19$ (Apomixis)				
amplexicaulis		32	Battaglia 1947a	H	C. & S. U.S.A.
bicolor		38	„ „	H	S: U.S.A.
hirta	Black-eyed Susan	38	„ 1947b	H	Canada, U.S.A.
laciniata	Cone Flower	38, 76	„ 1947a	H	E: N. America
speciosa		76	„ „	H	„ „

TITHONIA	$x = 17$				
rotundifolia		34	Heiser 1948	H	Mex., C. Amer.
tagetifolia		34	Bilquez, D. 1951	H	Mexico

VERBESINA	$x = 17$				
encelioides		34	Covas & S. 1946	H	Fla.—Mex.
subcordata		34	Schnack & C. 1947	—	Brazil

HELIANTHUS	$x = 17$				
grosse-serratus	Sawtooth S.	32	Cooper & M. 1932	H	E: U.S.A.
annuus	Sunflower	34	Geisler 1931	HO	cult (N. Amer.)
		(68)	Rybin 1939		
bolanderi		34	Heiser & W. 1948	—	California
giganteus	Giant S.	34	Geisler 1931	HO	Can., C: U.S.A.
maximilianii		34	„ „	H	C: U.S.A.
microcephalus		34	„ „	H	N. America
occidentalis		34	„ „	H	C: U.S.A.
salicifolius (orygalis)		34	„ „	H	„
argophyllus		34	Heiser 1948	H	Texas
jaegeri		34	„ „	—	California
petiolaris	Prairie S.	34	„ „	H	W: N. America
ruderalis	Wild S.	34	Klimochkina 1940	—	N. America
strumosus	Woodland S.	102	Wagner 1932	H	„
rigidus		102	„ „	H	W: N. America
tuberosus	Jerusalem Art.	102	„ „	R	E: N. America
tub. × annuus		68	Shchibra 1936	—	expt

BALSAMORRHIZA	$x = 19$				
careyana		38	Weber 1946	—	W: N. America
hookeri	Balsam Root	38	„ „	HR	„
incana		38	„ „	R	„
rosea		38	„ „	—	„
sagittata	Oregon S.	38	„ „	GHR	„
serrata		38	„ „	—	„

WYETHIA	$x = 19$				
amplexicaulis		38	Weber 1946	H	W: N. America
angustifolia		38	„ „	H	„
helenioides		38	„ „	—	„
mollis		38	„ „	—	„

TRIBE III: ASTEREAE

ASTRANTHIUM (BELLIS)	$x = 4$				
integrifolium		8	Baldwin 1941b	H	N. America.

ASTER *	$x = 5, 8, 9$				
amethystinus		10	Wetmore & D. 1939	H	E: U.S.A.
amplexicaulis		10	„ „	H	„
multiflorus		10	Delisle 1937	H	N. America

ASTER (*cont.*)

novae-angliae		10	Delisle 1937	H	N. America
sericeus		10	Annen 1945	H	,,
subulatus		10	Wetmore & D. 1939	—	,,
squamatus		20	Schnack & C. 1947	—	S. America

$x = 8$

adscendens		16, 32	J. Clausen *et al.* 1940	—	N. America

$x = 9$

alpinus		18	Sakai 1935	H	North Reg.
anomalus		18	Avers 1953	—	E: N. Amer.
fastigiatus		18	Tahara & S. 1926	—	Siberia
glehnii	& 8 spp.	18	Shimotomai & H. '42	H	Japan
montevidensis		18	Schnack & C. 1947	—	Brazil, Arg.
scaber		18	Shimotomai & H. '42	H	Japan
texanus		18	Avers 1953	—	E: N. Amer.
tripolium	Sea Aster	18	Shimotomai & H. '42	—	Eur., N. Afr., N. Asia
ageratoides		18, 19, 36	,, ,,	—	Himalayas
cordifolius		18, 36	Avers 1953	H	E: N. Amer.
sagittifolius		18, 36	,, ,,	H	,,
shortii		18, 36	,, ,,	H	,,
amellus		18	Annen 1945	H	Eur., Asia
garden forms		66, 76	,, ,,	H	*cult*
thomsonii	(3*x*)	27	,, ,,	H	Himalayas
alpinus	Rock Aster	36	S. & S. 1933	H	Alps—Altai
altaicus	& 2 spp.	36	Shimotomai & H. '42	H	Persia—N. Asia
drummondii		36	Avers 1953	H	E: N. Amer.
lowrieanus		36	,, ,,	H	,,
trinervius		36	Tahara & S. 1926	H	Himalayas
undulatus		36	Avers 1953	H	E: N. Amer.
frikartii		52, 54	Annen 1945	H	*cult*
flaccidus		54	S. & S. 1938	—	Altai
laevis	Michaelmas D.	54	Revell 1945*	H	E: U.S.A.
tataricus		54	Shimotomai & H. '42	H	Sib., China
ciliolatus		72	Avers 1953	—	N: N. Amer.

GRINDELIA $x = 6$

chiloensis		12	Covas & S. 1946	H	Argentine
pulchella		12	,, ,,	—	Chile
sp. aff. *chiloensis*		24	Schanck & C. 1947	—	Argentine
camporum		24	Heiser & W. 1948	—	N. America

FELICIA $x = 6, 8, 9$

bergeriana		12	Bilquez, D. 1951	H	S. Africa
amelloides	Blue Daisy	16	Sugiura 1936b	H	,,
tenella (*fragilis*)		16	Harling 1951b	H	,,
adfinis		18	Bilquez, D. 1951	H	,,

BACCHARIS $x = 9$

genistelloides		18	Bowden 1945a	H	Peru, Brazil
genistifolia		18	,, ,,	—	Brazil
halimifolia	Groundsel Bush	18	,, ,,	H	E: U.S.A.
phyteumoides		18	,, ,,	—	Brazil
pingraea		{18, 18	Covas & S. 1946	—	Chile
lanceolata		18	,, ,,	—	Peru

BELLIUM $x = 9$

bellidioides		18	Negodi 1935	H	Medit.

BOLTONIA (ASTEROMOEA) $x = 9$

indica		18	Tahara & S. 1926	H	Japan

CALLISTEPHUS $x = 9$

sinensis	China Aster	18	Tahara & S. 1926	H	Sib., China

GRANGEA $x = 9$

maderaspatana		18	Mitra 1947	—	Tr. Asia & Afr.

HETEROTHECA $x = 9$

grandiflora		18	Heiser & W. 1948	—	W: N. Amer.

LINOSYRIS (ASTER) $x = 9$

vulgaris (A. linosyris)		18	Annen 1945	H	Europe

PSEUDOBACCHARIS $x = 9$

retamoides		18	Schnack & C. 1947	—	Argentine

BELLIS $x = 9$

annua		18	Negodi 1935	—	N.W. Medit.
perennis	Daisy	18	„ „	H	Europe
sylvestris		36, 54	„ T. 1937	—	Medit.

ERIGERON $x = 9, 16$ (Polyploids Apomictic)

acris		18	L. & L. 1942	—	N. Temp.
alpinus		18	Chiarugi 1927b	H	Alpine & Arctic
aurantiacus	Orange Daisy	{ 18	Bergman 1942	H	Turkestan
		18	Harling 1951b		
aureus		18	„ „	H	W: N. Amer.
borealis		18	Chiarugi 1927b	—	Europe
canadensis	Fleabane	18	Okabe '34, Harling 1951b	H	Cosmop.
frigidus		18	Harling 1951b	H	Sierra Nevada
glabellus		18	„ „	H	N. America
polymorphus		18	Reese 1953	—	North & Arctic
uniflorus		18	Bøcher & L. 1950	H	Arctic
pulchellus		18	Harling 1951b	H	Caucasus
macranthus		{ 18	Bergman 1942	H	Rocky Mtns.
		26?	Holmgren 1919		
glabratus		{ 18	Sakai 1934	—	Switzerland
		36	M. & S. 1935		
annuus		27	Okabe 1934	—	N. America
karvinskianus		{ 32	Battaglia 1950a	H	Mex., C. Amer.
		36	Fagerlind 1947		
unalaschkense		36	Flovik 1940	—	Arctic
bonariensis		54	Holmgren 1919	—	S. America
compositus		54, 63	Bøcher & L. 1950	H	W: N. Amer.

GYMNASTER $x = 9$

pygmaeus		18	Shimotomai & H. '42	—	Japan
savatieri		18, 36	Inoue 1952	—	„
koraiensis		144	Shimotomai & H. '42	—	Korea

257

KALIMERIS $x = 9$

miqueliana		18	Shimotomai & H. '42 —	Japan
pinnatifida		18, 63, 64, 66	„ „ —	„
indica		54	„ „ —	„
incisa		72	Shimotomai & I. '51 H	Siberia
yomena		63 ± 9	„ „ H	*cult*

SOLIDAGO $x = 9$

canadensis		18	Brock unp. H	E: N. America
chilensis		18	Covas & S. 1946 —	Argentine
elongata		18	Clausen *et al.* 1940 H	W: N. America
multiradiata		18	„ „ —	„ „
rugosa		18	Goodwin 1937 H	E: N. America
virgaurea	Golden Rod	18	Scheerer, L. & L. '42 H(Ru)	Europe
sempervirens		18, 36	Goodwin 1937 H	E: N. America

HETEROPAPPUS $x = (9), 18$

arenarius	36	Shimotomai & H. '42 —	Japan, Mongolia
hispidus	36	„ „ —	„ „
leptocladus	36	„ „ —	„ „

GUTIERREZIA $x = 12$

species	24	Covas & S. 1947 —	S. America

TRIBE IV: INULEAE

ODONTOSPERMUM (ASTERISCUS) $x = 5$

spinosum	10	Tongiorgi 1935 —	Medit.

BUPHTHALMUM (TELEKIA) $x = 5$

grandiflorum Ox-eye	20	Sakai 1935 H	S. Europe
salicifolium	20	Tongiorgi 1935 —	„
speciosum	20	„ „ —	S. Eur., W. Asia

TESSARIA $x = 5$

absinthoides	20	Covas & S. 1946 —	Chile

PLUCHEA $x = 5$

camphorata Stinkweed	20	Baldwin & S. 1955a —	S. & E: U.S.A., W.I.
foetida Stinking Fleabane	20	„ „ —	„ „
purpurascens	20	„ „ —	S: U.S.A., Trop. Amer.

PULICARIA (INULA) $x = 5, 9$

vulgaris	18	Wulff 1937b —	Temp.
crispa	20	Singh 1951 —	N. & Trop. Afr., Arabia, India
dysenterica Fleabane	20	Rodolico 1933 —	Medit.

INULA $x = 5, 8, 9$

cordata	16	Tongiorgi 1935 —	Asia Minor
ensifolia (*bubonium*)	16	Reese 1953 H	Eur., N. Asia
grandiflora	16	S. & S. 1940 H	Cauc., Himal.
hirta	16	Tongiorgi 1942 H	S. Europe
orientalis (*glandulosa*)	16	„ „ H	Caucasus
thapsoides	16	„ „ H	Cauc., N. Persia

INULA (*cont.*)

britannica		$\begin{cases} 16, 24 \\ 32 \end{cases}$	Okabe 1937 Pólya, L. & L. 1948	H	Eur., Asia
conyza	Ploughman's Spikenard	32	Tongiorgi 1942	—	Eur., W. Asia
crithmoides	Golden Samphire	18	Castro & F. 1946	—	,, ,,
indica		18	Singh 1951	—	India
viscosa		18	Rodolico 1933	—	S. Europe
helenium	Elecampane	20	Rutland 1941	MV	N. Temp.
hookeri		20	Tongiorgi 1942	H	Himalayas
racemosa		20	,, 1935	H	Himal., W. China

GNAPHALIUM $x = 7$

luteo-album	Jersey Cudweed	14	Wulff 1937b	—	Cosmop.
uliginosum		14	,, ,,	—	S. Eur., W. Asia
supinum		28	Rutland 1941	—	N. Temp. & Arct.
norvegicum		56	L. & L. 1944b	—	,, ,,
sylvaticum		c. 58	S. & S. 1938	H	Eur., Cauc., N. America

HELICHRYSUM $x = 7$

arenarium		$\begin{cases} 14 \\ 28 \end{cases}$	Tongiorgi 1935 Scheerer 1939	—	Eur., Cauc.
bracteatum	Strawflower	28	Tongiorgi 1942	H	Australia
serotinum		28	Lorenzo-A. & G. '50	—	Europe
stoechas		28	,, ,, ,,	—	W. Medit.
thianschanicum		28	Tongiorgi 1935	H	W. China

ANAPHALIS $x = 7$

margaritacea	Pearly Everlasting	28	Maude 1939	H	N. America

FILAGO $x = 7$

arvensis		28	Wulff 1937b	—	Eur., N. Asia
germanica	Cudweed	28	,, ,,	—	Eur., S.W. Asia
minima		28	Reese 1952a	—	Eur., Siberia
spathulata		28	Hagerup 1941b	—	Eur., N. Afr., S.W. Asia

ANTENNARIA $x = 7$ (Apomictic)

dioica	Cat's Ear	28, 34	Bergman 1944	H	Eur., N. Asia, N. America
neglecta		28	Stebbins 1932	—	N. America
plantaginifolia		28	,, ,,	—	,,
solitaria		28	,, ,,	—	,,
brainerdii		42	,, ,,	—	,,
carpathica		40, 42	Bergman 1935b	—	N. Temp.
magellanica		56	,, 1937	—	Magellan
neodioica		c. 52	Stebbins 1932	—	N. America
glabrata		63	Bøcher & L. 1950	—	,,
alpina (*intermedia*)		84	Bergman 1935b	H	N. Temp.
canadensis		c. 84	Stebbins 1932	—	N. America
fallax		84	,, ,,	—	,,
parlinii		84	,, ,,	—	,,

HELIPTERUM x = 7, 11

roseum		14	Bilquez, D. 1951	H	Australia
manglesii		22	„ „	H	„

LEONTOPODIUM x = 7? 13

alpinum	Edelweiss	26	Sakai 1935	H	Europe
kurilense		26	„ 1934	H	Japan
campestre		49	S. & S. 1938	—	Siberia

AMMOBIUM x = 13

alatum	Everlasting	26	Avanzi 1948	H	Australia

EVAX x = 13

umbellata (*pygmaea*)	26	Tongiorgi 1942	—	Medit.

TRIBE V: CYNAREAE

XERANTHEMUM x = 6, 10

annuum	12	Poddubnaja 1931	H	Medit.
squarrosum	12	„ „	—	„
cylindraceum	20	„ „	—	„

CENTAUREA * x = 7, 8, 9, 10, 11, 12, 13
x = 7, 8, 9

scabiosa	{	14	Dark 1945 *		
		20	Roy 1937	—	Europe
		20 + 0–13**B**	Fröst 1948		
iberica		16	Poddubnaja 1931	—	Spain
solstitialis	St. Barnaby's Th.	16	Heiser & W. 1948	—	S. & S.E. Eur., W. Asia
diffusa		18	Moore & F. 1954	—	Eurasia
macrocephala		18	Poddubnaja 1931	H	Armenia
ossica		18	„ „	—	Caucasus
ovina		18	„ „	—	Sib., Asia Minor
maculosa		36	Moore & F. 1954	—	Europe

x = 10, 11, 12, 13

calcitrapa		20	Vignoli 1945b	—	Eur., N. Afr., Temp. Asia
macroacantha		20	„ „	—	Cauc., Asia Min.
reflexa		20	Poddubnaja 1931	—	Cauc., Armenia
salonitana		20	„ „	—	E. Europe
aspera	{	20	Lorenzo-Andreu 1951	—	S. Europe
		22	Maude 1939		
melitensis		22	Covas & S. 1947	—	Eur., S. Amer.
nervosa		22	Favarger 1953	H	S. Eur. mtns.
phrygia		22	Poddubnaja 1931	—	Europe
cyanus	Cornflower & 6 spp.	24	Fritsch 1935	H	Eur., Cauc.
repens	Russ. Knapweed	26	Moore & F. 1954	—	Asia

x = various

ruthenica		30	Poddubnaja 1931	H	Cauc., Siberia
fischeri		40	„ „	—	Eur., S.W. Asia
jacea	& 2 spp.	44	Roy 1937, Wulff '37b	—	Europe
bella	& 2 spp.	c. 55	Poddubnaja 1931	—	Caucasus
collina		60	Roy 1937	—	Medit.

PHAEOPAPPUS $x = 8$
steveni   16 Poddubnaja 1931   —   Caucasus

CARDUUS $x = 8, 11$
crispus   16 Poddubnaja 1931   —   Europe
nutans   Musk Thistle   16   ,,   ,,   —   Eur., Temp. Asia
acanthoides   22   ,,   ,,   —   Eur., Cauc.
defloratus   22 Reese 1952a   —   Europe

LEUZEA $x = 9$
conifera   18 Lorenzo-Andreu & G. H   Medit.
                                          1950

SAUSSUREA $x = 9, 13$
brachycephala   26 M. & S. 1935   —   Japan
sagitta   26   ,,   ,,   —   ,,
riederi   39   ,,   ,,   —   Kamchatka
alpina (affinis) $\left\{ \begin{array}{l} 36? \\ 54 \end{array} \right.$ Ishikawa 1916 / L. & L. 1944b   —   N. Eurasia

CARLINA $x = 10$
acanthifolia   20 Arata 1944   H   S. Eur., W. Asia
acaulis   20   ,,   ,,   H   S. Europe
corymbosa   20   ,,   ,,   —   Medit.
gummifera   20   ,,   ,,   —   ,,
lanata   20   ,,   ,,   —   ,,
vulgaris   Carline Thistle   20   ,,   ,,   —   Eur., N. Asia

CIRSIUM (CNICUS)* $x = 10, 17$
$x = 10$ (New World)
discolor   20 Ownbey 1951b   H   E: N. America
muticum   Swamp Thistle   20   ,,   ,,   H   ,,
$x = 17$ (Old World)
acaule   34 Wulff 1937b   —   Europe
arvense   34 Ehrenberg 1945   —   Temp. Eurasia
eriophorum   34 Reese 1952a   —   Eur., Asia Min.
heterophyllum   34 Wulff 1937b   —   Eur., N. Asia
oleraceum   34   ,,   ,,   —   Europe
japonicum   & 15 spp.   34 Aishima 1934   —   Japan
palustre   34 Poddubnaja 1931   —   Eur., N. Asia
vulgare (lanceolatum)   68   ,,   ,,   H   Eurasia
nipponicum   & 10 spp.   68 Aishima 1934   —   Japan
alpicolum   & 2 spp.   102   ,,   ,,   —   ,,

CNICUS $x = 11$
benedictus   Blessed Thistle   22 Vaarama 1947a   HMSp Medit., Cauc.

STEVIA $x = 11$
rabaudiana   Kaa He-e   22 EKJ   SuV Paraguay

SERRATULA $x = 11, 15$
tinctoria   22 Maude 1940   —   N. Eur., Asia
radiata   Sawwort   60 Poddubnaja 1931   —   Eur., Cauc.

ATRACTYLIS $x = 12$
lancea   24 Suzuka & K. 1949   —   Japan
lyrata   24   ,,   ,,   —   ,,
ovata   24 Suzuka 1950a   —   ,,

261

CARTHAMUS x = 8, 12

oxyacantha		24	Kishore 1951	—	Cauc., W. Asia
tinctorius	Safflower	24	Poddubnaja 1931	DO	O.W. Tropics
lanatus		64	„ „	O	Eur.—Persia

COUSINIA x = 13

carduiformis		26	Poddubnaja 1931	—	Caucasus

CRUPINA x = 14, 15

crupinastrum		28	Poddubnaja 1931	—	Medit.
vulgaris		30	„ „	H	„

JURINEA x = 15

cyanoides		30	Poddubnaja 1931	—	S. Eur., Cauc.

AMBERBOA x = 8

moschata		32	Poddubnaja 1931	—	S.W. Asia

ECHINOPS x = 8

sphaerocephalus	Globe Thistle	32	Poddubnaja 1927	H	Med.—N. Asia

ARCTIUM x = 16, 18

minus	Lesser Burdock	32	Wulff 1937b	—	Europe
lappa	Great B., Gobo	⌠ 32	Sugiura 1936	M	„
	(Japanese)	⌡ 36	Nakajima 1936	R	Japan
tomentosum		36	Poddubnaja 1931	—	Europe
vulgare	Wood B.	36	L. & L. 1944b	—	„

CYNARA x = 17

cardunculus	Cardoon	34	Covas & S. 1947	V	Medit.
scolymus	Globe Artichoke	34	E.K.J.	V	„

ONOPORDUM x = 17

acanthium	Scotch Th.	34	Poddubnaja 1931	—	Eur., W. Asia

SILYBUM (CARDUUS) x = 17

marianum	St. Mary's Th.	34	Heiser & W. 1948	H	Europe

TRIBE VI: SENECIONEAE

EMILIA (CACALIA) x = 5

sagittata	Flora's Paintbrush	⌠ 10	Afzelius 1924		
		⌡ 10	Baldwin & S. 1948b	H	India
sonchifolia		10	Baldwin 1946a	H	Tr. Afr. & Asia
coccinea		20	„ „	H	Trop. O.W.
sp.		20	Baldwin & S. 1949b	—	W. Africa

SENECIO (CINERARIA)* x = 5, 9, 11, 12, 23
x = 5

discifolius		10	Afzelius 1924	—	Trop. Africa
elegans	Purple Ragwort	20	„ „	H	S. Africa
isatideus		20	Goldsmith & K. '48	—	„
pendulus		20	Okabe 1931	—	Arabia
scandens		20	Afzelius 1924	H	China, Japan
squalidus	Oxford R.	20	„ „	—	Sicily, S. Italy
7 species		20	„ „ 1949		
tomentosus		20	Snoad unp.	H	S. Africa

262

SENECIO (*cont.*)

abrotanifolius		40	Afzelius 1924	H	C. Europe
adonidifolius		40	,, ,,	H	S. France, Spain
chordifolius		40	,, ,,	H	S. Africa
cineraria	Dusty Miller	40	,, ,,	H	Medit.
doria		40	,, ,,	H	S. & C. Europe
filaginoides		40	Covas & S. 1947	—	Chile
gillesianus		40	,, 1946	—	,,
hualtata		40	Schnack & C. 1947	—	,,
incanus		40	Favarger 1949b	H	Eur. Alps
jacobaea	Tansy Ragwort	40	Afzelius 1924	—	Europe
nemorensis		40	M. & S. 1935	—	Eur., N. Asia
viscosus		40	Afzelius 1924	—	Eur., Asia M.
vulgaris	Groundsel	40	,, ,,	—	Cosmop.
23 species		40	,, ,, 1949		
echinatus		60	,, 1949	—	Canaries
heritieri		60	,, 1924	H	,,
oxyriifolius		60	,, 1949	—	S. Africa
petasites	Calif. Geranium	60	,, 1924	H	Mexico
webbii		60	,, 1949	—	Canaries
soongaricus		60	,, ,,	—	C. & W. Asia
doronicum	Leopard's Bane	80	,, ,,	H	C. & S. Europe
uspallatensis		*c.* 80	Schnack & C. 1947	—	Chile
roberti-friesii		*c.* 180	Afzelius 1924	—	*cult*

$x = 9, 11, 12$

arenarius		18	Afzelius 1949	—	Cape Prov.
cladobotrys		24	S. & S. 1940	—	Caucasus
palmatus		{ 36	Suzuka & K. 1949	—	C. & E. Asia
		80	Afzelius 1949		
congestus (*palustris*)		48	,, 1924	—	Eur., N. Asia
caucasica		44	S. & S. 1940	—	Caucasus
resedifolius		46	,, 1938	—	Siberia
		46	,, 1938		
integrifolius (*campestris*)	{	48, 90	,, 1941	—	N. Temp.
		48	Rutland 1941		
spathulifolius		48, 50	Afzelius 1949	—	W. Europe
alpestris		48, 50	,, ,,	—	Europe

NOTONIA $x = 10$

grandiflora		20	Ganesan 1939	H	India

GYNURA (CRASSOCEPHALUM) $x = 10$

aurantiaca	Velvet Tree	20	Afzelius 1924	H	Java
rubens		20	,, ,,	—	Trop. Africa
crepidioides		40	,, ,,	—	,,

KLEINIA $x = 10$

articulata	Candle Plant	20	Afzelius 1949	H	S. Africa
cylindrica		20	,, ,,	H	,,
		c. 100	,, ,,		*cult*

OTHONNA $x = 10$

carnosa		20	Afzelius 1924	H	S. Africa
coronopifolia		20	,, 1949	—	Cape Prov.

ERECHTITES $x = 10$
hieracifolia	40	G. O. Cooper 1936	—	N. & S. Amer.

CACALIA $x = 10, 26$
suaveolens	40	Afzelius 1924	—	N. America
reniformis	50	„ „	—	„
aconitifolia	52	„ 1949	—	China
hastata	60	„ „	—	Eurasia
roborowskii	60	„ „	—	China

MALLOTOPUS $x = 9$
japonicus	18	M. & S. 1935	—	Japan

TRIDAX $x = 9$
trilobata	18	Hjelmqvist 1951	H	Mexico
procumbens	36	Raghavan & V. '41b	—	Trop. America

LIGULARIA $x = 24, 29, 30$
altaica	48	S. & S. 1938	—	Altai
hodgsonii	58	Afzelius 1949	—	China
macrophylla	58	„ 1924	H	Caucasus
clivorum & 6 spp.	60	„ 1924, 1949	H	China, Japan
tussilaginea (kaempferi)	60	Battaglia 1940	H	Japan

PETASITES (TUSSILAGO) $x = 26, 29, 30$
fragrans	Winter Heliotrope	52	Maude 1940	H	W. Medit.
hybridus	Butterbur	60	Langlet 1936	HM	Eurasia
albus		60	Scheerer 1939	—	„
frigidus		60	Flovik 1940	—	Arct., Temp.
niveus		60	Langlet 1936	—	Europe
spurius		60	„ „	—	„
japonicus		87	Yamamoto, K. 1931	HV	Sakhalin

TUSSILAGO (PETASITES) $x = 30$
farfara	Coltsfoot	60	Hagerup 1941b	M	Eurasia, N. Afr.
japonica		60	Langlet 1936	—	Japan

DORONICUM $x = 30$
austriacum	60	Wcisło 1951	—	Europe
cordatum	60	Lindqvist 1950	—	„
grandiflorum	60	Favarger 1949b	—	„
pardalianches	60	Lindqvist 1950	H	„
clusii	120	Wcisło 1951	—	C. Eur. mtns.
plantagineum	c. 120	Lindqvist 1950	H	Europe

ARNICA $x = ?$ (Apomixis)
montana	38	Favarger 1953	M	Eurasia
unalaschensis	c. 40	Sakai 1934	H	Unalaska
alpina	⎰56	L. & L. 1948		
	⎱60	Afzelius 1924	H	N. Reg.
	76	Bøcher & L. 1950		

HOMOGYNE $x = ?$
alpina	Alpine Coltsfoot c. 135	Langlet 1936	H	Europe

TRIBE VII: HELENIEAE

BLENNOSPERMA $x = 7, 9$
californicum	14	Heiser 1947	—	California
bakeri	18	„ „	—	„

SCHKUHRIA $x = 10. 11$
pinnata		20	Covas & S. 1946	—	Argentine
multiflora		22	Schnack & C. 1947	—	,,

HYMENOXYS* $x = 11, 15$
odorata		22	Speese & B. 1952	—	S.W: U.S.A.
argentea	& 11 spp.	30	,, ,,	—	,,
acaulis		30, 60	,, ,,	—	,,

TAGETES $x = 12$
erecta Afr. Marigold	24 (48)	Eyster 1939	H	Mexico
biflora	48	Covas & S. 1946	—	C. America
mendocina	48	Schnack & C. 1947	—	,,
patula French M.	48 (96)	Eyster 1939	H	Mexico
signata (*erecta* × *patula*)	36 (72)	,, ,,	H	*cult*

HELENIUM $x = 14, 17$
curtisii	28	Baldwin & S. 1952	—	N. America
autumnale Sneezeweed	34	E.K.J.*	H	E: N. America

THYMOPHYLLA $x = 16$
belenidium	32	Covas & S. 1946	—	C. America

FLAVERIA $x = 18$
bidentis	36	Covas & S. 1946	—	S. America

GAILLARDIA $x = 18$
aristata (*grandiflora*)	{ 36	Cooper & M. 1935	H	C: U.S.A.
	{ 72	Atwood 1937		
pulchella	{ 36	Morinaga *et al.* '29	H	S: U.S.A.
	{ 34 (68)	Schnack 1940		

TRIBE VIII: ARCTOTIDEAE

GAZANIA $x = 5$
rigens	10	La Cour 1945*	H	S. Africa

BERKHEYA $x = 7$
adlamii	14	Gelin 1936	H	S. Africa
bergiana	14	,, ,,	—	Rhodesia

URSINIA (SPHENOGYNE) $x = 8$
anethoides	16	Sugiura 1936b	H	S. Africa
anthemoides	16	,, ,,	H	,,
speciosa	16	,, ,,	H	,,

ARCTOTIS $x = 9$
acaulis	18	Bilquez, D. 1951	H	S. Africa
as *scapigera*	18	,, ,,	H	
stoechadifolia Afr. Daisy	18	,, ,,	H	,,
var. *grandis*	18	,, ,,		

VENIDIUM $x = 9$
decurrens v. *calendulaceum*	{ 18	Bilquez, D. 1951	H	S. Africa
	{ 18	Morrison 1952		
fastuosum	{ 18	Bilquez, D. 1951	H	,,
as *wyleyi*	{ 18	,, ,,		

CALENDULA $x = 7, 8, 9$

aegyptiaca	Egyptian M.	14	Negodi 1935	DH	Medit., Mesop.
officinalis	Pot Marigold	$\begin{cases} 28 \\ 32 \end{cases}$	" 1936a Weddle 1941	DH	S. Europe
suffruticosa	Shrubby M.	$\begin{cases} 28 \\ 32 \end{cases}$	Negodi 1936a Weddle 1941	H	E. Medit.
arvensis		36	Negodi 1936a	H	Eur., S.W. Asia

DIMORPHOTHECA $x = 9, 10$

aurantiaca	Cape Marigold	18	Harrison, T. 1937	H	S. Africa
pluvialis		18	Bilquez, D. 1951	H	"
pseudoaurantiaca		18	Harrison, T. 1937	H	"
sinuata		18	Bilquez, D. 1951	H	"
ecklonis		20	Harrison, T. 1937	H	"
barberiae		38-40	Pienaar unp.	H	"

ARTEMISIA * $x = 8, 9,$ $x_2 = 17$
$x = 8$

mongolica		16	Suzuka 1950b	—	E. Asia
3 species		16	" " 1951		
campestris	Sagewort	$\begin{cases} 16 \\ 18 \\ 36 \\ 36 \end{cases}$	" Weinedel 1928 Erlandsson 1939 Clausen *et al.* 1940b	M	N. Hemisphere

$x = 9$

absinthium	Wormwood	18	Weinedel 1928	DIP	Temp. Eurasia
annua	Sweet W.	18	Suzuka 1950b	H	S.W. & N. Asia
arborescens		18	Martinoli 1943	H	Medit.
cina	Levant W.	18	Weinedel 1928	IM	S.W. Asia
dracunculus	Tarragon	18	" "	Sp	S. Europe
lactiflora	White Mugwort	18	Suzuka 1950b	H	China
pontica	Roman W.	18	Weinedel 1928	H	C. Europe
stelleriana	Beach M.	18	Suzuka 1950b	H	N.E. Asia, N. Am.
vulgaris	Mugwort	18	Weinedel 1928	DI	N. Temp.
palmeri & 2 spp.		18	Ward 1953	—	California
14 species		$18\begin{cases} \\ \\ \\ \\ \end{cases}$	Suzuka 1950b, 1951 Clausen *et al.* '40a, b Nygren, L. &. L. '48 Favarger 1953		
borealis		18, 36	Erlandsson 1939	—	N. & Arctic
tridentata	Sagebrush & 4 spp.	$\begin{cases} 18, 36 \end{cases}$	Ward 1953	HM	W: N. Amer.
maritima	Santonin	$\begin{cases} 18 \\ 18 \\ 54 \end{cases}$	Weinedel 1928 Pólya 1948 Suzuka & K. 1949	DI	Eur., C. Asia
nitida		27	Chiarugi 1926	Fo	Italy
japonica		36	Suzuka 1950b	—	Japan
11 species		36	" " '51 Clausen *et al.* 1940b		
ludoviciana		36, c. 54	" " '40a	HM	N. America
koidzumii		$\begin{cases} 36 \\ 54 \end{cases}$	Suzuka 1951 " 1950b		

ARTEMISIA (*cont.*)

douglasiana	54	Clausen *et al.* '40a	HM	N. America
verlotorum	54	Vignoli 1945a	—	N. Temp.
montana	51–54	Shimotomai 1947		Arctic
iwayomogi	52–54	Suzuka 1950b	—	Japan
rothrockii	{ c. 72	Clausen *et al.* 1940a	H	W: N. America
	36, 54	Ward 1953		

$x_2 = 17$

dubia	34	Suzuka 1950b	—	N. Temp.
grenata	34	„ 1951	—	China, Japan
princeps	34	„ 1950b	—	„ „

ANACYCLUS $x = 9$

pyrethrum	18	Raves 1926	H	S.E. Europe
radiatus	18	Harling 1950	H	Medit.

ANTHEMIS $x = 9$

altissima	18	Harling 1950	H	S. Europe
arvensis	18	„ „	—	Eur., N. Afr., Asia Minor
austriaca	18	„ „	H	Austria
cotula Stinking May-Weed	18	„ „	—	Eur., N. & W. As.
cupaniana	18	Dowrick 1952a	H	Italy
maritima	18	Harling 1950	—	Medit.
montana (*macedonica*)	18	Dowrick 1952a	H	Eur., Syria
nobilis Chamomile	18	Suzuka & K. 1949	HM	Europe
rigescens	18	Harling 1950	H	Caucasus
rudolphiana	18	S. & S. 1940	—	„
ruthenica	18	Harling 1950	H	C. Europe
tinctoria Yellow Ch.	18	„ „	DH	Eur.—Persia
sancti-johannis	18	Dowrick 1952a	H	Bulgaria

CENIA $x = 9$

turbinata	18	Negodi 1935	—	S. Africa

CLADANTHUS $x = 9$

arabicus	18	Harling 1950	H	S. Spain, Morocco

LASIOSPERMUM $x = 9$

radiatum	18	Harling 1950	H	S. Africa

LONAS $x = 9$

inodora Afr. Daisy	18	Harling 1950	H	Medit.

NANANTHERA $x = 9$

perpusilla	18	Martinoli 1940	—	Corsica

OTANTHUS (DIOTIS) $x = 9$

maritimus Cotton Weed	18	Martinoli 1939	H	Medit.

SANTOLINA $x = 9$

pinnata	18	Martinoli 1939	H	Italy

TANACETUM (CHRYSANTHEMUM) $x = 9$

pseudachillea	18	Dowrick 1952a	—	Turkestan
vulgare Tansy	18	Shimotomai 1937b	HMSp	Eur., N. Asia

MATRICARIA $x = 9$

ambigua		18	Tahara 1921	—	Europe
chamomilla	Chamomile	18	L. & L. 1948	M	Medit.
matricarioides (discoidea)		{ 18 18	Rutland 1941, Suzuka 1950a	H	N.E. Asia
maritima (inodora)	Scentless May- Weed	⎧ 18 ⎨ 18 ⎪ 36 ⎩ 36	Hüser 1930, Hagerup 1941b, Vaarama 1950, Harling 1951a	H	Eur., S.W. Asia

ACHILLEA * $x = 9$

asplenifolia	& 2 spp.	18	Ehrendorfer 1952	—	Europe
atrata		18	Reese 1952a	H	C. Europe
cartilaginea		18	Lewitsky, T. 1937	—	Eur., S.W. Asia
nana		18	Favarger 1953	H	Alps
ptarmica	Sneezewort	18	Lewitzky, T. 1937	HMV	Eur., N. & W. As.
macrophyllum		18	Dowrick 1952a	—	N. Temp.
millefolium	Yarrow	⎧ 18 ⎨ 18 ⎪ 36, 54 ⎩ 54	Felfoldy 1947, Harling 1950, Turesson 1938, Ehrendorfer 1952	HM	Eur., W. Asia
collina		36	,, ,,	—	Europe
lanulosa		36	Lawrence 1947	—	N. America
borealis		54	,, ,,	—	W: N. America
stricta		54	Ehrendorfer 1952	—	Europe
pannonica		72	,, ,,	—	,,

CHRYSANTHEMUM $x = 9$

argenteum		18	Dowrick 1952b	H	S.W. Asia, Cauc.
boreale		18	,, ,,	—	China, Japan
cassium		18	,, ,,	—	S.W. Asia, Cauc.
catananche		18	,, ,,	H	Morocco
cinerariaefolium	Dalm. P.	18	,, ,,	HIM	Dalmatia
coccineum	Pyrethrum	18	,, ,,	HI	Cauc., Persia
filifolium		18	Shimotomai 1937b	—	Canaries
foeniculaceum		18	Harling 1951b	H	Teneriffe
flosculosum		18	Martinoli 1942	H	Medit.
lavandulaefolium		18	Shimotomai 1937b	I	Japan
lineare		18	,, ,,	—	,,
macrophyllum		18	Reese 1953	H	S.E. Eur., Cauc.
macrotum		18	Dowrick 1952b	—	Medit.
makinoi (japonicum)		18	Shimotomai & T. '36	H	Japan
mawii		18	Dowrick 1952b	H	Atlas
millefoliatum	18, 18 + iso.		,, ,,	—	S.W. Russia
myconis		18	,, ,,	H	C. & S. Europe
nipponicum		18	Shimotomai & T. '36	H	Japan
nivellei		18	Dowrick 1952b	—	Morocco
parthenium	Feverfew	{ 18 18	,, ,, Harling 1951a	H	Eurasia
rotundifolium		18	Shimotomai 1937b	H	Hungary
rupestre		18	Sugiura 1937a	—	Japan
serotinum		18	Dowrick 1952b	—	Medit.
uliginosum		18	,, ,,	H	Hungary
viscidi-hirtum		18	Battaglia 1951	—	S. Spain, N. Afr.
frutescens v. crithmifolium	Marguerite	{ 18 27	Harling 1951b Shimotomai 1937b	H	Canary Is., cult
alpinum		18, 36	,, ,,	H	Eur. Alps

268

CHRYSANTHEMUM (*cont.*)

atratum		$\{$ 18	Shimotomai 1937b	H	Eur., Alps
		36	Dowrick 1952b		
coronarium		18, 36	Shimotomai & H. '35	H	Medit.
corymbosum	18, 18 + *iso*, 36		Dowrick 1952b	H	Caucasus
oreades		18, 36	,, ,,	—	S.W. Asia, Cauc.
segetum	Corn M'gold	18, 36	,, ,,	H	Eur., N. Afr., W. Asia
balsamita	Costmary	$\{$ 18, 54	,, ,,	H	W. Asia
		18, 54	Harling 1951a		
ircutianum		36	Shimotomai 1937b	—	Siberia
praealtum		36	Dowrick 1952b	H	Caucasus
wakasaense		36	,, ,,	—	China, Japan
indicum		36, 54	,, ,,	BH	China
cultivated vars.		45–63	,, ,,		
leucanthemum	Ox-Eye D.	36, 54	,, ,,	H	Eur., N. Asia
camphoratum		54	Harling 1951b	—	California
ceratophylloides		54	Shimotomai 1937b	—	Europe
morifolium (*sinense*)		54	,, 1933	H	China, Japan
shimotomaii		54	,, ,,	—	Japan
sibiricum		54	Shimotomai & H. '35	—	Arctic
silvaticum		54	Dowrick 1952b	—	Europe
weyrichii		54	Shimotomai 1937b	—	Sakhalin
rubellum		$\{$ 63	Dowrick 1952b	H	*cult*
		70–80	Harling 1951b		
arcticum		72	Dowrick 1952b	H	Siberia
decaisneanum		72	Shimotomai 1933	—	Japan
ornatum		72	,, ,,	H	China
zawadskii		72	,, 1937b	—	Galicia
sonare		80	Dowrick 1952b	—	China, Japan
maximum	Shasta Daisy	85, 90, 126 148, 154, 160, 171 $\}$	,, ,,	H	N. Spain
pacificum (*marginatum*)		90	Shimotomai 1933	—	Japan
yezoense (*arcticum*)		90	,, ,,	—	,,
lacustre		198	Dowrick 1952b	H	Portugal

COTULA $x = 10$

coronopifolia	Brass Buttons	20	Castro & F. 1946	H	S. Africa

TRIBE XI: VERNONIEAE

VERNONIA $x = 9$

cinerea		18	Grant 1953	—	Burma

ELEPHANTOPUS $x = 11$

carolinianus	Elephant's Foot	22	Baldwin & S. 1955a	—	E. & C. U.S.A.
tomentosus	Devil's Grand-mother	22	,, ,, ,,	—	,, ,,
nudatus		22	,, ,, ,,	—	,, ,,

TRIBE XII: EUPATORIEAE

LIATRIS * $x = (9), 10$

elegans		18	Langlet 1925	H	E: N. America
chapmanii	& 12 spp.	20	Gaiser 1949–51	H	S.E. U.S.A.

19

LIATRIS (*cont.*)

aspera		20, 22	Gaiser 1951b	—	E: N. America
acidota		20, 30	„ 1949	H	„
angustifolia		20, 30, 40	„ 1950b	—	„
punctata		20, 30, 40	„ „	H	W: N. America
pychnostachya		$20 + 0\text{-}3\mathbf{B}$, 40	„ 1949	H	E: N. America
microcephala		20, 60	„ „	—	„
densispicata		40	„ 1950b	—	Minnesota
bracteata		60	„ „	—	Texas

AGERATUM $x = 10$

houstonianum (*mexicanum*)		20	Cooper & M. 1935	H	Mexico
conyzoides		20	Ishikawa 1916	HM	Tropics
		40	Mitra 1947		

EUPATORIUM * $x = 10, 17$ (Triploids Apomictic)

$x = 10$

cannabinum	Hemp Agrimony	20	W. F. Grant 1953	H	Eur., N. Asia
coelestinum	Mist Flower	20	„ „	H	N. America
ianthinum		20	Holmgren 1919	H	Mexico
patens		20	Krapovickas 1951a	—	Argentine
perfoliatum	Boneset & 14 spp.	20	Grant 1953	HM	N. America
recurvans	& 2 spp.	20, 30	„ „	—	„
purpureum		20, 40	„ „	HM	„
pilosum	& 3 spp.	30	„ „	—	„
pubescens		30, 40	„ „	—	„
mohrii	& 2 spp.	40	„ „	—	„
rothrockii		c. 80	„ „	—	„

$x = 17$

ageratoides		34	Holmgren 1919	H	N. Amer., W.I.
occidentale	& 2 spp.	34	Grant 1953	—	N. America
petiolatum		c. 34	Holmgren 1919	H	Mexico
purpusi		34	„ „	H	California
rugosum	White Snakeroot	34	Grant 1953	HM	Chile, Peru
		36	Cooper & M. 1935		
glandulosum		51	Grant 1953	H	Mexico

ADENOSTYLES $x = 19$

albifrons		38	Langlet 1936	H	Europe
alpina		38	„ „	H	„
leucophylla		38	Favarger 1953	H	W. Alps

MIKANIA $x = 19$

scandens	Cl. Hempweed	38	Mitra 1947	H	Temp. America

TRIBE XIII: MUTISIEAE

TRICHOCLINE $x = 18$

cineraria		36	Covas & S. 1947	—	S. America

MUTISIA $x = 23$

species		46	Snoad 1952	H	S. America

GERBERA (PERDICIUM) $x = 23, 25$

anandria		46	M. & S. 1935	H	Siberia, Japan
integripetala		46	Kishimoto 1936	H	Formosa
jamesoni	Barberton Daisy	50	„ „	H	Transvaal

CHAPTALIA $x = 24$				
integrifolia	48	Baldwin & S. 1947b	—	Trop. America
nutans	48	„ „	—	Mexico
CYCLOLEPIS $x = 27$				
genistoides	54	Covas & S. 1947	—	N. Patagonia
PLAZIA $x = 27$				
argentea	54	Covas & S. 1946	—	Argentina
PROUSTIA $x = 27$				
ilicifolia	54	Covas & S. 1946	—	Chile

Group XVI

GENTIANALES
239
H

PRIMULALES
240, 241
H

PLANTAGINALES
242
H

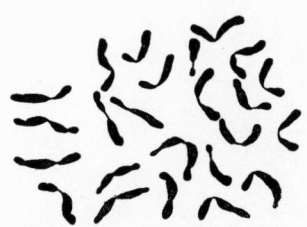

Primula sinensis

239 GENTIANACEAE

LOMATOGONIUM $x = 5$

rotatum		10	D. Löve 1953	—	Circumpolar

GENTIANA (incl. **GENTIANELLA**)* $x = 5, 6, 7,$ $x_2 = 11, 13$

tenella		10	Favarger 1949a	H	North Reg.
nivalis		14	„ „	H	Europe
utriculosa		22	„ 1952b	H	„
brachyphylla		24	Mattick, T. 1950	H	„
frigida		24	Skalinska 1951	H	„
algida		26	S. & S. 1938	H	Siberia
altaica		26	„ „	H	„
andrewsii	& 10 spp.	26	Rork 1949	H	E: N. America
septemfida		26	S. & S. 1938	H	Asia M.—Persia
makinoi		26	Sakai 1934	H	Japan
pneumonanthe		26	Scheerer 1939	H	Eur., N. Asia
scabra		26	Suzuka 1950	H	Manch., N. China
bavarica		28	Mattick, T. 1950	H	C. Europe
verna		{26	Skalinska 1950a	H	Eur., Asia
		28	Favarger 1949a		
acaulis	Stemless G.	36	Rork 1949	H	Europe
alpina		36	Favarger 1949a	H	„
amarella		36	D. Löve 1953	—	W. Eur.—Siberia
aurea		36	„ „	—	Arctic
austriaca		36	Favarger 1952b	—	Europe
campestris	Field G.	36	„ 1949a	H	„
clusii		{36	„ „	H	„
		36	Skalinska 1950a		
insubrica		36	Favarger 1952b	—	„
kochiana		36	„ 1949a	H	C. Europe
praecox		36	Skalinska 1951	—	Europe
prostrata		36	Favarger 1952b	H	N. Temp.
quinqueflora		36	Rork 1949	H	E: U.S.A.
saxosa		36	Favarger 1952b	H	New Zealand
tenuifolia		36	„ „	H	„
lutea	Gentian	40	„ 1949a	HM	Eur., Asia M.
punctata		{40	„ 1942b	H	Europe
		40	Skalinska 1951		
purpurea		40	Favarger 1949a	H	„
macrophylla		42	Rork 1949	—	Siberia
asclepiadea		{44	Favarger 1949a	H	Europe
		44	Skalinska 1951		
ciliata		44	Favarger 1949a	H	„
detonsa		44	D. Löve 1953	H	N. Eur., Arctic Russia
cruciata		52	Favarger 1949a	H	Eur., N. Asia
phlogifolia		52	Rork 1949	H	E. Eur., Asia
straminea		52	„ „	H	W. China
crinita		78	„ „	—	E: N. America
procera		78	„ „	—	„

CENTAURIUM (**ERYTHRAEA**) $x = 7$

littorale	Centaury	c. 38	Wulff 1937a	—	Europe
(vulgare)		c. 56	Warburg, M. 1939		

CENTAURIUM (*cont.*)
minus		42	Rork 1949	—	N. America
pulchellum		42	,, ,,	—	Eur., Temp. Asia

SWERTIA $x = 7, 9, 12$
cuspidata		18	Sakai 1940	—	N. Temp.
perennis		18	,, 1935		
		24	Woycicki 1937	H	,,
		28	Favarger 1952b		
bimaculata		24	Suzuka 1950	H	Himalayas

EXACUM $x = 9$
affine		36	Sugiura 1936	H	Socotra

LEIPHAIMOS (VOYRIA) $x = 9$
azurea		36	Winge 1925	—	Tropics

MENYANTHES $x = 9$
trifoliata	Buckbean	54	Rork 1949	M	N. Temp.

EUSTOMA $x = 9$
russellianum	Prairie Gentian	72	Rork 1949	H	Neb.—Tex.

NYMPHOIDES (LIMNANTHEMUM) $x = 9$
cristata		18	Mookerjea 1951	—	India, China
peltata	Water Fringe	24?	Wang, D. 1951	H	Eurasia
(*L. nymphoides*)		54	Scheerer 1939		
cordata	Floating Heart	36	Rork 1949	H	E: N. America

BLACKSTONIA (CHLORA) $x = 11$
perfoliata	Yellow-wort	44	Maude 1939	—	Eur., S.W. Asia, Morocco

HALENIA $x = 11$
elliptica		22	Favarger 1952b	H	Himalayas

BARTONIA $x = 13$
paniculata		52	Rork 1949	—	N. America
virginica		52	., ,,	—	,,

NEUROTHECA $x = 15$
loeselioides		30	Favarger 1952b	—	W. Trop. Africa

FAURIA $x = 17$
crista-galli		68	M. & S. 1935	H	N. Japan

ENICOSTEMA $x = 19$
littorale		38	Srinivasan 1941	—	Tropics

FRASERA $x = 13?$
caroliniensis		78	Rork 1949	H	E: N. America

240 PRIMULACEAE

CYCLAMEN $x = 5, 11, 12, 17$
balearicum		20	de Haan & D. 1951	H	Balearic Is.
repandum		20	,, ,,	H	France—Greece

CYCLAMEN (*cont.*)

creticum		22	de Haan & D. 1951	H	Crete
cilicium		30	,,	,,	H	Asia Minor
cyprium		30	,,	,,	H	Asia M., Cyprus
libanoticum		30	,,	,,	H	Syria
orbiculatum		30	,,	,,	H	S.E. Eur., As. M., Caucasus
pseudibericum		30	,,	,,	H	Asia Minor
europaeum		34	,,	,,	H	C. Europe
neapolitanum		34	,,	,,	H	France—Asia M.
africanum		68	,,	,,	H	Algeria
persicum	Florists' C.	48	,,	,,	H	E. Medit.
garden forms		48, 96	,,	,,	H	*cult*
graecum		84–85	,,	,,	H	E. Medit.

PRIMULA * $x = 8, 9, 10, 11, 12, 13$

S. 1. SOULIEI $x = 8$

rupicola	16	Bruun 1932b	—	Yunnan

S. 2. INAYATII $x = 8$

inayatii	16	Bruun 1932b	—	E. India

S. 3. FARINOSAE $x = 8, 9, 10, 11$

(i) *blandula*	16	Bruun 1932b	—	Burma, Tibet
caldaria	16	,, ,,	—	Yunnan
genesteriana	16	,, ,,	—	,,
glabra	16	,, ,,	—	Himalayas
knuthiana	16	,, ,,	—	China
sertulum	16	,, ,,	—	,,
stenocalyx	16	,, ,,	—	,,
(ii) *exigua*	18	,, ,,		North Reg.
farinosa Bird's-eye P. {	18, 72	,, ,,		
	18, 36	Davies 1953	H	,,
farinifolia	18	Bruun 1932b	—	Caucasus
frondosa	18	,, ,,	H	Thrace
fauriei	18	,, ,,	H	Japan
modesta	18	,, ,,	H	,,
longiflora	36	,, ,,	H	S.E. Europe
scotica	54	,, ,,	—	Scotland
scandinavica	72	,, ,,	—	S. Scandinavia
laurentiana	72	,, ,,	—	Quebec, etc.
capitellata	72	,, ,,	H	S.W. Asia
magellanica (*decipiens*)	72	,, ,,	—	Magellan
stricta	126	,, ,,	—	Arctic
(iii) *fasciculata*	18	,, ,,	—	Yunnan
chrysopa	20	,, ,,	H	China
yargonensis	20	,, ,,	H	Tibet
tibetica	20	,, ,,	—	,,
involucrata	22	,, ,,	H	Himalayas
sibirica {	22	S. & S. 1938	H	Arctic, Himal.
	44	Bruun 1932b		

S. 4. CAPITATAE $x = 9$

capitata	18	Bruun 1932b	H	Himalayas
crispata	18	,, ,,	H	Sikkim
lacteocapitata	18	,, ,,	—	,,

PRIMULA (cont.)

mooreana	18	Bruun 1932b	H	Sikkim
sphaerocephala	18	„ „	H	Yunnan

S. 5. MALACOIDES $x = 9$

effusa	18	Bruun 1932b	H	Yunnan
forbesii	18	„ „	H	China, Burma
malacoides	18, 36	„ „	H	W. China
garden forms	18, 36 (54)	Janaki Ammal 1952a	H	*cult*

S. 6. VERTICILLATA $x = 9$

floribunda	18	Bruun 1932b	H	Himalayas
verticillata	18	„ „	H	S. Arabia
kewensis (flor. × vert.)	36	„ „	H	*cult*

S. 7. AURICULA $x = 11$; $x_3 = 31 (9 + 11 + 12)$

palinuri	44	Wanner 1943	H	S. Italy
hortensis	54?	Bruun 1932b	H	*cult*
auricula	62	Wanner 1943	H	C. Europe
hirsuta	62	„ „	H	„
integrifolia	62	„ „	H	„
viscosa	62	„ „	H	„
glaucescens	62?	„ „	H	Alps
minima	62?	„ „	H	C. Europe
marginata	90?	Bruun 1932b	H	Alps

S. 8. MUSCARIOIDES $x = 10$

atricapilla	20 + 1-3B	Bruun 1932b	—	Tibet
bellidifolia	20	„ „	—	Himalayas
cernua	20 + 3B	„ „	—	China
littoniana	20	„ „	H	„
apoclita?	40	„ „	—	Tibet
cyanantha	40	„ „	—	„
deflexa?	40	„ „	H	W. China
lepta	40	„ „	H	Yunnan
menziesiana	40	„ „	H	Bhutan

S. 9. SOLDANELLOIDEAE $x = 10$

buryana	20	Bruun 1932b	—	Himalayas
nutans	20	„ „	H	Yunnan
reidii	20	„ „	H	Kumaon (Him.)
wollastonii	20	„ „	—	Himalayas

S. 10. YUNNANENSIS $x = 11$

yunnanensis	22	Bruun 1932b	—	China

S. 11. MINUTISSIMAE $x = 11$

reptans	22	Bruun 1932b	—	Himalayas

S. 12. CUNEIFOLIA $x = 11$

nipponica	22	Bruun 1932b	H	Japan
suffrutescens Sierra P.	44	„ „	H	California

S. 13. AURICULATA $x = 11$

rosea	22	Bruun 1932b	H	Himalayas
elliptica	22	„ „	—	„
algida	{ 18?	S. & S. 1938	H	W. Asia
	44	Bruun 1932b		
luteola	44	„ „	H	Caucasus
auriculata	45	S. & S. 1940	H	„

S. 14. DENTICULATA $x = 11$

denticulata	22 + 0-5B	Bruun 1932b	H	Himalayas
as *cachemiriana*	44 + 8B	„ „	—	
erythrocarpa	22 + 0-5B	„ „	—	Bhutan
crispa	44 + B	„ „	H	Himalayas

278

PRIMULA (*cont.*)

S. 15. SIKKIMENSIS $x = 11$

sikkimensis	& 11 spp.	22	Bruun 1932b	H	Himalayas

S. 16. CANDELABRA $x = 11$

pulverulenta	& 15 spp.	22	Bruun 1932b	H	China
japonica		44	,, ,,	H	Japan

S. 17. ROTUNDIFOLIA $x = 11$

gambeliana	22	Bruun 1932b	—	Himalayas

S. 18. NIVALES $x = 11$

chionantha	22 + 2–7B	Bruun 1932b	H	Yunnan
macrophylla	22	,, ,,	—	Himalayas
maximowiczii	22	,, ,,	—	N. China
nivalis	22	S. & S. 1938	H	C. Asia
obliqua	22	Bruun 1932b	—	Himalayas
purdomii	22	,, ,,	—	Kansu
russeola	22	,, ,,	—	Tibet
sinoplantaginea	22	,, ,,	—	Yunnan
tangutica	22	,, ,,	—	China
ellisiae	44	,, ,,	—	N. America
leucops	44	,, ,,	—	Szechuan
parryii	44	,, ,,	H	W: N. America
rusbyi	44	,, ,,	H	New Mexico

S. 19. PETIOLARES $x = 11$

winteri	22	Bruun 1932b	H	Himalayas

S. 20. VERNALES $x = 11$

elatior	Oxlip	22	Bruun 1932b	—	Eur., Asia Min.
juliae	& 17 spp.	22	,, ,,	H	Caucasus
veris	Cowslip	22	,, ,,	H	Eur., Asia Min.
vulgaris	Primrose	22	,, ,,	H	Europe

S. 21. MEGASEAEFOLIA $x = 11$

megaseaefolia	22	Bruun 1932b	—	Asia Minor

S. 22. GRANDIS $x = 11$

grandis	44	Bruun 1932b	H	Caucasus

S. 23. CORTUSOIDES $x = 11, 12, 13$

(i) *geraniifolia*	22	Bruun 1932b	H	Himalayas
heucherifolia	22	,, ,,	H	W. China
latisecta	22	,, ,,	—	Tibet
(ii) *maclareni?*	24	,, ,,	—	Korea
mollis	24	,, ,,	—	Himalayas
seclusa	24	,, ,,	H	Yunnan, Burma
septemloba	24	,, ,,	—	China
(iii) *pauliana*	24	,, ,,	—	Szechuan
(iv) *cortusoides* (*dentiflora*)	24	,, ,,	H	Siberia
hymenophylla	24	,, ,,	—	Tibet
lichiangensis	24	,, ,,	H	Yunnan
polyneura	24	,, ,,	—	China
saxatilis	24	,, ,,	H	Korea
veitchii	24	,, ,,	H	China
sieboldii	24, 36	,, ,,	H	Japan
(v) *jesoana*	26	,, ,,	H	,,

S. 24. BULLATAE $x = 12$

forrestii	24	Bruun 1932b	H	China
fruticosa	24	,, ,,	H	*cult*
redolens	24	,, ,,	—	Yunnan
rufa	24	,, ,,	H	,,

PRIMULA (*cont.*)
S. 25. SINENSIS $x = 12$

calciphila		24	Bruun 1932b	—	Hupeh
sinensis	Chinese P.	24	,, ,,	H	*cult*
		48	Darlington 1931a		

S. 26. OBCONICA $x = 12$

obconica	24, 48	Bruun 1932b	H	China
sinolisteri	24	,, ,,	—	Yunnan
werringtonensis	24	,, ,,	—	,,

S. 27. PYCNOLOBA $x = 12$

pycnoloba	24	Bruun 1932b	—	W. China

S. 28. REINII $x = 12$

reinii	24	Bruun 1932b	H	Japan

LYSIMACHIA $x = 9, 12, 14$

nemorum		18	Wulff 1938	—	Europe
clethroides		24	Sugiura 1936a	H	China, Japan
vulgaris	Yellow Loosestrife	28	Lewitzky 1934	H	Eurasia
nummularia	Creeping Jenny	36	Wulff 1938	H	Eur., Caucasus
punctata		30	Reese 1953	—	Austria—Cauc., Asia Minor

ANDROSACE $x = 9, 10$

villosa		72	S. & S. 1940	H	Cauc., Himal.
septentrionalis	Rock Jasmine	20	Dahlgren 1916	H	N. Hemisph.

HOTTONIA $x = 10$

palustris	Water Violet	$\left\{ \begin{array}{l} 20 \\ 20 \end{array} \right.$	Ehrenberg 1945, Wulff 1938	H	Europe

SOLDANELLA $x = 10$

carpatica	40	Satczek 1951	—	E. Europe
montana	40	,, ,,	H	,,

NAUMBERGIA (LYSIMACHIA) $x = 10?$

thyrsiflora	Tufted Loosestrife	*c.* 40	Dahlgren 1916	—	N. Temp.

ANAGALLIS $x = 10, 11$

tenella		22	Maude 1940	—	Europe
arvensis	Scarlet Pimpernel	40	Wulff 1937b	—	,,

CENTUNCULUS $x = 11$

minimus	Chaffweed	22	Hagerup 1941b		Eur., N. & S. Am.

CORTUSA $x = 12$

matthioli	24	Bruun 1932b	—	Eur., N. Asia

OMPHALOGRAMMA $x = 12$

farreri	48	Bruun 1932b	H	Burma
elwesianum	96	,, ,,	H	Himalayas

SAMOLUS $x = 12?$

valerandi	Brookweed	*c.* 24, *c.* 36	Wulff 1937a	—	Cosmop.

GLAUX $x = 15$

maritima	Black Saltwort	30	Wulff 1937a	—	Temp.

DODECATHEON $x = 22$

alpinum	44	Thompson 1953	H	California
conjungens	44	,, ,,	—	W: N. America

DODECATHEON (*cont.*)

cusickii		44	Thompson 1953	H	W: N. America
dentatum		44	,, ,,	—	,, ,,
frigidum		44	,, ,,	H	Behring Str.
jeffreyi		42, 44, 66	,, ,,	H	W: N. America
clevelandii		44, 66, 88	,, ,,	H	California
hendersonii		44, 66, 132	,, ,,	H	W: N. America
subalpinum		66	,, ,,	—	California
hanseni		88	,, ,,	—	,,
meadia	Shooting Star	88	,, ,,	H	N. America
poeticum		88	,, ,,	—	Oregon

TRIENTALIS *x* = ?

europaea	{	*c.* 112	L. & L. 1944b	—	Subarctic
	{	*c.* 160	Ehrenberg 1945		

241 PLUMBAGINACEAE

PLUMBAGELLA *x* = 6

micrantha		12	Phillips 1938	—	C. Asia

PLUMBAGO *x* = 7, 8

europaea	Common P.	14	Phillips 1938	M	S. Eur., Cauc.
capensis	Leadwort	{ 14	Dahlgren 1916	H	S. Africa
		{ 16	D'Amato 1940b		

CERATOSTIGMA *x* = 7, 9

plumbaginoides	{ 14	Phillips 1938	H	China
	{ 18	Sugiura 1944		

ARMERIA *x* = 8, 9

pinifolia		16	Sugiura 1939	—	Portugal
sardoa		16	,, ,,	—	Corsica, Sard.
alliacea		18	,, ,,	—	W. Medit.
arctica		18	,, 1944	—	N.W. Europe
berlengensis		18	,, ,,	—	Portugal
canescens		18	,, 1939	H	C. Europe
cariensis		18	,, 1944	—	Asia Minor
denticulata		18	,, 1939	—	Italy
filicaulis		18	,, ,,	—	Spain
juncea		18	,, ,,	H	S. France
juniperifolia		18	,, ,,	H	Spain, Portugal
longiaristata (*allioides*)		18	,, ,,	H	Spain
macrophylla		18	,, 1944	H	,,
plantaginea		18	,, 1939	H	W. Europe
pseudarmeria		18	Phillips 1938	H	S. Europe
scabra		18	Sugiura 1944	—	N. Asia
welwitschii		18	,, 1938	H	Spain
mauritanica		{ 18	Phillips 1938	H	N. Africa
		{ 54	Sugiura 1939		
maritima	Thrift,	{ 18	D'Amato 1940b	H	W. Eur., Sib., N.
	Sea Pink	{ 18	L. & L. 1944b		& S. America
v. *alpina*		{ 18	Phillips 1938		
		{ 36	Sugiura 1939		

LIMONIUM (STATICE) $x = 6, 7, 8, 9$ (Apomixis)

mucronatum		12	Baker unp.	—	Morocco
puberulum		14	„	H	Canary Is.
echioides		28	„	H	Medit., Asia M.
bicolor		16	Sugiura 1939	—	China
bonduellii		16	„ „	H	Algeria
cordatum		16	„ 1944	H	Medit.
dictyocladum		16	„ 1939	—	„
ferulaceum		16	Baker unp.	H	„
ovalifolium		16	„	—	W. Europe
spicatum		16	Sugiura 1936a	H	Casp.—Altai
thouinii		16	„ 1944	H	S.E. Eur., Cauc.
globulariaefolium		64	„ 1939	H	Medit., N. Afr.
vulgare	Sea Lavender	{ 32	Choudhuri 1942	H	Eur., N. Afr., Asia
		36	Castro & F. 1946		Minor
binervosum	(Apo.)	{ 32	Choudhuri 1942	H	W. Europe
		34, 35, 36	Baker unp.		
bellidifolium		18	Choudhuri 1942	H	Europe
latifolium		18	Baker unp.	H	Bulg.—S. Russia
sinuatum		18	Wulff 1937a	H	Medit.
suworowii		18	„ „	H	N.E. Persia—
					Turkestan
californicum		18	Baker unp.	—	California
mexicanum		18	„	—	„
suffruticosum		18	Aleskowsky 1930	—	Cauc.—C. Asia
gmelinii		{ 18, 27	„ „	H	E. Eur., Siberia
		36	Pólya 1948		
confusum	(Apo.)	27	D'Amato 1949b	—	Sicily
cosyrense	„	27	Baker unp.	H	„
recurvum	„	27	„	—	Portland Bill
transwallianum	„	27, 35	„	—	S. Wales, W. Irel.
humile		36	Choudhuri 1942	—	N.W. Europe
sareptans (*tomentella*)		36	Aleskowsky 1930	—	Russia
lychnidifolium (Apo.)		25	Baker unp.	—	W. Eur., N. Afr.
paradoxum	„	33	„	—	S. Wales, N. Irel.
girardianum	„	35	„	—	Portugal

GONIOLIMON $x = 8$

incanum		16	Sugiura 1936a	H	N. Afr.—Siberia
tataricum		{ 16	„ 1944	H	S.E. Eur.,—Sib.
		32	Baker unp.		

ACANTHOLIMON $x = 8$

androsaceum v. *creticum*	32	Baker unp.	H	E. Medit.

242 PLANTAGINACEAE

PLANTAGO * $x = 4, 5, 6$ $x_2 = 9 (4 + 5)$

$x = 4$

ovata	Isfghol	8	Hyde 1953	M	N.W. India

$x = 5$

amplexicaulis	10	MacCullagh 1934	—	Med.—N.W. Ind.
bellardi	10	„ „	—	Med., S.W. Asia
cretica	10	„ „	—	E. Medit.
serraria	10	„ „	—	Medit.
acanthophylla	10–12	„ „	—	S. Europe

PLANTAGO (*cont.*)

aristata	Indian Wheat	20	Heitz 1927	Fo	N. & S. Amer.
coronopus	Buck's Horn	10, 11, 30	Bøcher *et al.* 1953	V	Eur., N. Asia

$x = 6$

arborescens	& 14 spp.	12	MacCullagh 1934	—	Canary Is.
psyllium	Fleawort & 3 spp.	12	Heitz 1927	M	Med.—N.W. Ind.
sericea		12–14	MacCullagh 1934	—	Peru
maritima	Sea Plantain	12	Hagerup 1941b	V	Eur., N. Amer.,
		12 (18), 24	Earnshaw 1942		Arctic .
		12	Nakajima 1930,		
lanceolata	Ribwort	12, 13	Bøcher *et al.* 1953	Fo	Eur., N. Asia
		24, 96	MacCullagh 1934		
major	Great Pl.	12	Turesson 1938	Fo	Eur., Asia M.
v. *asiatica*		24	Ikeno 1929		
alpina (*borealis*)	& 7 spp.	24	MacCullagh 1934	—	C. Europe
tenuiflora		24	Tarnavschi 1938	—	E. Eur., N. Asia
japonica		36	Ono 1953	—	Japan

$x = 6, 10$

albicans		12	MacCullagh 1934	—	Medit.
		20	Lorenzo-Andreu 1951		
patagonica	Indian Wheat	24	MacCullagh 1934	Fo	N. & S. Amer.
		20	Covas & S. 1946		

$x_2 = 9$

raoulii		18	MacCullagh 1934	—	New Zealand

LITTORELLA $x = 6$

uniflora	Shoreweed	24	L. & L. 1942	—	C. & N. Europe

Group XVII

CAMPANALES
243–246
H(S)

POLEMONIALES
247, 248
H

BORAGINALES
249
HST

Campanula persicifolia

243 CAMPANULACEAE

JASIONE $x = 6, 7$

montana	Sheep's Bit $\begin{cases}\end{cases}$	12	Rosen 1931	H	Europe
		12, 14	Wulff 1937a		
perennis		60	Rosen 1931	H	W. Europe

ASYNEUMA (PHYTEUMA, PODANTHUM) $x = 6, 17$

limonifolium	24	Rosen 1931	H	S. Eur., Asia M.
sibthorpianum	24	„ „	H	Greece
canescens	34	Sugiura 1942	H	C. Eur., Cauc.
campanuloides	102	„ „	H	Caucasus

PHYTEUMA $x = (6), 12, 13, 14$

betonicifolium	24	Favarger 1953	H	Alps
lobelioides	24	Sugiura 1942	H	Asia Minor
michauxioides	24	„ „	—	—
halleri	26	„ „	H	S. Europe
nigrum	26	„ „	H	S.W. Europe
globulariifolium	28	Favarger 1953	—	Alps, Pyrenees
hemisphaericum	28	„ „	H	„ „
scheuchzeri	36	Rosen 1931	H	S. Europe
spicatum	Spiked Rampion 36	Armand 1912	H(R)	Europe

SPECULARIA (CAMPANULA) $x = 7, 10$

speculum	Venus' Looking $\begin{cases}\end{cases}$	14	Koller 1945*	H	S. Europe
	Glass	20	Sugiura 1942		
hybrida		20	„ „	—	Medit.
pentagonia		20	„ „	H	„

CODONOPSIS $x = 8$

clematidea	16	Rosen 1931	H	C: W. Asia
subsimplex	16	„ „	H	C. Asia

EDRAIANTHUS (WAHLENBERGIA) $x = 8$?

graminifolius	$\begin{cases}\end{cases}$	24	Rosen 1931	H	Dalmatia
		32	Sugiura 1942		
tenuifolius		32	„ „	H	„

PLATYCODON $x = (7?) 9$

grandiflorum	Chinese Bell $\begin{cases}\end{cases}$	18	Suzuka & K. 1949	H	E. Asia
	Flower	28	Kihara *et al.* 1931		
v. *mariesii*		18	Sugiura 1942		

CAMPANULA * $x = 8, 10, 12, 13, 14, 17$
$x = 8$

latiloba (*grandis*)	16	Marchal 1920	H	Siberia
pyrenaica	16	Sugiura 1942	H	Pyr., Balearic Is.
subpyrenaica	16	„ „	H	N.E. Spain
persicifolia	16, 17, 18, 32	Darlington & L. C. '50	H	Eur., Sib.
isophylla	32	Vilmorin & S. 1927b	H	Riviera
pulloides	48	Koller 1945*	H	*cult*
thyrsoidea	48	Sugiura 1942	H	Eur. Alps
phyctidocalyx	$\begin{cases}\end{cases}$ 16	La Cour 1945*	H	S.W. Asia
	102	Sugiura 1942		
carpatica	$\begin{cases}\end{cases}$ 32	Koller 1945*	H	Carpathians
	34	Sugiura 1942		

287

CAMPANULA *(cont.)*

alliariaefolia	{ 96	M. & S. 1935	H	Asia M., Cauc.
	{ 68	Sugiura 1942		

$x = 10$

macrostyla	20	Marchal 1920	H	Crimea
patula	20	Rutland 1941	H	S. Europe
propinqua v. *grandiflora*	20	Sugiura 1942	H	Armenia, Persia
rapunculus Rampion	20	Marchal 1920	HV	Eur., N. Africa
steveni v. *nana*	20	Koller 1945*	H	Cauc., Persia
divaricata	40	La Cour 1945*	—	N. America
ramosissima (*loreyi*)	{ 20	Marchal 1920	H	S. Europe
as *drabifolia*	{ 34	Sugiura 1942		

$x = 12$

colorata	24	Kishore 1951	H	Sikkim Himal.

$x = 13$

cervicaria	26	Sugiura 1942	H	Greece
peregrina (*primulaefolia*)	26	Marchal 1920	H	Spain, Portugal

$x = 14$

erinus	28	Koller 1945*	H	Medit., Canaries

$x = 17$

allionii	34	La Cour 1945*	H	Alps
barbata	34	Marchal 1920	H	,,
betonicaefolia	34	,, ,,	H	Greece
bononiensis & 16 spp.	34	Sugiura 1942	H	E. Eur., W. Asia
dasyantha	34	Sakai 1935	—	Sib., W: N. Am.
fragilis	34	Marchal 1920	—	Adriatic
hypopolia	34	La Cour 1945*	—	Temp. Asia
latifolia Giant C.	34	Vilmorin & S. 1927b	H	Eur.—Kashmir
longestyla	34	,, ,,	H	Caucasus
medium Canterbury Bell	34	Sugiura 1942	H	S. Europe
piperi	34	La Cour 1945*	H	W: N. America
punctata (*nobilis*)	34	Marchal 1920	H	Japan, Siberia
pyramidalis	34	,, ,,	H	Europe
pyraversi	34	Vilmorin & S. 1927b	H	*cult*
trachelium	34	Marchal 1920	H	Eur., Sib., N. Afr.
tubulosa	34	La Cour 1945*	—	Crete
van Houttii	34	Vilmorin & S. 1927b	H	*cult*
thyrsoidea	{ 34	Rosen 1931	H	Eur. Alps
	{ 48	Sugiura 1942		
cochlearifolia (*pusilla*)	{ 34	Marchal 1920	H	Alps
	{ 68	Sugiura 1942		
glomerata	34, 68	,, 1939	H	Eur.—C. Asia
rotundifolia Harebell	34, 68	Bøcher 1936	H	North Reg.
	34, 55–56, 68	Guinochet 1942		
v. *hostii*	68	Sugiura 1942		
portenschlagiana	{ 34	Marchal 1920	H	Dalmatia
	{ 102	Sugiura 1942		
raddeana	{ 34	Rosen 1931	H	Caucasus
	{ 102	Sugiura 1942		
abietina	68	Sugiura 1942	H	S.E. Europe
caespitosa	68	,, ,,	H	Alps
collina	68	,, ,,	H	Caucasus

CAMPANULA (*cont.*)

garganica	{ 68	Sugiura 1942	H	Alps
	102	„ 1937b		
kladniana	68	„ 1942	H	E. Europe
morettiana	68	„ „	H	Alps
pulla	68	„ „	H	„
scheuchzeri	68	Bøcher 1936	H	„
speciosa	68	Sugiura 1942	H	S.W. Europe
americana	102	„ „	H	N. America
caucasica	102	„ „	—	Caucasus
elegans	102	„ „	H	Siberia
laciniata	102	„ „	H	Greece
mirabilis	102	„ „	H	Caucasus
rapunculoides	102	„ „	HV	Eur., A.M., Cauc.
sibirica	102	„ „	H	C. Eur.—N. Asia

WAHLENBERGIA $x = (8?) 9$

gracilenta	18	Gulline unp.	—	Australia
gymnoclada	18	„	—	„
consimilis	36	„	H	„
quadrifida	54	„	—	„
saxicola	72	„	H	Tasmania
gracilis	64	Sugiura 1942	H	N. Caled., S.E. As.

ADENOPHORA $x = 17$

bulleyana	34	Sugiura 1942	H	Szechuan
diplodonta	34	Rosen 1931	H	China
forrestii	34	Sugiura 1942	—	„
remotifolia	37!	M. & S. 1935	H	Japan
thunbergiana	37!	„ „	—	„
stricta	34	Sugiura 1942	H	„
hakusanensis	34, 51	M. & S. 1935	—	„
liliifolia (*communis*)	{ 34	Modilewski 1934	H(R)	C. Eur.—Sib.
	102	Sugiura 1942		
ornata	102	„ „	H	W. China
palustris	102	„ „	H	E. Asia
potaninii	102	„ „	H	W. China
lamarckii	104	M. & S. 1936	H	E. Europe

MICHAUXIA $x = 17$

campanuloides	34	Sugiura 1942	H	Asia Minor

PRISMATOCARPUS $x = 17$

strictus	34	Sugiura 1942	—	S. Africa

SYMPHANDRA $x = 17$

hoffmanni	34	Vilmorin & S. 1927b	H	Bosnia

TRACHELIUM $x = 17$

coeruleum	34	Sugiura 1942	H	S. Europe

244 LOBELIACEAE

ISOTOMA $x = 7$

fluviatilis	14	Subramanyam 1951	—	Australia

LOBELIA * $x = 7, 9$?
$x = 7$

brevifolia	& 7 spp.	14	Bowden 1954	—	E: N. America
cardinalis	Cardinal Fl.	14	Vilmorin & S. 1927b	H	N. America
cliffortiana		14	Sugiura 1936b	—	Trop. Amer.
urens		14	Vilmorin & S. 1927b	—	Europe
siphilitica		14	Okuno 1937	HM	N. America
as *speciosa*		42	Sugiura 1936b		
triquetra		14, 42	Okuno 1937	—	S. Africa
amoena		28	Bowden 1954	H	E: N. America
elongata		28	„ „	—	„ „
glandulosa		28	„ „	H	„ „
sessilifolia		28	Sugiura 1937b	—	Kamchatka
erinus		28, 42	Vilmorin & S. 1927b	H	S. Africa
richardsonii		42	Sugiura 1937b	—	—
tupa	Blood L.	42	Vilmorin & S. 1927b	—	Chile, Peru

$x = 9$

ramosa	18	Sugiura 1936a	—	Australia
tenuior	18	„ 1937b	—	„

245 GOODENIACEAE

GOODENIA $x = 8$

elongata	16	W. D. Jackson unp.	—	Australia
geniculata v. *lanata*	16	„ „	—	„
ovata	16	„ „	H	„

SCAEVOLA $x = 8$

lobelia	16	Kausik 1939	—	Tropics

SELLIERA $x = 8$

radicans	16	W. D. Jackson unp.	H	Aust., N.Z., Chile

VELLEYA $x = 8$

montana	16	W. D. Jackson unp.	—	Australia
paradoxa	16	„ „	H	„

246 STYLIDIACEAE

STYLIDIUM $x = ?$

adnatum	36	Sugiura 1936a	H	Australia

247 POLEMONIACEAE

GYMNOSTERIS $x = 6$

nudicaulis	12	MacMillan 1949	—	N. America

HUGELIA $x = 7$

virgata	14	Flory 1937	H	N. America

PHLOX $x = 7$

amoena	14	Flory 1934	H	S.E: U.S.A.
amplifolia	14	„ 1937	H	„

PHLOX (cont.)

arendsii		14	Flory 1934	H	*cult*
bifida	Tenpoint Ph.	14	„ 1937	H	E: U.S.A.
carolina		14 + 0–2**B**	Meyer 1944	H	S.E: U.S.A.
divaricata	Blue Ph.	14 + 0–1**B**	„ „	H	E: N. America
drummondii		14 (28)	„ „	H	Texas
glaberrima	Meadow Ph.	14 + 0–3**B**	„ „	H	E: U.S.A.
maculata	Perennial Ph.	14	Flory 1934	H	E: N. America
nivalis		14 + 0–4**B**	Meyer 1944	H	S.E: U.S.A.
ovata		14	Flory 1934	H	„
paniculata		14 + 0–10**B**	Meyer 1944	H	E: U.S.A.
pilosa (argillacea)		14	Flory 1934	H	E: N. America
stellata		14	„ „	H	*cult*
stolonifera		14	„ „	H	E: U.S.A.
subulata	Moss Ph.				
		14 + 0–13**B**, 28	Meyer 1944	H	„
adsurgens	Periwinkle Ph.	14, 21	Flory 1934	H	W.: N. America
suffruticosa		14 + 0–1**B**, 21	Meyer 1944	H	*cult*
buckleyi		28	Flory 1937	H	W. Virginia
douglasii (diffusa)		28	„ 1934	H	W: N. America
hoodii		28	„ „	H	„ „

GILIA *x* = 7, 9
x = 7

aggregata	Skyrocket G.	14	Flory 1937	H	W: N. America
longiflora (collomia)		14	„ „	H	„ „
rubra	Texas Plume	14	„ „	H	N. America

x = 9

achilleaefolia	Yarrow G.	18	V. Grant 1953	H	California
angelensis		18	„ „	—	„
capitata		18	„ „	H	W: N. America
foetida		18	Covas & S. 1946	—	Chile
gilioides		18	Grant 1950b	—	W: N. America
laciniata		18	Langlet 1936	H	Peru, Chile, Arg.
latiflora		18	Grant 1950b	—	W: N. America
millefoliata		18	„ 1953	—	„ „
multicaulis		18	Sugiura 1936b	H	California
rigidula		18	Flory 1937	H	W: N. America
tricolor	Bird's-Eyes	18	Grant 1953	H	California
tenuiflora		18	„ 1950b	H	„
clivorum		36	„ „	—	„
sinuata		36	„ „	—	W: N. America

COLLOMIA (GILIA) *x* = 8

grandiflora		16	Flory 1937	H	W: N. America
heterophylla		16	„ „	—	„ „
linearis		16	„ „	H	„ „
coccinea (biflora)		32	„ „	H	Chile

LINANTHUS (GILIA) *x* = 9

aureus		18	Flory 1937	H	W: N. America
densiflorus		18	„ „	H	California
dianthiflorus		18	„ „	H	„
dichotomus		18	„ „	H	W: N. America
parviflorus		18	„ „	H	„ „

POLEMONIUM * $x = 9$

acutiflorum		18	Nygren, L. & L. '48	—	N. Temp.
boreale		16	Flovik 1940	—	Arctic Eurasia
caeruleum	Jacob's Ladder	18	Griesinger 1937	HM	Europe
reptans	Sweat Root	18	Flory 1937	M	N. America
13 species		18 {	„ „ Griesinger 1937		

CANTUA $x = ?$

buxifolia	Magic Fl.	*c.* 54	Flory 1937	H	Peru

COBAEA $x = ?$

scandens		52	Flory 1937, E.K.J.*	H	Mexico

248 HYDROPHYLLACEAE

ELLISIA $x = 5$

nyctelea	20	Cave & C. 1950	—	N. America

PHACELIA * $x = 5, 7, 8, 9, 11, 12, 13$

dubia	& 4 spp.	10	Cave & C. 1944, '47	—	W: N. America
maculata		10	„ 1950	—	„ „
divaricata		20	„ 1942	H	California
greenei		20	„ 1950	—	„
racemosa		14	„ 1947	—	„
ranunculacea		28	„ „	—	„
dalesiana		16	„ 1950	—	„
glabra		16	„ „	—	N. America
irritans		16	„ 1942	—	California
quickii		16	„ 1947	—	„
bipinnatifida		18	„ 1950	—	S.E: U.S.A.
purshii		18	„ „	—	S: U.S.A.
13 species		18	„ '42, '44, '47, '50		
grandiflora		22	„ 1944	H	California
linearis		22	„ „	H	W: N. America
parryi		22	„ 1947	H	S. California
sericea		22	„ 1942	H	W: N. America
tanacetifolia		22	„ „	H	California
viscida		22	„ 1947	H	„
whitlovia (*minor*)		22	Chittenden 1928	H	„
26 species		22	Cave & C. '42, '44, '47, '50		
californica		22, 44	„ 1944	—	„
5 species		22, 44	„ '42, '44, '47		
argentea		44	„ 1942	—	„
4 species		44	„ '42, '47		
lemmoni		{ 44 48	„ 1944 „ 1947	—	„
brachyloba		24	„ 1944	—	„
cooperae		24	„ 1947	—	„
suaveolens		24	„ 1950	—	„

292

PHACELIA (*cont.*)

bicolor	26	Cave & C. 1950	—	W: N. America
fremontii	26	„ 1942	—	California
glandulifera	26	„ 1950	—	„
gymnoclada	26	„ „	—	„
leibergii	26	„ „	—	„

EUCRYPTA $x = 5, 6$

micrantha	12	Cave & C. 1950	—	N. America
chrysanthemifolia	20	„ 1944	—	„

LEMMONIA $x = 7$

californica	14	Cave & C. 1950	—	California

ERIODICTYON * $x = 7$

angustifolium	28	Cave & C. 1950	—	W: N. America
californicum	28	„ 1947	—	California
3 species	28	„ '47, '50		

NAMA * $x = 7$

aretioides	14	Cave & C. 1950	—	N. America
demissum	14	„ „	—	W: N. America
stenocarpum	14	„ „	—	California
6 species	14	„ „		
densum	28	„ 1942	—	N. America
lobbii	28	„ „	—	„
jamaicense	28	„ 1950	—	W. Indies

HESPEROCHIRON $x = 8$

californicus	16	Cave & C. 1950	—	California

NEMOPHILA * $x = 7, 9$

phacelioides	14	Cave & C. 1950	H	E: N. America
maculata Spotted N.	18	„ „	H	„ „
menziesii	18	„. 1942	H	W: N. America
6 species	18	„ „		

DRAPERIA $x = 9$

systyla	18	Cave & C. 1947	—	California

HYDROPHYLLUM * $x = 9$

canadense	18	Bowden 1940a	H	E: N. America
capitatum	18	Cave & C. 1942	H	W: N. America
virginianum	18	„ 1950	H	E: N. America
4 species	18	„ '42, '50		

PHOLISTOMA $x = 9$

auritum	18	Cave & C. 1942	H	California
membranaceum	18	„ „	—	„
racemosum	18	„ 1947	—	„

EMMENANTHE $x = 9$

rosea	18	Cave & C. 1950	—	W: N. America
penduliflora Yellow Bells	36	„ 1942	H	California

ROMANZOFFIA $x = 11$

sitchensis	22	Cave & C. 1950	H	W: N. America

ROMANZOFFIA (*cont.*)
suksdorfi	22	Cave & C. 1942	—	W: N. America
tracyi	22	„ 1947	—	„ „

MILTITZIA $x = 12, 13$
glandulifera	24	Cave & C. 1950	—	W: N. America
lutea	24	„ „	—	„ „
parviflora	24	„ „	—	„ „
glaberrima	26	„ „	—	„ „

TURRICULA $x = 13$
parryi	26	Cave & C. 1947	—	W: N. America

WIGANDIA $x = 19$
kunthii	38	Cave & C. 1947	—	Trop. America
macrophylla	38	„ 1950	H	„ „
species	76	„ „	—	„ „
vigieri	44?	Sugiura 1936a	H	cult

HYDROLEA $x = 20$
spinosa	40	Svensson 1925	H	Trop. America

249 BORAGINACEAE

AMSINCKIA $x = 4, 5, 6, 7.$ $x_2 = 13, 15, 17, 19$
lunaris	8	Ray 1954	—	California
spectabilis	10	„ „	—	„
douglasiana	12	„ „	—	„
grandiflora	12	„ „	—	„
furcata	14	„ „	—	„
vernicosa	14	„ „	—	„
retrorsa	16, 26, 34	„ „	—	N. America
eastwoodiae	24	„ „	--	California
gloriosa	24	„ „	—	„
tessellata	24	„ „	—	„
lycopsoides	30	„ „	H	„
intermedia	30, 34, 38	„ „	H	„
inepta	36	„ „	—	L. California
angustifolia	32	Strey 1931	—	Chile

BRUNNERA (ANCHUSA) $x = 6$
	⎧ 12	Britton 1951		
macrophylla	⎨ 12	Smith 1932	H	Siberia, Cauc.
	⎩ 16?	Strey 1931		

CACCINIA $x = (6)\ 12$
crassifolia	24	Strey 1931	H	Armen.—Afghan.
strigosa	24	„ „	H	Persia

CYNOGLOSSUM * $x = (6)\ 12$
amabile		24	Britton 1951	H	China, Tibet
officinale	Hound's Tongue	24	„ „	—	Eur., Asia
zeylanicum	& 7 spp.	24	„ „	H	India
aequinoctiale		48	„ „	H	Kenya, Uganda

MERTENSIA $x = (6)\ 12$

elongata		24	Britton 1951	H	Kashmir
maritima	Oyster Plant	24	L. & L. 1948	H	W. Europe
sibirica		24	Strey 1931	H	E. Siberia
virginica	Virg. Cowslip	24	Britton 1951	H	E: U.S.A.
ciliata		24, 48	„ „	H	W: N. America

ADELOCARYUM (PARACARYUM) $x = 6$?

coelestinum		c. 24	Strey 1931	H	N. India

ASPERUGO $x = 6$?

procumbens		48	Reese 1953	M	Eur., W. Asia, N. Africa

LITHOSPERMUM $x = (6),\ 7,\ 8,\ 12$

canescens	Puccoon	14	Britton 1951	H	E: N. America
tenuiflorum		28	Strey 1931	—	Asia M.—India
apulum		28	Britton 1951	—	Medit.
fruticosum		28	Lorenzo-Andreu '51	H	S. Europe
erythrorhizon		28	Suzuka 1950	—	Japan
officinale	Gromwell	28	Britton 1951	B	Europe, W. Asia
arvense	Corn G.	16? / 28 / 28	Suzuka 1950 / Britton 1951, / L. & L. 1944b	—	Eurasia
purpureo-coeruleum		16	Reese 1952a	HM	Europe
zollingeri		16	Britton 1951	H	Java
croceum		24	„ „	—	N. America
incisum		24	„ „	—	„

OMPHALODES $x = (6),\ 7$

lusitanica (nitida)		24	Britton 1951	H	Spain, Portugal
linifolia		28	„ „	H	S.W. Europe
verna	Blue-eyed Mary	42	„ „	H	S. Europe

MYOSOTIS $x = 6,\ 7,\ 8,\ 9$

sylvatica	Wood For-get-me-not	14 / 18 / 18, 32	S. & S. 1941 / Britton 1951, / Geitler 1936	H	Eurasia
sparsiflora		18	„ „	—	Eur., N. Asia
alpestris (pyrenaica)	24, 48, c. 72		„ „	H	N. Reg.
hispida	Early F.	48	„ „	H	Eur., S.W. Asia, N. Africa
welwitschii		48	Britton 1951	H	Spain
arvensis	Common F.	c. 48 / c. 54	Strey 1931 / Geitler 1936	H	N. Temp.
palustris (scorpioides)		64	L. & L. 1942	H	Eurasia
caespitosa (laxa)		c. 80	Strey 1931	H	North Reg.

ANCHUSA $x = 6,\ 8,\ 9$?

affinis		16	Britton 1951	H	Abyssinia
barrelieri		16 / 18	Smith 1932 / Lewitzky 1940	H	S. Eur., Asia M.
capensis		16	Britton 1951	H	S. Africa
granatensis		16	„ „	H	Spain
officinalis	Alkanet	16	„ „	V	Europe
riparia		16	„ „	H	Cent. Europe
ochroleuca		24	„ „	H	Caucasus
azurea (italica)		32	„ „	H	Medit.
var. " Opal "		$32 + 1\text{–}4\mathbf{B}$	„ „		

CORDIA $x = 7, 8$

glabra		28	Britton 1951	H	Brazil
alba		32	„ „	H	Trop. America
angiocarpa		32	„ „	—	Cuba
boissieri		32	„ „	H	Texas—Mexico
leucosebestera		32	„ „	—	Cuba
sebestena	Aloe Wood	32	„ „	HM	W. Indies
alliodora		c. 72	„ „	W	Trop. America
rothii		c. 72	„ „	—	India
tremula		c. 80	„ „	—	W. Indies

PULMONARIA * $x = 7, 11$

officinalis	Lungwort	14	Tarnavschi 1935	HM	Eur., Caucasus
rubra	& 3 spp.	14	„ „	H	S.E. Europe
angustifolia		14, 28	„ „	H	Europe
saccharata	Jerusalem	⎰14, 16	Strey 1931	Sp	*cult*
	Sage	⎱22	Tarnavschi 1935		
affinis		22	„ „	H	France
tuberosa		22	„ „	—	Europe
mollis (*mollissima*)		28	„ „	H	C. Eur., N. Asia
montana		28	„ „	—	C. Europe

HELIOTROPIUM $x = 7–13$

mendocinum		14	Schnack & C. 1947	—	Chile
supinum		16	Britton 1951	M	S. Eur., S.W. Asia, N. Africa
arborescens Heliotrope (*peruvianum*)		18	„ „	HP	Peru
indicum		22	„ „	H	W. Indies
europaeum		⎰24	Svensson 1925	HM	Medit.
		⎱32	Britton 1951		
amplexicaule		⎰26	„ „	H	Argentine
		⎱28	Covas & S. 1947		
curassavicum		⎰26	Britton 1951	HM	U.S.A., W. Ind.
		⎱28	Schnack & C. 1947		

BORAGO $x = 8$

officinalis	Borage	16	Britton 1951	Sp	Eur , N. Afr., As. Minor
laxiflora		32	Strey 1931	H	Corsica

LOBOSTEMON * $x = 7$

fruticosus	& 9 spp.	14	Levyns 1934	H	S. Africa
echioides		14, 42	„ „	—	„
glaucophyllus		14, 28	„ „	H	„
bolusii		28	„ „	—	„
decorus		28	„ „	—	„
hispidus		28	„ „	—	„

ONOSMA $x = 7$

tauricum		14	Britton 1951	H	S.E. Europe
stellulatum		28	„ „	H	„

ECHIUM * $x = 7, 8$

hispidissimum		14, 28	Litardière 1943	—	Medit.
candicans	& 7 spp.	16	„ „	H	Madeira
lusitanicum		16	Britton 1951	H	Spain, Portugal

ECHIUM (*cont.*)

plantagineum	& 2 spp.	16	Britton 1951	HM	Medit.
aculeatum	& 3 spp.	16, 32	Litardière 1943	—	Canary Is.
rossicum		24	„ „	—	S. Eur., Cauc.
rosulatum		32	Britton 1951	—	Spain
vulgare	Viper's Bugloss	32	„ „	M	Eur., W. Asia
		16, 32	Litardière 1943		

NONNEA (NONEA) $x = 7, 8$

lutea	14	Britton 1951	—	Europe
rosea	16	„ „	H	Caucasus
versicolor	16	Gusuleac & T. 1935	—	„
decumbens	*c.* 32	Strey 1931	—	W. Medit.

LAPPULA (ECHINOSPERMUM) $x = 8?$

myosotis	*c.* 48	Strey 1931	M	Eur., S.W. Asia

LYCOPSIS (ANCHUSA) $x = 8$

orientalis		16	Strey 1931	—	S. Eur., S.W. Asia
arvensis	Bugloss	*c.* 54	Svensson 1925	—	Eurasia

MOLTKIA $x = 8$

petraea	16	Britton 1951	H	Greece

CERINTHE $x = 8, 9$

retorta		16	Strey 1931	H	Greece
major	Honeywort	16	Britton 1951	HM	Switzerland
glabra (*alpina*)		18	„ „	H	Eur., Alps
minor		18	„ „	HM	S. Europe

EHRETIA $x = 8, 10$

microphylla	Philippine Tea	32	Britton 1951	BH	S.E. Asia
(*buxifolia*)					
thyrsiflora		32	„ „	H	China, Japan
anacua		40	„ „	—	Texas, Mexico

SYMPHYTUM $x = 9, 10$

caucasicum		*c.* 36	Strey 1931	H	Caucasus
officinale	Comfrey	36	Suzuka 1950	HM	Eur., W. Asia
uplandicum		36	Vaarama, L. & L. '48	H	*cult*
peregrinum		36	Maude 1939	H	E. Caucasus
asperum	Prickly C.	40	Britton 1951	H	Russia—Persia
tauricum		40	„ „	H	S. Russia
bulbosum		*c.* 72	Strey 1931	H	Europe
tuberosum		*c.* 72	„ „	HM	Eur., S.W. Asia

ALKANNA $x = 11$

orientalis	22	Britton 1951	D?	E. Medit.

PENTAGLOSSA (CARYOLOPHA, ANCHUSA) $x = 11$

sempervirens	22	Britton 1951	H	W. Europe

Group XVIII

SOLANALES 250, 251 HS	**PERSONALES** 252–259 HS(T)

LAMIALES
260–264
HS(T)

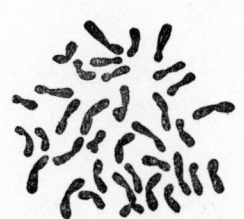

Glechoma hederacea

PETUNIA $x = 7, 9$

axillaris (nyctaginiflora)		14	Kostoff et al. 1935	H	Argentine
integrifolia (violacea)		14	Dermen 1931a	H	,,
		(28)	Levan 1937a		
hybrida (ax. × integ.)	(21, 28, 35)		Dermen 1931a	H	cult
parodii	14 + 0–1B		Sullivan 1947	—	Argentine
parviflora		18	Ferguson & C. 1932	—	N. & S. Amer.

CESTRUM $x = 8$

nocturnum	Night Jasmine	c. 16	Bhaduri 1933	H	W. Indies
parqui		16	Schnack & C. 1947	H	Chile
purpureum (elegans)		16	Carniel 1952	H	Mexico

FABIANA $x = 9$

imbricata	False Heath	18	Goodspeed 1933	M	Peru

NICANDRA $x = 9 +$ isochromosome

physaloides		19, 20 (40)	Darlington & J. '45	HM	Peru
		21?	Sinha 1951a		

NIEREMBERGIA $x = 9$

frutescens	Tall Cup Fl.	18	Goodspeed 1933	H	Chile

NICOTIANA $x = 9, 10, 12$
S. 1. PETUNIOIDES
$x = 9$

alata	Jasmine Tobacco	18	Goodspeed 1945	H	Brazil
bonariensis		18	,, ,,	—	,,
langsdorffii		18	,, ,,	—	,,
sanderae		18	,, ,,	H	cult
$x = 10$					
longiflora		20	,, ,,	H	Chile
plumbaginifolia		20	,, ,,	H	Mexico—Arg.
$x = 12$					
acaulis		24	,, ,,	—	Argentine
acuminata		24	,, ,,	—	S. America
attenuata	Coyote T.	24	,, ,,	M	Chile
corymbosa		24	,, ,,	—	Chile, Arg.
linearis		24	,, ,,	—	,, ,,
miersii		24	,, ,,	—	,, ,,
noctiflora (cavanillesii)		24	,, ,,	—	C. Argentine
pauciflora (caudigera)		24	Goodspeed 1945	—	Chile
palmeri		24	,, ,,	—	S.W: U.S.A.
petunioides (pampasana)		24	,, ,,	—	N. Argentine
sylvestris		24	,, ,,	—	N.W. Argentine
trigonophylla	Desert T.	24	,, ,,	M	S.W.: U.S.A., Mexico
undulata		24	,, ,,	—	Andes
wigandioides		24	,, ,,	—	,,
arentsii		48	,, ,,	—	Peru, Bolivia
bigelovii	Indian T.	48	,, ,,	M	W: U.S.A.
clevelandii		48	,, ,,	—	,,
nudicaulis		48	,, ,,	—	N. Mexico
nesophila		48	,, ,,	—	Mexico
repanda		48 (96)	,, ,,	—	,,
stocktonii		48	,, ,,	—	,,

21

NICOTIANA (*cont.*)

S. 2. RUSTICA

benavidesii		24	Goodspeed 1945	—	Peru
cordifolia		24	,, ,,	—	Juan Fern.
knightiana		24	,, ,,	—	S. Peru
raimondii		24	,, ,,	—	Peru
solanifolia		24	,, ,,	—	N. Chile
thyrsiflora		24	,, ,,	—	N.W. Peru
glauca	Tree T.	24	,, ,,	—	N.W. Argentine
paniculata		24	,, ,,	—	Peru
rustica	Aztec T.	48	,, ,,	IM	,,

S. 3. TABACUM

glutinosa		24	,, ,,	—	,,
tomentosa	Giant T.	24	,, ,,	—	,,
tomentosiformis (*rusbyi*)		24	,, ,,	—	Bolivia
otophora		24	,, ,,	—	Bolivia, Arg.
setchellii		24	,, ,,	—	N. Peru
tabacum	Common T.	48	,, ,,	IM	Peru, *cult*
		(72), (96)	Goodspeed 1930		
digluta (*glut.* × *tabacum*)		72	Clausen & G. 1925	—	*expt.*
tabacum × *Petunia parodii*		31	Pogliaga 1952	—	*expt.*

S. 4. SUAVEOLENTES

$x = 8$

exigua	32	Wheeler 1935	—	Queensland
maritima	32	,, ,,	—	S. Australia
velutina	32	,, 1945	—	Australia
suaveolens	32, 64	,, 1935	H	S.E. Australia

$x = 9$

gossei	36	,, ,,	—	C. Australia

$x = 10$

goodspeedii	40	,, ,,	—	S. Australia
megalosiphon	40	,, ,,	—	N.E. Australia

$x = 11$

rotundifolia	44	,, ,,	—	S.W. Australia

$x = 12$

debneyi	48	,, ,,	—	N.E. Austr., N. Caled.
fragrans	48	,, 1945	—	S. Pacific

$x_2 = (9 + 10)$

benthamiana	38	,, ,,	—	Australia
excelsior	38	,, ,,	—	,,

$x_2 = (10 + 11)$

occidentalis	42	,, ,,	—	,,

SCHIZANTHUS $x = 10$

pinnatus	20	Sugiura 1937b	H	Chile
retusus	20	,, ,,	H	Chile, Peru
wisetonensis	20	,, 1936b	H	*cult*

BROWALLIA $x = 11$

demissa	22	Sugiura 1936a	H	S. America
grandiflora	22	,, ,,	H	Peru
viscosa	22	,, ,,	H	S. America
speciosa	44	,, ,,	H	Colombia

BRUNFELSIA $x = 11$

americana		22	Bhaduri 1933	H	Trop. America
calycina		22	E.K.J. *	H	Brazil

QUINCULA $x = 10, 11$

lobata	20, 22, 24	Menzel 1950	H	Kans.—Mex.

SALPIGLOSSIS $x = 11$

sinuata	44	Vilmorin & S. 1928	H	Chile

ACNISTUS $x = 12$

parviflorus	24	Ratera 1943	—	Trop. America

CAPSICUM $x = 12$

annuum	Chilli, Red	24 (36, 48)	Pal *et al.* 1941	SpVVit	Trop. Amer., *cult*
	Pepper, Paprika	24	Sinha 1950a		
as *baccatum*		24	Huskins & L. C. '30		
		(12)	Christensen & B. '43		
as *frutescens*	Cayenne P.,	24	Sinha 1950a		
	Bird P.	(48)	Greenleaf 1947		
microcarpum		24	Schnack & C. 1947	—	W. Indies

CYPHOMANDRA $x = 12$

betacea	Tree Tomato	24	Vignoli 1945a	F	S. America

DATURA * $x = 12$

alba		24	Suzuka & K. 1949	—	O.W. Tropics
fastuosa		24	Vilmorin & S. 1927a	M	Tropics
ferox	& 4 spp.	24	Bergner 1943	M	China
meteloides	& 2 spp.	24	Satina 1953	M	W: N. Amer.
stramonium	Thorn A.	24 (12, 25)	Satina *et al.* 1941	HM	Cosmop.
	Jimson W.	(48)	Belling & B. 1923		

GRABOWSKIA $x = 12$

duplicata	24	Ratera 1943	—	S. America

JABOROSA $x = 12$

integrifolia	24	Vignoli 1945a	H	Argentine

LYCIUM $x = 12$

cestroides		24	Schnack & C. 1947	—	Brazil
chinense	Box Thorn	24	Sugiura 1936b	H	China
ciliatum		24	Ratera 1947	—	Brazil
cuneatum		24	„ 1943	—	Bolivia
elongatum		24	„ 1947	—	Chile

LYCOPERSICUM (SOLANUM) $x = 12$

esculentum	Tomato	24	Barton 1950	VF	*cult*, Peru
		(12, 25, 36, 48)	Rick 1945		
		(48)	Upcott 1935		
cheesemannii		24	Luckwill 1943	—	Galapagos
glandulosum		24	„ „	—	Peru
hirsutum		24	„ „	—	Peru, Ecuador
peruvianum		24	„ „	—	Peru
pimpinellifolium		24	„ „	—	„
pissisi		24	„ „	—	Peru, Chile

303

MARGARANTHUS $x=12$

solanaceus		24	Menzel 1950	—	Texas

SALPICHROA (WITHANIA) $x=12$

rhomboidea (origanifolia)	Huevo de Gallo	24	Vilmorin & S. 1928	V	Argentine

SCOPOLIA $x=12$

lurida		24	Vilmorin & S. 1928	H	Himalayas

SOLANDRA $x=12$

grandiflora		22–24	Campin 1924	H	Jamaica
		24	E.K.J.*		

PHYSALIS* $x=12$

alkekengi	Winter Cherry, Chinese Lantern Pl.	24	Menzel 1951	FH	Eur.—Japan
divaricata		24	Baldwin & S. 1951b	—	O.W. Tropics
francheti		24	Sinha 1951b	H	Japan
ixocarpa	Tomatillo	24	Menzel 1951	FH	S: U.S.A., Mex.
philadelphica	Purple W. Ch.	24	Vilmorin & S. 1928	FH	N. America
pruinosa	Strawb.-Tomato	24	Menzel 1951	F	E: U.S.A.
pubescens	Barbados G.	24	„ „	F	Trop. America
virginiana	& 20 spp.	24	„ „	F	N. America
viscosa		24 / 24	„ „ / Covas & S. 1946	F	S: U.S.A.—Arg.
peruviana	Cape Gooseb.	24 / 48	Yamamoto & S. '32 / Menzel 1951	F	S. America
angulata	Ground Cherry	48	„ „	F	Trop. Amer., Ind.
minima	Sunberry	48	Bhaduri 1933	FV	O.W. Tropics

SOLANUM * $x=12, 23$
(i) Non-Tuberous Group
$x=12$

aculeatissimum		24	Brock 1952	H	Trop. As. & Am.
adventitum		24	Westergaard 1948	—	Hungary
aethiopicum		24	Vilmorin & S. 1928	H	Trop. Afr. & Asia
angustifolium		24	Ratera 1943	—	Argentine
argentinum		24	„ „	—	„
auriculatum		24	Vilmorin & S. 1928	H	Trop. Asia
basilobum		24	Ratera 1943	—	Argentine
capsicastrum	Chritsmas Ch.	24	Vilmorin & S. 1928	H	Brazil
cornutum		24	„ „	H	Mexico
dillenianum		24	Westergaard 1948	—	Sweden
dulcamara	Bittersweet	24	Vilmorin & S. 1928	H	Eur., N. Asia
eleagnifolium		24	Heiser & W. 1948	—	U.S.A.
gracile		24	Vilmorin & S. 1928	HV	Trop. America
insulae-paschalis		24	Westergaard 1948	—	Easter Island
jasminifolium		24	Ratera 1943	—	Brazil
jasminoides		24	Vilmorin & S. 1928	H	„
indicum		24	Bhaduri 1935	M(V)	O.W. Tropics
integrifolium	Scarlet E.P.	24	Vilmorin & S. 1928	H	Africa
marginatum		24	„ „	—	Trop. Africa
melongena	Egg Plant, Aubergine	24 (36, 48)	Janaki-Ammal 1934	V	O.W. Tropics
muricatum	Pepino	24	Vilmorin & S. 1928	V	Peru
nitidi-bacatum		24	Westergaard 1948	—	Arg., Bolivia
ovigerum		24	Vazart 1950		

SOLANUM (cont.)

pearcei		24	Avanzi 1949	—	Chile
pinnatum		26 (24–28)	„ „	—	„
pseudocapsicum	Jerusalem Ch.	24	Vilmorin & S. 1928	H	Old World
sarachioides		24	Ratera 1943	—	Bolivia
seaforthianum		24	Sinha 1950b	—	Trop. America
tomatillo		24	Jørgensen 1928	V	Chile
torreyi		24	La Cour 1952	—	W: N. Amer.
torvum		24	Bhaduri 1933	V	O.W. Tropics
trilobatum		24	„ „	(V)	„
verbascifolium		24	Ratera 1943	(V)	„
violaefolium		24	„ „	—	Brazil
wendlandi		24	Vilmorin & S. 1928	H	Costa Rica
warszewiczii		24	Sinha 1950b	H	?
xanthocarpum	Thorny Nightsh.	24	Bhaduri 1933	HMV	O.W. Tropics
luteum (*nigrum*)		48	Jørgensen 1928	FV	Cosmop.
miniatum	& 8 spp.	48	Westergaard 1948	V	„
guineense Sunberry (*nigrum*)		72	Vilmorin & S. 1928	FV	„
memphiticum		72	Jørgensen 1928	—	„
		⎧ 24, 48, 72	Bhaduri 1933		
nigrum, s.l. B. Nightsh.		⎨ 24, 72	Stebbins & P. 1949	FV	„
		⎩ (96, 144)	Jørgensen 1928		
roberti-eliae		72	Westergaard 1948	—	
robinsonianum		72	Jørgensen 1928	—	Juan Fernandez

$x = 23$

aviculare	Poroporo	46	Baylis 1954	H	Australia, N.Z.
laciniatum		92	„ „	H	„ „

(ii) Tuberous Group
(a) Wild Species
$x = 12$

ehrenbergii	24	Hawkes unp.	—	Mexico
etuberosum	24	„	—	Chile
jamesii	24	H. B. Smith 1927	—	Peru
lanciforme	24	Hawkes 1944	—	Mexico
morelliforme	24	Hawkes unp.	—	„
phureja	24	Rybin 1933	R	Bolivia
pinnatisectum	24	Hawkes unp.	—	Mexico
polyadenium	24	Bukasov 1935	—	„
simplicifolium	24	Hawkes 1944	—	Argentine
tarijense	24	„	—	Bolivia
toralapanum	24	Hawkes unp.	—	„
vernei	24	„	—	Argentine
verrucosum	24	Bukasov 1935	—	Mexico
violacei-marmoratum	24	Hawkes unp.	—	Bolivia
vernei	24	Brücher & R. 1953	—	Argentine
capsicibaccatum	24	Hawkes 1954	—	Bolivia
sanctae-rosae	24	„ „	—	Argentine
yungasense	24	„ „	—	Bolivia
bulbocastanum	⎧ 24	Bukasov 1935	—	Mexico
	⎩ 36	Hawkes unp.		
chacoense	⎧ 24	H. B. Smith 1927	—	Paraguay
	⎩ 36	Hawkes unp.		

305

SOLANUM (*cont.*)

commersonii	Swamp P.	{ 24	Koopmans 1951	—	Argentine
		{ 36	Rybin 1933		
maglia	Maglia	{ 24	Hawkes unp.	R	Chile
		{ 36	Rybin 1933		
millanii		24, 36	Bukasov & L. 1935	—	Argentine
cardiophyllum		36	Hawkes 1944	R	Mexico
acaule		{ 36, 48	Brücher & R. 1953	—	Peru, Bol., Arg.
		{ 48	Swaminathan 1954		
antipoviczii		48	Rybin 1933	—	Mexico
colombianum		48	„ „	—	Ven., Col., Ecuad
fendleri	Navajo P.	48	Smith 1927	R	Mexico
longiconicum		48	Hawkes unp.	—	Costa Rica
polytrichon		48	„	—	Brazil
stoloniferum		48	„	—	Mexico
sucrense		48	Hawkes 1944	—	Bolivia
tuquerrense		48	Hawkes 1954	—	Colom., Ec.
demissum		72	Koopmans 1951	—	Mexico
spectabilis		72	Swaminathan & H. '54	—	„
querreroense		72	„ „	—	„
brachycarpum		72	Hawkes 1954	—	„
moscopanum		72	„ „	—	Colombia

About 100 other species, 70 diploid and 30 tetraploid, were given in the previous edition. These now seem to be of doubtful value and are therefore omitted pending further study.

(*b*) Cultigens, Clonal Species and Hybrids
$x = 12$

stenotomum		24	Rybin 1933	R	Peru, Bolivia
rybinii		{ 24 (48)	„ „ 1940	R	Colombia
		{ 36	Mitra 1949		
chaucha		36	Rybin 1933	R	Peru, Bolivia
andigenum		48	Swaminathan 1954	R	Andes
		(24)	Müntzing 1937c		
tuberosum	Potato	48	Swaminathan 1954	AR	Peru, *cult*
		(24)	Lamm 1937		
		(96)	Vilmorin & S. 1928		
curtilobum		60	Rybin 1933	R	Peru, Bolivia
edinense		60	„ 1930	R	Hab.?
salamanii		60	Hawkes 1944	—	Mexico
semidemissum		60	Rybin 1933	—	„
tub. × *antipoviczii*		72	Ivanov 1939	R	*expt.*
antipo-phureja		72	Koopmans 1951	R	„
antipo-chacoense		72	„ „	R	„
demisso-rosum		120	„ „	R	„

SARACHA $x = 12$

procumbens	24	Menzel 1950	—	Peru
viscosa	24	„ „	—	Peru, Chile
umbellata	48	Krenke 1930	H	Peru

WITHANIA $x = 12$

somnifera	48	Bhaduri 1933	M	O.W. Trop., Med., S.W. Asia

ATROPA $x = 12$

belladonna	Deadly Night-shade	{ 50	Homedes 1943	M	Eur., S.W. Asia,
		72	Vilmorin & S. 1928		India
baetica		72	Fardy 1940	—	Spain
acuminata		72	Dutt 1952a	—	Himalayas

HYOSCYAMUS $x = 14, 17$

muticus	Indian Henbane	28	Griesinger 1937	M	Egypt, Asia M.
niger	Henbane	{ 33, 34	,, ,,	M	Eur., W. Asia,
		34	Vaarama 1950		Himalayas

DUBOISIA $x = 30$

leichtardtii		60	Barnard ·1949	M	S.E. Australia
myoporoides		60	,, ,,	HM	E. Australia

250a NOLANACEAE

NOLANA $x = 12$

atriplicifolia	24	Datta 1933a	—	Chile, Peru
prostrata	24	,, ,,	H	,,
grandiflora	24	Sugiura 1936b	H	,,
tenella	24	,, ,,	H	,,

251 CONVOLVULACEAE

CUSCUTA * $x = 7, 15$

europaea	Gr. Dodder & 3 spp.	14	Finn 1937	Par	Eur., S.W. Asia
approximata		28	,, ,,	Par	Spain
monogyna		28	,, ,,	Par	Eur., S.W. Asia
reflexa		28	,, ,,	ParM	India
epilinum		42	,, ,,	Par	E. Eur., Asia
arvensis		56	,, ,,	Par	N. America
campestris		56	Fogelberg 1938	Par	,,
pentagona		c. 56	,, ,,	Par	,,
glomerata	& 3 spp.	30	,, ,,	Par	,,
gronovii		60	,, ,,	Par	,,
cephalanthi		60	,, ,,	Par	,,

CONVOLVULUS $x = 10, 11$

pluricaulis		20	Singh 1951	—	India
tricolor		20	Kano 1929	H	S. Europe
elongatus		22	Heitz 1926	—	Canaries
spithamaeus		22	Wolcott 1937	H	N. America
siculus		44	Heitz 1926	H	Medit.
undulatus		c. 22	,, ,,	H	,,
scammonia	Scammony	c. 24	,, ,,	M	E. Medit.
arvensis	Lesser Bindweed	50	Wolcott 1937	—	N. Temp.

CALYSTEGIA $x = 11, 12$

hederacea		22	Nakajima 1931	—	Ind., China, Afgh.
soldanella	Sea B.	22	Kano 1929	(V)	Temp.
sepium	Bindweed	{ 22	,, ,,	M(V)	,,
		24	Felfoldy 1947		

CRESSA   *x* = 14
truxillensis   28   Heiser & W. 1948   —   Peru

QUAMOCLIT (IPOMOEA, MINA)   *x* = 14, 15
coccinea   Star Glory   28   King & B. 1937   H   Arizona
angulata   ⎧ 28   Nakajima 1931   —   Brazil
                             ⎩ 30   Kano 1929
lobata (*versicolor*)   ⎧ 28   King & B. 1937   H   Mexico
                             ⎩ 30   Sugiura 1936b
pennata   Cypress Vine   30   King & B. 1937   H   Trop. America
sloteri (*pennata* × *coccinea*) 58   „   „   H   *cult*

EXOGONIUM (IPOMOEA)   *x* = 14?
purga   Jalap   24–28 Heitz 1926   HM   Mexico

ARGYREIA   *x* = 15
nervosa   30   Watanabe 1939   —   E. Asia

CALONYCTION (IPOMOEA)   *x* = 15
aculeatum   Moonflower   30   Kano 1929   H(V)   Tropics
  (*speciosum*)
muricatum   30   Nakajima 1931   H(V)   „

DICHONDRA   *x* = 15
repens   30   Covas & S. 1947   —   W. Indies

HEWITTIA   *x* = 15
sublobata (*bicolor*)   30   Watanabe 1939   H   O.W. Tropics

MERREMIA (IPOMOEA)   *x* = 15
distillatoria   Ulan   30   King & B. 1937   M   India, Malaya
  (*campanulata*)
gemella   58   Watanabe 1939   —   S.E. Asia—Trop.
                                                                    Aust.

OPERCULINA (IPOMOEA)   *x* = 15
dissecta   30   King & B. 1937   —   Trop. America
tuberosa   30   „   „   H   Tropics
turpethum   Ching-Chaw   30   Watanabe 1939   M   Tr. Afr. & Asia

STICTOCARDIA (IPOMOEA)   *x* = 15
campanulata   30   Watanabe 1939   —   Trop. Africa

IPOMOEA (PHARBITIS) *   *x* = 15
biloba   Pohne   30   Sugiura 1936a   FoSb(V) Tropics
carnea   30   Rao 1947a   —   S. America
carolina   30   Wolcott 1937   —   W. Indies
nil   Jap. M.G. & 14 spp. 30   King & B. 1937   H   Tropics
pandurata   Wild Potato Vine   30   „   „   H   S.E: U.S.A.
pulchella   30   Rao 1947a   H   Ceylon
reptans   30   „   „   —   O.W. Tropics
learii   Blue Dawnflower ⎧ 30   King & B. 1937   —   Trop. America
                             ⎩ 32? Rao 1940
staphylina   32?   „   „   —   India, Malaya

ramouri   60   King & B. 1937   —   Cuba
batatas   Sweet Potato   90   Ting & K. 1953   R   Trop. America

308

(1) NON-PARASITIC GROUP

ZALUZIANSKIA (NYCTERINIA)		$x = 6$			
capensis		12	Sugiura 1936a	H	S. Africa
villosa (selaginoides)		12	,, ,,	H	,,
ALONSOA	$x = 6$				
warscewiczii (grandiflora)		24	Propach 1934	H	Peru
LINARIA*	$x = 6, 7, 8$				
alpina		12	Favarger 1949b	H	Eur. Alps
barbata		12	M. & S. 1935	—	S. Africa
dalmatica		12	,, ,,	H	S.E. Europe
repens		12	Tjebbes 1928	H	Europe
reticulata	& 32 spp.	12	Heitz 1927	H	Port., N. Africa
vulgaris	Toadflax	12	Vaarama, L. & L. '48	M	Eur., Caucasus
triphylla		12, 14	East 1933	H	Medit.
pancicii		16	Heitz 1927	—	Macedonia
chalepensis		24	,, ,,	—	S. Eur., S.W. Asia
CHAENORRHINUM (LINARIA)		$x = 7$			
minus		14	Champagnat 1952	—	Eur., W. Asia
origanifolium		14	,, ,,	—	Iber. Penin.
littorale		$\begin{cases} 14 \\ 42 \end{cases}$	Heitz 1927 / Champagnat 1952	—	E. Medit.
COLLINSIA	$x = 7$				
bartsiaefolia		c. 14	Hiorth 1933	—	California
bicolor		14	,, ,,	H	,,
v. candidissima		14	Sugiura 1936b	H	,,
barts. × bicolor		(21, 28)	Hiorth 1933	—	expt.
DOPATRIUM	$x = 7$				
lobelioides		14	Raghavan & S. 1942	—	India
HEBENSTRETIA	$x = 7$				
dentata		14	Sugiura 1939	H	S. Africa
virgata		14	,, 1940	—	,,
ERINUS	$x = 7$				
alpinus		$\begin{cases} 14 \\ 14 \end{cases}$	Reese 1953 / Favarger 1953	H	S. Eur., N. Afr.
CYMBALARIA (LINARIA)		$x = 7$			
muralis	Wall Ivy	14	Eichhorn 1950	—	Europe
pallida		14	Heitz 1927	—	Italy
aequitriloba		c. 42	Bruun 1932b	—	Corsica
hepaticifolia		c. 42	Heitz 1927	H	,,
pilosa		42	Bruun 1932b	H	Italy
REHMANNIA	$x = 7$				
angulata		28	Sugiura 1936a	H	China
glutinosa		56	Suzuka & K. 1949	H	,,
STEMODIA	$x = 7$				
viscosa		42	Raghavan & S. 1942	—	Ind., Afghan.

VANDELIA $x = 7$
crustacea		42	Raghavan & S. 1940b	—	Tropics

DIGITALIS $x = (7)$ 28
ambigua	Yellow F.	56	Buxton & N. 1928	H	S. Europe
canariensis		56	Haase-Bessel, T. '31	—	Canary Is.
dubia		56	Regnart 1935	H	Balearics
nervosa		56	Buxton & D. 1934	—	Cauc., Persia
orientalis		56	,, ,,	H	Greece, Asia M.
purpurea	Foxglove	56	Buxton & N. 1928	HM	Europe
lanata	Grecian F.	56	Buxton & D. 1934	M	Danube
viridiflora		56	Buxton & N. 1928	—	Greece, Maced.
ferruginea		{ 56	Buxton & D. 1934	H	S. Eur., Asia M.
		70	Yakar 1945		
eriostachya		112	Buxton & D. 1934	—	S. Europe
lutea		112	,, ,,	H	,,
obscura		112	,, ,,	H	Spain
mertonensis (*purp.* × *ambigua*)		112	,, 1932	H	*cult*

MIMULUS (DIPLACUS) $x = 7, 8$
cardinalis	Monkey Flower	16	Sugiura 1940	H	W: U.S.A.
betonicifolia		32	,, ,,	—	Chile
guttatus (*langsdorfii*)		{ 28	Clausen *et al.* 1950	H	W: N. America
		48	Maude 1940		
tigrinus		{ 48	Sugiura 1944	H	*cult*
		c. 64	Brozek 1932		
quinquevulnerus (*luteus*)		*c.* 64	,, ,,	H	Chile
tigrinoides		*c.* 64	,, ,,	H	*cult*

VERONICA * $x = 7, 8, 9,$ $x_2 = 15, 17$ $x_3 = 26$
$x = 7$
filiformis		14	Lehmann 1944	H	Asia Minor
humifusa		14	Rutland 1941	—	N. & C. Europe
polita (*didyma*)		14	Beatus 1936	—	Eur., Sib., Africa
repens	& 4 spp.	14	Hofelich 1935	H	Corsica
arvensis	Field Speedwell	14, 16	Yamashita 1937	—	Eur., Asia, N. Afr.
cardiocarpa (*biloba*)		14, 16	Zündorf 1939	—	Himal., Cauc., Sib.
agrestis		{ 14, 28	Yamashita 1937	—	Eur., Asia, N. Afr.
		28	Wulff 1937b		
biloba		28	Zündorf 1939	—	Him., Cauc., Sib.
opaca (*agrestis*)		28	Beatus 1936	—	Eur., Asia, N. Afr.
persica (*tournefortii*)		28	,, ,,	—	O.W. Temp.
arguteserrata (*biloba*)		42	Zündorf 1939	—	Him., Cauc., Sib.
campylopoda		42	,, ,,	—	S.W. Asia
hederifolia		56	Hofelich 1935	—	Eur., S.W. & N. Asia
longifolia		70	S. & S. 1941	H	C.Eur.—N. Asia

$x = 8$
armena	& 1 sp.	16	Brandt 1953	—	Armenia
dillenii (*verna*)		16	Hofelich 1935	—	Eur., S.W. & N. Asia
fruticans		16	Huber 1927	H	Eur., Greenland
fruticulosa		16	Beatus 1936	H	Eur. mtns.
saturejoides		16	Brandt 1952	H	Dalmatia
verna		16	Hofelich 1935	—	Eur., S.W & N. Asia
prostrata		16, 32	Brandt 1953	H	Eur., N. Asia

VERONICA (*cont.*)

chamaedrys Germander S.	32	L. & L. 1944b	H	Europe
orbiculata (*prostrata*)	32	Scheerer 1937	—	,,
austriaca	{ 32	Brandt 1952	H	S.E. Europe
	{ 32, 48	Scheerer 1937		
gentianoides	48	Lehmann 1944	H	Caucasus
teucrium	·{ 64	Brandt 1952	H	Eur., N. Asia
	{ 68	Graze 1933		
variegata	64, 68	Simonet 1934d	H	*cult*

$x = 9$

alpina	18	Favarger 1949b	H	Alps, Arctic
anagalloides	18	Schlenker 1936	—	Greece—Persia
aphylla	18	Brandt 1952	H	S. Europe
beccabunga Brooklime	18	Schlenker 1936	—	N. Temp.
crista-galli	18	Hofelich 1935	—	Caucasus
montana	18	Simonet 1934d	—	Europe
oxycarpa (*anagallis*)	18	Schlenker 1936	—	N. Temp.
praecox	18	Hofelich 1935	—	Medit.
scutellata Marsh S.	18	Hagerup 1944	—	Eur., N. Amer.
stelleri	18	Sakai 1935	—	Aleutians
officinalis Common Sp.	18, 36	Bøcher 1944	HM	N. Temp.
panormitana (*cymbalaria*)	18, 36	Hofelich 1935	—	Medit., Asia M.
americana	36	Schlenker 1936	—	N. America
anagallis-aquatica	36	Ehrenberg 1945	—	N. Temp.
catenata	36	Schlenker 1936	—	Eur., N. Amer.
onoei	36	Yamazaki 1936	—	Japan
wormskjoldii	36	Bøcher & L. 1950	—	N. & Arctic

$x_2 = 15 \ (7 + 8)$

sibthorpioides	30	Hofelich 1935	—	France

$x_2 = 17 \ (8 + 9)$

longifolia (*maritima*)	34, 68	Graze 1935	H	Eur., As. M., Sib.
schmidtiana	34	Sakai 1935	—	Sakhalin
barrelieri (*spicata*) & 6 spp.	34	Graze 1933	H	Eur., N. Asia
plebeia	34	Frankel unp.	—	E. Australia
spicata	34 (35, 36)	Brandt 1953	H	Eur., N. Asia
spuria	34	Graze 1933	H	Europe
virginica Culvers Root	34	Huber 1927	HM	E: U.S.A.
crassifolia	68	Graze 1933	H	Balkans
incana (*candida*)	68	,, ,,	H	S.E. Eur., N. Asia

$x_3 = 26 \ (8 + 9 + 9)$

peregrina	52	Hofelich 1935	—	Eur., N. Amer.

HEBE (VERONICA) * $\ x = 20, 21$
$x = 20$

amplexicaulis & 25 spp.	40	Frankel unp.	H	New Zealand
diosmaefolia	40	Frankel 1941	H	,,
lycopodioides	40	Frankel & H. 1937	H	,,
mathewsii	40	Simonet 1934d	H	,,
pimeleoides	40	,, ,,	H	,,
speciosa	40	,, ,,	H	,,
townsoni	40	Frankel 1940	—	,,
vernicosa v. *canterburiensis*	40	Frankel & H. 1937	H	,,
v. *gracilis*	42	,, ,,	H	,,
leiophylla	40, 80	Frankel unp.	H	,,

311

HEBE (*cont.*)

parviflora	$\left\{\begin{array}{l}40\\80\end{array}\right.$	Simonet 1934d Frankel 1940	H	New Zealand
salicifolia	40	Frankel & H. 1937	H	,,
v. *egmontiana*	80	Frankel unp.		
traversii	40, 80, 120	,,	H	,,
buchanani	80	,,	H	,,
gigantea	80	,,	H	,,
macrocarpa	80	,,	H	,,
pinguifolia	80	Frankel & H . 1937	H	,,
subalpina	80, 120	Frankel unp.	—	,,
carsei (5x)	100	,,	—	,,
cockayniana	120	,,	—	,,
evenosa	120	,,	—	,,
laevis	120	,,	H	,,
montata	120	Frankel & H. 1937	—	,,

$x = 21$

cupressoides	42	Frankel & H. 1937	H	,,
epacridea	42	,, ,,	H	,,
formosa	42	Frankel unp.	H	S.E. Austr., Tasm.
hulkeana	42	Simonet 1934d	H	New Zealand
lavaudiana	42	Frankel unp.	H	,,
macrantha	42	Frankel & H. 1937	—	,,
raoulii	42	,, ,,	—	,,
salicornioides	42	Frankel unp.	H	,,
tetrasticha	42	Frankel & H. 1937	—	,,
buxifolia	42	Frankel unp.	H	,,
v. *odora*	84	Frankel & H. 1937		
v. *prostrata*	84	Frankel unp.		
armstrongii	124	,,	H	,,

PARAHEBE (VERONICA) $x = 20, 21$

$x = 20$

bidwillii	40	Frankel & H. 1937	H	New Zealand

$x = 21$

canescens	42	Frankel unp.	H	,,
catarractae	42	,,	H	,,
hookeriana	42	,,	H	,,
linifolia	42	Frankel & H. 1937	H	,,
lyallii	42	,, ,,	H	,,

PYGMAEA $x = 21$

ciliolata	42	Frankel & H. 1937	—	New Zealand
pulvinaris	42	Frankel 1941	—	,,
thomsoni	42	,, ,,	—	,,

ANTIRRHINUM* $x = 8$ (no natural polyploids)

glutinosum		16	Baur 1932	H	Spain
hispanicum		16	,, ,,	H	,,
majus	Snapdragon	16	Propach 1935	H	Medit.
		(32)	Sparrow *et al.* 1942		
molle		16	Lawrence 1930	H	Pyrenees
orontium		16	Heitz 1927	H	Europe
sempervirens		16	Baur 1932	H	Pyrenees
siculum		16	,, ,,	H	Sicily
tortuosum	& 6 spp.	16	,, ,,	H	W. Medit.

312

PENSTEMON (PENTSTEMON, CHELONE)* $x = 8$

albertinus	& 9 spp.	16	Keck 1945	H	W: N. America
barrettae		16	,, ,,	H	Oregon
barbatus		16	Sugiura 1936b	H	Colorado
cinereus		16	Keck 1945	H	Oregon
cyananthus	& 14 spp.	16	Clausen *et al.* 1940	H	W: U.S.A.
procerus		16, 32	Keck 1945	H	W: N. America
unicola		16, 32	,, ,,	—	,, ,,
wilcoxii		16, 32	,, ,,	H	N.W: U.S.A.
nemorosus		30!	Clausen *et al.* 1940	H	W: U.S.A.
aggregatus		32	,, ,,	—	,,
confertus		32	Keck 1945	H	,,
globosus		32	,, ,,	—	,,
pratensis		32	,, ,,	—	,,
rydbergii		32	,, ,,	H	,,
shastensis		32	,, ,,	—	,,
subserratus		32	,, ,,	—	,,
azureus		32, 48	J. Clausen 1933	—	California
frutescens!		40 (5*x*)	M. & S. 1935	—	Japan, Kamch.
attenuatus		48	Keck 1945	—	W: U.S.A.
euglaucus		48	,, ,,	H	Oregon
flavescens		48	,, ,,	—	W: U.S.A.
cobaea		64	Piotrowska, T. 1937	H	S.E: U.S.A.
neotericus (*laetus* × *azureus*)		64	J. Clausen 1933	—	California
laevigatus		96	La Cour 1931	—	S.E.: U.S.A

GRATIOLA $x = 8$

officinalis	32	Scheerer 1939	HM	Europe

TORENIA $x = 8, 9$

asiatica	16	Simon & L. 1930	H	S. India
baillonii (*flava*)	16	Sugiura 1936b	H	Indo-China
peduncularis (*edentula*)	18	Simon & L. 1930	H	India
fournieri	18 (36, 72)	Straub 1939	H	Indo-China

CALCEOLARIA $x = 8, 9, 30$

angustifolia	18	Srinath 1940	H	Chile
banksii	18	,, ,,	H	*cult*
cana	18	La Cour 1945*	—	Chile
clibranii	18	Srinath 1940	H	*cult*
crenatiflora	18	La Cour 1945*	H	Chiloe Is.
dentata	18	,,	H	Chile
integrifolia	18	,,	H	,,
pratensis	18	,,	H	,,
alba	36	,,	H	,,
polyrrhiza	36	,,	H	Patagonia
hyssopifolia	32	,,	H	Ecuador
mexicana	60	Srinath 1940	H	Mexico

ANARRHINUM (LINARIA) $x = 9$

bellidifolium	18	Heitz 1927	—	Medit.
laxiflorum	18	,, ,,	—	Spain

ASARINA (ANTIRRHINUM) $x = 9$

procumbens	18	Heitz 1927	—	Italy

DIASCIA $x = 9$

barbarea		18	Propach 1934	H	S. Africa

NEMESIA * $x = 9$

strumosa	& 7 spp.	18	Heitz 1927	H	S. Africa
versicolor		18	Propach 1934	H	,,
pulchella	& 7 spp.	18	La Cour 1945*	H	,,

KICKXIA (LINARIA, ELATINOIDES) $x = 7?, 9$

elatine		$\begin{cases} 18 \\ 36 \end{cases}$	Brunn 1932b Wulff 1939a	H	Eur., Asia
spuria	& 1 sp.	c. 14	Heitz 1927	—	Eur., N. Africa

SCROPHULARIA $x = 9, 10, 13$

canina		26	Rodrigues 1953	—	C. Eur., Medit.
nodosa	Figwort	36	Scheerer 1939	M	N. Temp.
vernalis		40	Håkansson 1926	—	C. & S. Eur. mtns.
aquatica	Water Betony	80	Maude 1940	M	W. Eur., N. Afr.
umbrosa		c. 52	Scheerer 1940	—	C. Eur., W. Asia

ANGELONIA $x = 10$

grandiflora (salicariaefolia)		20	Raghavan & S. '40b	H	Brazil
cubensis		20	,, ,,	H	Cuba

DIPLACUS $x = 10$

aridus		20	McMinn 1951	H	S. California
calycinus		20	,, ,,	—	California
clevelandii		20	,, ,,	—	,,
fascicularis		20	,, ,,	—	,,
puniceus		20	,, ,,	H	S. California

LIMOSELLA $x = 10$

subulata		20	Vachell & B. 1939	—	E: N. Amer., Wales
aquatica	Mudwort	40	,, ,,	—	N. Temp.
(sub. × aqu.)		30	,, ,,	—	Glamorgan

RUSSELIA $x = 10$

juncea		20	Raghavan & S. '40b	H	Mexico
rotundifolia		20	,, ,,	H	,,

SCOPARIA $x = 10$

dulcis		40	Raghavan & S. '40b	—	Tropics

PAULOWNIA $x = 10$

tomentosa (imperialis)		40	Westfall 1949	H	China, Japan

TETRANEMA $x = 10$

mexicana	Mex. Foxglove	20	Sugiura 1940	H	Mexico

MAURANDIA (ANTIRRHINUM) $x = 10?, 12$

scandens (lophospermum)		$\begin{cases} 20 \\ 24 \end{cases}$	Sugiura 1937a Heitz 1927	H	Mexico
antirrhiniflora		24	,, ,,	H	S.W: U.S.A.
barclaiana		24	,, ,,	H	Mexico
erubescens		24	,, ,,	H	,,
purpusii		24	,, ,,	H	,,
purpurea		24	Sugiura 1937a	—	,,

LAGOTIS	x = 11				
glauca		22	Sakai 1934	H	Asia, N. Amer.
takedana		22	„	—	Japan
SYNTHRIS	x = 12				
reniformis		24	MacMillan 1949	H	W: N. America
ILYSANTHES	x = 13				
parviflora		26	Raghavan & S. 1941	—	India, Trop. Afr.
VERBASCUM	x = 15, 16, 18				
nigrum	Dark Mullein	30	Håkansson 1926	HM	Eur., Caucasus
blattaria	Moth M.	30, 32	„ „	H	Eur., W. & C. Asia, N. Africa
chaixii	Nettle-leaved M.	32	„ „	H	S. & C. Europe
lychnitis	White M.	32	„ „	H	Eur., W. Asia
phlomoides	Woolly M.	32	„ „	H	S. & C. Eur., W. Asia
pulverulentum	Hoary M.	32	„ „	H	Europe
simplex		32	Fernandes 1950b	H	S.W. Eur., N. Afr.
thapsiforme		32	Håkansson 1926	HM	Eur., N. Africa
virgatum		32	„ „	H	Eur., A. Min., N. Africa
phoeniceum	Purple M.	{ 32 36	M. & S. 1935 Lawrence 1931	H	E. Eur., W. Asia
thapsus	Aaron's Rod	34, 36	Håkansson 1926	H	Eur.—Himal.
ternacha		48	„ „	—	Abyssinia
maurum		64	„ „	—	Morocco
CELSIA	x = 17, 20, 23, 24, 25, 26				
bugulifolia		34	Håkansson 1926	H	S.E. Europe
pontica		34	„ „	H	Armenia
horizontalis		40	„ „	—	Crete
roripifolia		c. 42	„ „	—	Thrace
battandieri		c. 46	„ „	—	Morocco, Alg.
brevipedicellata		46	„ „	—	E. Trop. Africa
faurei		46	„ „	—	Algeria
keniensis		46	„ „	—	Abyss., Kenya
arcturus		48	„ „	H	Crete
orientalis		48	„ „	H	Levant
rupestris		48	„ „	—	Thrace
maroccana		50	„ „	—	Morocco
cretica		52	„ „	H	Medit.
lyrata		52	„ „	—	„

(2) PARASITIC GROUP

RHINANTHUS (ALECTOROLOPHUS) *		x = 7			
minor & 5 spp.	Penny Grass	14	Witsch 1932	Par	Europe
major (serotinus)	Yellow Rattle	14 + 8B	Wulff 1939a	Par	„
PEDICULARIS *	x = 6, 8				
verticillata		12	Favarger 1953	Par	Arctic, Alps
amoena	& 2 spp.	16	S. & S. 1938	Par	Altai
foliosa	& 2 spp.	16	Witsch 1932	Par	Europe
sylvatica	Lousewort	16	L. & L. 1944b	Par	„
flammea	& 3 spp.	16	L. & L. 1948	Par	„

PEDICULARIS (*cont.*)
palustris — 16 — Reese 1953 — Par — Europe

MELAMPYRUM * $x=9$				
nemorosum	18	Reese 1952a	Par	Eur., Caucasus
pratense & 2 spp. Cow Wheat	18	Witsch 1932	Par	Eur., N. Asia

SOPUBIA $x=9$				
delphinifolia	36	K. Iyengar 1937	Par	India

ODONTITES $x=10$				
lutea	20	Witsch 1932	Par	Eur., Asia M.
verna (rubra)	$\begin{cases} 20 \\ 40 \end{cases}$	Fagerlind 1937 Witsch 1932	Par	Europe

TOZZIA $x=10$				
alpina	20	Witsch 1932	Par	Europe

STRIGA $x=10$				
densiflora	40	Kumar & A. 1941	Par	India
euphrasioides	40	„ „	Par	„
lutea	40	„ „	Par	Trop. Asia & Afr.
orobanchoides	40	„ „	Par	India, Trop. Afr.

EUPHRASIA * $x=11$				
montana	22	Witsch 1932	Par	W. Europe
rostkoviana Eyebright	22	„ „	MPar	Europe
anglica	22	Yeo 1954	Par	Britain
hirtella	22	„ „	Par	Eurasia
rivularis	22	„ „	Par	Britain
frigida	44	L. & L. 1948	Par	Arctic, Subarctic
minima	44	Witsch 1932	Par	C. & S. Europe
salisburgensis	44	„ „	Par	Europe
curta & 7 spp.	44	Yeo 1954	Par	Eur., Quebec
brevipila	44, 45	„ „	Par	N. & Alp. Eur., N.E.: N. Amer.
confusa Eyebright	44	„ „	Par	Britain
stricta	44	Reese 1952a	Par	Europe

BARTSIA (BARTSCHIA) $x=12, 14$				
alpina	$\begin{cases} 24 \\ 36 \\ 28 \end{cases}$	Favarger 1953 Doulat 1946 Bøcher & L. 1950	Par	Eur., N. Amer.

CASTILLEJA $x_2=11+12$				
arctica	46	S. & S. 1941	Par	Arctic

253 OROBANCHACEAE

OROBANCHE $x=(6)$ 12, 18, 19, 20				
ramosa	24	Gardé 1952a	Par	Eur., Cauc., W. Asia
uniflora	36, 72	Jensen 1951	Par	E: N. America
aegyptica	38	Srivastava 1939	Par	Egypt
crenata	38	Gardé 1952a	Par	Arabia

316

OROBANCHE (*cont.*)

lucorum		38	Palmgren 1943	Par	C. Europe
minor	Broomrape	38	Carter 1928	Par	Eur., N. Africa
reticulata		38	Favarger 1953	Par	C. & S. Europe
coerulescens		38, 40	Sugiura 1936b	Par	Eur., N. Asia
ammophila		40	„ „	Par	„ „

PHACELLANTHUS $x = 19$
tubiflorus		38, 57, 76	Matsuura & T. 1937	Par	Japan

CISTANCHE $x = 20$
phellipaea		40	Gardé 1952a	Par	Medit.

LATHRAEA $x = ?$
squamaria	Toothwort	36, 42	T. 1930, 1935	Par	Eur., N. Asia
clandestina		42	Dangeard 1937	Par	S. Europe

254 LENTIBULARIACEAE

PINGUICULA $x = 16$
alpina		$\begin{cases} 32 \\ 32 \end{cases}$	L. & L. 1944b Doulat 1947	C	Europe
grandiflora		32	„ „	C	W. Europe
vulgaris	Butterwort	64	„ „	HC	Eur., N. Asia, N. America

UTRICULARIA $x = ?$
minor		36–40	Reese 1952a	C	Eur., N. Asia, N. America
neglecta		36–40	„	C	Europe
ochroleuca		*c.* 40	„	C	„
vulgaris	Bladderwort	36–40	„	CH	Eur., N. Asia, & America

256 GESNERIACEAE

NAEGELIA (GESNERIA) $x = 12$
zebrina		24	Sugiura 1936b	—	Brazil

CORYTHOLOMA (GESNERIA) $x = 14$
cardinalis		28	Sugiura 1936b	H	Trop. America

SAINTPAULIA $x = 14$
ionantha	African Violet	28	Sugiura 1936b	H	Trop. Africa
kewensis	„ „	28	Holzer 1952	H	„

SINNINGA (GLOXINIA) $x = 14$
speciosa	Gloxinia	56	Sugiura 1936b	H	Brazil

STREPTOCARPUS * $x = 15, 16$
(i) $x = 15$: Stemmed Group
caulescens		30	Lawrence *et al.* 1939	—	Trop. E. Africa
holstii		30	„ „	—	„ „
kirkii		30	„ „	—	„ „
orientalis		30	„ „	—	Siam
saxorum		30	„ „	—	Trop. E. Africa

STREPTOCARPUS (*cont.*)
(ii) $x = 16$: Stemless Group

insignis		32	Lawrence 1945*	—	E. Cape Prov.
polackii		32	„ „	—	Transvaal
dunnii		32	Lawrence *et al.* 1939	H	„
rexii	& 15 spp.	32	„ „	H	Cape Prov.
saundersii		32	Sugiura 1940	—	Natal
kewensis × *grandis*		32, 64	Lawrence 1945*	H	*cult*
veitchii		32	Sugiura 1940	H	*cult*

CHIRITA (DIDYMOCARPUS) $x = 18$

lavandulacea	36	Sugiura 1940	H	Malaya

DIDYMOCARPUS $x = 18$?

tomentosa	54	Thathachar 1942	—	India

RAMONDA $x = 18$

nathaliae	36	Glišič, T. 1927	H	Balkans
serbica	72	„ „	H	„

257 BIGNONIACEAE

INCARVILLEA $x = 11$

compacta	{ 18?	Sugiura 1936b		China
	22	Bowden 1940a	H	
delavayi	{ 18?	Sugiura 1936b		W. China, Tibet
	22	Bowden 1940a	H	
grandiflora	22	„ „	H	W. China
olgae	22	„ „	H	Turkestan

SPATHODEA $x = 13$

campanulata Scarlet Bell	26	Raghavan & V. '40c	MHSh	Trop. Africa
nilotica	26	Venkatasubban 1945a	H	„

ARGYLIA $x = 15$

uspallatensis	30	Covas & S. 1946	—	Chile

MILLINGTONIA $x = 15$

hortensis Indian Cork T.	30	Narasinga Rao 1936	HW	Burma

OROXYLUM $x = 15$

indicum	30	Venkatasubban 1944	DM	India

TECOMARIA (TECOMA) $x = 17$

capensis	34	Venkatasubban 1944	H	S. Africa

JACARANDA $x = 18$

coerulea	36	Simmonds 1954	H	W. Indies
ovalifolia Jacaranda	36	Venkatasubban 1944	HSh	Brazil
as *mimosaefolia*	66	Pathak *et al.* 1949		

TECOMA $x = 18$?, 19?

smithii Austr. Trumpet Bush	36	Venkatasubban 1944	H	*cult*
chrysantha	38	„ „	H	Venezuela

CAMPSIS (TECOMA) $x = 18?, 19?, 20$

chinensis (*grandiflora*)	{ 36, 38 40 40	Venkatasubban 1944 Sax 1933b, Bowden 1945a	H	China, Japan
radicans Trumpet Vine	{ 40 40	Sax 1933b Venkatasubban 1944	H	E: U.S.A.
tagliabuana (*grand.* × *rad.*)	40	Vilmorin & S. '27a	H	*cult*

PANDOREA (TECOMA) $x = 19$

jasminoides	38	Nakajima 1936	H	Australia

PSEUDOCALYMMA $x = 19$

macrocarpum	38	Simmonds 1954	—	Cent. Amer.

ADENOCALYMMA $x = 20$

calycina	40	Venkatasubban 1944	—	Brazil

ANEMOPAEGMA (BIGNONIA) $x = 20$

chamberlaynii	40	Venkatasubban 1944	H	Brazil

ARRABIDAEA (BIGNONIA) $x = 20$

magnifica	40	Venkatasubban 1944	H	Colombia

BIGNONIA $x = 20$

capreolata Cross Vine	40	Bowden 1940a	H	S.E: U.S.A.
megapotamica	40	Venkatasubban 1944	—	Brazil
unguis-cati Cats' Claw	{ 40, 80	„ '45a	H	W. Indies—Arg.
(*tweediana*)	80	Bowden 1945a		

CALLICHLAMYS $x = 20$

latifolia	40	Simmonds 1954	—	Brazil, Peru

CATALPA $x = 20$

bignonioides Indian Bean	40	E. C. Smith 1941	HShW	S.E: U.S.A.
ovata	40	„ „	H	China
speciosa	40	„ „	HW	C: U.S.A.
hybrida	40	„ „	H	*cult*

CHILOPSIS $x = 20$

linearis Desert Willow	40	Bowden 1945a	H	S: U.S.A., Mex.

CLYTOSTOMA (BIGNONIA) $x = 20$

binatum (*purpureum*)	40	Venkatasubban 1944	H	Uruguay

CRESCENTIA $x = 20$

cujete Calabash Tree	40	Simmonds 1954	HTo	Trop. America
latifolia	40	„ „	—	„ „

CYDISTA (BIGNONIA) $x = 20$

diversifolia	40	Venkatasubban 1944	H	Mexico

DOLICHANDRONE $x = 20$

rheedii	40	Venkatasubban 1944	—	India, Malaya
stipulata	40	„ „	—	Burma

HETEROPHRAGMA $x = 20$

adenophyllum	40	Venkatasubban 1945a	—	India

319

KIGELIA $x = 20$
pinnata	Sausage Tree	40	Simmonds 1954	MSh	Trop. Africa

MARKHAMIA $x = 20$
hildebrantia		40	Venkatasubban '45a	H	Trop. Africa
platycalyx		40	„　　　„	H	Uganda

PAJANELIA $x = 20$
multijuga (rheedii)	40	Venkatasubban 1944	—	India, Burma

PARAGONIA (BIGNONIA) $x = 20$
pyramidata	40	Simmonds 1954	—	Brazil

PARMENTIERA $x = 20$
cereifera	Candle Tree	40	Simmonds 1954	H	Panama
edulis	Guajilote	40	Venkatasubban '45a	F	Mex., Guat.

PHAEDRANTHUS (BIGNONIA) $x = 20$
cherere	40	Venkatasubban 1944	H	Mexico

PHYLLARTHRON $x = 20$
comorense	40	Venkatasubban 1944	—	Madagascar

PHRYGANOCYDIA $x = 20$
corymbosa	40	Simmonds 1954	—	E: S. America

STENOLOBIUM (BIGNONIA) $x = 20$
stans	Yellow Bells	40	Bowden 1945a	H	W. Indies—Peru

STEREOSPERMUM $x = 20$
chelonoides		40	Venkatasubban 1944	W	India, Burma
suaveolens		40	„　　　„	HW	India
xylocarpum		40	„　　　„	W	„

TABEBUIA (TECOMA) $x = 20$
guyacan		40	Venkatasubban 1944	—	Panama
ipe	Lapacho	40	Covas & S. 1947	W	Paraguay
nodosa		40	„　　　„	—	Argentine
pallida	White Cedar	40	Simmonds 1954	HW	W.I., C. Amer.
rosea		40	Venkatasubban 1944	H	Mex.—Ecuador
serratifolia	Yellow Poui	{ 38?	„　　　'45a	HW	W. Indies
		{ 40	Simmonds 1954		
spectabilis		40	Venkatasubban '45a	H	Colombia

TANAECIUM $x = 20$
jaroba (albiflorum)	40	Venkatasubban 1944	—	Trop. America

AMPHILOPHIUM $x = 22$
mutisii	44	Venkatasubban 1944	—	W. Indies

258 PEDALIACEAE

PEDALIUM $x = 8$
murex	Burra Gokeru	16	Srinivasan 1942	M	India, Trop. Afr.

320

SESAMUM $x = 8, 13.$ $x_3 = 8 + 8 + 13 = 29$

alatum		26	Kedarnath 1950	V	S. Africa
capense		26	Shimamura 1951	—	,,
orientale (indicum)	Sesame	26	Raghavan & K. 1947	OMV	India, cult
		(52)	Richharia & P. 1940		
laciniatum		{ 28	Raghavan & K. 1945	—	India
		32	Ramanujam & J. 1948		
angolense		32	Kedarnath 1950	—	Trop. Africa
prostratum		32	Raghavan & K. 1947	—	India
occidentale		64	Sampath & R. 1949	—	,,
radiatum	Black Beniseed	64	John & R. 1941	OV	Trop. Africa
indicatum (orient. × prost.)	29 (58)	Raghavan & K. 1947	O	expt.

CERATOTHECA $x = 8$

sesamoides	32	Kedarnath 1950	OV	Trop. Africa

PROBOSCIDEA (MARTYNIA) $x = 15$

jussieui	Unicorn Plant	30	Sugiura 1936b	HV	S: U.S.A.
as M. louisiana		30	Martini 1939		
as M. fragrans		30	Gaiser et al. 1943		

IBICELLA (PROBOSCIDEA) $x = ?$

lutea	{ 30	Martini 1939	HV	Argentine
	32	Covas & S. 1947		

MARTYNIA $x = 18$

annua (diandra)	36	Srinivasan 1942	V	Trop. Amer.

259 ACANTHACEAE

THUNBERGIA $x = 7, 8, 9$

alata	Black-eyed Susan	{ 18	Grant 1955	H	Tr. Afr., E. Ind.
		32	Snoad 1952		
grandiflora		{ c. 28	E.K.J.*	H	India, Burma
		56	Snoad 1952		
laurifolia		56	Sugiura 1936b	H	Malaya

HYGROPHILA $x = 12, 16$

spinosa	Nirmulli, Water	{ 24	Sugiura 1940	(M)	E. Ind., Malaya
	Jasmine	32	Rangaswamy 1941		

JUSTICIA $x = 14$

debilis	28	Sugiura 1936a	H	Arabia
furcata	28	,, ,,	H	Mexico

JACOBINIA* $x = 14$

carnea & 2 spp.	28	Grant 1955	H	Brazil

RUELLIA* $x = 16, 17, 18$

tuberosa	Menow-weed	{ 32	Sugiura 1936b	H(R)	Trop. N. Amer.,
		34	Bowden 1940a		Jamaica
ciliosa		34	,, ,,	H	E: U.S.A.
malacosperma		34	,, ,,	H	C. America
nudiflora		34	,, ,,	H	S: U.S.A., Mex.
strepens		34	,, ,,	H	E: U.S.A.
graecizana & 18 spp.		34	Grant 1955	H	S. America

RUELLIA (*cont.*)
ciliata	36	Sugiura 1936b	—	India, Burma
squarrosa (*dipteracanthus*)	34	Grant 1955	—	Mexico

ADHATODA (JUSTICIA) $x = ?$
vasica	$\begin{cases} 34 \\ 56 \end{cases}$	Mukherjee 1952b Grant 1955	HDIM	India, Malaya

DICLIPTERA $x = 20$
resupinata	40	Sugiura 1939	—	Mexico

ERANTHEMUM (DAEDALACANTHUS) $x = 21$
pulchellum (*nervosus*)	42	Pathak *et al.* 1949	H	India
variegatum	42	„ „	H	*cult*

ACANTHUS $x = ?$
mollis (*lusitanicus*)	56	Sugiura 1936b	H	S. Europe
spinosus	$\begin{cases} 56 \\ 80 \\ 112 \end{cases}$	„ 1939 Drahowzal 1936 Sugiura 1937b	H	„

ELYTRARIA $x = ?$
virgata	50	Grant 1955	H	S.E: U.S.A.

SANCHESIA $x = ?$
nobilis	136	Singh 1951	H	Ecuador

260 GLOBULARIACEAE

GLOBULARIA $x = 8, 10$
vulgaris	16	L. & L. 1944b	H	S. Eur., Cauc.
cordifolia	Globe Daisy	20	Sugiura 1937a	H	S. Europe

262 SELAGINACEAE

HEBENSTRETIA $x = 7$
comosa	14	Sugiura 1936b	H	S. Africa
dentata	14	„ „	—	„

263 VERBENACEAE

DIOSTEA $x = 5$
scoparia	20	Covas & S. 1946	—	Chile, Arg.

JUNELLIA $x = 5$
asparagoides	20	Covas & S. 1946	—	Chile, Arg.
glauca	20	„ 1947	—	„
seriphioides	20	Schnack & C. 1947	—	„
aspera	60	Covas & S. 1946	—	Chile, Arg., Peru

VERBENA (incl. GLANDULARIA) * $x = 5, 7$
$x = 5$
dissecta	10	Schnack 1944	—	S. America
flava	10	Schnack & C. 1944	—	Argentine

VERBENA (*cont.*)

grandiflora		10	Dermen 1936a	—	Cuba
laciniata (*erinoides*)		10	Schnack & C. 1944	—	S. America
megapotamica		10	Schnack & G. 1945	—	Brazil—Arg.
mendocina		10	Schnack & C. 1945b	—	Argentine
parodii		10	Covas & S. 1944	—	,,
perakii		10	,, ,,	H	,,
peruviana		10 (20)	Schnack & C. 1945a	H	S. Braz., Peru, Ur.
phlogiflora		10	Schnack 1944	—	S. America
platensis (*teucrioides*)		10	Noack 1937	—	,,
radicans		10	Beale 1940	—	Chile, Arg.
santiaguensis		10	Schnack & G. 1945	—	Arg., Uruguay
hybrida	Garden V. {	10	Beale 1940	H	*cult*
		20 (40)	Furusato 1940		
crithmifolia		20	Covas & S. 1945	—	Ecuador, Arg.
hookeriana		20	,, ,,	—	Argentine
ambrosifolia		30	Dermen 1936a	—	N. America
canadensis	Clump V.	30	,, ,,	—	N. & S. Amer.
racemosa		30	,, ,,	—	N. America
tenera	Italian V.	30	Beale 1940	H	S. Braz.—Arg.

$x = 7$

officinalis	Vervain & 10 spp.	14	Dermen 1936a	H	Temp.
bonariensis		28	,, ,,	H	N. & S. Amer.
intermedia		28	Schnack & C. 1944	—	Brazil—Arg.
littoralis		28	Derman 1936a	—	Temp. & Tr. Am.
gracilescens		42	Schnack 1944	—	Bolivia—Arg.
montevidensis		42	Schnack & C. 1947	—	Uruguay
rigida (*venosa*)		42	Dermen 1936a	H	N. & S. Amer.
corymbosa		56	Noack 1937	H	S. America
sp. aff. *intermedia*		56	Schnack & C. 1947	—	Chile
ovata ($x_2 = 5 + 7$?)		72	Noack 1937	—	Brazil, Arg.

PRIVA $x = 6$

lappulacea	12	Patermann, T. 1938	—	Trop. America

VITEX $x = 6, 8$

agnus-castus	Chaste Tree	24	Patermann, T. 1938	H	Temp. & Sub.-Tr.
trifolia		32	Sugiura 1936a	M	Trop. Asia, Austr., E. Africa

PHRYMA $x = 7$

leptostachya	{ 14	Sugiura 1936b	—	N. Asia, Himal.,
	28	D. C. Cooper 1941		N America

NEOSPARTON $x = 8$

ephedroides	32	Covas 1950c	—	Chile, Arg.

CALLICARPA $x = 8?, 9?$

japonica	{ 16	Sugiura 1936b	H	E. Asia
	18	Patermann, T. 1938		

LIPPIA $x = 8?, 9?$

juncea (*baillonia*)		32	Junell 1934	—	Chile
citriodora	Lemon Verbena	36	Doulat, D. 1951	H	Chile, Arg.
nodiflora		36	Junell 1934	HM	O.W. Tropics

323

LANTANA $x = 8, 11$

camara	{ 32	Schnack & C. 1947	FHM	Tropics
	{ 44	Tjio 1948, Singh 1951		
polyacantha	44	,,	—	
trifolia	48	Patermann, T. 1938	H	Tr. Amer. & Asia

ACANTHOLIPPIA $x = 9$

seriphioides	36	Covas & S. 1947	—	Argentine

ALOYSIA $x = 9$

ligustrina	36	Covas & S. 1946	H	Texas—Arg.

PHYLA $x = 9$

nodiflora	36	Covas & S. 1946	—	Trop. & Sub-Tr.

CASTELIA $x = 11$

cuneato-ovata	44	Covas & S. 1946	—	S. America

CLERODENDRON $x = 12, 23?$

fargesii	24	Patermann, T. 1938	H	China
speciosissimum	48	Bowden 1945b	H	Tropics
thomsoniae	{ 46	Nishiyama & K. '42	H	,,
	{ c. 48	Bowden 1945b		
trichotomum	c. 46, c. 92	Bowden 1940a	H	China, Jap., Phil.
kaempferi	60	Bowden 1945b	—	E. Trop. Asia
bungei	108	,, ,,	H	Tr. Amer., China

DURANTA $x = 12?$

repens	Pigeon Berry	36	Patermann, T. 1938	H	Tropics
(plumieri)					

STACHYTARPHETA $x = ?$

cayennensis	48	Patermann, T. 1938	—	Tr. Amer., Afr.
angustifolia	56	Junell 1934	—	,, ,,
dichotoma	c. 112	,, ,,	H	Trop. America

264 LABIATAE

DRACOCEPHALUM $x = 5, 7$

imberbe	10	S. & S. 1938	H	Altai
moldavica	20	Panutina-M. 1933	H	Sib., Himal.
altaiense	14	S. & S. 1938	H	Altai
ruyschiana	14	L. & L. 1944b	H	Eur., Siberia

STACHYS (BETONICA) $x = 5, 8$

arvensis	Woundwort	10	Lang 1940	M	Eur., N. Africa
officinalis	Betony	16	,, ,,	M	Eur., Asia Min.
grandiflora		32	Lewitzky 1940	—	Asia M., Persia
sylvatica	Clownwort	{ 48	L. & L. 1942	M	Himal., N. Asia
		{ 66	Lang 1940		
palustris	Marsh Betony	{ c. 64	Wulff 1938	M	N. Temp.
		{ 102	Lang 1940		

TEUCRIUM $x = 5, 8, 13$

botrys	10	Junell 1934	—	Eur., Algeria
arduinii	32	,,	—	S. Europe

324

TEUCRIUM (*cont.*)

flavum		32	Junell 1934	—	Medit.
scorodonia	Wood Sage	{ 32 { 34	Scheerer 1940 Rutland 1941	H	W. Europe
chamaedrys		64	Reese 1952a	H	Eur., S.W. Asia, Morocco
polium		26	Lorenzo-A. & G. '50	—	Medit., S.W. Asia

SATUREIA *x* = 5?

montana	Winter Savory	30	Vaarama 1947a	HSp	S. Eur., Cauc.
hortensis	Summer Savory	{ 45 { 48	„ „ Mechelke 1954	HSp	Medit., S.W. Asia

HORMINUM *x* = 6

pyrenaicum		12	Favarger 1953	—	S. Eur. mtns.

HYSSOPUS *x* = 6

officinalis	Hyssop	12	Reese 1952a	DSp	Eurasia

PLECTRANTHUS *x* = 6

japonicus		24	Suzuka 1950	M	O.W. Tropics

ROSMARINUS *x* = 6

officinalis	Rosemary	24	Scheel 1931	Sp	Medit.

COLEUS *x* = 6, 7, 8

blumei		24	Furusato 1940	H	Java, *cult*
garden forms		48, 49, 72	Reddy 1952		
laciniatus		48	„ „	—	„
forskohlii		28	„ „	—	India
aromaticus (*amboinicus*)		32	Scheel 1931	M	„
rehneltianus		c. 48	„ „	—	Ceylon

PHLOMIS *x* = 6, 10, 11

lychnitis	Lampwick Pl.	20	Wagner 1948	H	S. Europe
purpurea		20	„ „	—	Spain, Portugal
tuberosa		22	Reese 1953	—	S. Eur., E. & N. Asia
alpina		24	S. & S. 1938	H	Siberia

THYMUS *x* = 6, 7, 9

serpyllum	Mother of T.	24	Pigott 1954	Sp	Eur., Asia, N. Afr.
alpestris		28	Jalas 1948	—	C. Europe
comosus		28	„ „	H	S.E. Europe
marschallianus		28	„ „	H	S.E. Eur., Cauc.
pulegioides		28	Pigott 1954	H	Europe
zheguliensis		28	Jalas 1948	—	C. Asia
caespititius		30	„ „	H	Pyrenees
vulgaris	Common Thyme	30	Vaarama 1947a	HMSp	S. Eur., N. Asia
citriodorus		42	„ „	H	*cult*
drucei	Mother of Thyme	54	Jalas 1948,	Sp	N. & Arctic
(*serpyllum, arcticus*)		50-56	Pigott 1954		
hirsutus (*doerfleri*)		54	Vaarama 1947a	—	Balkans
pallasianus (*odoratissimus*)		54	„ „	H	S. Russia
longidens (*lanicaulis*)		58	„ „	H	Balkans

MONARDA $x = 6, 8, 9$

punctata	Am. Horse Mint	24	Bushnell 1936	M	N. America
didyma	Bee Balm	32	,, ,,	H	E: N. America
fistulosa	Am. Bergamot	{ 32 36	,, ,, Suzuka & K. 1949	HSp	W: N. America

MENTHA $x = 6, 9, 10$

arvensis	Field Mint	{ 12, 60, 72 54 72 64, 92	L. & L. 1942 Wolf 1929 Ruttle 1931a Nagao 1941	SpP	Eur., N. Asia
requieni		18	Ruttle 1931a	P	Cors., Sard.
longifolia (*silvestris*)	Horse Mint, Jap. Peppermint	{ 18 24 24 48	Heimans 1938 Ruttle 1931a, Junell, L. & L. '42b Suzuka & K. 1949	Sp	North Temp.
rotundifolia	Apple Mint	{ 18 24 54	Heimans 1938 Nagao 1941, Schürhoff 1929b	PSp	Europe
niliaca	Egyptian M.	24, 56	Ruttle 1931a	P	Egypt
spicata	Spear Mint	{ 36 36, 48	Schürhoff 1929b L. & L. 1942	P	North O.W.
as *viridis*	White S.M.	36	Nagao 1941		
	Ital. Black S.M.	48	,, ,,		
	Am. Black S.M.	84	,, ,,		
aquatica	Water Mint	{ 36 c. 96	Schürhoff 1929b Ruttle 1931a	P	Eur., Asia, N. Afr.
piperita Peppermint		{ 36, 64 66, 68, 70	Glotov 1940 Ruttle 1931a	PSp	,, ,, ,,
v. *officinalis*	White P.	72, 84	Nagao 1941	P	
v. *vulgaris*	Black P.	68, 72 (128)	,, ,, Glotov 1940	P	
pulegium	Pennyroyal	20, 40	Ruttle 1931a	MSp	North O.W.

LAVANDULA $x = 6, 9,$ $x_2 = 15$

multifida		24	Garcia 1942	HP	W. Medit.
pedunculata		30	,, ,,	H	,,
stoechas		30	,, ,,	H	Medit.
viridis		30	,, ,,	—	Port., Madeira
spica	Spike L.	36	Laws 1930	HP	Medit.
vera v. *nana*	Lavender	48	E.K.J.*	HP	,,
v. *delphinensis*	,,	50	Makino 1951		
v. *fragrans*	,,	50	,, ,,		
officinalis	,,	54	Garcia 1942	HP	,,
lanata		54	,, ,,	—	Spain
latifolia		54	,, ,,	HP	Medit.

SALVIA $x = 6-11, 13, 17, 19$
 $x = 6$

hispanica		12	Scheel 1931	H	Trop. America
aethiopis		24	Felfoldy 1947	H	Medit.
carduacea		24	Stewart 1939	H	California
eremostachya		24	,, ,,	—	,,

SALVIA (*cont.*)

leucophylla		24	Stewart 1939	—	California
munzii		24	„ „	—	„

$x = 7$

dumetorum		14	Sugiura 1937a	—	N. Eurasia
officinalis	Sage	14	Hruby 1935	Sp	Medit.
superba	Violet S.	14	Benoist 1937	H	*cult*

$x = 8$

glutinosa		16	Hruby 1935	H	S. Eur.—Himal.
grandiflora		16	„ „	H	Asia Minor
sylvestris		16	„ 1941	H	E. Eur., N. Asia
verticillata	Lilac S.	16	„ 1934a	H	Eur., Asia M., Caucasus
columbariae	Chia	16 32	Stewart 1939 Carlson & S. 1936	GH	California
apiana		32	Stewart 1939	—	„
clevelandii		32	„ „	—	„
mellifera		32	„ „	—	„
sonomensis		32	„ „	—	„
splendens (i)	Scarlet S.	32	Carlson & S. 1936	H	Brazil
virgata		32	Benoist 1937	H	S.E. Eur., S.W. Asia
horminoides	Wild Clary	64	Yakovleva 1933	—	S. Eur., N. Afr.

$x = 9$

austriaca		18	Benoist 1937	—	S.E. Europe
patens	Gentian S.	18	Sugiura 1937a	H	Mexico
verbenacea	Vervain	54 64	Benoist 1937 Yakovleva 1933	H	Eur., S.W. Asia
pratensis	Meadow S.	18	Benoist 1937	H	Eur., Cauc.
v. *tenorii*		20	Sugiura 1936b		

$x = 10$

coccinea		20	„ „	H	Trop. N. Amer.
farinacea		20	„ „	H	Texas, Mexico
splendens (ii)		20	Furusato 1940	H	Brazil
podolica		20	Hruby 1941	—	Europe

$x = 11$

argentea		22	Sugiura 1936b	H	Medit.
jurisicii		22	Hruby 1948	H	Serbia
nemecii		22	„ „	—	Europe
nutans		22	Benoist 1937	H	S.E. Europe
sclarea	Clary	22	Suzuka 1950a	HM	S. Europe
carnosa v. *gilmani*		22	Stewart 1939	H	W: N. America
v. *pilosa*		32	„ „		

$x = 13 (6 + 7)$

spathacea		26	„ „	H	California

$x_2 = 17 (8 + 9)$

valentina		34	Benoist 1937	—	Spain

$x_2 = 19 (9 + 10)$

algeriensis		38	„ „	—	N. Africa
barrelieri (*pratensis*)		38	„ „	—	Eur., Cauc.

327

AJUGA $x = 7, 8$

chamaepitys	Ground Pine	28	Rutland 1941	—	Eur., S.W. Asia, N. Africa
genevensis		32	Scheerer 1940	H	Eur., S.W. Asia
pyramidalis		32	Favarger 1953	—	N. Eur., Alps
reptans	Bugle	32	Scheerer 1940	H	Eur., W. Asia, N. Afr.

PRUNELLA (BRUNELLA) $x = 7, 8?$

asiatica		28	Suzuka & K. 1949	—	E. Asia
grandiflora		{ 28 { 32	Bøcher 1949 Hruby 1932	H	Europe
vulgaris	Self Heal	{ 28 { 32	Bøcher 1949 Hruby 1932	H	N. Temp.
laciniata		32	„ „	—	Eur., W. Asia, N. Africa

TRICHOSTEMA $x = 7, 10, 19$

brachiatum		14	Lewis 1945	—	E: N. America
lanceolatum		14	„ „	—	W: N. America
oblongum		14	„ „	—	„ „
ovatum		14	„ „	—	California
austromontanum		28	„ „	—	„
lanatum	Blue Curls	20	„ „	H	„
parishii		20	„ „	—	„
dichotomum		38	„ „	H	E: N. America
setaceum		38	„ „	—	„ „

GALEOPSIS * $x = 8$

pubescens		16	Müntzing 1932	—	Europe
speciosa	& 3 spp.	16	„ „	—	„
tetrahit	Hemp Nettle	32	„ „	—	„
bifida		32	„ „	—	N. & C. Europe

MELISSA $x = 8$

officinalis	Balm	32	Reese 1952a	MSp	Eurasia

OCIMUM $x = 8$

basilicum	Basil	48	Vaarama 1947a	HMSp	Trop. Asia, Afr.
gratissimum		64	Golubinski, T. 1938	HP	India
sanctum	Tulsi	64	„ „	HM	O.W. Tropics
canum		64, 128	„ 1937	P	Trop. Asia & Afr.
canum × *grat.*		64 (128)	Lapin 1939	—	*expt.*

SCUTELLARIA * $x = 8?$

albida		32	Scheel 1931	—	S.E. Europe
galericulata	& 3 spp.	*c.* 32	„ „	H	N. Temp.
altissima		34	Reese 1953	—	S. Europe

ORIGANUM $x = 8?$

vulgare	Pot Marjoram	{ 30 { 32	Rutland 1941 Scheerer 1939	Sp	Eur., Asia, N. Afr.

ACINOS (CALAMINTHA) $x = 9$

alpinus		18	Reese 1953	—	Europe
arvensis (C. acinos)		18	Scheerer 1939	H	„

328

LAMIUM $x=9$

amplexicaule	Henbit	18	Bernström 1944	—	Eurasia, N. Afr.
album	Wh. Deadnettle	18	Turesson 1938	M	Eur., Himal.
maculatum		18	Jørgensen 1927a	H	Eur.—Altai
purpureum		18	Bernström 1944	—	S. Eur.—Altai
molucellifolium		36	,, ,,	—	N.W. Europe
hybridum		36	,, ,,	—	W. Eur., N. Afr.

GALEOBDOLON (LAMIUM) $x=9$

luteum	Yellow Archangel	18	Turesson 1938	—	Eur.—Persia
(*L. galeobdolon*)					

MOSLA $x=9$

punctata	18	Sugiura 1936b	—	Japan

LEONURUS $x=9, 10$

cardiaca	Motherwort	18	Rutland 1941	H	W. Europe
sibiricus		20	Suzuka 1950a	H	E. Asia

MARRUBIUM $x=9$?

vulgare	Wh. Horehound	{ 34	Rutland 1941	MSp	Eurasia
		{ 36	Wulff 1939b		

GLECHOMA (NEPETA) $x=9$

		⌈18	Scheerer, L. & L. '42		
hederacea	Ground Ivy	{ 24	L. & L. 1942a	H	Eurasia
		{ 36	Felfoldy 1947,		
		⌊36	Rutland 1941		

NEPETA $x = 9, 17$

macrantha		18	S. & S. 1938	H	Siberia
mussini		18	Floto & G. 1947	H	Cauc., Persia
nuda		18	Sugiura 1940	—	S. Europe
stachyoides		18	,, 1944	—	Algeria
cataria	Catmint	36	,, 1940	HM	Eur.—Himal.
grandiflora		36	,, ,,	—	Caucasus
kokanica		36	,, ,,	—	Turkestan
nepetella		34	Floto & G. 1947	H	S. Europe
pseudomussinii		26	,, ,,	H	*cult* (clone)
(*muss.* × *nepetella*)	(17 + 9)				

CLINOPODIUM (CALAMINTHA) $x = 10$

vulgare	Wild Basil	20	Scheerer 1939	—	N. Temp.

BALLOTA $x = 11$

nigra	Black Horehound	22	Rutland 1941	H	Eur., S.W. Asia

LYCOPUS $x = 11$

americanus		22	Ruttle 1932	—	N. America
europaeus	Gipsywort	22	,, ,,	—	S. Eur., N. Asia

PYCNOSTACHYS $x = 17$

eminii	34	Snoad 1952	—	Trop. Africa

PERILLA *x* = ?
 ocimoides   38, 40   Yamane 1950   —   E. Asia

PROSTANTHERA *x* = ?
 violacea (*thymifolia*)   *c.* 156   Snoad 1952   H   Australia

SIDERITIS *x* = ?
 spinulosa   22, 28, 30   Coutinho & L.-A. '48 —   Iber. Penin.
 hyssopifolia   *c.* 32   Reese 1953   —   S. Eur. mtns.

MONOCOTYLEDONS

Group I

BUTOMALES 265, 266 H	**ALISMATALES** 267–269 H
TRIURIDALES 270 H	**JUNCAGINALES** 271–273 H
APONOGETONALES 274, 275 H	**POTAMOGETONALES** 276–277 H
NAJADALES 278, 279 H	**COMMELINALES** 280–282 H
XYRIDALES 283, 284 H	**ERIOCAULALES** 285 H

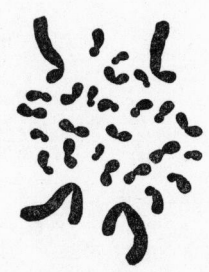

Hydrocharis morsus-ranae

265 BUTOMACEAE

TENAGOCHARIS $x = 7$
latifolia 14 Y. S. Rao 1953b — O.W. Tropics

HYDROCLEIS $x = 8$
nymphoides Water Poppy 16 Y. S. Rao 1953b H Brazil

LIMNOCHARIS $x = 10$
flava 20 Y. S. Rao 1953b H Trop. America

BUTOMUS $x = 13$
umbellatus Flowering Rush 26 Y. S. Rao 1953b H Temp. Eurasia
26, 39 (3x) L. & L. 1948

266 HYDROCHARITACEAE

ENHALUS $x = 7$
acoroides Sea Fruit 14 E.K.J.* T(V) N. Malaya, Austr.

HYDROCHARIS $x = 7$
morsus-ranae Frog's Bit 28 Maude 1940 H Eur., Temp. Asia

LAGAROSIPHON $x = 7, 11$
vaginalis 14 E.K.J.* Ma E. Africa, India
crispus 22 Eichhorn 1943 — E. Trop. Africa

BLYXA $x = 8$
sp. 16 Y. S. Rao 1950b — O.W. Tr. & Sub-Trop.

HYDRILLA $x = 8$
verticillata 16, 24 Sinoto 1929 FoMa W. Indies

ELODEA (HELODEA, ANACHARIS) $x = 8$
callitrichoides 16 Heitz 1927 H S. America
canadensis Ditch Moss { 24 Heppell 1945 * H N. America
{ 48 Santos 1924
densa 48 M. & S. 1935 H Argentine

HALOPHILA $x = 9$
ovata 18 Harada 1951 — Tr. Asia, Austr.

VALLISNERIA $x = 10$
spiralis 20 Jorgensen 1927b H Cosmop.
gigantea 40 ,, ,, H E. Indies

OTTELIA $x = 11$
alismoides { 22, 66 Y. S. Rao 1950b M(V) Trop. Asia & Austr.
{ 44 Islam 1950

BOOTIA $x = 11$
sp. 66 Y. S. Rao 1950b — O.W. Tropics

STRATIOTES $x = 12$
aloides Water Soldier 24 Schürhoff 1926 H Europe

335

267 ALISMATACEAE

ALISMA $x = 5, 6, 7, 13$

	10, 14, 16, 28	Wulff 1950		
	12	Palmgren 1943		
plantago-aquatica	14	Heppel, M. 1939	H	N. Temp.
Water Plantain	14	Woess 1948		
	14	Castro & W. 1950		
	14	Erlandsson 1946		
gramineum	14	Woess 1948	—	,,
	14	Erlandsson 1946		
triviale	14	Brown 1946	—	,,
	26	Castro & W. 1950		
	26	Woess 1948		
lanceolatum	26, 28	L. & L. 1944b	—	,,
	28	Erlandsson 1946		
subcordatum	28	Brown 1946	—	N. America

BALDELLIA (ALISMA, ECHINODORUS) $x = 7, 8, 9$

	14	Palmgren 1943		
ranunculoides	16	L. & L. 1944b	—	N. Europe
	18	Hagerup 1944		
	22	Clavier unp.		

ECHINODORUS $x = 11$
cordifolius	22	Baldwin & S. '55b	—	N. America

SAGITTARIA * $x = 11 (10)$

montevidensis Giant Alisma	20	Taylor 1925b	H	S. America
sagittifolia Arrowhead	20	Nawa 1928	H	N. Temp.
	22	L. & L. 1942		
aginashi	22	Shinke 1929	—	Japan
natans & 12 spp.	22	Brown 1946	—	N. America
latifolia	22	Oleson 1941	—	,,
trifolia	22	Morinaga & F. 1931	—	China, Japan

LIMNOPHYTON $x = 12$
obtusifolium	24	Murthy 1933	—	Tr. Asia & Afr.

268 SCHEUCHZERIACEAE

SCHEUCHZERIA $x = 11$
palustris	22	Manton 1949	—	N. Temp.

270 TRIURIDACEAE

SCIAPHYLLA $x = 12?$
japonica	48	Ohga & S. 1932	—	Japan

271 JUNCAGINACEAE

TRIGLOCHIN $x = 6, 8$
maritimum Arrowgrass	12	L. & L. 1944b	—	N. Temp.
	48	La Cour 1952		
palustre	24	L. & L. 1944b	—	,,

TRIGLOCHIN *cont.*)
barrelieri	30	Castro & F. 1946	—	Medit., Trop. & S. Africa
bulbosum	32	La Cour 1952	—	„ „

275 ZOSTERACEAE

ZOSTERA * $x = 6$
hornemanniana		12	Wulff 1937a	—	W. Europe
marina Eelgrass & 4 spp.		12	Harada 1948	Ma(Su)	W. Eur., N. Am.

276 POTAMOGETONACEAE

PHYLLOSPADIX $x = 10$
iwatensis	20	Harada 1944	—	Japan
japonica	16 ♂, 20 ♀	„ „	—	„

POTAMOGETON * $x = 13, 14$
$x = 13$
acutifolius		26	L. & L. 1942	—	Eur., Caus., Austr.
coloratus	& 9 spp.	26	Palmgren 1939	—	Europe
oxyphyllus		26	Harada 1942	—	Japan
panormitanus		26	„ „	—	N. & S. Temp.
anguillanus	& 9 spp.	52	„ „	—	Japan
fluitans		52	Kuleszanka, T. 1935	—	Temp. & Trop.
gramineus	& 2 spp.	52	Palmgren 1939	—	Europe
perfoliatus		52	Felfoldy 1947	—	N. & S. Temp.
filiformis		*c.* 78	L. & L. 1942	—	N. America
pectinatus		78	Harada 1942	—	N. & S. Temp.

$x = 14$
cristatus	28	„ „	—	America
monogynus	28	„ „	—	Europe
vaseyi	28	„ „	—	N. America
fauriei	29!	„ „	—	Japan
densus	30	Palmgren 1939	—	N. Temp.
apertus	42	Harada 1942	—	Japan
kamogawaensis	42	„ „	—	
vaginatus	*c.* 88	Palmgren 1939	—	N. & S. Temp.

277 RUPPIACEAE

RUPPIA $x = 8$
maritima	16	Wulff 1937a	—	Temp., Sub-Trop.

278 ZANNICHELLIACEAE

ZANNICHELLIA $x = 7$
palustris	28	Scheerer 1940	—	Cosmop.

337

279 NAIADACEAE

NAIAS $x = 6$

marina (major)	{ 12	Lewitzky 1931a	Fo	Temp. & Trop.
	12 ♀, 13 ♂	Harada 1943		
tenuicaulis	12 ♀, 13 ♂	„ „	—	Japan
ancistrocarpa	12, 24	„ „	—	„
flexilis	12, 24	Chase 1947	—	Eur., Egypt
minor	{ 12	Harada 1943	—	Temp. & Tr. O.W.
	24	Chase 1947		
foveolata	12, 24, 34	Harada 1943	—	Java
gracillima	{ 12	„ „	—	Temp. & Tr. O.W.
	24, 36	Chase 1947		
guadalupensis	{ 12, 36, 42		—	W. Indies
	48, 54, 60	„ „		
graminea	24	Harada 1943	—	Temp. & Tr. O.W.
muenscheri	24	Chase 1947	—	U.S.A.
oguraensis	24	Harada 1943	—	Japan
species	46	„ „		

280 COMMELINACEAE

POLLIA $x = 5, 19$

subumbellata	10	Darlington 1937b	—	Himalayas
japonica	38	Mitsukuri 1947	—	Japan

RHOEO $x = 6$

discolor	12 (24)	Walters & G. 1948	H	C. America

SETCREASEA (TRELEASEA) $x = 6$

brevifolia	{ 12, 24	Richardson 1935b	—	Texas
	36	Anderson & S. 1936		
pallida	12, 36	Celarier 1955	—	Mexico
tumida	24	„ „	—	„

ZEBRINA $x = 6$

pendula	24, 48	Darlington 1929a	H	Mexico

SPIRONEMA $x = 6$

fragrans	12	Darlington 1929a	H	Mexico

CALLISIA $x = 6$

repens	12	Anderson & S. 1936	—	S. America

CUTHBERTIA $x = 6$

graminea	12, 24, 25, 36, 37	Giles 1942	—	S.E: U.S.A.

WELDENIA $x = 6$

candida	{ 18	La Cour 1952	H	Mexico
	24	Atchison *et al.* 1949		

TRADESCANTIA $x = 6, 8, 12, 13, 15, 18$
$x = 6$ (*virginiana* group)

bracteata	12, 18	Anderson & S. 1936	—	E. & S. U.S.A.
canaliculata	12, 24	„ „	—	„ „

TRADESCANTIA (*cont.*)

edwardsiana		12	Anderson & S. 1936	—	E. & S. U.S.A.
ernestiana		12	,, ,,	—	,, ,,
hirsuticaulis		12	,, ,,	—	,, ,,
hirsutiflora		24	,, ,,	—	,, ,,
humilis		12	,, ,,	—	,, ,,
gigantea		12	,, ,,	—	,, ,,
longipes		24	,, ,,	—	,, ,,
occidentalis		12, 24	,, ,,	—	,, ,,
ozarkana		24	,, ,,	—	,, ,,
paludosa		12 + 0–12B	,, ,,	—	,, ,,
reverchoni		24	Brown *et al.* 1951	—	,, ,,
roseolens		24	Anderson & S. 1936	—	,, ,,
subaspera		24	,, ,,	—	,, ,,
tharpii		24	,, ,,	—	,, ,,
virginiana	Spiderwort	24 + 0–6B	Darlington 1929a	H	*cult*

$x = 6, 7, 8, 12$, etc.

iridescens		12	Atchison *et al.* 1949	—	Mexico
crassifolia		12 + 0–2B	Darlington 1929a	H	S. America
commelinoides		14	Celarier 1955	—	Mexico
rosea		24	Anderson & S. 1936	—	U.S.A.
reflexa		24, 26	Mitsukuri 1947	—	,,
micrantha		26	Anderson & S. 1936	—	Mexico
geniculata		{ 32	,, ,,	—	S. America
		{ 48	Simmonds 1954		
navicularis		32	Anderson & S. 1936	—	Peru
fluminensis	Wandering Jew	60	Anderson & S. 1936	H	,,
as *albiflora*		72	,, ,,	—	Brazil

CAMPELIA $x = 8$

zanonia		16	Darlington 1937b	—	Mex.—Brazil

TRIPOGANDRA (DESCANTARIA, NEODONNELLIA) $x = 8$

amplexicaulis	16	Celarier 1955	H	Cent. America
disgrega	16	Darlington 1937b	H	,, ,,
pflanzii	16	Celarier 1955	—	Bolivia
grandiflora	32	Wu 1941	H	Guatemala
cumanensis	48	Celarier 1955	—	Cent. America
elongata	{ c. 50	Simmonds 1954	—	C. & S. Amer.
	{ 60	Saura 1948b		

ANEILEMA $x = 10$

nudiflorum	Bird's Foot Gr.	20	Simmonds 1954	FoV	S.E.: Asia
keisak		30	Mitsukuri 1947	—	Japan
spiratum		40	Murthy 1934	FoV	India

CYANOTIS $x = 10, 12, 14$

axillaris	20	Islam & B. 1952	—	India
cristata	24 + 0–1B	,, ,,	H	India, Malaya
somaliensis	28	Anderson & S. 1936	H	E. Africa

COMMELINA $x = 11, 12?, 15?$

bengalensis	22, 68	Ganguly 1946, D. '29a	(Fo)V	O.W. Tropics
diffusa	30	Simmonds 1954	H	Tropics
communis	48, 90	Mitsukuri 1947	—	China
elegans	c. 52	Simmonds 1954	H	S: U.S.A.
nudiflora	56	Anderson & S. 1936	FoV	Tropics

COMMELINA (*cont.*)

hirtella	*c.* 58	Bowden 1940a	—	E: U.S.A.
coelestis	90	Anderson & S. 1936	—	Mexico
salicifolia	75	Sharma 1955	—	India
obliqua	150	,, ,,	—	,,

COMMELINANTIA $x = 13$

anomala	26	Anderson & S. 1936	H	Mexico

COLEOTRYPE $x = 18$

natalensis	36	Anderson & S. 1936	H	S. Africa

COCHLIOSTEMA $x = 19$

odoratissimum	38	Geitler 1939	H	Ecuador

DICHORISANDRA $x = 19$

thyrsiflora	38	Anderson & S. 1936	H	Brazil

TINANTIA $x = ?$

fugax	$\begin{cases} 64 \\ 68 \end{cases}$	Anderson & S. 1936 Darlington 1929a	—	Trop. America

PALISOTA $x = ?$

bracteosa	80	Anderson & S. 1936	H	Trop. Africa

285 ERIOCAULACEAE

ERIOCAULON $x = 8, 9$

cinereum	32	Erlandsson 1942a	—	Australia
truncatum	32	,, ,,	—	India
sexangulare	36	,, ,,	—	India, Madag.

Group II

BROMELIALES	ZINGIBERALES
286	287–292
H	H

Musa : " Gros Michel "

TILLANDSIA $x = 8$

usneoides	Old Man's Beard	32	Billings 1904	HT	Trop. America
lindeniana		64	Lindschau 1933	T	Brazil
streptophylla		64	„ „	HT	Mexico
juncea		c. 96	„ „	T	Trop. America

BROMELIA $x = 8$

fastuosa		c. 96	Lindschau 1933	HT	Trop. America
pinguin	Wild Pineapple	96	Collins & K. 1931	HT	„ „

CRYPTANTHUS $x = 9, 17$

acaulis		{ 34	M. & S. 1935	H	Brazil
		{ 36	Lindschau 1933		
zonatus		36	„ „	H	„
bivittatus		36, 54	„ „	H	S. America
beuckeri		54	„ „	H	Brazil

AREGELIA * $x = (9), 27$

marmorata	& 4 spp.	54	Lindschau 1933	H	Brazil
microps		c. 126	„ „	H	cult

BILLBERGIA * $x = (9), 27$

liboniana		54	M. & S. 1935	H	Brazil
ligulata	& 6 spp.	54	Lindschau 1933	H	S. America
vittata		72	„ „	H	Brazil
sp.		108	M. & S. 1935		—

NIDULARIUM * $x = (9), 27$

princeps	& 3 spp.	54	Lindschau 1933	H	Brazil

AECHMEA * $x = 25, 27$

comata	& 4 spp.	50	Lindschau 1933	H	Trop. America
hystrix		54	„ „	H	Brazil

CARAGUATA $x = 28$

zahnii	Caraguata	56	Lindschau 1933	T	Trop. America

ACANTHOSTACHYS $x = 25$

strobilacea		50	Lindschau 1933	—	Brazil

CANISTRUM $x = 25$

roseum		50	Lindschau 1933	H	Brazil

MACROCHORDIUM $x = 25$

tinctorium		50	Lindschau 1933	—	Brazil

DYCKIA $x = 25$

altissima		50	Lindschau 1933	H	Brazil
sulphurea		50	„ „	H	„

PUYA $x = 25$

spathacea		50	Lindschau 1933	H	Argentine

HECHTIA $x = 25$

ghiesbreghtii		50	Lindschau 1933	H	Mexico

PITCAIRNIA * $x = 25$

andreana	& 4 spp.	50	Lindschau 1933	H	Ecuador—Venez.
muscosa		50	M. & S. 1935	H	Brazil
punicea		50	Lindschau 1933	H	Mexico

ANANAS $x = 25$

microstachys		50	Collins 1933	FTVit	Brazil
comosus	Pineapple	50, 75, 100	Collins & K. 1935	FTVit	*cult*, Brazil

PSEUDANANAS (ANANAS) $x = 25$

macrodontes	*c.* 100	Lindschau 1933	—	Brazil

LINDMANNIA $x = 25$?

penduliflora	*c.* 120	Lindschau 1933	—	Peru

287 MUSACEAE

ENSETE $x = 9$

edule			HT	Trop. Africa
as *buchanani*	18	Cheeseman 1947		Nyasaland
as *davyae*	18	„ „		Transvaal
as *Musa ensete*	18	Cheeseman & L. 1935		Abyssinia
as *livingstoniana*	18	Cheeseman 1947		Nyasaland
gilletti	18	„ „	—	Trop. Africa
pechelli	18	E.K.J.	—	New Guinea
superba	18	Agharkar & B. 1935	—	E. Indies

MUSA $x = 10, 11$

S. 1. AUSTRALIMUSA $x = 10$

textilis	Manila Hemp	20	Cheeseman & L. 1935 T	Philippines
fehi	Fei, Borabora	20	Dodds 1946 F	Oceania
lolodensis		20	Simmonds & D. 1949 —	New Guinea
peekelii		20	„ „ „ —	„
erecta		20	Simmonds 1953 —	Solomon Is.
angustigemma		20	„ „ —	New Guinea

S. 2. CALLIMUSA $x = 10$

borneensis	20	Simmonds & D. 1949 —	Sarawak
coccinea	20	Cheeseman & L. 1935 TH	China
violascens	20	Simmonds & D. 1949 —	Malaya

S. 3. EUMUSA $x = 11$ (Bananas or Plantains)

acuminata (incl. *banksii*, *malaccensis*, etc.)	22	Simmonds & D. 1949 —	S.E. Asia
edible & exp. forms 22, 33, 44 etc. (*paradisiaca, cavendishii*, etc.)		Dodds & S. 1948 F	*cult*
balbisiana	22	Simmonds & D. 1949 —	S.E. Asia
edible & exp. forms 22, 33, 44 etc.		Dodds & S. 1948 F	*cult*
acuminata × *balbisiana* edible & exp. forms 22, 33, 44, etc. *sapientum*, etc.		„ „ F	*cult*
basjoo Bashofu	22	Simmonds & D. 1949 HT	Liukiu
itinerans	22	„ „ —	Burma
nagensium	22	Wilson 1946 —	India

MUSA (*cont.*)
S. 4. RHODOCHLAMYS   *x* = 11

laterita		22	Simmonds & D. 1949	—	Burma
ornata		22	Cheeseman & L. 1935	H	N.E. India
sanguinea		22	Simmonds & D. 1949	H	Assam
velutina		22	,, ,,	—	,,

288 STRELITZIACEAE

STRELITZIA   *x* = 7, 11

nicolai		14	Sato 1948	H	S. Africa
reginae	Bird of Paradise Fl.	14	Cheeseman & L. 1935	H	,,
augusta		22	Simmonds 1954	H	,,

HELICONIA   *x* = 8, 11, 12 (13)

metallica		16, 18, 20, 22	Agharkar & B. 1935	H	Ecuador—Colom.
seemannii		22	Cheeseman & L. 1935	H	India
bihai	False Plantain	24	,, ,,	HV	W.I., Tr. S. Am.
as *aureo-striata*		24	Venkatasubban 1946		*cult*
brevispatha		24	Cheeseman & L. 1935	—	Mexico
brasiliensis		{ 24	Venkatasubban 1946,	H	Brazil, Guiana
		24	Chakravorti 1949		
illustris		24	Venkatasubban 1946	H	Pacific Is.
insignis		24	Cheeseman & L. 1935	H	S. America
psittacorum	Parrot P.	24	,, ,,	H	,,
rubra		26	Venkatasubban 1946	—	?

RAVENALA   *x* = 11

madagascariensis	Travellers' T.	22	Cheeseman & L. 1935	H	Madagascar

290 ZINGIBERACEAE

COSTUS   *x* = 9

cylindricus		18	Simmonds 1954	T	Trinidad
bicolor		18	Venkatasubban 1946	—	Cameroons
discolor		18	Raghavan & V. 1943	H	Brazil
friedrichsenii		18	Simmonds 1954	H	Cent. America
igneus		18	Raghavan & V. 1943	H	Brazil
malortieanus		18	Gregory 1936	HT	Cent. America
as *elegans*		18	Venkatasubban 1946		
niveopurpureus		18	Simmonds 1954	—	Martinique
speciosus		{ 18	Sato 1948	H	India, Malaya
		36	Raghavan & V. 1943		
as *sericeus* (3*x*)		27	Simmonds 1954		
afer	Ginger Lily	36	Venkatasubban 1946	HSp	Trop. Africa
pictus		36	,, ,,	H	Mexico
musaicus		*c.* 102	,, ,,	H	Congo, *cult*

ZINGIBER   *x* = 11, 12

cassumunar		22	Raghavan & V. 1943	M	Trop. Asia
zerumbet	Wild Ginger	22	,, ,,	V	,,
mioga	Jap. Wild G.	55	Morinaga *et al.* 1929	Sp	Japan
officinale	Ginger	{ 22	Raghavan & V. 1943	Sp	Malaya, *cult*
		22 + 2B	E.K.J.*		

345

KAEMPFERIA $x = 9, 11, 12$

atrovirens		22	Venkatasubban 1946	H	Borneo
speciosa		22	,, ,,	—	India
gibsoni		24	Raghavan & V. 1943	—	—
gilbertii		36	,, ,,	H	India, Burma
galanga		54	,, ,,	MSp	India
rotunda		54	,, ,,	H	India, Java

ALPINIA $x = 12$

allughas	Tara	48	Raghavan & V. 1943	M	India
calcarata		48	,, ,,	M	India, China
chinensis		48	Sato 1948	—	China
galanga	Siamese G.	48	Raghavan & V. 1943	Sp	Trop. Asia
japonica		48	Sato 1948	—	Japan
nutans		48	Raghavan & V. 1943	H	India
rafflesiana (*vittata*)		48	,, ,,	·H	Malaya
sanderae		48	Venkatasubban 1946	H	*cult*

AMOMUM (PHAEOMERIA) $x = 12$

magnificum	48	Venkatasubban 1946	H	E. Indies
	52	Chakravorti 1952		

ELETTERIA $x = 12$

cardamomum Malabar Card.	48	Gregory 1936	MSp	S. Ind., Burma
	52	Chakravorti 1952		

GLOBBA $x = 12$

bulbifera	48	Raghavan & V. 1943	—	Malaya

PHAEOMERIA (NICOLAJA) $x = 12$

atropurpurea	48	Boehm 1931	H	Malaya

CURCUMA $x = 16, 21$

longa Turmeric		32	Sato 1948		
(*domestica*)		62	Raghavan & V. 1943	DSp	Malaya, *cult*
		64	Sugiura 1931		
amada	Mango G.	42	Raghavan & V. 1943	SpV	India
aromatica	Yellow Zedoary	42	,, ,,	MSp	
petiolata		64	Venkatasubban 1946	DHSp	E. Asia
zedoaria	Zedoary	64	,, ,,	DHSp	India

BRACHYCHILUS $x = 16$

horsfieldii	32	Holzer 1952	H	Java

HEDYCHIUM $x = 9?, 17, 26$

flavescens		34	Raghavan & V. 1943	H	India, Masc. Is.
spicatum		34	Sato 1948	H	India
greenii		36	Raghavan & V. 1943	H	,,
coccineum v. *angustifolium*		52	Venkatasubban 1946	H	India, Burma
flavum		52	Raghavan & V. 1943	H	Himalayas
coronarium	Ginger Lily	54	,, ,,	H	India, China
gardnerianum		54	,, ,,	H	Himalayas
elwesii		66	Gregory 1936	HP	Assam
gracile		66	Raghavan & V. 1943	HSp	India

346

291 CANNACEAE

CANNA $x = 9$

discolor		18	Offerijns 1935	H	Trop. W. Indies
glauca	Arrowroot C.	18	Honing 1928	HR	W. Ind., Mexico
flaccida		18	Belling, T. 1931	H	N. America
humilis		18	Offerijns 1935	H	China
edulis	Queensland A.	18 / 27	Simmonds 1954 / Venkatasubban 1946	HR	Trop. America
indica	Indian Shot	18 / 27	Honing 1928 / Belling 1925	HR	Trop. America
limbata (aureo-vittata)		18, 36	Honing 1928	H	Brazil

292 MARANTACEAE

THALIA $x = 6$

dealbata	12	Suessenguth 1921	HT	S.E: U.S.A.

CALATHEA $x = 4, 11, 12, 13$

veitchiana	8 / 26	Sato 1948 / Venkatasubban 1946	H	Peru
mediopicta	22	,, ,,	H	Brazil
insignis	22	Sato 1948	H	,,
grandiflora	24	Venkatasubban 1946	H	,,
lietzei	24, 26	,, ,,	H	,,
zebrina	24, 26	,, ,,	H	,,
lindeniana	26	,, ,,	H	,,
makoyana	26	,, ,,	H	,,
roseo-picta	26	,, ,,	H	,,
taeniosa	52	Sato 1948	H	,,
as *Maranta asymmetrica*	24	Venkatasubban 1946		

MARANTA $x = 6, 13$

nitida-picta?	8	Venkatasubban 1946	—	—
arundinacea v. *variegatum*	18	Sato 1948	HR	Trop. Amer., W.
W.I. Arrowroot	48	Simmonds 1954		Indies
as *Phrynium*	46	Venkatasubban 1946		
bicolor	24	,, ,,	H	Brazil, Guiana
tigrina	24	,, ,,		—
nitida	26	,, ,,		—
leuconeura v. *massangeana*	26	,, ,,	H	Brazil
striata	26	Sato 1948	—	?

CTENANTHE $x = 9$

oppenheimiana	18	Sato 1948	H	Brazil

MONOTAGMA $x = 9$

smaragdinum	27	Sato 1948	H	Ecuador

STROMANTHE $x = ?$

sanguinea	24 / 44	Suessenguth 1920 / Venkatasubban 1946	HR	Brazil

347

Group III

LILIALES
293–298
H

ARALES
302, 303
H

AMARYLLIDALES
306
H

ALSTROEMERIALES
299–301
H

TYPHALES
304, 305
H

IRIDALES
307
H

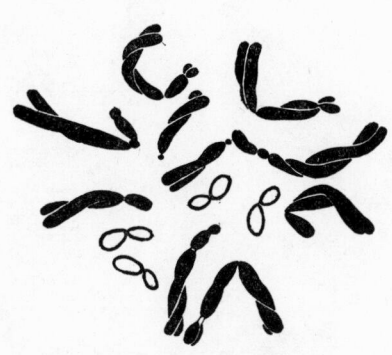

Puschkinia libanotica

293 LILIACEAE

Order of the Tribes with their Basic Numbers

I	Scilleae: 3–15	XIV	Veratreae: 8, 10, 11
II	Allieae: 5–9	XV	Asparageae: 10
III	Tulipeae: 6–12	XVI	Bowieae: 10
IV	Kniphofieae: 6	XVII	Anguillarieae: 10, 11
V	Agapantheae: 6, 15	XVIII	Tricyrtideae: 13
VI	Aloineae: 7	XIX	Narthecieae: 12, 13, 14, 15, 17
VII	Asphodeleae: 7–13	XX	Heloniadeae: 12, 17
VIII	Uvularieae: 7, 8, 11	XXI	Ophiopogoneae: 18
IX	Polygonateae: 6–11	XXII	Peliosantheae: 18
X	Colchiceae: 7–27	XXIII	Aspidistreae: 18, 19
XI	Johnsonieae: 8	XXIV	Convallarieae: 19
XII	Milliganieae: 8	XXV	Herrerieae: 27
XIII	Dianelleae: 8, 9		

TRIBE I: SCILLEAE

ORNITHOGALUM $x = 3, 5, 6, 7, 8, 9$, etc.

virens		6	Quintanilha & C. '47	H	Mozambique
graminifolium		10	Therman 1951	H	S. Africa
libanoticum		10	Geitler 1929b	—	Syria
cydni		12	Delaunay 1923	—	Asia Minor
fimbriatum		12	„ 1926	H	„
leptophyllum		12	Pienaar unp.	—	Transvaal
pretoriense		12	„	—	„
nanum		12	Delaunay 1926	—	Greece, Asia M.
thyrsoides Chincherinchees		12	Neves 1952	H	Cape
zeyheri		12	„ 1953	H	S. Africa
tenuifolium		16	Delaunay 1926	H	S. Eur., Asia M.
as *gussonei*		18	Polya 1949		
pyrenaicum French Asparagus	16 + 0–3B	Neves 1952	HV	S. Eur., S.W. Asia
v. *flavescens*	16 + 0–1B, 24	„ „		
exscapum		18	Martinoli 1950	H	Dalmatia
tempskyanum		18	Delaunay 1926	—	Asia Minor
umbellatum Star of Bethlehem	18 + 0–6B, 27 + 0–1B, 36, 43, 45, 52, 54, 72	Neves 1952	H	Eur., Asia M., N. Africa
pyramidale		24	„ „	H	Medit.
boucheanum		28	Lauber 1947	—	S.W. Asia
nutans	{ 30	Nakajima 1936	H	S. Europe,
	{ 42	Holzer 1952		Asia Minor
arcuatum		32	Neves 1952	—	Caucasus
lacteum		32	Nakajima 1936	H	S. Africa
unifolium	34 + 0–1B	Neves 1952	H	W. Medit.
concinnum	36 + 0–6B	„ „	—	„
arabicum (3x)		51	„ „	H	Medit.
caudatum		54	Therman 1951	H	S. Africa
divergens		54	Neves 1952	H	S. Europe
narbonense	54 + 0–11B	„ „	H	Medit., S.W. Asia

BELLEVALIA (HYACINTHUS) $x = 4$

(i) *desertorum*	8	Feinbrun 1939	—	Palestine
flexuosa	8	„ „	—	„

BELLEVALIA (*cont.*)

romana	8	Feinbrun 1939	H	Italy, Greece
sessiflora	8	,, ,,	—	Libya, Egypt

(ii) *ciliata*	8	,, ,,	—	Algiers—Greece
longipes	8	,, ,,	—	Assyria
speciosa	8	,, ,,	—	Transcaucasia
wilhelmsii	8	,, ,,	—	Caucasus
palmyrensis	16	,, ,,	—	Syria
stepporum	16	,, ,,	—	,,

(iii) *dubia*	8	Chiarugi 1949	—	W. Medit.
fomini	8	Feinbrun 1939	—	E. Caucasus
hackeli	8	Levan 1944	—	Europe
macrobotrys	8	Feinbrun 1939	—	E. Caucasus
trifoliata	8	,, ,,	—	N.E. Medit.
webbiana	{ 8 16	,, ,, Chiarugi 1949	—	Tuscany
warburgii	16	Feinbrun 1939	—	Palestine
alexandrina	24	,, ,,		Alexandria

(iv) *formiculata*	8	Delaunay 1926	—	—
acutifolia	8	,, ,,	—	—

DIPCADI $x = 4, 9$

serotinum	{ 8 8 + 0–1B 8 + 2–16B	Levan 1944 Fernandes *et al.* 1948 Resende & F. 1946	H	S. Eur., N. Africa
glaucum	18	La Cour unp.	H	S. Africa
fulvum	34	Battaglia 1954	H	N. Africa

SCILLA $x = 4, 6, 7, 8, 9, 10, 11$

obtusifolia	8	Martinoli 1949	—	Sard., N. Africa
sibirica	12	Sato 1935a	H	E. Eur., Asia M.
permixta	14 + 0–2B	,, 1936	H	—
hughii	16	Maugini 1953a	—	Marettimo
italica	16	Dark 1934	H	S. Europe
lingulata	16	Sato 1942	H	Alg., Morocco
peruviana	{ 16	,, 1935a	H	Medit. (*sic*)
Cuban Lily	{ 14, 16, 22, 23, 28	Battaglia 1949a, c, '50b	H	
as *ughii*	15, 17, 19, 20, 22	Sato 1942	H	
pratensis	{ 28 26	Maude 1940 Sato 1942	H	Croatia
autumnalis	{ 14 28, *c*. 42 29	Battaglia 1952b Maude 1939, 1940 Sato 1942	H	Medit., Cauc.
bifolia	18	,, 1935a	H	Eur., Asia
chinensis	18, 26, 34, 35	,, 1942	H	China
numidica	18	Battaglia 1953	—	Algeria
hyacinthoides	20	Sato 1935a	H	S. Europe
monophylla	20	Fernandes *et al.* '48	H	Portugal, Spain
ramburei	20	,, ,,	—	W. Europe
verna	22	Maude 1940	H	,,
japonica	26, 34, 36, 42, 44	Sato 1935a	H	Japan
indica	{ 30 44, 45, 46, 58	Sheriff & M. 1946 Y. S. Rao 1953a	HM	Trop. Asia

PUSCHKINIA $x = 5$

scilloides	{ 10 { 16	Greeves, T. 1930 Sato 1942	H	Asia M., Syria
v. *libanotica*	{ 10 { 10 + **4B**	,, ,, Darlington 1936b	H	,, ,,

URGINEA $x = 5$

maritima Sea Onion	{ 10 + **2B** { 20 + **1–4B**, 30 { 20, 30, 40	Geitler 1929a, b Raghavan & V. '40 Giuffrida 1950	HM	Medit.
indica	20	Raghavan 1935	—	Ind., Bur., Tr. Afr.
polyphylla	20	,, & V. '40	M	India
undulata	20	Martinoli 1949	H	Medit.
fugax	21, 24	,, ,,	—	,,

LACHENALIA $x = 7, 8, 11, 13$

(i) *rubida*	14	Moffett 1936	H	S. Africa
membranacea	14	,, ,,	H	,,
tricolor	14, 21	,, ,,	H	,,
glaucina	28	,, ,,	H	,,
pendula	42	,, ,,	H	,,
(ii) *rosea* (*isopetala*)	14	,, ,,	H	,,
elegans	28	,, ,,	H	,,
(iii) *liliiflora*	16	,, ,,	H	,,
nervosa	16	,, ,,	H	,,
pallida	16	,, ,,	H	,,
purpureo-coerulea	16	,, ,,	H	,,
unicolor fragrans (*versicolor*)	16	,, ,,	H	,,
orchioides	16, 17	,, ,,	H	,,
pustulata	32	Sato 1942	H	,,
(iv) *unifolia*	22	Moffett 1936	H	,,
sp.	26	,, ,,	H	,,

ENDYMION (SCILLA) $x = 8$

hispanicus (*S. campanulata*)	16	Sato 1935a	H	Spain
non-scriptus Bluebell (*S. nutans*)	16	,, ,,	H	Europe

GALTONIA $x = 8$

candicans Summer Hyac.	16	Newton 1924	H	S. Africa

DRIMIOPSIS $x = 8$

maculata	64	Sato 1942	H	S. Africa
botryoides	80	M. & S. 1935	—	,,

HYACINTHUS $x = 8, 9, 14$

orientalis Hyacinth	16	Darlington *et al.* '51	H	Greece, Asia M.
garden forms	16–31	,, ,,		
azureus	18	Chiarugi 1950	H	Asia Minor
amethystinus	28	Darlington 1932b	H	Pyrenees
pouzolzii (*fastigiatus*)	28	Chiarugi 1950	H	Cors., Sard.

ALBUCA $x = 9$

nelsoni	18	Sato 1942	H	Natal

353

MUSCARI $x = 9$

alpinum		18	Chiarugi 1950	H	Asia Minor
argaei		18	Delaunay 1926	—	Greece
caucasicum		18	,, ,,	H	Caucasus
comosum	Feather H.	18	,, ,,	H	Medit., S.W. Asia
as *tenuiflorum*	$18 + 0-2B$		,, ,,		
latifolium	$18 + 0-2B$		,, ,,	H	Asia Minor
longipes		18	,, ,,	H	Palestine
moschatum	Musk H.	18	,, ,,	H	Asia Minor
polyanthum	$18 + 0-2B$		,, ,,	H	,,
armeniacum		⌠18	Greeves, T. 1931	H	,,
		⌡36	Haque 1952		
commutatum		⌠18	Chiarugi 1950	H	Sicily
		⌡45	Delaunay 1926		
botryoides	Grape Hyacinth	⌠36	,, ,,	H	Eur., S.W. Asia
		⟨ c. 48	M. & S. 1935		
		⌡63	Sato 1942		
conicum		36	Greeves, T. 1931	H	S. Europe
pallens		36	Delaunay 1926	H	Caucasus
racemosum		⌠36	Chiarugi 1950		
		⟨45	Delaunay 1926	H	Medit., Cauc.
		⌡54	Wunderlich 1937		
neglectum		⌠45	Delaunay 1926	H	Medit.
		⌡54	Sato 1942		

CHIONODOXA $x = 9, 10$

sardensis	18	Greeves, T. 1930	H	Asia Minor
luciliae	⌠18	Müller 1912	H	,,
	⌡20	Sato 1942		

CAMASSIA $x = 15$

esculenta	Quamash	30	Nakajima 1936	HR	U.S.A.
cusickii		30	Greeves, T. 1931	H	Oregon
leichtlinii		30	F. H. Smith 1942	H	California

EUCOMIS $x = 15, 16$

bicolor	⌠30	M. & S. 1935	H	Natal
	⌡32	Darlington 1932b		
autumnalis (*undulata*)	⌠30	Koeperich 1930	H	S. Africa
	⌡60	Sato 1942		
comosa (*punctata*)	60	M. & S. 1935	H	,,
pallidiflora	60	Sato 1935a	H	,,

VELTHEIMIA $x = 20$

glauca	40	Sato 1942	H	S. Africa
viridifolia	40	Coleman 1940	H	,,

TRIBE II: ALLIEAE

BRODIAEA $x = 5, 6, 7, 8$

californica	⌠10	Johansen 1932	H	California
	⌡12	Burbanck 1941		
stellaris	12	,, ,,	H	,,
minor (*purdyi*)	⌠12, 32	,, ,,	H	Argentine
	⌡14	Johansen 1932		
elegans	32	Burbanck 1941	H	California
coronaria (*grandiflora*)	⌠42	,, ,,	HR	,,
	⌡36	K. 1931		

TRITELEIA (BRODIAEA) $x = 5, 7, 8$

ixioides v. *scabra*		10, 10 + **B**	Burbanck 1941	H	California
v. *analina*		50	„ „		
peduncularis		14, 28	„ „	H	„
hyacinthina	Wild Hyacinth	28	„ „	H	„
lactea		42–48	F. H. Smith 1933	H	W: N. America
laxa	Grass-Nut	18, 28, 42, 48	Burbanck 1941, '44	H	California
bridgesii		16	„ 1941	H	Cal., Oregon
crocea		16	„ 1941	H	California
hendersoni		32	„ 1941	H	Oregon

IPHEION (BRODIAEA, TRITELEIA) $x = 6$

uniflorum	{ 12	Saez 1949b	H	Argentine
	12	Battaglia 1952a		

BLOOMERIA $x = 9$

aurea	18	Sato 1942	H	S. California
crocea	18	Burbanck 1944	H	California

DICHELOSTEMMA (BRODIAEA) $x = 9$

volubile		{ 18	Burbanck 1941	H	California
		36	Johansen 1932		
pulchellum	Blue Dicks	{ 18	Burbanck 1941	H	W: U.S.A.
(*capitata*)		72	Johansen 1932		
congestum (*B. pulchella*)		36	Burbanck 1941	H	„

BREVOORTIA (DICHELOSTEMMA) $x = 8$

ida-maia	Floral Fire	c. 40	Johansen 1932	H	California
	Cracker	48	Burbanck 1941		

ALLIUM * $x = 7, 8, 9$ (Apomixis)

$x = 7$

allegheniense		14	Levan 1932	—	N. America
carmeli		14	Feinbrun 1950	—	Palestine
cernuum	Wild Onion	{ 14	Levan 1935	(V)	N. America
		16!	Brumfield 1941		
moly (apo.)	Lily Leek	14	Levan 1932	H	Europe
ardelii		14	Feinbrun 1950		
hirsutum		14	„ „	—	Palestine
narcissiflorum	Narcissus O.	14	Levan 1932	H	Europe
scorzoneraefolium		14	Mensinkai 1940	—	S. Europe
stellatum	Prairie O.	14	Anderson 1931	(R)	N. America
ursinum	Ramsons	14	Levan 1932	HRV	Eur., N. As., Cauc.
pendulinum		14, 18!	„ 1935	H	Eur., N. Africa
amplectens (apo.)		(14), 21, 28	„ 1940b	—	W: U.S.A.
macranthum		{ 14	„ 1934	—	Himalayas
		28	Mensinkai 1940		
neapolitanum	Daffodil O.	{ 14	Levan 1935	HRV	Eur., S.W. Asia
		21, 35	Kefallinos unp.		
		28	Feinbrun 1950		
bidwelliae		28	Mensinkai 1939	H	California
validum	Pacific O.	28	Levan 1935	—	N. America
tartaricum	Tartar O.	28–32	„ 1931	V	E. Eur., Siberia

$x = 8$

artemisietorum		16	Feinbrun 1950	—	Palestine
ascalonicum	Shallot & 5 spp.	16	Levan 1931	RV	*cult*
aschersonianum		16	Szelubsky 1950	—	S.W. Asia

ALLIUM (*cont.*)

callidictyon		16	Araratian & T. 1945	—	S.W. Asia
canadense	Tree O.	16	La Cour 1945 *	V	N. America
chloranthum		16	Feinbrun 1950	—	S.W. Asia
coppoleri		16	„ „	—	„ „
desertorum		16	„ „	—	Egypt
dumetorum		16	Szelubsky 1950	—	Palest., Leb.
fistulosum	Welsh O.	16	Levan 1935	V	Siberia
fuscoviolaceum		16	Araratian & T. 1945	—	Caucasus
fuscum		16	Diannelidis 1951	—	Eur., S.W. Asia
kunthianum		16	Araratian & T. 1945	—	Caucasus
lusitanicum	Perenn. Welsh O.	16	La Cour 1945 *	V	Medit.
materculae		16	Araratian & T. 1945	—	Caucasus
meteoricum		16	Diannelidis 1951	—	Greece
modestum		16	Feinbrun 1950	—	S.W. Asia
moschatum		16	Billeri 1954	—	Eur., S.W. Asia
pallasii (*pallyssium*)		16	Ono 1935	—	Siberia
proliferum		16	„ „	RV	Persia, Bal.
pyrenaicum		16	„ „	—	Pyrenees
sativum	Garlic & 17 spp.	16	Levan 1935	SpV	C. Asia
stamineum		16	Diannelidis 1951	—	S.W. Asia
tel-avivense		16	Szelubsky 1950	—	Palestine
thunbergii		16	Ono 1935	—	China, Japan
viviparum	& 11 spp.	16	Mensinkai 1940	—	Siberia
ammophilum		16, 32	Levan 1935	—	Europe
carinatum		16, 24, 25, 26	Woess 1947	—	„
cepa	Garden O.	16, 32	D'Amato 1948	RV	*cult*, Persia
margaritaceum		16, 32	Mensinkai 1940	—	Eur., S.W. Asia
nipponicum		{ 16	Ono 1935	—	Japan
		{ 32	Katayama 1936		
odorum	Fragrant-Fl. G.	16, 32	Håkansson 1951	H(V)	Siberia
ramosum (*odorum*)		16, 32	La Cour 1945 *	H	„
schoenoprasum	Chives	16, 24, 32	Levan 1936	V	N, Temp.
scorodoprasum	Racambole	16, 24	Woess 1947	RV	Eur., Cauc., Syria
victorialis		{ 16	Levan 1935	—	S. Eur., Asia
		{ 32	M. & S. 1935		
yunnanense (*mairei*)		16, 32	Levan 1935	—	China
angulosum	Mouse Garlic	16–100 !	„ „	V	Siberia
nutans		16–108 !	„ „	—	„
condensatum		17	Sato 1942	—	„
ampeloprasum	Wild Leek	· 32	La Cour 1945 *	V	Medit., S.W. Asia.
bakeri		32	Katayama 1936	—	China, Japan
ciliare		32	Ono 1935	—	Eur., S.W. Asia
cyaneum		32	Mensinkai 1940	H	China
deseglisei		32	„ 1939	—	Europe
porrum	Leek	32	Levan 1931	V	*cult*, Persia
rotundum		32	„ „	—	Eur., Asia M.
sikkimense		32	„ „	—	Himalayas
splendens		32	Sakai 1934	H	Siberia
tuberosum	Gynmigit	32	La Cour 1945 *	V	Him., China, Jap.
oleraceum	Field Garlic	{ 32	Levan 1937b	Sp	Eur., Cauc.
		{ 40	Woess 1947		
vineale	Crow G.	{ 32	Ono 1935	SpV	Eur., Cauc., Leb.
		{ 40	Fernandes *et al.* '48		

ALLIUM (*cont.*)
roseum	32	Levan 1935	V	Medit.
v. *bulbiferum*	48	Messeri 1931		
senescens	$\begin{cases} 32 \\ 48 \end{cases}$	Ono 1935 Mensinkai 1940	R	Eur., Siberia
babingtonii (*ampeloprasum*)	$\begin{cases} 40 \\ 48 \end{cases}$	Ono 1935 Maude 1940	V	Ireland, S.W. Eng.

$x = 9$
karataviense	18	Levan 1935	H	Turkestan
pseudoflavum	18	Araratian & T. 1945	—	Caucasus
triquetrum	18	Levan 1935	—	Eur., N. Africa
zebdanense	18	„ „	—	Syria, Armenia

NOTHOSCORDUM (ALLIUM) $x = 8, 9$ (Triploids Apomictic)
fragrans	$\begin{cases} 16, 24 \\ 18 \\ 16\text{–}22 \\ 19 \end{cases}$	Messeri 1931 Levan 1935 Garber 1944 D'Amato 1949c	HSp	Mexico
striatum	16	Levan 1935	—	S.E.: U.S.A.,
as *bivalve*	18	Beal 1932		Mexico

CALOSCORDUM $x = 8$
neriniflorum	16, 17	Sato 1942	—	China

MILLA $x = 13$?
biflora	39	Sato 1942	H	Mexico

TRIBE III: TULIPEAE

CALOCHORTUS $x = 6, 7, 8, 9, 10$
(i) *superbus*	12, 14	Beal & O. 1943	H	California
catalinae	14	„ „	H	„
flexuosus	14	„ „	H	Utah
leichtlinii	14	„ „	H	W: N. America
palmeri	14	„ „	H	California
splendens Lilac M.L.	14	„ „	H	„
venustus Wh. Mariposa L.	14 + 0–1B	„ „	H	„
luteus Sego Lily	14 + 0–1B, 20, 21	„ „	HR	„
davidsonianus	28	„ „	H	„
vesta	28	„ „	H	N. America
(ii) *macrocarpus*	14	„ „	H	W: N. America
(iii) *clavatus*	16	„ „	H	California
kennedyi	16	„ „	H	„
nuttallii Sego Lily	16	„ „	H	W: N. America
aureus	32	„ „	H	S.W: U.S.A.
(iv) *ambiguus*	18	„ „	H	W: N. America
gunnisoni	18	„ „	H	S.W: U.S.A.
(v) *plummerae*	18	„ „	H	California
weedii	18	„ „	H	„
(vi) *barbatus*	36	„ „	H	Mexico
(vii) *albus*	20	„ „	H	California
amabilis Golden Globe T.	20	„ „	H	„
amoenus Purple Gl. T.	20	„ „	H	„
pulchellus	20	„ „	H	„
(viii) *apiculatus*	20	„ „	H	W: N. America

357

CALOCHORTUS (*cont.*)

elegans		20	Beal & O. 1943	H(R)	Oregon
lobbii		20	,, ,,	H	N. America
monophyllus	Yellow Star T. (benthami)	20	,, ,,	H	California
tolmiei (maweanus majus)		20	,, ,,	H	Oregon
(i\) nudus		20	,, ,,	H	California
umbellatus		20	,, ,,	H	,,
uniflorus		40	,, ,,	H	,,
(x) howellii		20	,, ,,	H	Oregon
lyallii		20	,, ,,	H	W: N. America
nitidus		20	,, ,,	H	,, ,,
persistens (greenei)		20	,, ,,	H	,, ,,
longebarbatus		20, 30	,, ,,	H	,, ,,
pavonaceus (douglasianus)		40	,, ,,	H	,, ,,
lilacinus		40	Fanshawe unp.	H	,, ,,

FRITILLARIA $x = 12$: by fusion and fragmentation, 9, 13
OLD WORLD GROUPS (little or no heterochromatin)

(i) ruthenica		18	Darlington 1936c	H	S.E. Eur., Cauc.
nigra (tenella, caussolensis)		$18 + 0$–3B	La Cour 1951a	—	S. Eur., Cauc.
(ii) acmopetala		24	Darlington 1936c	H	Asia M., Syria
askabadensis		24	,, ,,	—	Transcaucasia
aurea		24	La Cour 1951a	—	Asia Minor
camtschatcensis		24, 36	Matsuura 1935	H	N.W. Amer., N.E. Asia, Japan
caucasica (armena)		24	La Cour 1951a	—	Cauc., Asia Min.
cirrhosa		24	,, ,,	H	Himalayas
citrina		24	Darlington 1936c	H	Asia Minor
conica		24	La Cour 1951a	—	Greece
dasyphylla		24, 36	Darlington 1936c	H	Asia Minor
drenovskii		24	,, & L.C. '41	—	Balkans
eggeri		24	,, 1936c	—	N.W. Persia
elwesii		24	,, ,,	—	W. Asia Minor
gracilis		24	,, ,,	—	Dalm., Monten.
graeca		24	La Cour 1951a	—	Greece, S. Maced.
hispanica		24	Darlington 1936c	—	Spain
imperialis	Crown Imperial	$24 + 0$–12B	,, ,,	H	Persia, Himal.
involucrata		24	,, & L. C. '41	—	N.W. Italy, S.E. France
karadaghensis		24	,, 1936c	—	N. Persia
latifolia		24, 36	,, ,,	H	Caucasus
libanotica		24	,, ,,	—	Syria, Palestine
lusitanica		24	La Cour 1951a	—	Portugal
macrandra		24	,, ,,	—	Greece
meleagris	Snake's Head L.	24	Darlington 1936c	H	Cauc., N. & C. Europe (?)
meleagroides		24	,, ,,	H	C. Asia, S. Russia, Bulgaria
messanensis		24	La Cour 1951a	—	Sicily
obliqua		$24 + 2$B	Darlington 1936c	H	Greece
oranensis		24	,, ,,	—	N.W. Morocco, Algeria, Tunis
pallidiflora		24	,, ,,	H	S. Siberia
pontica		24	,, ,,	H	S. Bal., Asia M,

FRITILLARIA (*cont.*)

pyrenaica	24, 36	La Cour 1951a	H	Pyrenees
tubiformis	24	„ „	H	Marit. Alps
verticillata (*thunbergii*)	24	Sato '42, Suzuka '50a	H	C. As., China, Jap.

NEW WORLD GROUPS (much heterochromatin)

(iii) *biflora* Mission Bells	24	La Cour 1951a	H	California
purdyi	24	Beetle '44, La C. '51a	H	„
liliacea	24	„	H	„
mutica	24	La Cour 1953	H	„
falcata	{ 24 { 24, 25	Beetle 1944 La Cour 1951a	H	„
pluriflora Adobe L.	{ 24 { 24 + 2B	Beetle 1944 Darlington 1936c	H	„
lanceolata	{ 24+1B, 36 { 24+0-8B, 36, 48	„ „ Beetle 1944	H	W: N. America
recurva (*coccinea*)	{ 24 { 24+1B, 36	„ „ Darlington 1936c	H	S. Ore.—Calif.
phaeanthera	{ 24 { 36	„ „ Beetle 1944	—	California
(iv) *pudica*	26, 39	Darlington 1936c	H	W: N. America

KOROLKOWIA (FRITILLARIA) $x = 12$

sewerzowi	24	La Cour 1951a	—	C. Asia

NOMOCHARIS $x = 12$

mairei	24	Darlington 1936b	H	S.W. Szechuan, N. Yunnan
pardanthina	24	„ „	H	W. Yunnan
saluenensis	24	„ „	H	N.W. Yun., S.E. Tibet, N. Assam
nana	48	„ „	H	Himalayas

NOTHOLIRION $x = 12$

campanulatum	24	La Cour 1952	H	Up. Bur., Tibet, S.W. China
macrophyllum	24	La Cour unp.	H	Himalayas
thompsonianum	24	Wylie unp.	H	N. Him.—Afgh.

CARDIOCRINUM (LILIUM) $x = 12$

cordatum (*L. cordifolium*)	24	Sansome & L.C. '34	H	Japan
giganteum	24	M. Sato 1932	H	Himalayas

LILIUM $x = 12$

amabile	24	Sansome & L.C. '34	H	Korea
auratum Goldband L.	24 + 0–1B	Stewart 1947	HR	Japan
bolanderi	24	Sansome & L.C. '34	H	California
brownii	24	Sato 1932	H	China
bulbiferum v. *croceum*	24	Sansome & L.C. '34	H	S. Europe
callosum	24	Stewart 1947	H	C. China, Japan
canadense Meadow L.	24 + 0–1B	Stewart 1943, 1947	HR	E: N. America
candidum Madonna L.	24	Sansome & L.C. '34	H	S. Eur., Syria
catesbaei	24	Stewart 1947	H	S.E: U.S.A.
cernuum	24	Sansome & L.C. '34	H	N. Asia
chalcedonicum Sc. Turk's Cap	24	„ „	H	Greece
columbianum	24	„ „	H	W: N. America
concolor (*coridium*)	24	M. Sato 1932	HR	C. China

LILIUM (*cont.*)

v. *pulchellum*		24	Kumazava & K. '47	H	N.E. Asia
dauricum	Candlestick L.	24	M. Sato 1932	H	„
davidi		24	Beal 1942	H	W. China
v. *willmottiae*		24 + 0–1B	Stewart 1943, 1947	H	C. & W. China
duchartrei		24	Stewart 1947	H	W. China
formosanum		{ 24 + 0–2B (48)	M. Sato 1932 Emsweller & B. 1940	H	Formosa
grayi		24	M. Sato 1932	H	S.E: U.S.A.
hansoni		24	„ „	H	Korea
henryi		{ 24 + 1–2B 24 + 0–2B	Mather 1935 Stewart 1947	H	C. China
humboldti		24	Sansome & L.C. '34	H	California
japonicum		24 + 1–2B	„ „	HR	Japan
leichtlinii v. *maximowiczii*		24	M. Sato 1932	H	Japan, Korea
leucanthum				H	China
v. *chloraster*		24	Stewart 1947	H	Hupeh
longiflorum	Easter L.	24 (48)	Goodspeed *et al.* '35 Emsweller & L. 1943	H	Japan
martagon		24 + 0–3B	Fernandes 1950b	HR	S. Europe
medeoloides	Wheel L.	24	Sansome & L.C. '34	H	Japan
michauxii (*carolinianum*)		24	Stewart 1347	H	S.E: U.S.A.
michiganense		24	„ „	H	E: N. America
monodelphum		24	„ „	H	Caucasus
neilgherrense		24	Abraham 1939	H	Mtns, S. India
occidentale		24	Stewart 1947	H	S. Ore., N. Calif.
pardalinum	Leopard L.	24	Sansome & L.C. '43	H	California
v. *angustifolium* (*roezlii*)		24	„ „	H	„
parryi		24	Stewart 1947	H	Calif., Arizona
philadelphicum Orange Cup L.		24	Sansome & L.C. '34	H	E: N. America
philippinense		24	„ „	H	Philippines
pumilum (*tenuifolium*		24	„ „	H	N.E. Asia
Coral L.		24 + 0–2B	Stewart 1943		
pyrenaicum	Yellow T. C.	24	Sansome & L.C. '34	H	Pyrenees
regale	Royal L.	24	„ „	H	W. China
sargentiae		24 + 0–1B	Stewart 1947	H	Szechuan
speciosum		24	Sansome & L.C. '34	HR	Japan
sulphureum (*myriophyllum*)		24	Stewart 1947	H	W. China—Up. Burma
superbum	Turks' Cap	24	„ „	H	E: U.S.A.
tsingtauense		24 + 0–1B	„ 1943, 1947	H	E. China, Korea
wardii		24	„ 1947	H	S.E. Tibet
tigrinum Tiger L.		{ 24 36 + 0–1B	M. Sato 1932 Sansome & L.C. '34	HR	China, Japan
v. *flaviflorum* (as *lancifolium* v. *fl.*)		24	Kumazava & K. '47	H	Kyushu
hollandicum (*umbellatum*) (*bulbiferum* × *maculatum?*)		24	Sansome & L.C. '34	H	*cult*
maculatum (*elegans*)				H	Japan, *cult*
v. *batemanniae* (*dauricum* × *concolor?*)		24 + 1B	Stewart 1943	H	*cult*
testaceum Nankeen L. (*chalcedonicum* × *candidum*)		24	Sansome & L.C. '34	H	„

TULIPA* $x = 12$
S. 1. ERIOSTEMONES

australis	& 11 spp.	24	Upcott & L. C. '36	H	S Eur., N. Afr.
saxatilis		36	„ „	H	Crete

TULIPA (cont.)

sylvestris	48	Upcott & L. C. '36	H	Europe
turkestanica	48	,, ,,	H	S. Russia
whittalli	48	,, ,,	H	Asia Minor

S. 2. LEIOSTEMONES (brackets enclose species with mere colour differences)

(i) batalini & 2 spp.	24	Upcott & L. C. '36	H	Bokhara
⌠ chrysantha	24, 48	,, ,,	H	Persia
⎸	24	,, ,,	H	Kashmir
⎨ clusiana Lady Tulip	48	,, ,,	H	Himalayas
⌡	60	,, ,,	H	Medit.

(ii) altaica	24	,, ,,	H	C. Asia
ferganica	24	La Cour *	H	,,
ostrowskiana	24	Upcott & L. C. '36	H	E. Turkestan
sprengeri	24	,, ,,	H	Asia Minor
kolpakowskiana	24, 48	,, ,,	H	Turkestan
korolkowi	24, 48	,, ,,	H	,,

(iii) borsczowi	24 + 0–6B	,, ,,	H	Pers., C. Asia
cypria & 5 spp.	24	,, ,,	H	Cyprus
aleppensis	36	,, ,,	H	Syria
lanata	36	,, ,,	H	C. Asia
praecox	36	,, ,,	H	S. Fr., N. Italy

(iv) ⌠ armena	24	,, ,,	H	Asia Minor
⌡ galatica	24 + 2–12B	,, ,,	H	,,
boetica	24	,, ,,	H	Greece
planifolia	24	,, ,,	H	Europe
rhodopea	24	,, ,,	H	Bulgaria
suaveolens	24	,, ,,	H	S. Russ., Asia M.
gesneriana Garden Tulip	24, 36	,, ,,	H	cult, Persia
(v) kaufmanniana & 8 spp.	24	,, ,,	H	Turkestan

AMANA (TULIPA) $x = 12$

latifolia	24	Sato 1942	—	Japan
edulis	48	,,	R	,,

ERYTHRONIUM* $x = 12$

dens-canis Dog's Tooth V.	24	Hruby 1934b	H	Eur., N. Asia
californicum	24	La Cour *	H	California
hendersonii & 3 spp.	24	F. H. Smith 1955	H	Oregon
grandiflorum (iaponicum)	24	Sato 1942	H	W: N. America
revolutum	24	F. H. Smith 1955	H	,, ,,
albidum	44	Cooper 1939	H	E: N. America
americanum	48	Haque 1951	H	,, ,,

GAGEA $x = 12$

graminifolia	24	Romanov 1936	—	Transcasp.
minima	24	Westergaard 1936	—	Eur., N. Asia
soleirolii	36	Martinoli 1950a	—	S. Europe
tenera	36	Romanov 1936	—	Turkestan
arvensis	48	T. 1938	H	Medit.
sylvatica (lutea)	72	Westergaard 1936	H	Eur.—Himal.
fistulosa	c. 80	Bianchi 1946	H	Tyrol
spathacea	c. 102	Westergaard 1936	—	Europe

LLOYDIA $x = 12$

serotina	$\begin{cases} 24 \\ 24 \end{cases}$ Newton 1927, Bianchi 1946	H	Europe

TRIBE IV: KNIPHOFIEAE

KNIPHOFIA $x = 6$

abyssinica	12	Janaki-Ammal 1950	—	Abyssinia
breviflora	12	„ „	H	S. Africa
burchellii	12	Moffett 1932b	H	„
caulescens	12	Janaki-Ammal 1950	H	„
comosa	12	„ „	H	Abyssinia
foliosa	12	„ „	H	„
galpini	12	„ „	H	Transvaal
kirkii	12	„ „	H	Trop. S.W. Afr.
leichtlinii	12	Moffett 1932b	H	Abyssinia
macowani	12	Janaki-Ammal 1950	H	S. Africa
modesta	12	„ „	H	„
multiflora	12	„ „	H	„
natalensis	12	Moffett 1932b	H	„
nelsonii	12	„ „	H	„
northiae	12	„ „	H	„
praecox	12	Janaki-Ammal 1950	H	„
sarmentosa	12	Moffett 1932b	H	„
zululandiae	12	Janaki-Ammal 1950	—	„
uvaria (*aloides*) R. Hot Poker	12, 13	Webber 1932	H	„
snowdenii (3x) (12), 18, (24)		Janaki-Ammal 1950	H	Uganda

TRIBE V: AGAPANTHEAE

TULBAGHIA $x = 6$

aloides	12	Sato 1942	—	S. Africa

AGAPANTHUS $x = 15$

orientalis African L. (*umbellatus*)	30	Darlington 1933a	H	S. Africa

TRIBE VI: ALOINEAE

CHAMAEALOE $x = 7$

africana	14	Viveiros 1949	—	S. Africa

LEPTALOE $x = 7$

albida	14	Müller 1945	—	S. Africa
saundersii	14	„ „	—	„

LOMATOPHYLLUM $x = 7$

orientale	14	Resende 1937	—	Mascarene Is.

POELLNITZIA $x = 7$

rubriflora	14	Viveiros 1949	H	S. Africa

ALOË* $x = 7$

arborescens	14	Snoad 1951	H	S. Africa
aristata	14	„ „	H	„
brevifolia	14	„ „	H	„
ferox	14	Sato 1942	HM	„

ALOE (*cont.*)

greenii	14	Snoad 1951	H	S. Africa
humilis	14	Sato 1942	H	,,
plicatilis	14	Snoad 1951	HM	,,
saponaria	14	,, ,,	HM	,,
striata	14	Müller 1945	H	,,
succotrina	14	Resende 1937	HM	,,
variegata	14	Snoad 1951	H	,,
vera	14	Marshak 1934	HMV	Medit.

ciliaris	{ 42	Schnarf & W. 1939,	H	S. Africa
	42	Snoad 1951		
f. *gigas* (5*x*)	35!	Resende 1938		

110 spp.	14		—	Africa

Ferguson 1926, Fernandes 1931, Kondo & M. 1943, Johansen 1929d, Müller 1945, Resende 1937, Sato 1937, 1942, Suto 1936, Snoad 1951

ASTROLOBA (APICRA) *x* = 7

aspera	14	Ferguson, 1926	H	S. Africa
deltoidea	14	Resende 1937	H	,,
foliolosa	14	,, ,,	H	,,
spiralis	14	,, ,,	H	,,
bicarinata (3*x*)	21	,, ,,	H	,,
pentagona	28	,, ,,	H	,,

ASTERIA* *x* = 7

verrucosa	14	Resende 1937	H	S. Africa
maculata	{ 14	,, ,,	H	,,
	28	Sato 1942		
nigricans	{ 14	,,		
	(21)	Riley 1948a	H	,,
	28	Ferguson 1926		
cheilophylla	14, 28	Sato 1937	H	,,
44 spp.	14		H	,,

Ferguson 1926, Marshak 1934, Resende 1937, Sato 1942, Snoad 1951, Suto 1936

ASTERIA × ALOË *x* = 7

4 hybrids	{ 14	Sato 1937,	—	expt.
	14	Riley 1948b, 1950		
1 hybrid	28	Sato 1937		

HAWORTHIA* *x* = 7

aristata	14	Snoad 1951	H	S. Africa
cymbiformis	14	,, ,,	H	,,
fasciata	14	Sato 1942	H	,,
glabrata	14	Snoad 1951	H	,,
margaretifera	14	Sato 1942	H	,,
maughanii	14	Snoad 1951	H	,,
planifolia	14	,, ,,	H	,,
tortuosa	14	,, ,,	H	,,
truncata	14	,, ,,	H	,,
61 species	14		H	,,

Ferguson 1926, Kondo & M. 1943, Pinto-Lopes 1944, 1946, Resende 1937, Resende & F. 1946, Sato 1937, 1942, Snoad 1951

363

HAWORTHIA (*cont.*)

attenuata	{ 14	Snoad 1951	H	S. Africa
	28	Kondo & M. 1943		
limifolia	14, 28	Resende 1937	H	,,
herrei	{ 14	Snoad 1951	H	,,
	42	Pinto-Lopes 1944		
reinwardtii	{ 14, 21, 28	Snoad 1951, 1952	H	,,
	42	Sato 1942		
tessellata	{ 14, 28,	Resende 1937		
	28, 42, 56, *c*. 58		H	,,
	c. 61, 63	Viveiros 1949		
resendeana (3*x*)	21	Snoad 1952		
carissoi	28	Pinto-Lopes 1944	H	,,
chalwinii	28	Resende 1937	H	,,
greenii	28	Pinto-Lopes 1944	H	,,
subfasciata	*c*. 28	Ferguson 1926	H	,,
glauca	{ 28	Snoad 1951	H	,,
	29	Resende 1939		
brotereana	35	Pinto-Lopes 1944	H	,,
rewendetii	35	,, ,,	H	,,
rubrobrunea	35	Snoad 1951	H	,,
sampaiana	35, 36	,, ,,	H	,,
armstrongii	42	Pinto-Lopes 1944	H	,,
coarctata	42	Snoad 1951	H	,,
coarctatoidea	42	,, ,,	H	,,

TRIBE VII: ASPHODELEAE

EREMURUS *x* = 7

altaicus	14	Burström 1929	H	Manch., Siberia
elwesii	14	Sato 1942	H	*cult*
himalaicus	14	Burström 1929	H	Himalayas
robustus	14	,, ,,	H	Turkestan
spectabilis	14	Upcott 1936a	HV	Asia M., Persia

BULBINELLA *x* = 7

robusta	14	Hair unp.	—	S. Africa

CHRYSOBACTRON (BULBINELLA) *x* = 7

hookeri	14	Hair 1942	H	New Zealand
rossii	14	Hair unp.	H	Campbell Is.

ASPHODELINE *x* = 7

lutea Asphodel	{ 28	Sato 1942,	H	Italy—Arabia
	28	La Cour 1952		

ASPHODELUS *x* = 7

fistulosus	28	Lorenzo-Andreu 1951	H	S. Eur.—Afghan.
albus	56	La Cour 1952	H	S. Europe
ramosus	{ 56	,, ,,	H	,,
	52	Sato 1942		
lusitanicus	56	Fernandes 1950b	—	Portugal

ANTHERICUM *x* = 7, 8

ciliatum	14	M. & S. 1935	—	Venezuela
roseum	32	Stenar 1928	—	Tanganyika

ANTHERICUM (*cont.*)

ramosum		32	Elvers 1932a	H	W. & S. Europe
liliago	St. Bernard Lily	$\left\{\begin{array}{l}30\\32\\64\end{array}\right.$	Bowden 1945a Fernandes 1950b Elvers 1932a	H	S. Eur., N. Afr.

CHLOROPHYTUM (ANTHERICUM) $x = 7, 8$

inornatum	14	Baldwin & S. 1951c	—	W. Trop. Africa
laxum	14	,, ,,	—	O.W. Tropics
natalensis	14	Sato 1942		
ursaubiriensis	14	,, ,,		
comosum (*sternbergianum*)	28	R. Yamazaki 1936	H	S. Africa
elatum	28	Sato 1942	H	,,
orchidastrum	28	Baldwin & S. 1951c	—	O.W. Tropics
viviparum	28	,, ,,	—	,, ,,
alismifolium	16	,, ,,	—	Trop. Africa
sternbergianum	32	Schnarf & W. 1939	H	S. Africa

BULBINE $x = 7, 12, 13$

annua	14	Straub 1938	H	S. Africa
asphodeloides	14	,, ,,	—	,,
caulescens	14	,, ,,	H	,,
latifolia	14	Snoad unp.	—	,,
longiscapa	14	,, 1952	—	,,
mesembryanthemoides	14	,, ,,	—	,,
praemorsa	14	Straub 1938	—	,,
rostrata	14	Snoad unp.	—	,,
succulenta	14	,, 1952	—	,,
tetraphylla	14	Straub 1938	—	,,
triebneri	14	,, ,,	—	,,
bulbosa	24, 48	Gulline unp.	H	E. Australia
semibarbata	26	Straub 1938	H	Australia

ECHEANDIA $x = 8$

terniflora	16	Schnarf & W. 1939	H	C. America

SIMETHIS $x = 8$

planifolia	48	Fernandes 1950b	H	S.W: Eur., N. Afr.

CHLOROGALUM $x = 9$

pomeridianum	36	Cave 1949	H	California

ALECTORURUS $x = 10$

yedoensis	40	Sato 1942	H	Japan

ANEMARRHENA $x = 11$

asphodeloides	22	Sato 1942	H	N. China

ARTHROPODIUM $x = 11$

candidum	22	Hair 1942	H	New Zealand
milleflorum	22	W. D. Jackson unp.	—	Australia
cirrhatum	$\left\{\begin{array}{l}44\\36\end{array}\right.$	Hair 1942 Sato 1942	H	New Zealand

CHAMAESCILLA $x = 11$

corymbosa	44	W. D. Jackson unp.	—	Australia

25   365

DICHOPOGON (ARTHROPODIUM) $x = 11$
strictus		66	Gulline unp.	H	S. Australia

PARADISEA $x = ?$

liliastrum	St. Bruno Lily	⎧ 30 ⎨ 32 ⎩ 48	Bowden 1945a Stenar 1928 Sato 1942	H	S. Europe
lusitanica		32, 64	Fernandes 1950b	—	Portugal

THYSANOTUS $x = ?$

patersoni	*c.* 80	W. D. Jackson unp.	—	S. Australia

TRIBE VIII: UVULARIEAE

UVULARIA $x = 7$

grandiflora	14	Anderson & W. 1934	H	E:N. America
perfoliata	14	„ „	H	„ „
sessile	14	„ „	H	„ „

OAKESIELLA (OAKESIA) $x = 8$

sessilifolia	16	Sato 1942	H	N. America

LITTONIA $x = 9, 11$

modesta	⎧ 18 ⎨ 22	La Cour unp. Sato 1942	H	S. Africa

GLORIOSA $x = 11$

simplex	22	E.K.J.*	HM	Mozambique
rothschildiana	⎧ 22 ⎨ 66	E.K.J.*,Tjio 1948 La Cour 1951b	H	Trop. Africa
superba	⎧ 22 ⎨ 88	E.K.J.*, Tjio 1948 La Cour 1951b	HM	Trop Asia & Afr.
carsonii	66	La Cour 1952	H	Trop. Africa
verschurii	88	„ „	H	?

TRIBE IX: POLYGONATEAE

DISPORUM $x = 6, 8, 9, 11$

maculatum	12	Ownbey 1953	—	N. America
sessile	16	M. & S. 1935	H	Japan
smilacinum	16	Hasegawa 1932	—	Japan, Siberia
smithii	16	Jones 1951	—	W: N. America
pullum	16	Hasegawa 1932	H	Ind., E. Ind., Ch.
hookeri	18	Jones 1951	H	California
lanuginosum	18	„ „	H	E: N. America
trachycarpum	22	„ „	H	N.W: N. Amer.

CLINTONIA $x = 7, 8$

andrewsiana	28	Walker 1944	H	California
umbellulata	28	„ „	H	N. America
uniflora	Queen Cup	28	„ „	H	„
udensis (*alpina*)	28	M. & S. 1935	H	E. Asia, Himal.
borealis	32	Walker 1944	H	N. America

STREPTOPUS $x = 8$

japonicus	16 + 2B	M. & S. 1935	H	Sib., N. Amer.
amplexifolius	32	„ „	H	N. Temp.
streptopoides	*c.* 54	„ „	H	Japan

MAIANTHEMUM $x = 8?, 9?$

bifolium	May L.	30, 36, 42 42 54	Stenar 1935 L. & L. 1942 Sato 1942	H	N. Temp.
dilatatum		32? 36 54	M. & S. 1935 Palmgren 1943 Sato 1942	—	W: N. Amer., Japan

SMILACINA $x = 9$

amplexicaulis	36	Rattenbury 1948	—	W: N. America
japonica	36	M. & S. 1935	H	Japan
sessilifolia	36	Cave 1948a	—	W: N. America
stellata	36	Stenar 1935	H	,, ,,

POLYGONATUM $x = 9, 10, 11, 14$

falcatum		18 20	Berg 1933 Sato 1942	—	Japan
latifolium		18 20	Hasegawa 1933 Suomalainen 1947	H	Europe
giganteum	18, 28, 29, 30		,, ,,	H	N. America
multiflorum Solomon's Seal		18, 24 18, 30 18, 20, 28	Eigsti 1942 Dark, M. 1939 Soumalainen 1947	HV	N.Temp.
cobrense		20	Therman 1950	—	N. America
humile		20	Hasegawa 1933	H	Eur., Siberia
lasinianthum		20	,,	—	Japan
maximowiczii		20	M. & S. 1935	—	,,
maximum		20	Suomalainen 1947	—	,,
silvicolum		20	Hasegawa 1933	—	,,
sibiricum		20, 21 26	Suomalainen 1947 Therman 1953	—	Himal., N. Asia
japonicum Amatokoro		20 29	Hasegawa 1933 Suomalainen 1947	HV	Japan
biflorum Small S.S.		20, 40	Therman 1950	H	E. Asia
pubescens		20, 40	,, ,,	—	,,
odoratum Solomon's Seal (*officinale*)		20 26–30	Suomalainen 1947 Maude 1939	HMV	Eur., N. Asia
commutatum (*giganteum*)		20, 40, 60 28	Therman 1950 Suomalainen 1947	—	N. America
canaliculatum		40	Eigsti 1942	—	E. Asia
hondoense		22?	M. & S. 1935	—	Japan
roseum		28	Therman 1953	H	Siberia
verticillatum		27, 28 30, 84 28, 60, 86–91	Berg 1933 Dark, M. 1939 Therman 1953	H	Eur., N. Asia
hookeri		30	,, ,,	H	S.W: China, Tibet
kingianum		64	,, ,,	—	Burma

DRYMOPHILA $x = 10$

cyanocarpa	20	W. D. Jackson unp.	—	Australia

DISPOROPSIS $x = 10$

arisanensis	40	Sato 1942	—	China

TRIBE X: COLCHICEAE

COLCHICUM $x = 7, 9, 10.$ $x_2 = 17, 19$

ritchii		14	Feinbrun unp.	H	N. Afr., Palest.
schimperi		14	,, ,,	H	Palest., Arabia
hierosolym		18	,, ,,	H	Palestine
bivonae		36	Levan 1940a	H	Sicily, Sardinia
fimbriatum		36	Sato 1942	H	?
sibthorpii		36	,, ,,	H	Greece
luteum		38	Mehra & K. 1948a	H	N. India—Turkes.
autumnale	Autumn Crocus	38	Takenaka 1950	HM	Europe
neapolitanum		38	Levan 1940a	H	S. Italy, S. France
speciosum		38	,, ,,	H	E. Medit., Cauc.
byzantinum		40	,, ,,	H	cult
giganteum		40	,, ,,	H	cult
bornmülleri		42	,, ,,	H	Asia Minor
variegatum	Levant A.C.	44	,, ,,	H	S. Europe
latifolium		54	,, ,,	H	Greece, Crete
montanum		54	,, ,,	H	S. Europe
decaisnei		54	Feinbrun unp.	H	E. Medit.
steveni		54	,, ,,	H	Palest., Syria
tunicatum		54	,, ,,	H	Palestine
lusitanicum		102	de Castro 1945b	—	Portugal

BULBOCODIUM $x = 11$

vernum	22	Levan & S. 1947	H	Europe

MERENDERA (COLCHICUM) $x = ?$

bulbocodium	60	Fernandes 1950b	H	Spain, Portugal

TRIBES XI, XII, XIII: JOHNSONIEAE, MILLIGANIEAE, DIANELLEAE

LAXMANNIA (BARTLINGIA) $x = 8$

sessiliflora	16	W. D. Jackson unp.	—	Australia

ASTELIA $x = 8$

velutina	16	Sato 1942	—	?
alpina	c. 80	W. D. Jackson unp.	—	Australia

DIANELLA $x = 8$

intermedia	16	Hair 1942	H	New Zealand
laevis	16, 32	Curtis 1952	H	E. Australia
coerulea	16, 32, 48	,, ,,	H	,,
revoluta	16, 32, 48	,, ,,	—	,,
tasmanica	16, 64, 76, 80, 84	,, ,,	H	Tasmania
ensifolia	32	Sato 1942	H	Asia, Austr., Haw.

STYPANDRA $x = 9$

caespitosa	18	W. D. Jackson unp.	H	Australia

TRIBE XIV: VERATREAE

SCHOENOCAULON $x = 8$
officinale	Cebadilla	16	de Zerpa 1951	M	Mexico

VERATRUM $x = 8$
japonicum		16	Sato 1942	—	Japan
longebracteatum		16	M. & S. 1935	—	,,
maximowiczii		16	,, ,,	—	,,
oxysepalum (album)		32	,, ,,	—	Eur., N. Asia
stamineum		32 + 2B	,, ,,	—	Japan
album	White Hellebore	32	Stenar 1932	HM	Eur., N. Asia
nigrum	Black H.	64	Miller 1930	HM	Eur., Asia Min.

ZYGADENUS $x = 8, 11$
fremonti		22	Miller 1930	—	California
chloranthus		32	,, ,,	H	N. America
elegans		32	,, ,,	H	,,

STENANTHIUM $x = 10$
robustum	Feather Fleece	20	Sato 1942	H	E. & C. U.S.A.

TRIBE XV: ASPARAGEAE

ASPARAGUS $x = 10$
crispus		20	Nagao 1938	H	S. Africa
lucidus		20	,, ,,	R	China, Japan
medeoloides	Smilax A.	20	,, ,,	H	S. Africa
myriocladus		20	,, ,,	H	Natal
officinalis	Asparagus	20	,, ,,	MV	Eur., Siberia
plumosus	Fern A.	20	,, ,,	H	S. Africa
tenuifolius		20	,, ,,	H	S. Europe
scandens		20	Gardé & G. 1953	H	S. Africa
umbellatus		20	,, ,, ,,	H	Canary Is.
sp.		40	Nagao 1938	—	
splendens		60	Sato 1942		
sprengeri		60	Nagao 1938	H	S. Africa

TRIBE XVI: BOWIEAE

BOWIEA $x = 10$?
volubilis	$\begin{cases} 20 \\ (18-23) \\ 21 \end{cases}$	D'Amato 1949a			
		Sato 1942	H	S. Africa	

TRIBE XVII: ANGUILLAREAE

DIPIDAX $x = 10$
triquetrum		20	Hair unp.	H	S. Africa

ANGUILLARIA $x = 10$
dioica		20, 40	W. D. Jackson unp.	—	Australia

BAEOMETRA $x = 11$
columellaris		22	Miller 1930	H	S. Africa

TRIBE XVIII: TRICYRTIDEAE

TRICYRTIS (BRACHYCYRTIS)* $x = 13$

macropoda		26	Sinoto & K. 1932	H	Japan, China
stolonifera	Toad Lily & 2 spp.	26	Miller 1930	H	Formosa
yatabeana	& 6 spp.	26	Sato 1942	H	Japan, *cult*
formosana		25, 26, 52	„ „	H	Formosa

TRIBE XIX: NARTHECIEAE

JAPONOLIRION (TOLFIELDIA) $x = 12$

osense	24	Sato 1942	—	Japan

NARTHECIUM $x = 13$

ossifragum	Bog Asphodel	26	Wulff 1935	H	W. Europe

ALETRIS $x = 13$

foliata	52	Sato 1942	—	E. Asia

METANARTHECIUM $x = 13$

luteo-viride	52	Sato 1942	—	Japan

TOLFIELDIA $x = 14, 15$

calyculata	28	Miller 1930	H	Eur., N. Amer.
pusilla (palustris)	30	„ „	—	N. Temp., Arctic
nuda	30	Sato 1942	—	Japan
nutans	30	M. & S. 1935	H	Japan, N. Amer., E. Siberia
japonica	60	„ „	H	Japan

HELONIOPSIS $x = 17$

breviscapa	34	Ono 1926	H	Korea
japonica	34	Sato 1942	H	Japan
orientalis	34	Nakajima 1933	—	„
pauciflora	34	Sakai 1934	—	„

TRIBE XX: HELONIADEAE

CHIONOGRAPHIS $x = 12$

japonica	24	Sato 1942	H	Japan

HELONIAS $x = 17$

bullata	Swamp Pink	34	Miller 1930	H	E: U.S.A.

TRIBE XXI: OPHIOPOGONEAE

LIRIOPE $x = 18$

graminifolia v. *minor*	36	M. & S. 1935	H	Japan
v. *koreana*	108	Sato 1942		
muscari	72	Westfall 1950	H	China, Japan
	72, 108	Oinuma 1949		

OPHIOPOGON (MONDO) $x = 18$

jaburan	Lily Turf	36	M. & S. 1935	H	Japan
japonicus		36, 72	Sato 1942	H	„
planiscapus		36, 72	Oinuma 1949	—	„

TRIBE XXII: PELIOSANTHEAE

PELIOSANTHES $x = 18$
arisanensis 36 Sato 1942 — S.E: Asia

TRIBE XXIII: ASPIDISTREAE

ASPIDISTRA $x = 18$
lurida (elatior)   { 32, 36 K. 1931, T. 1937   H   China
                       36 Sato 1942
ROHDEA (RHODEA) $x = 19$
japonica   { 36? Yamamoto, K. 1931
              { 38 M. & S. 1935   H   Japan
              { 38 Sato 1942

TRIBE XXIV: CONVALLARIEAE

CONVALLARIA $x = 19$
majalis Lily of the Valley 38 L. & L. 1944b   H   N. Temp.
keiskii 38 M. & S. 1935   H   Japan

REINECKIA $x = 19$
carnea   { 38 Noguchi 1936   H   China, Japan
            { 42 Hosono, K. 1931

TRIBE XXV: HERRERIEAE

HERRERIA $x = 27$
salsaparilha 54 Sato 1942   H   Brazil

294 TECOPHILAEACEAE

ODONTOSTOMUM $x = 10$
hartwegii 20 Cave 1949 — California

CYANASTRUM $x = 11, 12$
cordifolium   { 22 Sato 1942   —   Trop. Africa
                 { 24 Nietsch 1941
TECOPHILAEA $x = 12$
cyano-crocus 24 La Cour 1945 *   H   Chile

295 TRILLIACEAE

PARIS $x = 5$
polyphylla 10 + 0–1B Darlington 1941 (G)H Himalayas
formosana 10 + 2B Gotoh & K. 1937 — Formosa
tetraphylla 10 Darlington 1941 — Japan
hexaphylla 10, 15 ,, ,, — ,,
obovata 10, 15 ,, ,, — ,,
quadrifolia Herb P. 20 ,, ,, H Europe
japonica (Kinagusa) 40 ,, ,, — Japan

TRILLIUM $x = 5$
chloropetalum 10 Warmke 1937 — California
declinatum (gleasonii) 10 + 3B Gotoh 1937 — C: U.S.A.

371

TRILLIUM (*cont.*)

decumbens		10	Bailey 1951	—	N. America
erythrocarpum (*undulatum*)		10	La Cour 1951a	—	E: N. America
grandiflorum		10	Darlington & L.C. '40	H	,, ,,
kamtschaticum		10	Haga 1937a	—	Japan, Kam.
lancifolium		10	Bailey 1951	—	N. America
luteum (*sessile*)		10	La Cour 1951a	—	,,
ovatum		10	Warmke 1937	—	W: N. America
petiolatum		10	,, ,,	—	N.W: U.S.A.
pulsillum		10	Baldwin *et al*. 1949	H	E: N. America
recurvatum	10 + 0–2B		Gotoh 1937	—	C: U.S.A.
rivale		10	Warmke 1937	—	Oregon, Calif.
sessile		10	Darlington & L.C. '40	H	E: U.S.A.
stamineum		10	Bailey 1951	—	N. America
stylosum		10	Darlington & L.C. '40	H	S.E: U.S.A.
undulatum		10	Wilson & B. 1941	H	E: N. America

		10	Darlington & L.C. '40		
erectum	⎰ 10 + 0–4B		Sparrow *et al*. 1952	H	E: N. America
	⎱ 15 + 2–3B		,, ,,		

hagae		15, 30	Haga 1951	—	Japan
smallii (*apetalon*)		20	,, 1937a	—	,,
tschonoskii		20	,, 1937b	—	,,
amabile		30	Amano 1944	—	,,

MEDEOLA $x = 7$
virginica	Ind. Cucumber	14	Stewart & B. 1942	R	S.E.: U.S.A.

SCOLIOPUS $x = 7$
bigelovii		14	Johansen 1932	—	N. America

296 PONTEDERIACEAE

EICHHORNIA $x = 8$
martiana		16	Bowden 1945b	H	Brazil
azurea		32	,, ,,	H	,,
crassipes	Water Hyacinth	32	Taylor 1925c	H	Trop. America

PONTEDERIA $x = 8$
cordata	Pickerel Weed	16	Bowedn 1945b	H	E: N. America

MONOCHORIA $x = 14, 26$
hastaefolia		28	Majumdar 1953	(V)	Trop. Asia
vaginalis		52	Morinaga & F. '31a	(V)	Trop. Afr. & Asia

HETERANTHERA $x = 15$
dubia		30	Bowden 1945b	H	Trop. America

297 SMILACACEAE

SMILAX $x = 13, 14, 15, 16$
herbacea	Carrion Flower	26	Lindsay 1930	H	N. Amer., Japan
glauca	Cat Greenbriar	28	Jensen 1937a	HM	N. America
aspera		32	Carvalho 1948	H	S. Eur.—India

SMILAX (*cont.*)

medica	Mexican S.	32	Suzuka 1950a	M	Mexico
oldhami		32	Jensen 1937a	M	Japan
rotundifolia	Greenbriar	32	Speese 1939	HMR	N. Amer., W.I.
sieboldii		32	Nakajima 1933	M	Japan
hederacea		30	,, 1937	M	,,
china	China Root	60	,, ,,	HMRT	Cochin-Ch.—Jap.

HETEROSMILAX *x* = ?

japonica		62	Sato 1942	—	Japan

298 RUSCACEAE

DANAE *x* = 20

racemosa	Alexandria	40	Sato 1942	H	Greece—Persia
(*laurus*)	Laurel				

RUSCUS *x* = 20

aculeatus	Butcher's Broom	40	Martinoli 1951	HT	Eur., S.W: Asia
hypoglossum		40	,, ,,	H	S. Europe
hypophyllum		40	,, ,,	H	Canary Is.—Cauc.

299 ALSTROEMERIACEAE

ALSTROEMERIA *x* = 8

aurantiaca	16	Whyte 1929	H	Chile
brasiliensis	16	,, ,,	H	Brazil
haemantha	16	,, ,,	H	Chile
pulchella (*psittacina*)	16	,, ,,	H	S. America
ligtu	16	La Cour 1945 *	H	Chile
rosea	16	,, ,,	H	,,
campaniflora	16	,, ,,	H	Brazil
chilensis	16	D. Sato 1938	H	Chile
species aff. *ligtu*	32	Goodspeed 1940	—	Andes

BOMAREA *x* = 9

caldasiana	18	Whyte 1929	H	Guatemala
carderi	18	,, ,,	H	Peru, Colombia
edulis W.I. Jer. Artichoke	18	,, ,,	HR	Trop. America
patacocensis	18	,, ,,	H	Andes, Guat.
salsilla	18	D. Sato 1938	R	Chile

302 ARACEAE

CALLA *x* = 7, 9

palustris Water Dragon	{ 36, 72	Hagerup 1941b	R	N. Temp.
	63, 69, 70	Ehrenberg 1945		

AGLAONEMA *x* = 8

pictum	16	Gow 1908	H	Malaya

DIEFFENBACHIA *x* = 8

picta	16	Gow 1908	H	S. America

373

ACORUS $x = 9, 11, 12$

calamus Sweet Flag	⎧ ⎨ ⎩	18 18 24, 36, 48	Dudley 1937, D. 1951 Wulff 1954	HIMP	N. Temp.
v. *angustatus*		44	Kurakubo 1940		
gramineus	⎧ ⎨ ⎪ ⎩	18 22 24 24	D. 1951 Kurakubo 1940 Wulff 1940a Ito 1942	HM	Himal.—Japan
asiaticus		44	,, ,,	—	N.E. Asia

AMBROSINIA $x = 11$
bassii	22	Vignoli 1939	H	Medit.

POTHOS $x = 12$
scandens	24	Snoad 1952	H	O.W. Tropics

XANTHOSOMA $x = 12, 13$
violaceum	24	D. 1951	H	W. Indies
sagittifolium Coco Yam	26	E.K.J.*	R	Trop. America
helleborifolium	39	Simmonds 1954	—	Venez., Brazil

COLOCASIA $x = 12, 14$

antiquorum Taro Yam, (*esculenta*) Dasheen	⎧ ⎨ ⎩	28 36 48	Ito 1942 Rao 1947b D. 1951	R	India, *cult*
v. *nymphaefolia*		28	Sharma & D. 1954		
v. *gigantea*	⎧ ⎨ ⎩	28 42 42	Kurakubo 1940 Nakajima 1936, E.K.J.*		

MONSTERA $x = 12, 14$

deliciosa Ceriman	⎧ ⎩	24 56	E.K.J.* D. 1951	FH	Mexico
latevaginata		56	,, ,,	H	Trop. America

ORONTIUM $x = 12, 14$

aquaticum Golden Club	⎧ ⎩	24 28	D. 1951 Huttleston unp.	FFoH	E: N. America

TYPHONIUM $x = 13$
trilobatum	26	Simmonds 1954	H	India, Malaya
divaricatum	52	Ito 1942	H	Trop. Asia

AMORPHOPHALLUS $x = 13, 14$

linumaana		26	Kishimoto 1941	—	?
satsumaensis		26	,, ,,	—	?
sylvaticus		26	Asana & S. 1937	—	India
titanum		26	Tjio 1948	H	Sumatra
rivieri (*konjac*) Konjak	⎧ ⎨ ⎩	26 26 32	Kishimoto 1941 Ito 1942 D. 1951	R	Cochinch.—Japan
v. *kiusiana*	⎧ ⎩	26 39	Ito 1942 Tjio 1948		Japan
bulbifer		36	Chandler 1943	H	India
campanulatus	⎧ ⎩	26 28	Asana & S. 1937 Patel & N. 1937	HR(V)	Trop. Asia

ARISAEMA* $x = 13, 14$

ambiguum		26	Bowden 1945a	—	China
serratum		{ 26	Nakajima 1933	H	Japan
		28!	Ito 1942		
japonicum		28	Kishomoto 1941	H	,,
murrayi		28	Asana, T. 1936	—	Himalayas
quinatum		28	Bowden 1940a	R	S.E: U.S.A.
ringens	& 13 spp.	28	Ito 1942	H	Japan
taihokensis		28	Kishimoto 1941		Formosa
thunbergii		28	Nakajima '33, Ito '42	—	Japan
sazenzoo		28	Kurakubo 1940	—	Japan, China
limbatum		{ 28	Ito 1942	—	Japan
		32!	,, ,,		
concinnum		56	Bowden 1940a	R	Himalayas
dracontium	Dragon Root	{ 28, 56	Huttleston unp.	H	E: U.S.A.
		56	Bowden 1940a		
triphyllum	Indian Turnip	28, 56	Huttleston 1949	HR	E: N. America
kiushianum		56	Ito 1942	—	Japan
ovale		56	,, ,,	—	,,
robustum		56	,, ,,	—	,,
sadoense		56	,, ,,	—	,,
heterophyllum		c. 140	,, ,,	—	,,

PINELLIA $x = 13, 14$

tripartita	{ 26	Kurakubo 1940	H	S. Japan
	52	Ito 1942		
ternata (tuberifera)	{ 28	Huttleston unp.	H	Japan, China
	116	Ito 1942		
	128	D. 1951		

ALOCASIA $x = 14$ (13?)

cucullata	28	Ito 1942	—	India
fornicata	28	Sharma & D. 1954	—	,,
macrorrhiza	{ 26	M. & S. 1935,	R	O.W. Tropics
	28	Kurakubo 1940,		
	28	Ito 1942		

CRYPTOCORYNE $x = 14$

ciliata	28	Tjio 1948	H	India, Malaya

EMINIUM (HELICOPHYLLUM) $x = 14$

crassipes	28	Lotfy 1951	—	Palestine

GONATANTHUS $x = 14$

pumilus (sarmentosus)	28	Sharma & D. 1954	H	Himalayas

PISTIA $x = 14$

stratiotes	Water Lettuce	28	Blackburn 1933	MaM(V) Tropics

ARUM $x = 14, 16$

maculatum	{ 28	L. & L. 1942		Eur. (Sweden)
	56, 84	Maude 1940	(R)	(Britain)
	64	D. 1951		(France)
italicum	64	,, ,,	R	Medit.

CALADIUM	$x = 15$	⎧ 28 (30–32)	Sharma & D. 1954		
		30	Kurakubo 1940		
bicolor		30	Simmonds 1954	H	Trop. America
		⎩ 48	Ito 1942		

SYMPLOCARPUS	$x = 15$				
foetidus	Skunk Cabbage	30	Ito 1942	H	E: N. Am., N.E. Asia

EPIPREMNUM	$x = 15$				
mirabile	Tonga Plant	60	Ito 1942	H	Mal.—Tr. Aust.

PHILODENDRON	$x = 15, 16, 17$				
giganteum		30	Simmonds 1954	H	Trop. America
houlletianum		32	D. 1951	—	Guiana
andreanum		34	M. & S. 1935	H	Colombia

ANTHURIUM*	$x = 15, 16, 22$				
andraeanum		30	Ito 1942	H	Colombia
gracile	& 30 spp.	30	Gaiser 1927	H	Guiana
hookeri		30	Kurakubo 1940	H	W.I., Br. Guiana
scherzerianum		⎧ 30	„ „		
		30	Ito 1942	H	Guatemala
		⎩ 32	D. 1951		
magnificum		32	Haase-Bessel 1928	H	Colombia
scandens		c. 48	Gaiser 1927	H	Trop. America
radicans		c. 48	„ „	H	Brazil
calamus		44	Kurakubo 1940	—	?
crassinervium		c. 60	Gaiser 1927	H	Panama, Venez.
digitatum		c. 60	„ „	H	W. Indies, Venez.
wallisii		c. 60	„ „	H	Colombia

CULCASIA	$x = 16$				
scandens		32	D. 1951	H	Trop. Africa

DRACUNCULUS	$x = 16$				
vulgaris		32	D. 1951	HM	S. Europe

SAUROMATUM	$x = 16$				
guttatum		32	D. 1951	H	N.W. India

ZAMIOCULCAS	$x = 16$				
zamiifolia		32	D. 1951	H	E: Trop. Africa

ZANTEDESCHIA	$x = 16$				
aethiopica	Arum Lily	32	Ito 1942	HMV	S. Africa

SCINDAPSUS	$x = ?$				
pictus	Silver Vine	112	D. 1951	H	Malaya, Java

ARIOPSIS	$x = 20?$				
peltata		80	D. 1591	H	Himalayas

PELTANDRA	$x = 22$				
undulata		c. 44	Duggar 1900	H	E: U.S.A.
virginica	Green Arrow Arum	88	Huttleston unp.	H	N.E. America

376

303 LEMNACEAE

LEMNA (SPIRODELA) $x = 10, 11$

minor	Duckweed	40	Blackburn 1933	H	Cosmop.
polyrrhiza		40	„ „	—	„
trisulca		44	„ „	—	Eur., Siberia
gibba		64	„ „	—	N. Hemisphere

WOLFFIA $x = ?$

arrhiza	$\begin{cases} c.\ 44\text{–}46 & \text{Lawalrée 1943} \\ c.\ 50 & \text{Blackburn 1933} \end{cases}$	—	Temp.

304 SPARGANIACEAE

SPARGANIUM* $x = 15$

angustifolium		30	L. & L. 1942	—	N. Amer., Austr.
friesii		30	„ „	—	Europe
hyperboreum		30	„ 1948	—	N. Europe
minimum	Bur Weed	30	Wulff 1938	—	Europe
ramosum	Bede Sedge	30	„ „	T	„
simplex		30	Hagerup 1941b	—	„
yamatense	& 4 spp.	30	Harada 1947	—	Japan
stenophyllum		30, 45	„ „	—	Manchuria

305 TYPHACEAE

TYPHA $x = 15$

angustata		30	Harada 1947	—	E. Medit., S.W: Asia
angustifolia	Sm. Reed Mace	30	L. & L. 1942	HT	Am., Eur., Asia
latifolia	Cat-tail	30	Harada 1947	HT	N. Am., Eur., As.
orientalis		30	„ „	H	China, Japan

306 AMARYLLIDACEAE

HABRANTHUS $x = 6$

robustus		$\begin{cases} 12 & \text{D. Sato 1938,} \\ 12 & \text{Flory 1948} \end{cases}$	H	Uruguay
andersoni		$\begin{cases} 21 & \text{D. Sato 1938} \\ 24 & \text{Flory 1948} \end{cases}$	H	Argentine
as *texana*		24	„ „	H	(Texas)
brachyandrus		24	„ „	H	S. Brazil

ZEPHYRANTHES $x = 6, 7$ $x_3 = 19$

tauberti		12	D. Sato 1938	H	S. America
atamasco	Atamasco L.	24	Flory 1943	H	S.E: U.S.A.
treatiae		24	„ „	H	„
verecunda		24	La Cour 1952	H	Mexico
tubispatha		25!	Flory 1943	H	W. Indies
flammea		14	Schnack & C. 1947	—	Peru
candida		38	Inariyama 1937	H	Argentine
macrosiphon		46, 48	Flory 1943	H	Mexico

ZEPHYRANTHES (*cont.*)

grandiflora (*carinata*)	48	Coe 1954	H	C. Amer., W.I.
pulchella	48	Flory 1943	H	Texas
simpsonii	48	,, ,,	H	Florida
lindleyana	*c.* 96	La Cour unp.	H	Mexico
ajax	42	Sato 1942	H	*cult*
brazosensis	48, 55–59	Coe 1954	—	S: U.S.A.
longifolia	(24) 44–50	,, ,,	H	S: U.S.A., Mex.

LYCORIS   *x* = 6, 9, 11 (by fusion from 11)

sanguinea	22	Inariyama 1937	H	Japan
sprengeri	22	,, 1944	H	,,
radiata v. *pumila*	22	,, ,,	H	China
radiata (3*x*)	33	,, ,,	H	,,
v. *alba*	39	D. Sato 1938	H	,,
albiflora	17	Inariyama 1937	H	*cult*
straminea	16	,, ,,	H	China
aurea	12, 13, 14	,, ,,	H	China, Japan
squamigera (3*x*)	27	,, ,,	H	Japan

COOPERIA   *x* = 12

traubii	Prairie Lily	24	Coe 1954	H	Texas
drummondii	(24), 48	,, ,,	H	Texas, Mexico
pedunculata	48	Sato 1942, Coe 1953	H	,, ,,
brasiliensis	69 + **B**	Traub 1945	—	Brazil

GALANTHUS   *c* = 12

byzantinus	24	La Cour 1946	H	S.E: Europe
cilicicus	24	,, ,,	H	Taurus
platyphyllus (*latifolius*)	24	,, ,,	H	Cauc., Asia M.
plicatus	24	Sato 1942	H	Crimea
nivalis Snowdrop	{ 24, 25, 28 24, 36	,, ,, La Cour 1946	H	Europe, Cauc.
elwesii	24, 48	Sato 1938	H	Asia Minor

IXIOLIRION   *x* = 12

montanum (*tataricum*)	24	Traub 1942	H	W. Asia, Siberia

LEPTOCHITON   *x* = 12

quitoensis	24	Snoad 1952	H	Ecuador

UNGERNIA   *x* = 12

sewerzowii	24	Baranov & P. 1925	—	Persia

LEUCOJUM   *x* = 7, 8, 9, 11

autumnale	14	Neves 1939	H	Medit.
trichophyllum	14	,, ,,	H	W. Medit.
roseum	16	,, ,,	H	Corsica
hiemale	18	,, ,,	H	Riviera
aestivum	22	,, ,,	H	Eur., S.W: Asia
v. *pulchellum*	22	,, ,,	H	Balearics
vernum Snowflake	22	,, ,,	H	Europe

NARCISSUS $x = 7, 10, 11$

(i) $x = 7$

asturiensis	$14 + 0\text{–}2B$	Wylie 1952	H	C. & N. Sp. & Portugal
atlanticus	14	,, ,,	(H)	Atlas
bulbocodium	14, 21, 28, 35, 42	Fernandes 1934	H	Sp., Port., S.W.
Hoop Petticoat	$14 + 0\text{–}4B$	,, 1949a		France, N.W.
v. *citrinus*	$14 + 0\text{–}2B$	Wylie 1952		Africa
genuinus	14	Fernandes 1934		
nivalis	14	,, ,,		
obesus	26!	,, & N. '41		
conspicuus	28	,, ,, ,,		
monophyllus foliosus	28	,, 1951		
romieuxii	29!	Wylie 1952		Morocco
calcicola	$14 + 0\text{–}2B$	,, ,,	H	Portugal
cyclamineus	$14 + 0\text{–}1B$	,, ,,	H	N. Portugal
fernandesii	14	Fernandes 1951	—	Portugal
gaditanus	14	,, 1939b	—	S.W: Sp. & Port.
jonquilla Jonquil	14	Nagao 1933	H	S. Sp. & Port.
juncifolius	$14 + 1B$	Fernandes 1939c	H	Spain, S. France
minor	14	,, & F. '46	H	Pyrenees
v. *pumilus*	14	,, ,, ,,		
	$14 + 1B$	Wylie 1952		
minutiflorus	14	Fernandes 1939b	—	S.W: Sp. & Port.
poeticus Pheasant's Eye	14, 21	Nagao 1929	H	S. Europe
v. *radiiflorus*	14	Wylie 1952		E. Adriatic
recurvus	21	,, ,,		cult
pseudonarcissus Daffodil	14	Fernandes & F. '46	H	W. Europe
v. *pallidiflorus*	15	Philp 1934b		
hispanicus (*maximus*)	21	,, ,,		cult
tortuosus	21	Fernandes & F. '46		,,
bicolor	28	,, ,, ,,		,,
nobilis	28	,, 1951		,,
rupicola	14	,, 1939b	H	Spain, Portugal
scaberulus	14	,, ,,		Portugal
triandrus	14	,, 1949b	H	Sp., Port., Britt.
viridiflorus	28	,, 1943	(H)	Gib., N.W. Afr.
watieri	14	,, 1939b	H	Morocco

(ii) $x = 10, 11$

broussonetii	22	Fernandes 1940	—	Morocco
elegans	20	,, 1943	—	W. Medit.
serotinus	30	,, ,,	—	Medit.
tazetta Polyanthus N.	22	,, 1937b	H	,,
	20–22, 30–32	Nagao 1933		Japan, *cult*
v. *italicus*	22	Maugini 1952		S. France, Cors., Italy
v. *aureus*	22	,, 1953c		Medit.
bertolonii	20, 22	,, ,,		Italy
patulus	20, 22	,, ,,		Italy, Greece
cypri	30, 33	,, ,,		E. Medit.

(iii) HYBRID SPECIES

bernardi (*ps. nar. x poet.*)	$14 + 1B$	Wylie 1952	H	Pyrenees
gracilis (*jon. x poet.*)	14	Pereira 1940	H	*cult*
odorus (*ps. nar. x jon.*)	14	Fernandes 1934	H	,,
tenuior (*jon. x poet.*)	14	Pereira 1940	H	,,
johnstonii (*ps. nar. x triandrus*)	21	Wylie 1952	H	Portugal

NARCISSUS *(cont.)*

jonquilloides (jon. x gad.)	21	Fernandes 1939a	—	S.W. Iber. Penin.
intermedius (jon. x taz.)	17	Nagao 1933	H	N.E. Spain (?)
biflorus (poet. x taz.)	{ 17	Fernandes 1934	H	S. France (?)
	24	Nagao 1933		
dubius (junc. x taz.)	50	Fernandes 1937a	H	S. Fr., N.E. Sp.

TAPEINANTHUS $x = (7)$ 14

humilis	28	Fernandes & F. '45	—	S.E. Spain, Mor.

CRYPTOSTEPHANUS $x = (7)$ 14

vansonii	28	Gouws 1949	—	S. Africa

ANOIGANTHUS $x = 8$

breviflorus	16	Gouws 1949	H	S. Africa

VALLOTA $x = 8$

speciosa (purpurea)	16	Sato 1942	H	S. Africa

HAEMANTHUS $x = 8, 9$

albiflos	16	Sato 1938	H	S. Africa
	16 + 2B	„ „	H	cult
coccineus	16	„ „	H	S. Africa
hirsutus	16	Gouws 1949	—	„
nelsonii	16	„ „	H	Transvaal
katherinae	18	Snoad 1952	H	Natal
magnificus	18	Gouws 1949	H	„
multiflorus	18	Snoad 1952	H	Trop. Africa

CYRTANTHUS $x = 8, 11$

parviflorus	16	Taylor 1925a	H	S. Africa
tuckii	16	Gouws 1949	H	„
obliquus	22	D. Sato 1938	H	Cape Prov.

HIPPEASTRUM $x = 9, 11$

advenum	18	Ficker 1951	H	Chile
chilense	18	„ „	H	„
pratense	18	Sato 1942	H	„
aulicum	22	Snoad 1952	H	Brazil, Paraguay
calyptratum	22	Neto 1948	H	Brazil
equestre	22	Snoad 1952	H	Trop. America
solandriflorum	22	Baldwin & S. 1947a	H	Trop. S. Amer.
stylosum	22	Neto 1948	H	Brazil, Guiana
rutilum v. *fulgidum*	{ 22	Snoad 1952	H	Brazil, Ven.
	44	Sato 1942		
candidum	33	Snoad 1952	H	Argentine
reginae	33	Neto 1948	H	Brazil
ruiri	33	Snoad 1952	H	cult
vittatum	{ 43	„ unp.	H	Peru
	44	Inariyama 1937		
hybridum	44	Inariyama 1937	H	cult
blumenavia (as *Griffinia*)	77	Sato 1938	H	Brazil

MIERSIA $x = 10$ (11)
chilensis

chilensis	20, 21	Cave & B. 1943	H	Chile

AMARYLLIS $x = 11$

belladonna Cape Plant	22	Sato 1938,	H	S. Africa
(*Brunsvigia rosea*)	22	Gouws 1949		

AMMOCHARIS $x = 11$

coranica	22	Gouws 1949	—	S. Africa

BOÖPHONE $x = 11$

disticha	22	Gouws 1949	H	S. Africa
guttata	22	„ „	—	„

BRUNSVIGIA $x = 11$

cooperi	22	Gouws 1949	—	S. Africa

CLIVIA $x = 11$

caulescens	22	Gouws 1949	—	S. Africa
miniata	22	Inariyama 1937	H	Natal
nobilis	22	„ „	H	S. Africa
cyrtanthiflora	18?	Wittlake 1940	H	*cult*
(*miniata* × *nobilis*)				

CRINUM $x = 11$

abyssinicum	22	Dolcher 1950	H	Abyssinia
asiaticum	22	Inariyama 1937	H	Trop. Asia
buphanoides	22	Gouws 1949	—	S. Africa
crispum	22	„ „	H	Transvaal
forbesianum	22	„ „	H	Delagoa Bay
gigas	22	Inariyama 1937	H	Bonin Is.
latifolium	22	„ „	H	India
lineare	22	D. Sato 1938	H	S. Africa
longifolium (*capense*) {	22	Dolcher 1950	H	„
	22 + 2B	Inariyama 1937		
moorei	22	D. Sato 1938	H	„
grandiflorum	22	Sato 1942	H	*cult*
octobris	22	„ „	H	„
powellii	22	Dolcher 1950	H	„
rattrayi	22	D. Sato 1938	H	Trop. Africa
yemense	22	Snoad 1952	H	Arabia
macrantherum ($3x$)	33	D. Sato 1938	—	Melanesia
bulbispermum	72	Gouws 1949	H	S. Africa

CYBISTETES $x = 11$

longifolia	22	Gouws 1949	H	S. Africa

LAPEIDRA $x = 11$

martinezii	22	Fernandes 1950a	—	S.E: Spain

PANCRATIUM $x = 11$

maritimum	22	Fernandes 1933	H	Medit.
illyricum {	22	Brumfield 1941	H	S. Europe
	44	Sato 1938		

26   381

STERNBERGIA $x = 11, 12?$

lutea	⎧ 22	Inariyama 1937		
	⎨ 22, 33	Battaglia 1949b	H	Medit.
	⎩ 24	Amico 1947		

NERINE $x = 11, 12$

angustifolia	22	Janaki Ammal 1951b	H	S. Africa
appendiculata	22	„ „ „	H	Natal
duparquetiana	22	Gouws 1949	—	S. Africa
falcata	22	„ „	—	„
frithii	22	„ „	—	„
laticoma	22	„ „	—	„
lucida	22	Janaki Ammal 1951b	—	„
marginata	22	„ „ „	—	„
bowdenii	22, 24	„ „ „	H	Cape Pen.
filifolia	22, 24	„ „ „	H	S. Africa
masanorum	⎧ 22	„ „ „	—	Kalahari
	⎩ 24	Gouws 1949		
curvifolia	22, 24, 33	Janaki Ammal 1951b	H	Cape Pen.
sarniensis Guernsey Lily	22, 24, 33	„ „ „	H	„
flexuosa	22, 33	„ „ „	H	Transvaal
humilis	22, 33	„ „ „	H	Table Mt.
pudica	22, 33	„ „ „	H	*cult*
undulata	22, 33	„ „ „	H	S. Africa
moorei	33	„ „ „	H	Cape Prov.
Garden forms	22–26, 28, 33, 36	Janaki Ammal & B.	H	*cult*
	44	1951		

HEMEROCALLIS* $x = 11$

flava Common Day Lily	22	Dark 1932b	H	Eur., T. Asia
& 3 spp.				
koreana	22	Takenaka 1952	—	Korea
forrestii & 7 spp.	22	Stout 1932	H	China
fulva			H	Eur., T. Asia
v. *longituba*	22	Sato 1942		
v. *Kwanso*	33	„ „		
	36?	Suzuka 1950a		
as *disticha*	22, 33	Takenaka 1952		

HESPEROCALLIS $x = 12$

undulata	48	Cave 1948b	H	Colo., Ariz.

LEUCOCRINUM $x = 14$

montanum	28	Cave 1948b	H	W: U.S.A.

ELISAENA $x = 23$

longipetala	46	Snoad 1952	H	Peru

HYMENOCALLIS $x = 23$

amancaes	46	Snoad 1955	H	Chile, Peru
littoralis	46	D. Sato 1938	H	S. America
speciosa Spider Lily	⎧ 46	Sato 1938	H	W. Indies
	⎩ 90–100	Heitz 1926		
lacera	69	D. Sato 1938	H	N. America
macrostephana	46, 92	Snoad 1955	H	S. America
senegambica	69	„ „	H	Guinea
calathinum	86–23!	„ 1955	H	S. America

382

PAMIANTHE	$x = 23$				
	peruviana		46	La Cour unp.	H	Peru

PAMIANTHE $x = 23$
peruviana — 46 — La Cour unp. — H — Peru

PHAEDRANASSA $x = 23$
carmioli — 46 — Snoad 1952 — H — Costa Rica

EUCHARIS $x = ?$
grandiflora Amazon L. — 68 — Sato 1938 — H — Colombia

SPREKELIA $x = ?$
formosissima — { *c.* 117 Sato 1938 / *c.* 121 Snoad unp. } — H — Mexico

307 IRIDACEAE

CROCUS $x = 3, 4, 5, 6, 7,$ etc.

$x = 3, 4$

balansae	6	Mather 1932	H	S.W. Asia
candidus v. *subflavus*	6	Karasawa 1943	H	Asia Minor
graveolens	6	Mather 1932	H	,,
hyemalis	6 + **4B**	,, ,,	H	Syria, Palestine
olivieri	6	,, ,,	H	S.E. Europe
suterianus (*aucheri*)	6	,, ,,	H	Asia Minor
biflorus Cloth-of-Silver	7, 8, 15, 20	Karasawa 1943	H	Eur., Asia Min.
flavus (*aureus*)	8	Mather 1932	H	S.E. Eur., As. M.
danfordiae	8	,, ,,	H	Asia Minor
kotschyanus (*zonatus*)	8	,, ,,	H	,,
aerius	8, 14	,, ,,	H	,,
chrysanthus	8, 9, 10	,, ,,	H	Greece, Asia M.
etruscus	{ 8 / 11 }	{ Karasawa 1943 / Mather 1932 }	H	Italy
stellaris	8, 11	,, ,,	H	*cult*
vernus	8, 16–32	Karasawa 1943	H	Eur., *cult*

$x = 5–8$

hueffelianus	{ 9! / 14 }	{ Karasawa 1943 / Mather 1932 }	H	Hungary
ancyrensis	10	Karasawa 1950	H	Asia Minor
ochroleucus	10	Mather 1932	H	Syria, Palestine
reticulatus	10	,, ,,	H	Caucasus—Italy
cancellatus	10, 16	Karasawa 1943	HV	Greece—Persia
pulchellus	12	Mather 1932	H	Greece, Asia M.
angustifolius Cloth-of-Gold C. (*susianus*)	12	Karasawa 1950	H	Crimea, Cauc.
speciosus	{ 12, 14, 16 / 12, 18 }	{ ,, 1940 / Mather 1932 }	H	Asia M., S. Russ., Persia
sativus Saffron	{ 14, 15 / 16, 40 / 24 }	{ ,, ,, / Karasawa 1940 / Sugiura 1931 }	HMSp	Italy—Kurdistan *cult*
sieheanus	16	Karasawa 1943	H	Asia Minor
tomasinianus	16	Mather 1932	H	Dalmatia
hadriaticus	{ 16 / 24 }	{ ,, ,, / Karasawa 1943 }	H	Greece, Albania

$x = 10–15$

fleischeri	20	Mather 1932	H	Asia Minor
karduchorum	20	,, ,,	—	Kurdistan

CROCUS (*cont.*)

korolkowii	20	Mather 1932	H	Turkestan
leichtlinii	20	,, ,,	H	Asia Minor
asturicus	22	,, ,,	H	Spain
corsicus	22	,, ,,	H	Corsica
dalmaticus	22	Karasawa 1943	H	Dalmatia
medius	22	,, ,,	H	Riviera
sieberi	22	Mather 1932	H	Greece
boryi v. *marathoniseus*	24	,, ,,	H	,,
malyi	24	,, ,,	H	Dalmatia
minimus	24	Karasawa 1943	H	Cors., Sardinia
salzmannii	24	Mather 1932	H	Spain, Morocco
byzantinus (*iridiflorus*)	26	,, ,,	H	E. Europe
imperati	26	,, ,,	H	Italy
laevigatus v. *fontenayi*	26	,, ,,	H	Greece
niveus	26	Karasawa 1932	H	,,
versicolor	26	Mather 1932	H	Eur. Alps
longiflorus (*odorus*)	28	Karasawa 1943	H	S. Italy, Sicily
pestalozzae	28	,, ,,	H	Greece, Turkey
tournefortii	30	Mather 1932	H	Greece
nudiflorus	*c.* 46	,, ,,	H	S.W. Europe

CYPELLA $x = 5, 7$

purgans	10	Sakai 1952	—	Brazil
herbertii	14	,, ,,		
	14 + 0–1B	Covas & S. 1947	H	Argentine

BABIANA $x = 6? \ 7?$

stricta	12	Brittingham 1934		
	14	Sugiura 1931	H	S Africa

NEOMARICA (MARICA) $x = 7$

northiana	14	M. & S. 1935	H	Brazil

SPARAXIS $x = 7?, 10?$

tricolor	14	Sugiura 1931		
	20	Nakajima 1936	H	S. Africa

IRIS* $x = 7 \ 8 \ 9, 10, 12$, etc.
(i) Bulbous Group
S. 1. Xiphium $x = 7, 8, 9.$ $x_2 = 15, 17, 25$

tingitana	28	Simonet 1934a	H	Morocco
	42	,, ,,	H	*cult*
xiphioides	42	,, ,,	H	Pyrenees
filifolia	32	,, 1952	H	S. Spain, N. Afr.
juncea	32	,, 1934a		
as *lusitanica*	34	,, ,,	H	Sicily, N. Africa
xiphium	34	,, ,,	H	W. Medit.
v. *battandieri*	36	,, ,,	H	N. Africa
boissieri	36	,, 1952	H	Portugal
sp. 119	30	,, ,,	—	Tangiers
sp. 117	50	,, ,,	—	,,

S. 2. Reticulata $x = 8, 10, 14$

histrioides	16, 17	Simonet 1934a	H	Asia Minor
winogradowii	16	,, ,,	H	Caucasus

IRIS (*cont.*)

bakeriana	20	Simonet 1952	H	Asia M., Mesop.
histrio	20	,, 1934a	H	Asia Minor
vartanii	20	,, ,,	H	Palestine
reticulata	20	,, ,,	H	Caucasus
danfordiae	28	,, ,,	H	Asia Minor

S. 3. JUNO $x = 9, 11, 12, 13,$ $x_2 = 25$

caucasica	18	Simonet 1934a	H	Cauc., Asia Min., Persia
willmottiana v. *alba*	21	,, 1952	H	Tashkent
bucharica	22	,, 1934a	H	Bokhara
orchioides	22	,, ,,	H	,,
sindjarensis	22	,, ,,	H	Mesopotamia
alata	24	,, ,,	H	W. Medit.
warleyensis	24	,, ,,	H	Bokhara
persica	26	,, ,,	H	Asia M.—Persia
vicaria	26	,, 1952	H	C. Asia
graeberiana	50	,, ,,	H	Turkestan

S. 4. NEPALENSIS $x = 12, 14$

decora (*nepalensis*)	24	La Cour unp.	H	N.W. Him.—Yun.
collettii	28	Simonet 1934a	H	Burma—Yunnan

(ii) RHIZOMATOUS GROUP
S. 5. APOGON $x = 7, 8, 10, 11, 12$, etc.

$x = 7$

orientalis	28	Simonet 1934a	H	Manch., Kor., Jap.
sibirica	28	,, ,,	H	Eur., W. Russia
tenuis	28	,, ,,	H	Oregon
fulva	42	,, ,,	H	S.E: U.S.A.
prismatica	42	,, ,,	H	E: N. America
verna	42	,, ,,	H	S: U.S.A.

$x = 8$

sintenesii	16, 32	Simonet 1934a	H	Italy—Asia M.
rossii	32	Kurita 1940	H	Korea, China

$x = 9$

kerneriana	18	La Cour unp.	H	Asia Minor
humilis	72	Simonet 1934a	H	Trans., Cauc., Alt.

$x = 10$

urumovii	20	,, ,,	H	Europe
aurea	40	,, ,,	H	Kashmir
bracteata	40	Foster 1937	H	Oregon
bulleyana	40	Simonet 1934a	H	W. China
chrysographes	40	,, ,,	H	,,
delavayi	40	,, ,,	H	,,
douglasiana (*watsoniana*)	40	,, ,,	H	California
foetidissima	40	,, ,,	HM	Eur., N. Africa
forrestii	40	,, ,,	H	W. China
gormanii	40	,, ,,	H	Oregon
hartwegii v. *australis*	40	Lenz 1950	H	S. California
innominata	40	,, unp.	H	Oregon
munzii	40	,, 1950	—	California
ochroleuca	40	Simonet 1934a	H	W. Asia Minor
pabularia (*ensata*)	40	,, ,,	H	C. Asia—Korea
purdyi	40	Foster 1937	H	Ore., N. Calif.

IRIS (*cont.*)

tenax	40	Simonet 1934a	H	Wash., Oregon
wilsoni	40	,, ,,	H	W. China

$x = 11$

minuta	22	Simonet 1934a	H	Japan
spuria	22	Westergaard 1938	H	Europe
chrysophaeanicia	43	Randolph 1934	H	S.E: U.S.A.
brevicaulis (*foliosa*)	44	Simonet 1934a	H	,,
carthaliniae	44	,, ,,	H	Caucasus
halophila	44	,, ,,	H	C. Asia
hexagona	44	Snoad 1952	H	S.E: U.S.A.
lilacina	44	La Cour unp.	H	Persia?
missouriensis	88	Snoad 1952	H	S.E: U.S.A.

$x = 12, 13, 15, 16, 17, 19$

aschersoni	24	Simonet 1952	H	Cilicia
grant-duffii	24	,, 1934a	H	Palestine
kaempferi	24	,, ,,	H	Manch.—Japan
melanostica	24	,, 1952	H	Jordan
pseudacorus Yellow F. {	24, 30, 34	L. &. L. 1942	(B)P	Eur., Cauc., Sib.
	32, 34	Ehrenberg 1945		
laevigata Blue Flag	32	Kazao 1929	HM	E. & N. Asia
unguicularis (*stylosa*)	38	Simonet 1934a	H	E. Medit., Algeria
v. *lazica*	32	,, 1952	H	E. Asia Minor
v. *speciosa* {	36	La Cour 1952	H	E. Medit.
	38	Simonet 1952		
v. *alba*	48	La Cour 1952	H	,,
graminea	34	Simonet 1934a	H	S. Eur., Cauc.
maritima	38	,, ,,	H	W. Eur., N. Afr.
setosa	38	,, ,,	HR	N. Asia, Alaska, Lab., E: U.S.A.
virginica	54, 56, 70	Anderson 1936	H	E: N. America
ruthenica	c. 84	Simonet 1934a	H	Transylv.—Korea
longipetala	c. 86	,, ,,	H	California
montana	c. 86	,, ,,	H	W: U.S.A.
versicolor Blue Flag	72, 84, 105	,, ,,	HM	E: N. America

S. 6. POGONIRIS $x = 8, 10, 11, 12, 13$

$x = 8$

attica	16	Simonet 1934a	H	Greece, Cauc.
pseudopumila	16	,, 1952	H	S. Italy, Sicily
mellita	24	,, 1934a	H	Greece, Turkey
reichenbachii {	24, 32	,, ,,	H	Balkans
	40	Randolph 1935		
as *balkana*	24, 48	Simonet 1934a		
pumila	32, 36	,, ,,	H	E. Europe

$x = 10$ (Dwarf Bearded Irises)

chamaeiris (*olbiensis*)	40	Simonet 1934a	H	S. Europe
subbiflora (*biflora*)	40	,, ,,	H	Port., Sp., N. Afr.

$x = 11$ (or $10 + 12$)

flavissima	22	Simonet 1934a	H	Hungary—Mong.
albicans	44	,, ,,	H	S. Eur., Asia M., Yemen
biliottii	44	,, 1952	H	N.E. Asia Min.
kashmiriana	44	,, 1934a	H	Himalayas
kochii	44	,, ,,	H	*cult*
germanica Orris Root	44	,, ,,	HP	Europe, *cult*

IRIS (cont.)
germanica

	⌠24	Simonet 1934a		
as *florentina*	⟨28	Sakai 1952		
	⌡48	Kazao 1929		
as *amas* (*macrantha*)	48	Simonet 1934a		

$x = 12$ (Tall Bearded Irises)

alberti	24	Simonet 1934a	H	Turkestan
imbricata	24	,, ,,	HP	Transcauc., N. Persia
pallida (*cengialtii*)	24	,, ,,	HP	Tyrol
variegata	24	,, ,,	H	Balkans, *cult*
aphylla	24, 48	,, ,,	H	E. Eur., Cauc., Siberia
belouini	48	,, 1952	—	Morocco
cypriana	48	,, 1934a	H	Cyprus
junonia	48	,, 1952	H	Asia Minor
mesopotamica	48	,, 1934a	H	Syria?
trojana	48	,, ,,	H	Asia Minor

	145 vars.	24 (25)⌉		
Bearded	23 ,,	36 (35)		
Irises	247 ,,	48 (46–53) ⟩ Randolph 1944	H	*cult*
	3 ,,	60 (63)⌡		

$x = 13$

bloudowii	26	Simonet 1952	H	C. Asia

S. 7. PARDANTHOPSIS $x = 8$

dichotoma	32	Simonet 1934a	H	Sib.—N. China

S. 8. ONCOCYCLUS $x = 10$

acutiloba	20	Simonet 1934a	H	Transcauc.
antilibanotica	20	,, 1952	H	Anti-Lebanon
atrofusca	20	,, ,,	H	Palestine
atropurpurea	20	,, 1934a	H	Syria
auranitica & 10 spp.	20	,, 1952	H	,,
ewbankiana	20	,, 1934a	H	Asia M., N. Pers.
iberica	20	,, ,,	H	Cauc., N. Persia
barnumiae (*mariae*)	20	,, ,,	H	S. Palest., Sinai
paradoxa	20	,, ,,	H	Transcauc., N. Persia
sari	20, 21	,, ,,	H	Asia Minor
sofarana	20	,, ,,	H	Lebanon
susiana	20	,, ,,	H	Persia
urmiensis	20	,, ,,	H	Asia Minor

S. 9. REGELIA $x = 11$

korolkowii	22, 33, 44	Simonet 1934a	H	Turkestan
hoogiana	33, 44	,, ,,	H	Kashmir, W. Tib.
stolonifera (*leichtlinii, vaga*)	44	,, ,,	H	Bokhara, Turkest.

S. 10. PSEUDO-REGELIA $x = 11?, 12?$

kumaonensis	⌠22	Simonet 1952	H	Himalayas
	⌡24	La Cour unp.		

S. 11. EVANSIA $x = 13, 14, 15, 16, 17, 18, 22$

tectorum Wall Iris	⌠24	Sakai 1952	HR	S.W. China, N. Burma
	⌡28	Simonet 1934a		
milesii	26	,, ,,	H	Himalayas
formosana	28	Yasui 1939	H	Formosa

IRIS (*cont.*)

confusa (as *wattii*)		{ 30 { 30	Simonet 1934a Snoad 1952	H	W. China
cristata	Crested Iris	32	Simonet 1934a	HSp	E: U.S.A.
v. *lacustris*		42	,, ,,	H	N. Am. (Gr. Lak.)
japonica		{ 34, 54 { 36, 54	Kazao 1929 Yasui 1939	HR	China, Japan (*cult*)
gracilipes		36	Simonet 1934a	H	Japan
speculatrix		44	Snoad 1952	H	Hong Kong

HELIXYRA (IRIS) $x = 12$
sisyrinchium	Spanish Nut	24	Simonet 1934a	HSp	Medit.—N.W. Ind.

HERMODACTYLUS (IRIS) $x = 10$
tuberosus	Snake's Head Iris	20	Simonet 1928a	H	Levant

BELAMCANDA $x = 8$
chinensis	Blackberry Lily	32	Nakajima 1936	H	China, Jap. N. Ind.

CHASMANTHE (ANTHOLYZA) $x = 8$
aethiopica	32	Nakajima 1936	H	S. Africa

LAPEYROUSIA $x = 8$
cruenta	16	Brittingham 1934	H	S. Afr. (Cape)

SISYRINCHIUM $x = 8, 9$
sp.	16	Bowden 1945a	—	Chile
labidum	32	,, ,,		W. Indies
bellum	32	,, ,,	H	California
montanum	32, *c.* 96	Bøcher & L. 1950	—	N. America
sp.	64	Bowden 1945a	—	Chile
angustifolium	96	,, ,,	H	N. America
iridifolium	18	,, ,,	H	Brazil—Chile
macrocarpum	18	Covas & S. 1946	—	Argentine
striatum	18	Vilmorin & S. 1927b	H	Chile
californicum	{ 34 { 36	Maude 1940 Bowden 1945a	H	California
brachypus	36	,, ,,	H	,,
sp.	90	,, ,,		

WATSONIA $x = 9$
iridifolia	18	Nakajima 1936	H	S. Africa

DIERAMA $x = 10$
pendulum	20	Vilmorin & S. 1927b	H	Trop. Africa

IXIA $x = 10$
crateroides	20	Brittingham 1934	H	S. Africa
viridiflora	20	Collins unp.	H	,,
maculata	30	Nakajima 1936	H	,,
hybrida	40	Brittingham 1934	H	*cult*
speciosa (*Gl. coccinea*)	60	Bamford 1935	H	S. Africa

TRITONIA $x = 10$
crocata	20	Brittingham 1934	H	S. Africa

MORAEA $x = 10, 14$

iridioides	$\begin{cases} 20 \\ 40 \end{cases}$	Sakai 1952 Snoad unp.	H	S. Africa
ramosa	20	Sakai 1952	H	,,
edulis	28	,,　　,,	H	,,

CROCOSMIA $x = 11$

pottsii	22	Nakajima 1936	H	S. Africa
crocosmiiflora M'bretia	22, 33, 44	Brittingham 1934	H	*cult*
(*T. aurea* × *C. pottsii*)	22–24, 33	Meurman & S. 1946		

FREESIA $x = 11$

refracta	22	Brittingham 1934	H	S. Africa
v. *leichtlinii*	22	La Cour 1945 *		
hybrida	22, 33, 44	Lawrence 1945 *	H	*cult*

HOMERIA $x = 12$

collina	24	Sakai 1952	H	S. Africa
elegans	36	Brittingham 1934	H	,,

CURTONIS (ANTHOLYZA) $x = 13$

paniculatus	26	Brittingham 1934	H	S. Africa

TIGRIDIA * $x = 13?, 14?$

pavonia Tiger Flower	26	Brittingham 1934	H	Mexico
2 vars.	28	Sakai 1952		

GLADIOLUS * $x = 15$

(i) *alatus* (*namaquensis*)	30	Bamford 1935	H	S. Africa
permeabilis	30	,,　　,,	H	,,
formosus	45	,,　　,,	H	*cult*
(ii) *cardinalis*	30	,,　　,,	H	S. Africa
carmineus	30	,,　　,,	H	,,
splendens	30	,,　　,,	H	,,
(iii) *blandus* & 6 spp.	30	,,　　,,	H	,,
papilio	75	,,　　,,	H	,,
(iv) *byzantinus*	$\begin{cases} 60 \\ 90 \end{cases}$	Mensinkai 1939b Bamford 1935	H	Medit.
illyricus	$\begin{cases} 60 \\ 90 \end{cases}$	Fernandes 1950b Bamford 1941	H	,,
atroviolaceus	90	,, 1935	H	Syria, Persia
communis	90, 180	,, 1941	H	Medit.
segetum	120	,, 1935	H	,,
(v) *angustus* & 9 spp.	30	,, 1935	H	S. Africa
(vi) *saundersii*	30, 45	,,　　,,	H	,,
platyphyllus	60	,,　　,,	H	,,
primulinus	60	,,　　,,	H	,,
quartinianus	75	,,　　,,	H	Abyss., *cult*
dracocephalus	$\begin{cases} 75, 90 \\ 80 \end{cases}$	,,　　,, Mensinkai 1939b	H	Natal
psittacinus	75, 90	Bamford 1935	H	S.E. Africa
colvillei	30, 45	,,　　,,	H	*cult*
nanus	30, 45, 60	,,　　,,	H	,,

HOMOGLOSSUM (GLADIOLUS) $x = 15$

watsonius	30	Bamford 1941	H	S. Africa

ROMULEA $x = 17$

bulbocodium	34	Fernandes *et al.* '48	H	W. Medit.
parviflora	*c.* 60	M. & S. 1935	H	S. Africa

Group IV

DIOSCOREALES
308–311
H

AGAVALES
312–313
HS

PALMALES
314
HST

PANDANALES
315
ST

CYCLANTHALES
316
H

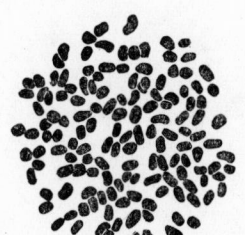

Dioscorea batatas

310 ROXBURGHIACEAE

STEMONA $x = 7$
japonica   14   Suzuka & K. 1949   MR   Japan

311 DIOSCOREACEAE

DIOSCOREA $x = 10$

caucasia		20	B. W. Smith 1937	—	Caucasia
quinqueloba	Japanese Yam	20	,, ,,	R	Japan
gracillima		20	Nakajima 1933	—	,,
tokoro		20	,, ,,	—	,,
japonica		40	,, ,,	—	,,
discolor		40	,, ,,	H	S. America
macroura		40	B. W. Smith 1937	—	Trop. Africa
alata Lisbon or White Y. {		40	Simmonds 1954	R	Trop. Asia
		c. 81	Nakajima 1936		
sativa	Yam	60	,, ,,	R	S.E. Asia, *cult*
villosa		60	B. W. Smith 1937	—	N. America
reticulata		61	,, ,,	—	Chile
fargesii		64	,, ,,	—	China
bulbifera	Air Yam	80	Nakajima 1936	HR	Trop. Asia
cayennensis	Attoto Yam	c. 140	B. W. Smith 1937	R	Guiana, Brazil
oppositifolia	E. Indies Y.	c. 140	,, ,,	R	E. Indies
batatas	Chinese Yam	c. 144	,, ,,	R	China, *cult*
pentaphylla		c. 144	,, ,,	(R)V	Trop. Asia

BORDEREA (DIOSCOREA) $x = 12$
chouardii	24	Heslot 1953	—	Pyrenees
pyrenaica	24	,, ,,	—	,,

TAMUS $x = 12$
communis	Black Bryony	48	Meurman 1925	HM	Eur., Pers., N. Afr.

312 XANTHORRHOEACEAE

XANTHORRHOEA $x = 11$
hastile	Grass Tree	22	J. T. Waterhouse unp. T		E. Australia
media		22	,, ,,	—	,, ,,
preissii		22	,, ,,	—	W. Australia

313 AGAVACEAE

PHORMIUM $x = 16$
tenax	N.Z. Flax	32	Sato 1932	HT	New Zealand
colensoi	Mtn. Flax	—		HT	,, ,,

NOLINA $x = 18, 19$
microcarpa	36	Sato 1942	HT	S.W: U.S.A.
parryi	38	Lenz 1950	H	S. California

393

CORDYLINE $x = 19$

australis	Cabbage Tree	$\begin{cases} 38 \\ 120 \end{cases}$	Bowden 1945a M. & S. 1935	HT	New Zealand
indivisa		38	Sato 1942	HT	,, ,,

DASYLIRION $x = 19$

acrotrichum	38	Sato 1942	AHTV	Mexico
longissimum (*quadrangulautm*)	38	,, ,,	AHTV	,,
texanum	38	Sato 1935b	AHTV	Texas
wheeleri	38	,, ,,	AGTV	Mexico

DRACAENA (CORDYLINE) $x = 19$

arborea	38	McKelvey & S. 1933	T	Trop. Africa
deremensis	38	Sato 1942	H	,, ,,
draco Dragon Tree	38	Bowden 1940a	HReT	Canary Is.
terminalis (*spicata*)	38	Sato 1935b	HT	E. Indies
fragrans	$\begin{cases} 38 \\ 42 \end{cases}$	Whitaker 1934a Guard & H. 1941	T	Trop. Africa
cylindrica	39	Sato 1942	H	W. Tr. Africa
thalioides	40	,, ,,	H	Trop. Africa
cannaefolia	c. 114	,, 1935b	T	Australia
congesta (*stricta*)	c. 114	,, ,,	M	Mal., Austr.

SANSEVIERIA $x = 20, 21$

zeylanica Nagaset, Ceylon Bowstring Hemp	$\begin{cases} 40,42 \\ 42 \end{cases}$	M. & S. 1935 E.K.J.*	HT	Ceylon
roxburghiana Indian B. H.	40	Patel & N. 1937	HT	India
metallica	40	Sato 1942	H	*cult*
grandis	100	,, ,,	T	Trop. Africa
cylindrica Ife H.	102–104	Heitz 1926	HT	,, ,,

DORYANTHES $x = 24$

excelsa	48	Sato 1938	H	Australia
guilfoylei	48	,, ,,	H	,,
palmeri	48	,, ,,	H	,,

BESCHORNERIA $x = 30$

tubiflora	60	Sato 1938	H	Mexico

BRAVOA $x = 30$

geminiflora	60	Sato 1942	H	C. Mexico

FURCRAEA (FOURCROYA) $x = 30$

gigantea Mauritius H.	60	M. & S. 1935	HT	C. Amer., W. Ind.
pubescens	60	,, ,,	HT	Mexico
bedinghausii	60	McKelvey & S. '33	H	,,
selloa	60	Devidé unp.	H	Guatemala

HESPEROYUCCA (YUCCA) $x = 30$

whipplei	60	McKelvey & S. '33	H	California

HESPERALOË $x = 30$

parviflora	60	McKelvey & S. '33	H	California

MANFREDA (AGAVE) $x = 30$

virginica	60	McKelvey & S. '33	T	S.E: U.S.A.

394

POLYANTHES (POLIANTHES) $x = 30$

tuberosa	Tuberose	60	Sato 1938	HP	Mex., *cult*

RUNYONIA $x = 30$

longiflora		60	Granick 1944	—	Mexico

SAMUELA $x = 30$

faxoniana	Date Yucca	60	McKelvey & S. '33	H	W. Texas

YUCCA * $x = 30$

alofiolia	Spanish Bayonet	60	Watkins 1936	H	Mex., W. Indies
arkansana	& 4 spp.	60	,, ,,	H	S: C. U.S.A.
australis		60	Snoad 1952	H	Mexico
wrightii		60	M. & S. 1935	—	—
filamentosa	& 6 spp.	60	McKelvey & S. '33	(F)H	S.E: U.S.A.

AGAVE * $x = 30$

amaniensis		60	Doughty 1936	T	*cult*
bouchei	& 4 spp.	60	Vignoli 1936, 1937		C. America
brevispina	& 4 spp.	60	Granick 1944		N.E. Mexico
consociata	& 2 spp.	60	McKelvey & S. 1933	T	California
deserti		60	Lenz 1950		Colo. Desert, Cal.
lespinassei		60	Doughty 1936	—	Yucatan
shawii		60	Lenz 1950		California
vivipara	& 3 spp.	60	Sato 1935, 1942	T	W. Ind., Guatem.
angustifolia	Ketki	{ 60	Doughty 1936	T	W. Indies
		{ 120	Granick 1944		
americana	Century Pl. 60, 120, 180		,, ,,	HT	Mexico, Arizona
v. *albo-marginata*		120, 226	Sato 1935		
candelabrum		*c.* 90	Vignoli 1936	T	Mexico
cantala	Kantala	90	Doughty 1936	T	,,
lurida		*c.* 90	Vignoli 1936	T	,,
zapupe		{ 90	Sato 1942	T	,,
		{ 110	Doughty 1936		
melliflua	& 7 spp.	120	Granick 1944	AT	,,
salmiana		120	Vignoli 1936	T	,,
variegata		120	Sato 1935		C. America
fourcroyoides	Henequen	138	Doughty 1936	T	Yucatan
sisalana	Sisal Hemp	{ 138	,, ,,	T	Mexico
		{ *c.* 149	Granick 1944		
atrovirens		180	Sato 1938	T	,,
ghiesbrechtii		180	Vignoli 1936	T	,,

HOSTA (FUNKIA) $x = 30$ (Apomixis) [from Liliaceae]

lancifolia (*japonica*)		60	Akemine 1935	H	Japan
fortunei		60	Yasui 1935	H	,,
plantaginea	Plantain L.	60	,, ,,	H	Jap., China
sieboldiana		60	,, ,,	H	Japan
venusta		60	,, ,,	—	,,
ventricosa		60	Sato 1942	—	,,
clausa		90	Yasui 1935	—	Korea

395

314 PALMAE

NIPA $x = 8$?
  fruticans   Nipa Palm   16 Radermacher 1925   ASuT   Ceylon, Burma—
                                                             Australia

LICUALA $x = 8, 14$
  grandis (as *Pritchardia*)   16 Venkatasubban '45b   H   New Britain
  peltata   28   „   „   T   India, Burma

WASHINGTONIA (BRAHEA) $x = 18$?
  filifera   Skirt Palm   36 Sato 1952   HSh   S.W: U.S.A.

CHAMAEDOREA $x = 13$?
  sartorii   c. 12 Suessenguth 1920   HT   Mexico
  corallina   c. 26 Söderberg 1919   HT   Venezuela
  elatior (*karwinskyana*)   26 Suessenguth 1920   —   Mexico
  glaucifolia?   26   „   „   HT   „

COLLINIA (CHAMAEDOREA) $x = 13$
  elegans   26 E.K.J.*   H   Mexico

CALAMUS $x = 14$
  caryotoides   28 E.K.J.*   HT   Australia

DIDYMOSPERMA $x = 14$
  porphyrocarpum   28 Gassner 1941   —   India, Malaya

PINANGA $x = 14$
  disticha   28 Gassner 1941   —   India

ZALACCA $x = 14$
  affinis   28 Bosch 1947   —   Malaya

CHRYSALIDOCARPUS (DYPSIS) $x = 14$?, 16?, 18?
  lutescens   ⎰28 Gassner 1941   H   Madagascar
    as *Areca*   ⎱32 Venkatasubban 1945b
  madagascariensis   36   „   „   H   „

ACTINOPHLOEUS (KENTIA, PTYCHOSPERMA) $x = 16$
  angustifolius   32 Rawi, D. 1951   New Guinea
  macarthuri   32 Sato 1946   H   „   „
  sanderianus   32 Venkatasubban 1945b H   „   „

ARECA $x = 16$
  catechu   Betel Nut   32 Sato 1946   DMToW Trop. Asia, *cult*
  triandra (*aliciae*)   ⎰c. 32 E.K.J.*   HV   India, Malaya
                          ⎱32 Rawi, D. 1951

ARECASTRUM (COCOS) $x = 16$
  romanzoffianum Queen P.   32 E.K.J.*, Sato 1946   HV   Trop. S. Amer.

ARENGA $x = 16$
  pinnata   Sugar Palm   ⎧26 E.K.J.*
    (*saccharifera*)   ⎨32 Sato 1946   AStSuVT India, Malaya
                       ⎩32 Venkatasubban 1945b
  engleri   32 Sato 1946   HT   Formosa

ARIKURYROBA (COCOS) $x = 16$
  schizophylla   32 Venkatasubban '45b H   Brazil

396

ATTALEA $x = 16$
  cohune   Cohune Palm   32 Sato 1946   AOT   Honduras
  spectabilis   32 Gassner 1941   Brazil

BUTIA (COCOS) $x = 16$
  bonnetii   32 Sato 1946   H   Brazil
  capitata   Yatay Palm   32   „   „   E.K.J.* H   „

CARYOTA $x = 16$
  urens   Kitul   32 Sato 1946   AHStSuTW Trop. Asia

COCOS $x = 16$
  nucifera   Coconut   { 32 Santos 1928,   ABNOSuTToW
                             { 32 E.K.J.*   Pacific, *cult*

CYRTOSTACHYS $x = 16$
  lakka   Sealing Wax P. 32 Rawi, D. 1951   H   Mal., E. Indies

DICTYOSPERMA $x = 16$
  album   32 Venkatasubban '45b H   Mascarene Is.

ELAEIS $x = 16$
  guineensis Oil Palm   { 32 Sato 1946, E.K.J.* AHMOTV
                            { 32 Venkatasubban '45b   Trop. Africa

EXORRHIZA $x = 16$
  savoryana   32 Sato 1946   —   Bonin Is.

HETEROSPATHE $x = 16$
  elata   32 Venkatasubban '45b H   Philippines

HYOPHORBE $x = 16$
  verschaffeltii Spindle P. 32 Sato 1946   H   Mascarene Is.

JUBAEA $x = 16$
  spectabilis Coquito   32 Sato 1946   HNSuTW Chile

LATANIA $x = 16$
  commersonii (*rubra*)   32 Venkatasubban '45b FHT   Mascarene Is.
  verschaffeltii (*aurea*) 32 Bosch 1947   HW   „   „

NEPHROSPERMA $x = 16$
  van houtteana   32 Venkatasubban '45b H   Seychelles

ONCOSPERMA $x = 16$
  filamentosum Nibung P.   32 Venkatasubban '45b TVW   Malaya

ORBIGYNA $x = 16$
  lydiae   32 Gassner 1941   —   Brazil

RAPHIA $x = 16$
  ruffia   Raffia   32 Sato 1946   HT   E. Afr., Madag.

STEVENSONIA $x = 16$
  borsigiana (*grandiflora*) 32 Rawi, D. 1951   H   Seychelles

27   397

AIPHANES (MARTINEZIA) $x = 16, 18$
caryotaefolia		$\left\{\begin{array}{l}32 \\ 32\end{array}\right.$ Sato 1946 / Venkatasubban '45b	H	S. America
erosa		36 Gassner 1941	—	W. Indies

HOWEA $x = 16, 18$
forsteriana	32 Venkatasubban '45b	H	Lord Howe Is.
belmoreana	36 Sato 1946	H	,, ,,

RHAPIS $x = 16, 18$
excelsa (flabelliformis	$\left\{\begin{array}{l}32 \\ 36 \\ 36\end{array}\right.$ Bosch 1947 / Sato 1946 / Venkatasubban '45b	HTo	S. China
humilis	36 Sato 1946	H	,,

BORASSUS $x = 18$
flabellifer	Palmyra P.	$\left\{\begin{array}{l}36 \\ 36\end{array}\right.$ Venkatasubban '45b / Bosch 1947	AFMSuTVW	India, Mal.

CHAMAEROPS $x = 18$
humilis	Fan P.	36 Sato 1946	HT	W. Medit.

COCCOTHRINAX (THRINAX) $x = 18$
argentea	$\left\{\begin{array}{l}36 \\ 36\end{array}\right.$ Sato 1946 / Venkatasubban '45b	H	San Domingo

COPERNICIA $x = 18$
cerifera	Carnauba Wax P.	36 E.K.J.*	FMOStSuTW	W. Ind., Brazil

EUPRITCHARDIA (PRITCHARDIA) $x = 18$
pacifica	36 Venkatasubban '45b	HT	Fiji
filifera	36 ,, ,,	FH	W: N. America

HYPHAENE $x = 18$
wildbrandi	36 Sato 1946	FT	Trop. Africa

LIVISTONIA $x = 18$
chinensis	Chinese Fan P.	36 Venkatasubban '45b	HT	C. China
v. subglobosa		36 Sato 1946		
rotundifolia		36 Venkatasubban '45b	HSt	Malaya

PHOENIX $x = 18$
canariensis		36 Beal 1937	FTW	Canary Is.
dactylifera	Date Palm	$\left\{\begin{array}{l}28? \\ 36\end{array}\right.$ Doulat 1944 / Beal 1937	AFTW	Persia, cult
humilis (hanceana)		36 ,, ,,	FHT	Ind., Bur., China
paludosa		36 Venkatasubban '45b	HT	Bengal—Cochin.
pusilla (farinifera)		36 Patel & N. 1937	AFStSuT	India, Ceylon
reclinata		36 Beal 1937	AFH T	Trop. Africa
sylvestris		36 ,, ,,	AMSuT	India

SABAL $x = 18$
bermudana	Ber. Palmetto	36 Sato 1946	HT	Bermuda
(blackburniana)				
causiarum	P.R. Hat P.	36 Bowden 1945b	TW	Puerto Rico
minor	Dwarf Palmetto	36 ,, ,,	H	S.E: U.S.A.

SABAL (*cont.*)
palmetto	Cabbage P.	36	Bowden, 1945b	HTVW	S.E : U.S.A.
umbraculifera		36	Venkatasubban '45b	H	Hispaniola

THRINAX $x = 18$
excelsa	36	Venkatasubban '45b	H	Jamaica
morrisii	c. 36	E.K.J.*	H	W. Indies

TRACHYCARPUS (CHAMAEROPS) $x = 18$
fortunei	Windmill P.	36	Sato 1946	HTV	China, Jap., Bur.
(*excelsa*)					

TRITHRINAX $x = 18$
brasiliensis	36	Sato 1946	H	S. Braz., Parag.

CORYPHA $x = 18$
umbraculifera	Talipot P.	36	Olah 1954	T	India, Ceylon

ROYSTONEA (OREODOXA) $x = 18, 19$
oleracea	Cabbage P.	36	Simmonds 1954	V	W. Indies
regia	Cuba Royal P.	{ 36	Venkatasubban '45b	H	,,
		38	Sato 1946		

315 PANDANACEAE

PANDANUS $x = 30, 32$
pacificus	60	Tjio 1948	H	Pacific Is.
pygmaeus	60	,, ,,	H	Madagascar
boninensis	c. 64	Harada 1947	H	Pacific Is.

316 CYCLANTHACEAE

CARLUDOVICA $x = ?$
palmata		18	E.K.J.*	HT	S. America
latifolia		30	Harling 1946	—	W. Indies
insignis	Panama-hat Pl.	32	E.K.J.*	H	W. I., Trop. Amer.

Group V

HAEMODORALES
317–322
H(ST)

BURMANNIALES
323-325
H

ORCHIDALES
326
H

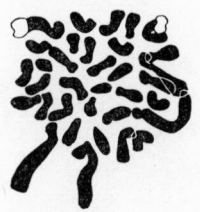

Cephalanthera erecta

317 HAEMODORACEAE

ANIGOZANTHUS $x = 6$
flavidus Kangaroo Paw 12 Stenar 1927 H Australia

318 HYPOXIDACEAE

RHODOHYPOXIS $x = 6$
baueri 12 Sato 1942 H S. Africa

CURCULIGO $x = 9$
recurvata (capitulata) 18 Sato 1938, Tjio 1948 H Tr. Asia, Austr.
sumatrana 18 Tjio 1948 — Trop. Asia
orchioides { 18 Sheriff 1946 HM(R) ,,
{ *c.* 50 Sato 1938
HYPOXIS $x = 11$
pusilla 22 W. D. Jackson unp. — Australia

321 TACCACEAE

TACCA $x = 15$
involucrata 30 Baldwin & S. 1951a — Trop. Africa

326 ORCHIDACEAE

VANDA $x = 9?, 19$
tricolor { 18, 36 Hoffmann 1930
{ 28 Heim 1941 H Java
{ 38 Woodard 1952
coerulea 38 Storey 1953 H Assam, Bur., Siam
hookeriana 38 ,, ,, H Borneo
sanderiana 38 ,, ,, H Philippines
teres 38 ,, ,, H Burma, Siam
  Garden vars. 38, 95 ,, ,, H *cult*

PLEIONE $x = 10$
pricei 20 + 1B La Cour 1952 H Formosa
formosana 40 Miduno 1940 H ,,

SPIRANTHES $x = 10$
sinensis 20 Miduno 1939 H Tr. & Temp. Asia
spiralis 30 Hagerup 1944 H Eur., N. Afr.,
      Asia Minor

CYPRIPEDIUM $x = 10, 11$
acaule 20 Belling 1926 H E: N. America
pubescens 20 ,, ,, HM N. America
reginae (spectabile) 22 Hoffmann 1930 H E: N. America
  as *hirsutum* 20 Humphrey 1934
calceolus Lady's Slipper 22 Francini 1931 H Eurasia
parviflorum 20 Carlson 1945 H N. America

403

DENDROBIUM $x = 10, 19$

nobile	{ 20	Hoffmann 1930	H	Himal., China
	{ 40	Heim 1941		
bronckartii	40	,, ,,	H	Annam
chrysotoxum	40	Hoffmann 1930	H	Burma
infundibulum	40	,, ,,	H	,,
superbum	40	Heim 1941	H	Philippines
thyrsiflorum	40	Hoffmann 1930	H	Burma
wardianum v. giganteum	40	,, ,,	H	,,
monile (catenatum)	38	Miduno 1940	H	China, Japan

EPIPACTIS $x = 10, 16, 18, 19$

helleborine Helleborine	{ 20, 40	Weijer 1952	—	Eur., N. Asia, N.
(latifolia)	{ 38, 40	Hagerup 1947		Africa
shizuoi	32	Miduno 1938	—	Japan
leptochila	36, 40	Hagerup 1947	—	Europe
atrorubens (atropurpurea)	40	,, ,,	—	Eur., N. As., Cauc.
microphylla	40	,, ,,	—	Asia M., Cauc.
palustris	40	,, ,,	—	Eur., N. Afr., T. Asia
confusa (persica)	40	,, ,,	—	Persia
thunbergii	40	Miduno 1938	—	Japan

GOODYERA $x = 11, 14, 15$

procera	{ 22	Afzelius 1943	—	Ind., Mal., China
	{ 42	Miduno 1939		
hachijoensis	28	,, ,,	—	Japan
matsumurana	28	,, ,,	—	Luikiu Is.
macrantha	30	,, ,,	H	Japan
repens	30	Richardson 1935	H	N. Temp.
maximowicziana	42	Miduno 1939	—	Japan

HIMANTOGLOSSUM $x = 12$

hircinum Lizard O.	24, 36	Heusser 1938	—	C. & S. Eur., N. Africa

THELYMITRA $x = 13$

longifolia	26	Hair 1942	—	New Zealand

ONCIDIUM $x = 13, 14$

bicallosum	28	Hoffmann 1930	H	Guatemala
flexuosum	28	,, ,,	H	Brazil
varicosum	56	,, ,,	H	,,
excavatum	52	Heim 1941	H	Peru

PAPHIOPEDILUM * $x = 13, 14, 16, 17, 18, 19$

bellatulum & 13 spp.	26	Duncan 1947	H	Burma
philippinense	26	Duncan & M. 1949b	H	Philippines
concolor	26	,, ,, 1948	H	Burma
hirsutissimum	26, 27–28	Duncan 1947	H	Assam, India
insigne	26, 28	,, ,,	H	Nepal
v. Harefield Hall	39	Mehlquist 1947	H	cult
rothschildianum	26, 28	Duncan 1947	H	Papua
spicerianum	26, 28, 30	,, & M. 1949a	H	Assam
praestans	28	,, 1947	H	Papua
callosum	32	,, ,,	H	Cochin China

404

PAPHIOPEDILUM (*cont.*)

chamberlainianum	32	Duncan & M. 1949c	H	New Guinea
mastersianum	32	,, 1947	H	Malaya
dayanum	34	,, ,,	H	Borneo
tonsum	34	,, ,,	H	Sumatra
wardii	34 + 6–9**B**	,, ,,	H	Up. Burma
curtisii	36	,, ,,	H	Sumatra
glaucophyllum	36	,, ,,	H	Java
javanicum	36	,, ,,	H	Java, Borneo
lawrenceanum	36	,, ,,	H	Borneo
barbatum	38	,, ,,	H	Malacca
superbiens	38	,, ,,	H	,,
venustum	42	,, ,,	H	Nepal
sublaeve	58	,, & M. 1950	H	Borneo, Siam
maudiae	34	McQuade 1949	H	*cult*
Garden forms	26–29, 39–42, 53–56, 70	Duncan 1947	H	,,

CALYPSO *x* = 14

bulbosa	28	Hagerup 1944	H	N. Temp.

HAMMARBYA (MALAXIS) *x* = 14

paludosa	Bog O.	28	Hagerup 1944	—	Eur., Sib., N. Am.

HABENARIA *x* = (7), 14, 21

oldhami		28	Miduno 1940	H	Japan
sagittifera		28	,, 1939	—	Manch., Japan
dilatata	Bog Orchis	42	Humphrey 1934	H	N. America
straminea		42	Harmsen 1943	—	Arctic
dentata (*geniculata*)		62	Miduno 1939	H	India, Burma

MALAXIS *x* = 15?

monophylla	*c.* 30	Hagerup 1944	—	N. Temp.

LIPARIS *x* = 15, 16, 21

krameri	30	Miduno 1939	—	Japan
kumokiri	30	,, ,,	—	Korea, Japan
makinoana	30	,, ,,	—	Japan
loeselii	32	Hagerup 1941b	H	N. Temp.
nervosa	42	Miduno 1940	—	Japan, China

LIMODORUM *x* = 16

abortivum	64	Malvesin-F. & E. '49	—	Europe

STELIS *x* = 16

ciliaris (*atropurpurea*)	32	Hoffmann 1930	H	Mexico
miersii	32	,, ,,	H	Brazil

VANILLA *x* = 16

aromatica		32	Heim 1950	H	Brazil, W. Ind.
fragrans (*planifolia*)	Vanilla	32	,, ,,	HP	W. Indies
hartii		32	,, ,,	—	,,
imperialis		32	,, ,,	H	Trop. Africa
moonii		32	,, ,,	—	Ceylon
papino		32	,, ,,	—	—
pompona	W. Indian V.	32	,, ,,	HP	Trop. America
thartii		32	,, ,,	—	—

BLETILLA (BLETIA) $x = 16, 18$
striata (hyacinthina)	32	Miduno 1954	H	China, Japan
formosana	36	„ „	—	Formosa

CEPHALANTHERA $x = 16, 17, 18$
longifolia	32	Hagerup 1947	—	Eur., N. Afr., W. & N. Asia
damasonium Helleborine	{ 32	„ „	—	Eur., N. Afr.,
(grandiflora)	36	Barber 1942		Cauc.
falcata	34	Miduno 1938	H	Japan

LISTERA $x = 17–21$
ovata Twayblade	{ 34 + 1B	MacMahon 1936		
	34, 36, 38	L. & L. 1944b	—	Eur., Cauc., Sib.
	(17)	Hagerup 1947		
cordata	{ 38	S. & S. 1940	—	N. Temp.
	42	Blackburn, T. 1936		

ANACAMPTIS $x = 18$
pyramidalis	36	Barber 1942	H	Eur., N. Afr., S.W. Asia

ASCOTAINIA (TAINIA) $x = 18$
laxiflora	36	Miduno 1940	H	Liukiu Is.

NEOTTIA $x = 18$
nidus-avis Bird's Nest O.	36	Barber 1942	—	Eur., Cauc., Sib.

OPHRYS $x = 18$
apifera Bee O.	36	Barber 1942	—	Eur., N. Africa
insectifera Fly O.	36	„ „	—	Europe
fuciflora Late Spider O.	36	Heusser 1938	—	C. & S. Eur., S.W. Asia
sphegodes Early S.O.	36	„ „	—	Eur., N. Africa

SARCANTHUS $x = 18$
rostratus	36	Hoffmann 1930	H	China

SERAPHIAS $x = 18$
vomeracea	36	Heusser 1938	—	S. Europe

ORCHIS (incl. DACTYLORCHIS) $x = 16, 18, 19, 20, 21$
papilionacea	32	Heusser 1938	H	S. Europe
morio Green-Winged O.	36	Hagerup 1938	—	Eur., Cauc., Sib.
coriophora	38	Vermeulen 1949	—	Europe
aristata	40	Miduno 1939	—	N.E. Asia
cruenta	40	Vermeulen 1947	H	Europe
foliosa (maderensis)	40	„ „	H	Madeira
fuchsii (maculata) Spotted O.	40	„ „	—	Europe
pallens	40	Heusser 1938	H	„
purpurea Lady O.	{ 40	Heim 1941	H	Eur., Asia Min.,
	42	Vermeulen 1947		Caucasus
sambucina	{ 40	„ 1947	—	Europe
	42	Hagerup 1938		
strictifolia Marsh O.	40	„ „	—	„
as latifolia	40, 80	Maude 1939		
traunsteineri	40, 80, 120, 122	Vermeulen 1947	—	Eur., S.W. Asia

ORCHIS (cont.)

elodes (ericetorum)		79, 80	Maude 1939	—	Eur.—Persia
caucasica		80	S. & S. 1940	—	Caucasus
maculata	Spotted O.	80	Vermuelen 1947	H	N.W. Europe
majalis		80	,, ,,	—	Europe, etc.
munbyana		80	,, ,,	—	N. Africa
purpurella		80	,, ,,	—	N.W. Europe
sesquipedalis		80	,, ,,	—	Spain, Portugal
praetermissa		80, 82	Maude 1939	—	N. Europe
fuchsii × praetermissa		60	J. Heslop-Harrison '53	—	nat. hybrid
fuchsii × purpurella		60	,, ,,	—	,, ,,
				—	
globosa		42	Diannelidis 1949	—	Eur., Asia Min.
laxiflora		42	Vermuelen 1947		Eur., N. Afr., S.W. Asia
mascula	Early Purple O.	42	,, ,,	H	Eur., N. Afr., N. & W. Asia
militaris	Soldier O.	42	,, ,,	H	Eur., As. M., Sib.
palustris		42	Heusser 1938	—	Eur., N. Afr., S.W. Asia
provincialis		42	,, ,,	H	Europe
rotundifolia		42	Humphrey 1932	H	E: N. America
simia	Monkey O.	42	Heusser 1938	—	Eur., N. Afr., Caucasus
spectabilis		42	Humphrey 1932	H	E: N. America
tridentata		42	Heusser 1938	H	S. Europe
ustulata	Dark-Winged O.	42	Vermuelen 1947	—	Eur., Cauc.. Sib.

PLOCOGLOTTIS $x = 19$

javanica		38	Afzelius 1943	H	Java

AERIDES $x = 19, 20$

japonicum		38	Sugiura 1936a	H	Japan
lawrenceae		40	Heim 1941	H	Philippines

ANAGRAECUM $x = 20$

leonis		40	Heim 1941	H	Comoro Is.

BRASSAVOLA $x = 20$

nodosa		40	Kamemoto 1950	H	C. Amer., Brazil
perrinii		40	Afzelius 1943	H	Brazil

CALANTHE * $x = 20$

discolor	& 5 spp.	40	Miduno 1940	H	Japan

CATTLEYA * $x = 20$

aurantiaca	& 14 spp.	40	Kamemoto 1950	H	Cent. America
labiata		40, 41, 42	,, ,,	H	Brazil
bowringiana		41	,, ,,	H	Cent. America
Garden forms	40, 42, 60–62, 80, 83, 84		,, ,, 1952	H	cult

COELOGLOSSUM $x = 20$

viride	Frog O.	40, 80	Afzelius 1943	—	Eur., W. Asia, N. America

COELOGYNE $x = 20$

fimbriata		40	Hoffmann 1930	H	Himalayas

COELOGYNE (*cont.*)
flexuosa	40	Hoffmann 1930	H	Java
fuliginosa	40	,, ,,	H	N. India

CYMBIDIUM * $x = 20$
insigne & 12 spp.	40	Mehlquist 1952	H	Annam
bicolor	40	Swamy 1941	**H**	Ceylon
sinense	40	Sugiura 1936a	H	China
Garden forms	40, 60, 80	Mehlquist 1952	H	*cult*

DENDROCHILUM (PLATYCLINIS) $x = 20$
glumaceum	40	Hoffmann 1930	H	Philippines

ELEORCHIS $x = 20$
conformis	40	Miduno 1939	—	Japan
japonica	40	,, ,,	—	,,

EPIDENDRUM * $x = 20$
atropurpureum & 9 spp.	40	Kamemoto 1950	H	Brazil
ramiferum	40	Hoffmann 1930	H	Mexico
ciliare	40, 80, 160	Geitler 1940a	H	Trop. America
nocturnum	{ 40 { c. 80	Hoffmann 1930 Kamemoto 1950	H	,, ,,
radicans	40, 70	,, ,,	H	Guatemala
xanthium	60	,, ,,	H	Brazil

GONGORA $x = 20$
galeata	40	Hoffmann 1930	H	Mexico

GYMNADENIA $x = 20$
conopsea Fragrant O.	{ 40 { 40, 80	Diannelidis 1949 S. & S. 1940	H	Eur., N. & W. A.
odoratissima	40	Heusser 1938	H	Europe
chidori	42	Miduno 1940	H	Japan

LUISIA $x = 20$
boninensis	40	Miduno 1940	—	Bonin Is.

HERMINIUM $x = 20$
monorchis Musk O.	40	Heusser 1938	—	Eur., Cauc., Temp. Asia

LAELIA $x = 20$
anceps	40	Kamemoto 1950	H	Mexico
purpurata	40	,, ,,	H	Brazil
rubescens	40	,, ,,	H	Mexico
gouldiana	40, 60	,, ,,	H	,,
autumnalis	41, 42	,, ,,	H	,,
albida	42, c. 63	,, ,,	H	Guatemala

LAELIOCATTLEYA $x = 20$
Hybrids	60–63, 80	Kamemoto 1950	H	*cult*

NIGRITELLA $x = 20$ (16?)
nigra	{ 40 { 64	Heusser 1938 Afzelius 1943	H	Eur. Mtns.
rubra	80	Heusser 1938	—	,, ,,

PHALAENOPSIS * $x = 19$
schilleriana & 6 spp.	38	Woodard 1951	H	Philippines
amabilis	38, c. 114	,, ,,	H	*cult*

STANHOPEA $x = 20$				
oculata	40	Afzelius 1943	H	Mexico
insignis	40	Hoffmann 1930	H	Brazil
hernandezii (tigrina)	40	,, ,,	H	Mexico

ZYGOPETALUM $x = 20$				
mackaii	40	Hoffmann 1930	H	Brazil

ACERAS $x = 21$				
anthropophora Man O.	42	Barber 1942	H	Eur., N. Africa

CHAMAEORCHIS $x = 21$				
alpina	42	Heusser 1938	—	Europe

CORALLORHIZA $x = 21$				
innata	42	Miduno 1940	H	Eur., N. Amer.
trifida Coral Root	42	L. & L. 1948		Eur., Sib., N. Am.

LEUCORCHIS $x = 21$				
albida	42	Heusser 1938	—	Eur., W. Sib.

PLATANTHERA (HABENARIA) $x = 21$				
bifolia Lesser Butterfly O.	42	Diannelidis 1949	H	Eur., N. Afr., N. Asia
chlorantha Greater B. O.	42 (21)	Hagerup 1947	H	Eur., Cauc., Sib.
hologlottis	42	Miduno 1940	H	N. China
hyperborea	{ 42	Humphrey 1934	—	N. Temp.
	84	Harmsen 1943		
oligantha	126	Afzelius 1922	—	Dahuria

TRAUNSTEINERA $x = 21$				
globosa	42	Heusser 1938	—	Eur., Asia M.

ZEUXINE $x = 22$				
sulcata	44	Seshagiriah 1941	H	India, Mal.,China

PECTEILIS $x = 24$				
radiata	48	Miduno 1940	H	Japan

ORNITHIDIUM $x = 24$?				
densum	c. 48	Hoffmann 1930	H	Mexico

Group VI

JUNCALES

327–330

H(S)

CYPERALES

331

H

GRAMINALES

332

H(ST)

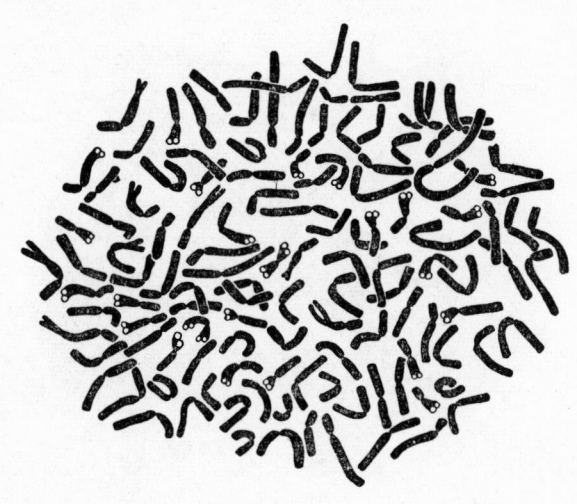

Sieglingia decumbens

327 JUNCACEAE

LUZULA * $x = 3$–36 (Chromosomes polycentric)

purpurea		6	Nordenskiöld 1952	—	Canary Is.
bulbosa	& 8 spp.	12	„ „	—	E: N. America
lactea		12	Malheiros & G. '47	—	Iber. Penin.
nemorosa	& 1 sp.	12	Wagner 1949	—	Eur., W. Asia
campestris	Sweep's Brush	12, 36	Nordenskiöld 1951	—	Cosmop.
comosa		12, 24	„ „	—	W: N. America
henriquesii		12 c. 84	„ „ Fernandes 1950b	—	Portugal
multiflora		12 24, 36, 48	Malheiros & G. '47 Gardé & G. 1952	—	Cosmop.
pallescens		12 36	Nordenskiöld 1951 Wagner 1949		C. & N. Eur.— Japan
spicata	Spiked Woodrush	12, 14, 24	Nordenskiöld 1951		North Reg.
orestra		20, 22	„ „	—	California
alopecurus		24	Wagner 1949	—	S. S. Amer.
forsteri	& 7 spp.	24	Nordenskiöld 1951	—	Eur., W. Asia, N. Africa
wahlenbergii		24 36	„ „ L. & L. 1944a	—	Arctic
frigida		36	Nordenskiöld 1951	—	Scandinavia Mts.
arcuata		36, 42	„ „	—	North Reg.
congesta		36, 48	„ „	—	W. Europe
sudetica		36 48 54	L. & L. 1944a Nordenskiöld 1951 Michalska 1953	—	N. Eur. Mts.
acuminata		48	Nordenskiöld 1951	—	N. America
confusa		48	L. & L. 1948	—	N. & Arctic
johnstonii		42	Nordenskiöld 1951	—	E. Trop. Africa
rufescens		52	„ „	—	Siberia
pilosa	Hairy Woodrush	66 72	„ „ Hagerup 1944	—	North Reg.

OXYCHLOË $x = 8$

andina		16	Sasaki 1937	—	S. America

JUNCUS $x = 10$ (8?)

tenuis (macer)		30 32	L. & L. 1948 Sasaki 1937	T	N. & S. Amer.
trifidus		30	L. & L. 1944a	—	N. Reg., Alpine
acutiflorus		40	Timm & C. 1940	—	Eur., N. Asia, E: N. America
alpinus		40	L. & L. 1944a	—	North Reg.
anceps		40	Wulff 1937a	—	W. & S. Europe
bulbosus (supinus)		40	L. & L. 1944a	—	Eur., W. Asia, N. Africa
castaneus	Chestnut Rush	40	„ 1948	—	North Reg.
conglomeratus		40	„ „	—	Asia M.—Nfld.
effusus	Soft Rush	40	„ 1944a	HT	Cosmop.
emmanuelensis		40	Fernandes et al. '48	—	Europe
inflexus	Hard Rush	40	L. & L. 1948	—	Eurasia, N. Afr.
maritimus	Sea Rush	40	„ 1944a	T	N. & S. Temp.
squarrosus	Heath Rush	40	„ 1948	—	Eur., Arctic
subnodulosus		40	Richards & C. 1941	—	Eur., N. Asia, N. Afr., E: N. Am.
filiformis		40, c. 80	L. & L. 1948	T	N. Reg., Patag.

28   413

JUNCUS (*cont.*)

triglumis		50	L. & L. 1944a	—	North Reg.
articulatus	Jointed R.	{ c. 60 80	Wulff 1937a Timm & C. 1940	T	N. Temp.
acutiflorus × *articulatus*		60	,, ,,	—	nat. hybrid
bufonius Toad Rush	*c.* 60, *c.* 120		Wulff 1937a	T	N. & S. Temp.
prominens	*c.* 64		Sasaki 1937	—	Japan
gerardi (*bottnicus*) Mud Rush	80		Wulff 1937a	T	N. Temp.
nodulosus		80	L. & L. 1948	—	N.W. Eur., N. Am.
arcticus	*c.* 100		,, 1944a	—	North & Arctic

331 CYPERACEAE

BULBOSTYLIS *x* = 5

barbata	10	Tanaka 1941	—	Australia
capillaris	84	,, 1937	T	N. America

FIMBRISYTLIS * *x* = 5, 6, 8, 11

autumnalis		10	Tanaka 1939a	—	N. & S. America
miliacea		10	,, ,,	—	Tropics
sub-bispicata		10	,, ,,	Fo	Trop. Asia
complanata		16	,, ,,	—	Tropics
aestivalis	& 3 spp.	20	,, ,,	—	Trop. Asia, Austr., America
makinoana		24	,, ,,	—	Japan
sericea		44	,, ,,	—	Tr. Asia & Austr.

ELEOCHARIS (HELEOCHARIS) *x* = 5, 8, 9 (Chromosomes polycentric)

parvula		10	Wulff 1937a	—	Eur., N. Amer., Afr., Japan
palustris		{ 10, 16 36 38	Levitsky 1940 Hicks 1929 Håkansson 1954	—	Europe
japonica		20	Tanaka 1937	—	Japan
multicaulis		20	Håkansson 1928	—	Eur., N. Africa
acicularis	Spike Rush	{ 20 *c.* 56?	Tanaka 1937 Hicks 1929	—	N. & S. Temp.
tuberculosa		30?	,, ,,	—	N. America
uniglumis		{ 16, 32 46 *c.* 69, 92	L. & L. 1948 Walters 1949 Hartshorne unp.	—	Eur., W. Asia, N. Africa
quinqueflora		80, *c.* 100	A. Löve 1954	—	N. & Arctic

CAREX * *x* = 6, 7, 8, 9, 10, 13, etc. (Chromosomes polycentric)

siderosticta	12, 24	Tanaka 1940	—	China
divisa	14	Tarnavschi, T. 1950	—	Eur., Him., S. Afr.
bicolor	16	Reese 1953	—	Arctic, Alp.
lasiolepis	16	Tanaka 1939b	—	Japan
grallatoria	18	,, ,,	—	Kiu-Siu Is.
pilulifera	18	Heilborn 1924	—	Eur., N. Asia
oxyandra	18, 20	Tanaka 1949	—	Japan
reinii	26	,, 1939b	—	,,
communis	28	Wahl 1940	—	N. America
ericetorum	30	Heilborn 1939	—	Eur., Cauc., Sib.
novae-angliae	30	Wahl 1940	—	N. America
umbellata	30	,, ,,	—	,, ,,
panicea	32	Heilborn 1939	—	Eur., Temp. Asia

CAREX (*cont.*)

pilosa	32, 57	Okuno 1940	—	Italy
firma	34	Reese 1953	—	Europe
nigromarginata	34	Wahl 1940	—	N. America
conica	34, 38, 42	Okuno 1940	—	Japan
pennsylvanica	36	Wahl 1940	—	N. America
atrofusca	36, 40	L. & L. 1948	—	North Reg.
parciflora	38, 39, 44	Tanaka 1949	—	Japan
parallela	44	L .& L. 1942	—	North Reg.
davalliana	46	Heilborn 1939	—	N. Temp.
tomentosa	48	,, ,,	—	Europe
bushii	{ 48	Wahl 1940	—	N. America
	52	Okuno 1940		
capitata	50	Heilborn 1939	—	Eur., N. Amer.
gracillima	50, 52, 54	Wahl 1940	—	N. America
rariflora	50, 54	L. & L. 1948	—	N. & Arctic
canescens	54, 56	,, 1942	—	Temp.
tenuiflora	58, 62	,, ,,	—	N. Temp.
flava s.l.	60, 68, 70	Davies 1955	—	Eur., Sib.
scirpoidea	{ 64	,, 1948	—	,, ,,
	65	Heilborn 1939		
leporina	66, 68	L. & L. 1942	—	Eur., N. Amer.
podogyna	{ 68, 72	Tanaka 1941	—	Japan
	76	Okuno 1940		
rostrata	{ 76	L. & L. 1944b	—	Eurasia
	82	Wahl 1940		
myabei	90	Okuno 1940	—	Japan
adelostoma	106	L. & L. 1942	—	O.W. Arctic
hirta	112	Heilborn 1939	—	Eur., Temp. Asia
220 spp.	36–112	The same authors and:		

Bøcher 1938a, Clausen *et al.* 1940, Ehrenberg 1945, Harling 1945, Levan & L. 1942, Reese 1952a, 1953, Tanaka 1939c, 1948, Wulff 1939a, Davies 1953b, 1955.

CYPERUS $x = 8, 9$

alternifolius	Umbrella Pl.	32	Tanaka 1937	HT	Madagascar
hakonensis		36	,, ,,	T	Japan
sanguinolentus		48	,, ,,	T	Tropics
fuscus		c. 72	L. & L. 1944b	—	Eur., As., N. Afr.
papyrus	Papyrus Gr.	c. 102	Tanaka 1937	HT	Trop. Africa
esculentus	Tiger Nut,	108?	Hicks 1929	BR	Cosmop.
as *rotunda*	Chufa	108	Tanaka 1937		

CLADIUM $x = 9$

mariscus		36	Pfeiffer 1942	Temp. & Sub-Tr.

SCIRPUS $x = ?$

mucronatus		42	Tanaka 1937	—	Cosmop.
radicans		58	Heilborn 1939	—	,,
sylvaticus	Wood Club R.	64	Ehrenberg 1945	—	N. Temp.
maritimus	{	80	Rodrigues 1953		
		86	Blackburn, T. 1936	T	Cosmop.
		110	Tanaka 1937		

ISOLEPIS (SCIRPUS) $x = 14?$

setacea	28	Scheerer 1940	—	Cosmop.

BLYSMUS (SCIRPUS) $x = 20, 22$
rufus	40	Wulff 1937a	—	N. Eur., Sib.
compressus	44	Håkansson 1928	—	Eur., Temp. Asia

SCHOENOPLECTUS (SCIRPUS) $x = 20, 21$
triquetrus	40	Tanaka 1949	—	Cosmop.
lacustris	38, 40, 42	„ 1938	—	„
tabernaemontani	42	Wulff 1938	—	Eur., Temp. Asia
americanus	c. 80	„ 1937a	—	Amer., S.W. Eur., Australia

TRICHOPHORUM (SCIRPUS) $x = 00$
alpinum (*S. hudsonianus*)	58	Heilborn 1939	—	N. Temp.
caespitosum	104	Scheerer 1940	—	Eur., N. Amer., Himalayas

ELEOGITON (SCIRPUS) $x = 30$
fluitans	60	Scheerer 1940	—	Cosmop.

RHYNCHOSPORA $x = 13$, etc.
alba	White Beak Sedge	{ 26	Scheerer 1940	—	Eur., Siberia
		42	L. & L. 1942		
fusca	Brown B. S.	32	Scheerer 1940	—	Eur., Russia
japonica		62	Tanaka 1941	—	Japan

SCLERIA $x = 14$
tesselata	28	Tanaka 1941	—	Tr. Asia & Austr.

DULICHIUM $x = 16$
arundinaceum	32	Hicks 1929	—	N. America

LIPOCARPHA $x = 23$
microcephala	46	Tanaka 1937	—	E. Asia, Austr.

ELYNA $x = 26$
myosuroides	52–59	Heilborn 1939	—	Azores

ERIOPHORUM $x = 29$, etc.
latifolium		{ c. 54	Scheerer 1940	—	N. Temp. & Arc.
		72	L. & L. 1948		
brachyantherum		58	„ 1944b	—	N. Scand., N. Am.
russeolum		c. 58	„ 1948	—	N. Temp. & Arc.
scheuchzeri		58	„ „	—	„ „
vaginatum	Hare's Tail	58	Tanaka 1949	H	N. Temp.
virginianum		58?	Hicks 1929	—	N. America
angustifolium Cotton Gr. (*polystachyum*)		58, 60	L. & L. 1948	HT	N. Temp., Arctic
gracile		{ 60	Tanaka 1949	—	C. & N. Europe
		76	Hagerup 1944		

KOBRESIA $x = 26, 36$
bellardii	52	Bøcher 1938a	Fo	N. Temp.
simpliciuscula	72	L. & L. 1948	—	N. Reg., Alpine

SCHOENUS $x = 27, 38$
nigricans	54	Rodrigues 1953	—	W. Eur., S. Afr., Amer.
ferrugineus	76	L. & L. 1944b	—	Eur., Russia

KYLLINGA $x = 60$
brevifolia	120	Tanaka 1941	—	Trop. & Subtr.

Order of the Tribes with their Basic Numbers

I	Maydeae: 5, 9 (10)		XIII	Lygeeae: 20
II	Andropogoneae: 5, 9 (10), 11, 12, 14, 17, 19		XIV	Agrosteae: 5, 7
			XV	Phalarideae: 5, 6, 7
III	Paniceae: 7, 9, 10, 12, 15, 17, 19		XVI	Festuceae: 5, 6, 7, 8, 9, 11, 13
IV	Arundinelleae: 9, 10, 12, 14		XVII	Aveneae: 4, 6, 7, 9, 13
V	Eragrosteae: 8, 9, 10, 12		XVIII	Hordeae: 7
VI	Sporoboleae: 8, 9, 10, 12, 14		XIX	Stipeae: 4, 9, 10, 11, 12, 14, 17, 19, 23
VII	Zoisieae: 9, 10			
VIII	Chlorideae: 7, 9, 10		XX	Oryzeae: 12, 15
IX	Pappophoreae: 9, 10		XXI	Arundineae: 12
X	Aristideae: 11, 12, 19		XXII	Centotheceae: 12
XI	Leptureae: 7, 9, 13		XXIII	Bambuseae: 12 (no 2x)
XII	Nardeae: 13			

TRIBE I: MAYDEAE

COIX $x = 5$

aquatica	Bead Coix	10	Mangelsdorf & R. 1939, E.K.J.*	FoTo	Trop. Asia
lacryma-jobi	Job's Tears	20	Mangelsdorf & R. '39		*cult*, Malaya
v. " *adlai* "	Adlay	20	E.K.J.*	FoGH	
v. *mayuen*, v. *stenocarpa*		20	Mangelsdorf & R. '39	FoGTo	
gigantea	Giant Coix	20, 40	E.K.J.*	FoTo	Trop. Asia

CHIONACHNE (POLYTOCA) $x = (5) 10$

koenigii		20	E.K.J.*	Fo	Trop. Asia
as *barbata*		20	Mangelsdorf & R. '39		
semiteres		20	E.K.J.*	Fo	,,

SCLERACHNE $x = (5) 10$

punctata		20	Mangelsdorf & R. '39	Fo	Java

POLYTOCA $x = (5) 10$

macrophylla		40	Avdulov 1931	Fo	New Guinea, etc.
		40	Simmonds 1954		

EUCHLAENA $x = (5) 10$

mexicana	Teosinte	20	Mangelsdorf & R. '39	FoG	Mexico
perennis	Perennial T.	40	,, ,,	Fo	,,

ZEA $x = (5) 10$

mays	Maize	20 + 1–7B	Randolph 1928	GFoOV	Mexico, *cult*
	Indian Corn	20 + 1–7B	Darlington & U. '41 *cf*. Rhoades 1950		
		(10, 40, 80)	Randolph 1932		
		(30)	Beadle 1930		

TRIPSACUM $x = (9) 18$

australe		36	Simmonds 1954	Fo	S. America
floridanum	Florida Gama	36	Longley 1937	Fo	Florida
dactyloides	Eastern G.	36, 72	Mangelsdorf & R. '39	Fo(G)	Tr. & Sub-Tr. Am.
latifolium		72	,, ,,	Fo	C. America

TRIPSACUM (*cont.*)

laxum		72	Mangelsdorf & R. '39	Fo	C. America
pilosum	Guatemala G.	72	„ „	Fo	„

TRIBE II: ANDROPOGONEAE

SORGHUM $x = 5$

brevicallosum		10	Garber 1950	—	N. Australia
intrans		10	„ „	—	„ „
matarankense		10	Garber & S. 1951	—	„ „
purpureo-sericeum		$10 + 1$–6B	{ Janaki Ammal 1940b, Darlington & T. 1941	Fo	Trop. Africa
spp. *deccanense*		10	Garber 1950	Fo	W. India
dimidiatum		10	„ „	Fo	Sudan
stipoideum		10	„ „	—	N. Australia
versicolor		10	„ „	Fo	E. Trop. Africa
arundinaceum	Kamerun G.	20	Longley 1932	Fo	Trop. Africa
australiense		20	Garber & S. 1951	—	N. Australia
cernuum	White Durra	20	Huskins & S. 1934	FoG	*cult*
dochna	Sorgo, Sugar S.	20	„ „	GSu	„
drummondii	Chicken-Corn	20	Karper & C. 1936	Fo	„
durra	Cholam	20	Huskins & S. 1932	GFo	„
effusum	Kamerun G.	20	Karper & C. 1936	Fo	Trop. Africa
hewisonii		20	„ „	Fo	Sudan
leiocladum		20	Garber 1954	—	S.E. Asia, N. Aus.
margaritiferum	Guinea Corn	20	Huskins & S. 1934	FoG	*cult*
melaleucum	Shelsheleih	20	„ „	FoG	Sudan, *cult*
nitidum		20	Garber 1950	—	E. Australia
plumosum		20 (30)	„ 1954	—	N. Australia
roxburghii	Shallu	20	E.K.J.*	FoG	*cult*
stapfii		20	Krishnaswamy & A. 1940	Fo	India
subglabrescens	Milo	20	Huskins & S. 1934	FoG	*cult*
sudanense	Sudan Grass	{ 20 (40)	„ „ Salomon 1940	Fo	N. Africa
verticilliflorum	Wild S. Tabuki	$20 + 1$B	Huskins & S. 1934	Fo	Trop. Africa
virgatum	Tunis Grass	20	„ „	Fo	N. Africa
vulgare	Great Millet	20	Kuwada 1915	FoGSu	*cult*, Abyssinia
halepense	Johnson Gr.	{ 20, 40 40	E.K.J.* Huskins & S. 1934	Fo	Trop. Asia, Medit.
almum		40	Saez & N. 1943	Fo	Argentine
laxiflorum		40	Garber 1950	—	N. Australia
macrospermum		40	„ „	—	„ „
friesii		40	Moffett & H. 1949	—	Trop. Africa
rigidifolium		60	Garber 1950	—	E. Trop. Africa

HYPARRHENIA $x = 10, 15$

aucta		20	Krupko 1953	Fo	S. Africa
edulis		20	Brown 1953	Fo	Sudan
hirta		30, 44 $(3x$–$1)$	Krupko 1953	Fo	Trop. Africa
dissoluta		40	Moffett & H, 1949	FoT	Trop. & Sub-Tr.
newtonii		40	„ „	Fo	Angola

SORGHASTRUM $x = 10$

elliottii		20	Garber 1950	—	S.E: U.S.A.
pellitum		20	Saura 1948a	—	S. America
secundum		20	Garber 1950	—	S.E: U.S.A.
nutans	Indian Grass	{ 20	Saura 1948a	Fo	E. & C: U.S.A.,
		40	Brown 1950		Mexico

CAPILLIPEDIUM (ANDROPOGON) $x = (5)\ 10$

parviflorum	Scented Golden-	20	Church 1940	Fo	O.W. Tropics
(as *A. micranthus*)	beard				

DIECTOMIS $x = (5)\ 10$

fastigiata	20	Moffett & H. 1949	Fo	Tropics

ELYONURUS $x = (5)\ 10$

barbiculmis	20	Brown 1951	Fo	Tex., Ariz., Mex.
tripsacoides	20	,, ,,	Fo	S: U.S.A.—Arg.

MONOCYMBIUM $x = (5)\ 10$

ceresiiforme	20	Moffett & H. 1949	FoT	Trop. Africa

POGONATHERUM $x = (5)\ 10$

paniceum	20	E.K.J.*	H	Trop. Asia

TRACHYPOGON $x = (5)\ 10$

montufari	Crinkle-Awn	20	Brown 1951	—	S.W. U.S.A.-Arg.
capensis		40	de Wet 1954b	FoT	S. Africa

VETIVERIA $x = (5)\ 10$

lawsoni		20	E.K.J.*	T	India
zizanioides	Kus Kus Grass	20	,,	FoHPT	Trop. Asia

AMPHILOPHIS (ANDROPOGON) $x = (5)\ 10$

foulkesii	20	Ramanathan 1950	—	India
pertusa	40	Sampath & R. 1949	—	O.W. Tropics

APLUDA $x = (5)\ 10$

mutica	{ 20	Hunter 1934	Fo	Trop. Asia
	40	Avdulov 1928		

CHRYSOPOGON (ANDROPOGON) $x = (5)\ 10$

aciculatus	Love G.	20	E.K.J.*	FoH	Trop. Asia
montanus		20	,,	Fo	,, ,,
zeylanicus		20	,,	T	India
gryllus		40	Avdulov 1931	Fo	Medit.

SCHIZACHYRIUM $x = (5)\ 10$

glabrescens	20	Moffett & H. 1949	—	Angola
jeffreysii	40	,, ,,	—	Trop. Africa
semiberbe	{ 30	de Wet 1954b		Tr. Afr. & Amer.
	50	Krupko 1953		

CYMBOPOGON $x = (5)\ 10$

excavatus	Turpentine G.	20	de Wet 1954b	—	O.W. Tr. & Subtr.
validus		20	,, ,,	—	S. Africa
caesius		{ 20	E.K.J.*	P	India
		22	Babu 1936		
goeringii		20	Moriya & K. 1949a	—	Tropics

419

CYMBOPOGON (*cont.*)

nardus	Citronella G.	20	Kuwada 1919	HMPSp	Trop. Asia
polyneurus	Camphor G.	20	Babu 1936	P	India
flexuosus	Malabar L.G.	20, 40	,, ,,	MP	,,
coloratus	Myet-Sat	40	,, ,,	P	Burma
martinii	Palmarosa, Ginger G.	40	,, ,,	P	India
citratus	Lemon G.	40, 60	,, ,,	HMP	Trop. Asia
plurinodes		40	de Wet 1954b	Fo	S. Africa

THEMEDA $x = (5)\ 10$

arguens		20	Avdulov 1928	Fo	Malaya—Austr.
triandra (*forskalii*)	Rooi G.	60	,, 1931	Fo	Africa
japonica		80	Tateoka 1954	Fo	Japan

ANDROPOGON $x = (5)\ 10$

agrostoides		20	Saura 1948a	—	Argentine
cirratus	Texas Beard G.	20	Brown 1950	Fo	S.W: U.S.A., Mexico
elliottii		20	Hunter 1934	Fo	E: N. America
eucomus		20	Moffett & H. 1949	—	Tr. & S. Africa
glomeratus		20	Brown 1950	—	S: U.S.A., C. Am.
micranthus		20	Church 1940	—	Trop. Asia, Austr.
monticola		20	Krishnaswamy 1940	—	India
paniculatus		20	Saura 1948a	—	Trop. & Subtrop.
pumilus		20	Krishnaswamy 1940	—	India
virginicus	Broom Sedge	20	Church 1936	Fo	E: U.S.A., C. Am.
amplectens		40	Moffett & H. 1949	Fo	S. Africa
annulatus	Angleton G.	40	Warmke *et al.* 1946	Fɔ	N. Afr., India, Australia
distachyum		40	Saura 1943	Fo	Medit.
gayanus	Gamba	40	Moffett & H. 1949	FoT	Trop. Africa
schinzii		40	,, ,,	—	,, ,,
schirensis		{ 20 / 40 }	de Wet 1954b / Moffett & H. 1949	Fo	Abyssinia
scoparius	Prairie Beard G.	40	Hunter 1934	Fo	U.S.A.
ischaemum		40	Brown 1950	—	Temp. & Tr. O.W.
provincialis		40, 60	Church 1940	Fo	U.S.A.
foveolatus		45	Krishnaswamy 1940	—	Tr. Afr. & Asia
caricosus		50	,, ,,	—	Tr. Asia, Masc. Is.
edwardsianus		60	Gould 1953	Fo	Tex., Arg., Parag.
exaristatus		60	,, ,,	Fo	S: U.S.A.
ternarius		60	Church 1940	Fo	,, ,,
furcatus	Blue Joint T.F.	{ 60 / 70 }	Nielsen 1939 / Church 1929b	Fo	N. America
hallii	Turkey Foot	{ 60, 70 / 60, 100 }	Nielsen 1939 / Brown 1950	Fo	C: U.S.A.
perforatus		120	Gould 1953	Fo	Texas, Mexico
barbinodis		180	,, ,,	Fo	S: U.S.A.—Arg.

HETEROPOGON $x = 10,\ 11$

contortus	Tangle-head, Spear Grass	{ 20 / 60 / 44 }	E.K.J.* / Brown'51, de Wet'54b / Moffett & H. 1949	FoT	Cosmop.
melanocarpus		22	,, ,,	—	Tropics

420

HEMARTHRIA $x = 10$
altissima   20   de Wet 1954b   —   Tropics

MICROSTEGIUM $x = 10$
japonicum   20   Tateoka 1954   —   India, Japan
vimineum v. *polystachyum*   40   Ono & T. 1953   —   „   „

ECCOILOPUS $x = 10$
cotulifer   40   Ono & T. 1953   —   Japan

EUCLASTA (ANDROPOGON) $x = 10$
condylotricha (*piptatherus*)   40   Avdulov 1931   Fo   Tr. Afr. & Amer.

DICHANTHIUM $x = 10$
aristatum   20   de Wet 1954b   Fo   O.W. Tropics
annulatum   Marvel G.   ⎰40   Karper & C. 1936   Fo   N. & Trop. Afr.,
                                ⎱40   E.K.J.*   Trop. Asia
nodosum   40   Oke 1950   —   Trop. Asia
caricosum   40   „   „   Fo   „   „

EREMOPOGON (ANDROPOGON) $x = 10$
foveolatus   ⎰40   Sampath & R. 1949,   Fo   N. Afr., Tr. Asia
                                ⎱40   E.K.J.*

BOTHRIOCHLOA (ANDROPOGON) $x = 10$
glabra   40   de Wet 1954b   Fo   O.W. Tropics
insculpta   60   „   „   Fo   „   „
intermedia   40, 60 Oke 1950   Fo   Tr. Asia & Austr.
saccharoides Silver Beard 60, 120 Gould 1953   Fo   S: U.S.A.—Arg.
                G.

ISCHAEMUM (ANDROPOGON) $x = 10$
arcuatum   20   de Wet 1954b   Fo   S. Africa
guianense   40   Krishnaswamy 1940   Fo   Trop. America
crassipes   56   Moriya & K. 1949a   Fo   China, Japan
anthephoroides   68   Kuwada 1919   Fo   Japan

IMPERATA $x = (5) 10$
cylindrica   Alang Alang   20   Janaki Ammal 1941   FoT   Tr. & Subtr. O.W.
  as *arundinacea*   Blady G.   20   Bremer 1924

ERIANTHUS (SACCHARUM) $x = (5) 10$
ravennae   Plume G. $20 + 0–1B$ Janaki Ammal 1941   HT   Medit., S.W. Asia
pollinioides   30   Li & M. 1951a   —   China
strictus   30   Brown 1951   —   S.E: U.S.A.
elegans   40   Bremer 1924   T   India
arundinaceus   ⎰40, 60 „   1934   HT   India, China
                           ⎱40   Janaki Ammal 1941
formosanus   60   Li & M. 1951a   —   Formosa
sara (*bengalense*)   60   Rümke 1934   T   India, Afghan.

NARENGA (SACCHARUM) $x = 5$
porphyrocoma   30   Janaki Ammal 1941   T   India, Malaya
  as *S. narenga*   30   Bremer 1924

SACCHARUM $x = 10, 12$
arundinaceum   ⎰   40   E.K.J.*   T   India, China
                          ⎱40, 60 Bremer 1934

421

SACCHARUM (*cont.*)

spontaneum	Kans G.	⎧ 54–128 ⎨ 48–80 ⎪ 96, 112 ⎩ 48–128	Singh 1934 Janaki Ammal 1936 Bremer 1936 Moriya 1941	T	Polynesia— Turkestan
officinarum	Sugar Cane	80	Janaki Ammal 1941		
Cult vars. (*off.* × *spont.*, etc.)		⎧ 80–156 ⎨ 70–173 ⎩ 80–136	Bremer 1923 Li & M. 1951a Li & L. 1948	Su	*cult*, E. Indies
robustum		⎧ 42 ⎩ 60–144	„ „ Weller 1939	Su	Mal. & Polyn.
barberi		82–124	Bremer 1931	Su	*cult*, India
sinense		⎧ 118–120 ⎩ 117, 123	„ „ Li & M. 1951a	Su	*cult*, China

SCLEROSTACHYA *x* = 12

fusca	Yekkda	48, 96	Janaki Ammal 1940a	T	India, Burma

MISCANTHUS *x* = 14, 19

sinensis	⎧ 28 ⎨ 38 ⎪ 38 ⎩ 40	Moriya & K. 1949b Leung & L. 1949 Takizawa 1952 Tateoka 1954	—	China, Japan
japonicus	⎧ 38 ⎨ 38 + 3B, 57 ⎩ 36	Leung & L. 1949 Li & M. 1951b Avdulov 1931	HT	E. Asia, Polyn.
transmorrosinensis	38	Leung & L. 1949	—	Formosa
formosanus	38	„ „	—	„
chinensis	42	Church 1929b	HT	E. Asia
saccharifera	64	Hunter 1934	H	„
sacchariflorus	76	Takizawa 1952	—	E. Asia
tinctorius	76, 114	„ „	—	Japan

EREMOCHLOA *x* = 9

ophiuroides	Centipede G.	18	Brown 1950	H	S.E. Asia

ARTHRAXON *x* = 9

langsdorffi (*ciliaris*)	36	Avdulov 1931	Fo	O.W. Tropics
hispidus	36	Tateoka 1954	Fo	Japan

CLEISTACHNE *x* = 9

sorghoides	36	Garber 1950	—	E. Trop. Afr., Ind.

ISEILEMA *x* = 9

laxum	36	Ramanathan 1950	—	India, Ceylon

COELORRACHIS (ROTTBOELLIA) *x* = 9

glandulosa	54	Avdulov 1931	Fo	Trop. Asia

ROTTBOELLIA (MANISURIS) *x* = 9, 10

cylindrica	18	Mangelsdorf & R. '39	Fo	N. America
japonica	18	Moriya & K. 1949a	—	Japan
exaltata	⎧ 20 ⎩ 36	Moffett & H. 1949 Krishnaswamy *et al.* 1954	FoT	Trop. Afr. & Asia

SEHIMA *x* = 17

nervosum	34	Sampath & R. 1949	—	O.W. Tropics

PENNISETUM (PENICILLARIA) $x = 7, 9$

$x = 7$

spicatum	Pearl Millet	14	Avdulov 1931	Fo	Tropics
typhoideum	Spiked	14–17	Li & Li 1943	FoG	Trop. Afr., Asia
(glaucum)	Millet	14 (21)	Krishnaswamy & A.'41		
purpureum	Dry Napier	28	Simmonds 1954		
	Grass	27	Parodi 1946	FoT	Trop. Africa
		28, 56	Krishnaswamy & R. '48b		

$x = 9$

alopecuroides		18	Ono & T. 1953	H	China
alopecurus		18	Hrishi 1952	—	India
hohenackeri		18	,, ,, E.K.J.*	Fo	,,
setaceum (3x)	Fountain Grass	27	,, ,,	FoH	N. Afr., S.W. Asia
clandestinum	Kikuyu G.	36	,, ,,	Fo	E. Africa
latifolium		36	Parodi 1946	—	Argentine
nervosum		36	,, ,,	Fo	Ecuador—Argent.
subangustum		36	Krishnaswamy et al. 1954	Fo	India
orientale		36	Hrishi 1952	Fo	N. Afr.—India
v. triflorum		45	Krishnaswamy 1940		India
villosum	Feathertop	45	,, ,,	FoH	N.E. Trop. Afr.
polystachyon	Mission G.	54	Krishnaswamy & R. 1949	Fo	India
frutescens		63	Parodi 1946	—	Argentine
macrourum		45	Avdulov 1931	Fo	S. Africa
setosum		54	,, ,,	Fo	Trop. America

PANICUM * $x = 7, 9, 10$

$x = 7$

reptans		14	Brown 1950	Fo	Tropics

$x = 9$

antidotale	& 2 spp.	18	Burton 1942	Fo	Trop. Asia
capillare	Witchgrass	18	Avdulov 1928	Fo	N. America
lanuginosum		18	Brown 1948	Fo	S.E: U.S.A., W.I.
scribnerianum	& 50 spp.	18	,, ,, 1951	Fo	N. America
tuberculatum	& 1 sp.	18	Krishnaswamy 1940	Fo	Trop. Asia
anceps		18	Brown 1948	Fo	N. America
		36	Burton 1942		
boscii		18, 36	Brown 1948	Fo	E: U.S.A.
virgatum	Switch	18, 36, 54, 72, 90, 108	Nielsen 1944	Fo	N. & C. Ame
	Grass	21–36	Brown 1948		
amarum		36	,, ,,	Fo	E: U.S.A., W.I.
bisulcatum (acroanthum)		36	Avdulov 1931	Fo	E. Asia
		54	de Wet 1954b		
deustum		36	,, ,,	Fo	S. Africa
fasciculatum	Browntop Millet	36	Burton 1942	Fo	Trop. America
purpurascens	Para Grass	36	,, ,,	Fo	Tro. Afr. (Amer.)
miliaceum	Indian Millet	36	Avdulov 1931	G	cult, India
	Proso M.	(72)	Arenkova 1940	Fo	
miliare	Little M.	36	Rau 1929a	FoG	Trop. Asia
urvilleanum	& 7 spp.	36	Parodi 1946	Fo	Cal., Arg., Chile
verrucosum	& 3 spp.	36	Brown 1948	Fo	E: U.S.A.
texanum	Texas M.	36	,, 1950	Fo	Temp. America
		54	Burton 1942		

PANICUM (*cont.*)

maximum	Guinea Grass	$\left\{\begin{array}{l}18\\36\\32,48\end{array}\right.$	de Wet 1954b E.K.J.* Warmke 1951	FoT	Trop. Africa

esculentum		54, 58	Krishnaswamy 1940	Fo	Japan (*cult*)
fultum		54	Parodi 1946	—	S. America
jubiflorum		54	Burton 1942	—	Australia
psilopodium		54	Ramanathan 1950	—	India
plenum		54	Brown 1951	—	Tex., Ariz., Mex.
bulbosum		$\left\{\begin{array}{l}54,72\\70\end{array}\right.$	„ „ Krishnaswamy 1940	Fo	„ „

x = 10

hians		20	Brown 1951	Fo	S: U.S.A.
milioides		20	Parodi 1946	—	N. America
prionitis		20	„ „	—	Brazil
elephantipes		30	Covas 1949b	—	„
obtusum	Vine-Mesquite	20, 40	Brown 1951	Fo	S: U.S.A., Mex.
geminatum		40	„ „	—	Trop., Sub-trop.
laxum	Woodland G.	40	Warmke *et al.* 1946	Fo	Trop. America
repens		40	Krishnaswamy 1940	FoSb	Sub-tropics
teneriffae		40	„ „	—	Medit., S.W. Asia
" *makarikari* "		44	Moffett & H. 1949	Fo	S. Africa
altissimum		60	Krishnaswamy 1940	—	Guiana

UROCHLOA   *x* = 7, 9, 15

trichopus	14	P. T. Thomas unp.	FoG	Sudan
pullularis	28	Moffett & H. 1949	—	E. Trop. Africa
mosambicensis	42	„ „	—	Mozambique
bolbodes	36	„ „	—	Abyssinia
panicoides	$\left\{\begin{array}{l}36\\30\end{array}\right.$	„ „ de Wet 1954b	Fo	O.W. Tropics
brachyura	30	„ „	Fo	S. Africa

BRACHIARIA   *x* = 7, 9

marlothii		14	P. T. Thomas unp.	—	S. Africa
comata		28	„ „	—	Abyssinia
eruciformis		18	Avdulov 1931, E.K.J.*	Fo	Tr. Afr. & Asia
ciliatissima		36	Brown 1951	Fo	Ark., Texas
decumbens		36	Zerpa 1952	Fo	Trop. America
distachya		36	Krishnaswamy 1940	Fo	Trop. Asia, Austr.
extensa		36	Parodi 1946	—	S.E: U.S.A., W.I.
nigropedata		$\left\{\begin{array}{l}18\\36\end{array}\right.$	de Wet 1954b Moffett & H. 1949	—	S. Africa
paspaloides		36	E.K.J.*	Fo	Trop. Asia
serrata		36	Moffett & H. 1949	Fo	S. Africa
viridula		36	„ „	—	E. & C. Trop. Afr.
dictyoneura		42	„ „	—	Trop. Africa
brizantha	Large-seeded P.	54	„ „	FoH	Trop. & S. Africa

AMPHICARPUM   *x* = 9

purshii	18	Brown 1948	—	E: U.S.A.

ANTHEPHORA   *x* = 9

hermaphroditica	18	Avdulov 1928	Fo	Trop. America
as *elegans*	18	Mimeur 1950		

424

SPINIFEX	$x = 9$				
littoreus		18	E.K.J.*	Sb	India—Malaya
SETARIA	$x = 9, 19$				
flabellata		18	de Wet 1954b	—	S. Africa
italica	Italian Millet	18	Avdulov 1928	G	*cult*, China
longiseta		18	Moffett & H. 1949	Fo	Trop. Africa
viridis	Green Bristle G.	18	Tateoka 1954	Fo	Cosmop.
pallidefusca (*glauca*)	Kavatta G.	18 / 36	Krishnaswamy & A. 1935b / Moffett & H. 1949	FoG	O.W. Tropics
verticillata	Bur B. G.	18 / 36	de Wet 1954b / Avdulov 1931	FoG	Cosmop.
faberi		36	Kishimoto 1938	—	China
intermedia		36	Krishnaswamy & R. 1949	—	Cosmop.
magna	Giant B. G.	36	Brown 1948	Fo	E: U.S.A., W.I.
phragmitoides		36	Moffett & H. 1949	—	Trop. & S. Africa
plicata		36	Avdulov 1928	Fo	Trop. Asia
glauca (*lutescens*)	Yellow B. G.	36 / 72	„ 1931 / Brown 1948	Fo	Eur., Temp. Asia
sphacelata	Rhodesian Tim.	36, 54	Moffett & H. 1949	Fo	Trop. Africa
chevalieri	Buffel Grass	54	„ „	FoT	„ „
palmifolia		54	Krishnaswamy *et al.* 1954	H	India
splendida		63	Moffett & H. 1949	Fo	Trop. & S.E. Afr.
geniculata		72	Brown 1948	—	America
macrostachya		72	„ 1950	—	S.W: U.S.A., Mex.
chondrachne		38	Ono & T. 1953	—	Tropics
TRICHACHNE (PANICUM)		$x = 9$			
californica	Cottontop	18 / 36	Krishnaswamy 1940 / Brown 1951	Fo	S.W: U.S.A., Mex.
insularis	Sourgrass	36	„ „	—	S: U.S.A.—Arg.
patens		72	„ „	—	Texas
ACROCERAS	$x = 9$				
macrum		36	Moffett & H. 1949	—	Trop. & S. Afr.
ALLOTEROPSIS	$x = 9$				
semialata		54	Moffett & H. 1949	—	O.W. Tropics
CHLORIDION	$x = 9$				
cameronii		54	Moffett & H. 1949	—	Trop. Africa
ECHINOCHLOA	$x = 9$				
cruspavonis		36	Parodi 1946	Fo	Trop. & Sub-tr.
crusgalli	Cockspur G.	36 / 42 / 48 / 54	Brown 1948 / Church 1929b / Rau 1929 / Tateoka 1954	FoG	N. Temp.
colona	Jungle Rice	36 / 48 / 54 / 72	Brown 1950 / Krishnaswamy & R. 1949 / de Wet 1954b / E.K.J.*	FoG	Trop. & Sub-tr.

425

ECHINOCHLOA (*cont.*)

frumentacea	Jap. Barny. M.	{ 36	Hunter 1934	FoG	Trop. Asia
		{ 56	Church 1929b		
stagnina		54	Krishnaswamy & R. 1949	AFoG SuT	Tr. Afr. & Asia
pyramidalis	Antelope G.	72	Parodi 1946	FoGT	,,　　,,

ERIOCHLOA $x = 9$

contracta	Prairie Cupgrass	36	Brown 1950	Fo	S: U.S.A.
montevidensis		36	Parodi 1946	—	Argentine
sericea		54	Brown 1951	Fo	Tex., Oklah.
villosa		54	Tateoka 1954	Fo	E. Asia

LASIACIS $x = 9$

divaricata	Tibisee	36	Parodi 1946	Fo	Trop. America

LEPTOLOMA $x = 9$

cognatum	36, 72	Brown 1951	Fo	E. & S: U.S.A.

MELINIS $x = 9$

minutiflora	Molasses G., Efwatakala G.	36	Avdulov 1931	Fo	Tr. Afr. & Amer.
macrochaeta		36	Moffett & H. 1949	—	Trop. Africa

PASPALIDIUM (PANICUM) $x = 9$

paludivagum	36	Burton 1942	Fo	E: U.S.A.
jubiflorum	54	,,　　,,	Fo	Australia

OPLISMENUS $x = 9$

undulatifolius		54	Avdulov 1931	—	S. Eur.—E. Asia
compositus	Basket Grass	72	,,　　,,	H	Tropics
as *burmannii*		72	,,　　,,		
setarius		c. 72	Brown 1948	—	S.E: U.S.A., Tr. America

TRICHOLAENA $x = 9$

monachne	36	de Wet 1954b	Fo	S. Africa

RHYNCHELYTRUM (TRICHOLAENA) $x = 9$

minutiflorum	36	Moffett & H. 1949	—	Trop. Africa
nyassanum	36	,,　　,,	—	Nyasaland
repens (*rosea*) Natal Grass	36	de Wet 1954b	FoH	Trop. Africa
setifolium	36	Moffett & H. 1949	—	S. Africa

SACCIOLEPIS $x = 9$

angusta	18	Tateoka 1954	—	O.W. Tropics
glaucescens	36	Moffett & H. 1949	—	Mashonaland
striata	36	Brown 1948	—	E: U.S.A., W.I.

STENOTAPHRUM $x = 9$

secundatum	St. Augustine G.	{ 18	Brown 1950,		
		{ 18	Warmke *et al.* 1946	H	S.E: U.S.A.
		{ 20!	Brown 1948		

DIGITARIA (PANICUM) $x = 9, 15, 17$

brazzae		18	Moffett & H. 1949	—	Trop. Africa
chinensis		18	Ono & T. 1953	—	China
didactyla	Blue Couch	18	E.K.J.*	Fo	Mauritius, Austr.

DIGITARIA (*cont.*)

eriantha	Woolly Finger-G.	{18 40	Moffett & H. 1949 de Wet 1954b	Fo	S. Africa
gazensis		18	Moffett & H. 1949	—	Gazaland
milanjiana		18	,, ,,	—	Trop. Africa
smutsii		18	Ramanathan 1950	—	Transvaal
swazilandensis		18	Moffett & H. 1949	—	Swaziland
filiformis		36	Brown 1948	Fo	E: U.S.A.
horizontalis		{36 30	Avdulov 1928 P. T. Thomas unp.	Fo	Tropics
ischaemum	Smooth Crabgr.	36	Brown 1948	Fo	Eurasia
sanguinalis	Crabgrass	{34 36–48 54	P. T. Thomas unp. Brown 1948 Covas & S. 1947	FoG	Sub-tropics
pentzii		{36 54	Burton 1942 Moffett & H. 1949	Fo	S. Africa
adusta		72	Parodi 1946	—	Brazil
marginata		72	Ramanathan 1950	Fo	Tr. Asia & Afr.
timorensis		72	E.K.J.*	Fo	Trop. Asia
exilis	Fundi	54	Hunter 1934	FoG	W. Africa
valida		30	de Wet 1954b	Fo	S. Africa
decumbens		30	Burton 1942	Fo	,,
polevansii		34	,, ,,	Fo	,,
longiflora		34	P. T. Thomas unp.	—	Trop. Africa

CENCHRUS $x = 9, 17$

ciliaris (Apo.)		{34 36 32, 36, 40, 54	E.K.J.* Moffett & H. 1949 Fisher *et al.* 1954	Fo	Trop. & S. Africa India
pauciflorus	Field Sandbur	36	Brown 1948	Fo	America
myosuroides		{54 70	,, 1950 Avdulov 1931	SbFo	Trop. America
brownii (*inflexus*)		34	,, ,,	Fo	Austr., Tr. Amer.
echinatus	Hedgehog G.	34	,, ,,	Fo	Trop. America
setigerus (Apo.)	Anjan G.	{34 36	E.K.J.* Fisher *et al.* 1954	Fo	N.E. Tr. Afr.— India
tribuloides	Dune Sandbur	34	Brown 1948	Sb	E: N. & Tr. Am.

OPLISMENOPSIS $x = 10$

najada		20	Parodi 1946	—	Uruguay

LEPTOCORYPHIUM $x = 10$

lanatum		40	Parodi 1946	—	Mexico

AXONOPUS $x = 10$

iridaceus		20	Parodi 1946	—	S. America
furcatus		40	Brown 1950	Fo	E: U.S.A.
compressus	Carpet Grass	{40 *c.* 60	E.K.J.* Parodi 1946	FoH	Trop. America
affinis		80	Brown 1948	Fo	S: U.S.A.

ISACHNE $x = 10$

globosa		60	Tateoka 1954	—	Australia

PASPALUM * $x = 10, 12$

ciliatifolium		20	Burton 1940	Fo	E: U.S.A., W.I.

PASPALUM (*cont.*)

gayanum		20	Saura 1943	Fo	Argentine
haumanii		20	„ 1941	Fo	„
paniculatum		20	Burton 1940	Fo	Tr. Amer. & Afr.
racemosum (*stoloniferum*)		20 + 1–3B	Avdulov & T. 1933	FoH	Peru, Ecuador
rufum		20	Saura 1948a	—	Brazil
supinum		20	Burton 1942	Fo	S.E: U.S.A.
thunbergii		{ 20 { 40	Moriya & K. 1949a Tateoka 1954	—	O.W. Tropics
vaginatum		20	Brown 1948	Fo	N. America
notatum	Bahia G.	20, 40	Saura 1948a	Fo	Trop. America
plicatulum		{ 20 { 40	Brown 1950 Saura 1941	Fo	S.E:U.S.A.—Arg.
praecox		20, 40	Brown 1948	Fo	S.E: U.S.A.
quadrifarium		{ 20 { 30 { 60	Saura 1941 Burton 1942 Krishnaswamy 1940	Fo	Argentine
boscianum	Bull P.	40	Burton 1940	Fo	E: U.S.A.—Brazil
commune	& 11 spp.	40	Saura 1941, '43, '48a	Fo	Argentine
commersonii		40	Moffett & H. 1949	—	O.W. Tropics
conjugatum	Sour G.	40	E.K.J.*	FoH	Tropics
dissectum		40	Brown 1951	Fo	E: U.S.A.
laeve		40	„ 1948	Fo	E: „
lanceolatum		40	Krishnaswamy 1940	—	S. America
longifolium		40	E.K.J.*	Fo	Tr. Asia & Austr.
malacophyllum		40	Burton 1940	Fo	Brazil
pauciciliatum		40	Parodi 1946	—	S. America
scrobiculatum	Koda M.	40	Avdulov 1928	FoG	*cult*, India
setaceum		40	Brown 1948	Fo	E: U.S.A., Mex.
dilatatum	Dallis G. Large Water G.	{ 40 { 50?	Brown 1948 Krishnaswamy 1940	FoH	S. America
distichum	Knotgrass, Water Couch	{ 40 { 48 { 60	Brown 1948 Burton 1942 Parodi 1946	SbFo	Sub-Tropics
langei		{ 40 { 60	Brown 1951 Burton 1942	Fo	S.E: U.S.A., W.I., Venezuela
urvillei	Vasey Grass	{ 40 { 40, 60	Brown 1950 Nielsen 1939	FoTo	S: U.S.A.—Arg.
longipilium		60	Burton 1942	Fo	E: U.S.A.
pubescens		60	Brown 1948	Fo	„
pubiflorum		60	„ 1951	Fo	S.E: U.S.A.,Mex., Cuba
epile		80	Saura 1941	Fo	E: U.S.A., C. Am.
virgatum	Cortadero	80	Avdulov 1931	Fo	S. Tex.—S. Amer.
giganteum		120	Burton 1942	Fo	S.E: U.S.A.
floridanum		120, 160	Brown 1950	Fo	E. & S: U.S.A.
almum	Coomb's Pasp.	24	Burton 1942	Fo	Tex., S. America

TRIBE IV: ARUNDINELLEAE

DANTHONIOPSIS *x* = 9

dinteri	18	de Wet 1954a	—	E. Africa

ARUNDINELLA $x = 10, 14$

setosa		20	Ramanathan 1950	—	Nepal
hirta		$\begin{cases} 28 \\ 56 \end{cases}$	Moriya & K. 1949a Tateoka 1954	—	Japan

TRISTACHYA $x = 10, 12$

welwitschii	40	Moffett & H. 1949	—	Trop. Africa
hispida	· 24	de Wet 1954a	Fo	S. Africa

LOUDETIA $x = 10, 12$

simplex	60	Moffett & H. 1939	FoT	Trop. & S. Afr.
flavida	24	de Wet 1954a	—	S. Africa

TRIBE V: ERAGROSTEAE

TRIODIA (TRIDENS) * $x = 8$

pilosa		$\begin{cases} 16 \\ 16 \end{cases}$	Covas 1945, Brown 1950	Fo	S: U.S.A., Mex.
texana		16	,, ,,	—	Texas, Mexico
elongata	& 4 spp.	32	,, ,,	Fo	S: U.S.A.

ELEUSINE $x = 9$

tristachya		18	Avdulov 1928	Fo	S. America
oligostachya		18	Krishnaswamy 1940	Fo	Brazil
indica	Goose Grass	$\begin{cases} 18 \\ 36 \end{cases}$	Avdulov 1931, E.K.J.* Moffett & H. 1949	FoG	Trop., Sub.-Trop.
lagopoides (*brevifolia*)		36	Krishnaswamy & A. 1935c	Fo	India
coracana Ragi, Finger Mil.		36	Avdulov 1931	ASuFoG	*cult*, Abyssinia
v. *tocussa*		39?	Krishnaswamy 1940		
compressa (*flagellifera*)		45	,, ,,	Fo	W. Asia, Tr. Afr.

AELUROPUS $x = 10$

littoralis	20	Avdulov 1933	Sb	Medit.

TETRACHNE $x = 10$

dregei	20	Moffett & H. 1949	—	S. Africa

TRIRAPHIS $x = 10$

andropogonoides	20	de Wet 1954b	Fo	S. Africa

LEPTOCHLOA $x = 10$

filiformis Red Sprangletop	20	Brown 1950	—	S: U.S.A., Tr.Am.
neesii (*polystachya*)	20	Avdulov 1928	Fo	Australia
obtusiflora	20	E.K.J.*	Fo	E. Afr., India
chinensis	40	Avdulov 1928	Fo	Trop. Asia
virgata	40	Parodi 1946	—	S: U.S.A., Tr. Am.
dubia Sprangletop	60	Brown 1950	Fo	S: U.S.A., Mex., Argentine

ERAGROSTIS * $x = 10$

aspera & 7 spp.	20	Moffett & H. 1949	Fo	Tr. & S. Afr., Ind.
cambessediana	20	Hagerup 1932	—	Trop. Africa
cilianensis Sterile Grass	20	Moffett & H. 1949	FoG	Trop., Sub-Trop.
japonica	20	Avdulov 1928	Fo	Trop. Asia, Austr.
albida	40	Hagerup 1932	Fo	Sudan

29   429

ERAGROSTIS (*cont.*)

bifaria	40	E.K.J.*	Fo	Trop. Asia
brownii	40	,,	Fo	Trop. Asia, Austr.
beyrichii	40	Brown 1950	—	S: U.S.A.
chariis (*gangetica*)	40	E.K.J.*	Fo	Trop. Afr. & Asia
curtipedicellata	40	Brown 1951	—	S: U.S.A.
curvula	{40 50	Nielsen 1939 de Wet 1954b	H	S. Africa
echinochloidea & 7 spp.	40	Moffett & H. 1949	Fo	,,
superba & 3 spp.	40	de Wet 1954b	Fo	S. Africa
pilosa Ind. Love G. & 2 spp.	40	Ono & T. 1953	Fo	Temp.
secundiflora	40	Brown 1950	—	S: U.S.A.
sessilispica	40	Nielsen 1939	—	,,
spectabilis Purp. Lovegrass	{40 42	,, ,, Nielsen & H. 1937	Fo	S: U.S.A., Mex.
spicata	40	Brown 1950	—	Calif., Tex., Arg., Paraguay
capensis	{40 60	Avdulov 1928 Moffett & H. 1949	Fo	S. Africa
tef (*abyssinica*) Teff Grass	40	,, ,,	FoG	*cult*, Abyssinia
barrelieri	60	,, ,,	—	Medit., N. Afr.
mexicana Mex. Lovegrass	60	Avdulov 1928	Fo	Texas, Arizona
habrantha	60, 90	Moffett & H. 1949	Fo	Trop. Africa
linearis (*pallescens*)	80	Hagerup 1932	Fo	W. Africa
ferruginea	80	Tateoka 1954	Fo	Japan

DIPLACHNE $x = 10$

dubia	40	Covas 1949b	Fo	Argentine

CLEISTOGENES (DIPLACHNE) $x = 10$

serotina	40	Avdulov 1931	—	S. Eur.—C. Asia

POGONARTHRIA $x = 10$

squarrosa	{40 40, 42	de Wet 1954b Moffett & H. 1949	—	S. Africa

DACTYLOCTENIUM (ELEUSINE) $x = 10, 12$

aegyptium Crowfoot Gr.	{20 36 48 34?	P. T. Thomas unp. Moffett & H. 1949 Avdulov 1931, E.K.J.*Fo Krishnaswamy & A. 1935c		Trop., Sub-Trop.
scindicum	48	Krishnaswamy & A. 1940	Fo	India

TRIBE VI: SPOROBOLEAE

CRYPSIS (HELEOCHLOA) $x = 8, 9$

aculeata	{16 54	Polyá 1948 Stebbins, Myers 1947	Fo	Europe
schoenoides	36	Avdulov 1931	Fo	Medit., Temp. As.

MUHLENBERGIA $x = 9, 10, 21$

filiformis	18	Stebbins, Myers 1947	—	W: N. America
andina Foxtail Muhly	20	,, ,, ,,	—	,, ,,

430

MUHLENBERGIA (*cont.*)

asperifolia	Scratchgrass	20	Stebbins, Myers, 1947	—	N. Amer., Temp. S. America
lindheimeri		20	Brown 1950	—	Texas
polycaulis		20	„ 1951	—	Tex., Ariz., Mex.
porteri	Bush M.	20	„ „	—	S.W: U.S.A.,Mex.
brachyphylla		40	„ 1950	—	C: U.S.A.
emersleyi	Bullgrass	40	„ „	Fo	Tex., Ariz., Mex.
mexicana	Wire-Stem M.	40	Avdulov 1931	—	E: N. America
monticola	Mesa M.	40	Brown 1951	—	Tex., Ariz., Mex.
racemosa	Marsh Muhly	40	Avdulov 1931	Fo	N. America
reverchoni		40	Brown 1951	—	Texas
rigens	Deer Grass	40	Stebbins & L. 1941	Fo	Tex., Calif., Mex.
squarrosa	Mat M.	40	„ „ „	Fo	N. America
sylvatica (*umbrosa*)		40	Avdulov 1931	Fo	E: N. America
pungens		{ 42	Nielsen & H. 1937	Fo	S: U.S.A.
		{ 60	Nielsen 1939		
repens	Creeping M.	60	Brown 1951	—	Texas, Arizona
hugelii		42	Ono & T. 1953	Fo	Himalayas
japonica		42	„ „	Fo	Japan

SPOROBOLUS $x = 9, 10, 12$
$x = 9$

fimbriatus		18	Moffett & H. 1949	—	S. Africa
virginicus		18	Brown 1950	—	S.E: U.S.A., W.I., Brazil
indicus		{ 18, 36	Avdulov 1931	Fo	Tropics
		{ 24	Warmke *et al.* 1946		
cryptandrus	Sand Dropseed	{ 18	Nielsen 1939	FoG	N. America
		{ 36	Brown 1950		
capensis		{ 18	de Wet 1954b	—	S. Africa
		{ 36	Moffett & H. 1949		
diander		36	Avdulov 1928	Fo	Tr. Asia & Austr.
elongatus		36	Ono & T. 1953	Fo	Australia
neglectus		36	Brown 1950	—	U.S.A.
poiretii	Smut Grass	36	Avdulov 1931	Fo	Trop As. (*intr.* America)
wrightii	Sacaton	36	Brown 1950	Fo	Tex., Calif., Mex.
asper		54, 108	„ „	—	U.S.A.
heterolepis	Prairie Dropseed	72	Nielsen 1939	—	E. & C: U.S.A.
airoides	Alkali D'seed	{ 108	Brown 1951	Fo	W: N. America
	Bunchgrass	{ 126	Stebbins & L. 1941		

$x = 10, 12$

tremulus		20	E.K.J.*	Fo	E. Asia
japonicus		40	Ono & T. 1953	Fo	China, Japan
tenuissimus		40	Hunter 1934	Fo	Tropics
panicoides		24	Moffett & H. 1949	—	Abyssinia
wallichii		24	E.K.J.*	Fo	Trop. Asia
pyramidalis	Rat's Tail G.	24, 30	Moffett & H. 1949	FoGHT	Trop. Africa

LYCURUS $x = 10, 14$

phleoides	Texas Timothy,	{ 28	Brown 1951	Fo	S.W: U.S.A.—
	Wolftail	{ 40	Avdulov 1931		Argentine

TRIBE VII: ZOISIEAE

HILARIA $x = 9$

mutica	Tobosa G.	36	Brown & C. 1951	Fo	Tex., Ariz., Mex.
belangeri	Curly Mes.	36, 72	,, ,,	Fo	,, ,, ,,

TRAGUS $x = 10$

berteronianus	20	Brown 1950	—	Medit.—Afghan.
racemosus	40	de Wet 1954b	Sb	Medit., N. & S. Africa

PEROTIS $x = 10$

patens	40	Moffett & H. 1949	Fo	Natal

ZOYSIA $x = 10$

japonica	Korean Lawn G.	40	Forbes 1952	H	Korea, Japan
matrella	Manila G.	40	,, ,,	HSb	S.E. As., S. Austr.
tenuifolia	Mascarene G.	40	,, ,,	H	S.E. Asia

TRIBE VIII: CHLORIDEAE

BECKMANNIA $x = 7$

erucaeformis	Slough G.	14	Avdulov 1931	Sb	S. Eur., W. Asia
syzigachne	American S. G.	14	Nielsen & H. 1937	FoSb	E. Asia, N. Amer.

BOUTELOUA $x = 7, 10$ (Apomixis)

chondrosioides		14?	Brown 1950	Fo	Tex., Ariz., Mex.
		20	Freter & B. 1955		
filiformis	Slender	14?	Brown 1950	Fo	,, ,, ,,
		20, 21, 22	Snyder & H. 1953		
heterostega		20	,, ,, ,,	Fo	W. Indies
radicosa		20	Freter & B. 1955	Fo	Calif., Mex.
uniflora		20	,, ,, ,,	Fo	Tex., Mex.
rothrockii		22	Fults 1942	Fo	Ariz., Calif., Mex.
breviseta		21	,, ,,	Fo	Texas, Mexico
		28	Brown 1950		
eriopoda	Black Grama	21	Fults 1942	Fo	S.W: U.S.A., Mex.
		28	Brown 1950		
hirsuta	Hairy	21, 37, 42	Fults 1942	Fo	U.S.A., Mexico
	Grama	28	Brown 1951		
trifida		28	,, 1950	Fo	S: U.S.A.
rigidiseta		28	,, ,,	Fo	S.W: U.S.A., Mex.
		35	Fults 1942		
gracilis	Blue	28, 35, 42,	,, ,,	Fo	W. & C: U.S.A., Mexico
	Grama	61, 77			
		20, 40, 60,	Snyder & H. 1953		
		42, 84			
as *oligostachya*		50	Avdulov 1931		
curtipendula	Side-oats	28, 35, 40,	Fults 1942	Fo	U.S.A.—Arg.
	Grama	42, 56, 70			
		85–101	Harlan 1949		
	(sex.)	40, 52	Freter & B. 1955		
	(apo.) 74, 80, 82, 86, 96		,, ,, ,,		
simplex	Mat Grama	40	Covas 1945	Fo	S: U.S.A.—Arg.

SPARTINA $x = 7$

patens	Salt Meadow C.G.	28	Church 1936	Sb	E: N. America
v. *juncea*		42 56	,, 1940		

SPARTINA (cont.)

pectinata	Prairie C. G.	28	Church 1929a	SbT	N. America
as michauxiana		42, 84	„ 1940		
bakeri		42	„ „	Sb	S.E: U.S.A.
caespitosa		42	„ „	Sb	„
cynosuroides	Big Cord G.	42	„ „	Sb	„
gracilis	Alkali C. G.	42	„ „	Sb	W. & C: U.S.A.
leiantha		56	„ „	Sb	California
maritima (stricta)		56	Huskins 1930	Sb	Europe
alterniflora	Smooth C. G.	56	Church 1940	Sb	E: N. America
v. pilosa		70	Huskins 1930		(Eur., intr.)
townsendii	Rice G.	126	„ „	SbT	S. England, cult
(alterniflora × maritima)					

CRASPEDORACHIS x = 9

rhodesiana		27	Moffett & H. 1949	—	Trop. Africa

CYNODON x = 9, 10

bradleyi		18	Hurcombe 1946	—	S. Africa
diploideum	Giant Star G.	18	E.K.J.*	Fo	Trop. Africa
hirsutus		18	Covas 1949b	—	S. Africa
plectostachyum	E. Afr. {	18	Sampath & R. 1949	Fo	E. Africa
	Star G. {	18, 54	Moffett & H. 1949		
dactylon	Bermuda G. {	36	Brown 1950	FoHM	Cosmop.
	{	40	Hurcombe 1947		
transvaalensis	Florida G.	20	„ „	—	S. Africa
magennisii		30	„ „	—	„

DINEBRA x = 10

retroflexa		20	Avdulov 1931	—	Africa—India

TRICHONEURA x = 10

grandiglumis		20	Moffett & H. 1949	—	S. Africa

CHLORIS* x = 10

distichophylla		20	Krishnaswamy 1940	Fo	S. America
virgata	Sweet G. {	20	Moffett & H. 1949	FoH	Tropics
	{	26	P. T. Thomas unp.		
as caudata	{	40	Krishnaswamy 1940		
barbata	{	20	Avdulov 1928	Fo	Tropics
	{	40	E.K.J.*		
gayana	Rhodes G. {	20	Brown 1950	Fo	Trop. & S. Africa
	{ 20, 40		Moffett 1944		
gracilis		30	Krishnaswamy 1940	—	Tropics
pilosa		30	P. T. Thomas unp.	Fo	Sudan
acuminata		40	Avdulov 1928	—	S. America
pycnothrix	{	30	de Wet 1954b	—	Trop. Africa
	{	36	P. T. Thomas unp.		
	{	40	Moffett & H. 1949		
uliginosa		40	Parodi 1946	—	Argentine
cucullata		40	Avdulov 1928	Fo	Tex., New Mex.
truncata	Star G.	40	„ „	Fo	Australia
verticillata	Windmill G.	40	Brown 1950	Fo	C: U.S.A.
	& 3 spp.				
bournei	{	40	E.K.J.*	Fo	India
	{	50	Krishnaswamy 1940		

CHLORIS (*cont.*)

submutica	$\begin{cases} c.\ 65 \\ 80 \end{cases}$	Krishnaswamy 1940 Avdulov 1931	Fo	Mexico

ENTEROPOGON $x = 10$
| *monostachyos* | 20 | Ramanathan 1950 | — | India |

SCHEDONNARDUS $x = 10$
| *paniculatus* Tumblegrass | 30 | Brown 1950 | Fo | C: U.S.A., Arg. |

ASTREBLA $x = 10$
| *lappacea* | 40 | Brown 1950 | — | Australia |

GOUINIA $x = 10$
| *latifolia* | 40 | Parodi 1946 | — | Argentine |

MICROCHLOA $x = 10$
| *kunthii* | 40 | Moffett & H. 1949 | — | Trop. America |

TRICHLORIS $x = 10$
| *mendocina* | 40 | Avdulov 1931 | H | S: U.S.A., S: S. America |
| *pluriflora* | 60 | Brown 1951 | — | S. Tex., Mex., S: S. America |

BUCHLOË $x = ?$
| *dactyloides* Buffalo G. | $\begin{cases} 56 \\ 60 \end{cases}$ | Nielsen 1939
Avdulov 1931 | Fo | Sask.—S. Mex. |

TRIBE IX: PAPPOPHOREAE

ENNEAPOGON $x = 9, 10$
elegans	20	E.K.J.*	Fo	N.E. Afr.—India
wrightii Spike Pappus G.	20	Covas 1945	Fo	S.W: U.S.A., Peru, Bolivia
cenchroides	36	P. T. Thomas unp.	Fo	S. Africa
scoparius	36	de Wet 1954b	Fo	,,

COTTEA $x = 10$
| *pappophoroides* | 20 | Covas 1945 | Fo | S.W: U.S.A.— Argentine |

PAPPOPHORUM $x = 10$
| *bicolor* | 60 (40) | Brown 1950 | — | Tex., Ariz., Mex. |
| *mucronulatum* | 60 | ,,   ,, | Fo | S. Amer., Mex. |

TRIBE X: ARISTIDEAE

ARISTIDA $x = 11, 12, 19$
adscensionis	22	Covas & B. 1945	FoT	Tropics
congesta	22	Moffett & H. 1949	—	S. Africa
macilenta	22	,, ,,	—	,,
mendocina	22	Covas & B. 1945	—	Chile
meridionalis	22	Moffett & H. 1949	—	S.W. Africa
scabrivalvis	22	,, ,,	—	Trop. Africa
spegazzinii	22	Covas & B. 1945	—	Uruguay
submucronata	22	de Wet 1954b	—	S. Africa

434

ARISTIDA (*cont.*)

depressa	44	E.K.J.*	Fo	India
hamulosa	44	Stebbins & L. 1941	Fo	S.W: U.S.A.— Guatemala
leucophaea	44	Moffett & H. 1949	—	Rhodesia
subulata	44	Covas & B. 1945	—	Argentine
barbicollis	24	de Wet 1954b	—	S. Africa
junciformis	24	,, ,,	—	,,
canescens	48	,, ,,	—	,,
rhiniochloa	38	P. T. Thomas unp.	—	Sudan

TRIBE XI: LEPTUREAE

PSILURUS $x = 7$

nardoides	14	Avdulov 1931	—	S. Eur.—Afghan.

PHOLIURUS (LEPTURUS) $x = 7$

pannonicus	14	Avdulov 1931	—	S. Eur., Cauc.

PARAPHOLIS (PHOLIURUS) $x = 7, 9?$

strigosa (*filiformis*)	14	Castro & F. 1946	—	S. Eur., N. Afr.
incurva	c. 32	,, ,,		
	36	Avdulov 1931	Sb	W. Eur., Medit.
	38	Rodrigues 1953		

MONERMA (LEPTURUS) $x = 13$

cylindrica (*subulata*)	26	Avdulov 1931	Fo	Medit.—S. Afr.
	52	Hunter 1934		

TRIBE XII: NARDEAE

NARDUS $x = 13$

stricta	Mat Grass	26	Avdulov 1928	—	Eur., N. As., Cauc.

TRIBE XIII: LYGEEAE

LYGEUM $x = 20$

spartum	Esparto	40	Ramanujam 1938	T	Medit.

TRIBE XIV: AGROSTEAE

APERA $x = 7$

interrupta	14	Maude 1939	—	Europe
spica-venti	14	Avdulov 1931	—	Eur., Siberia

CHAETURUS $x = 7$

fasciculatus	14	Avdulov 1931	—	Spain, Portugal

CORNUCOPIAE $x = 7$

cucullatum	14	Avdulov 1931	—	E. Medit.

GASTRIDIUM $x = 7$

ventricosum	Nit Grass	14	Rutland 1941	Fo	W. Eur., Medit.

435

LAGURUS $x = 7$

ovatus	Hare's-tail G.	14	Avdulov 1931	FoH	W. France, Med., Canary Is.

MIBORA $x = 7$

minima (*verna*)	14	Avdulov 1931	—	W. Eur., Greece, Algeria

PHLEUM $x = 5, 7$

echinatum		10	Ellerström & T. '50	—	S. Europe
arenarium	Sand Timothy	14	Wulff 1937a	Sb	W. Eur., Medit.
hirsutum (*michelii*)		14	Nordenskiöld 1937	—	Eur., Cauc.
subulatum		14	Myers 1941	Fo	N. America
nodosum	Cat's tail	14, 21	Nordenskiöld 1941	Fo	N. Temp.
alpinum	Mountain T.	14, 28	Litardière 1949a	Fo	Arctic, Alpine
commutatum (*alpinum*)		$\begin{cases} 14 \\ 28 \end{cases}$	„ 1948b Nordenskiöld 1941	Fo	„ „
phleoides (*boehmeri*)		$\left.\begin{array}{l} 14 + 0\text{--}4\mathbf{B}, \\ 28 + 0\text{--}2\mathbf{B} \end{array}\right\}$	Bøcher 1950	—	Eur., N. Afr., Sib., Turkestan
paniculatum (*asperum*) Rough T.		28	Avdulov 1928	—	Eur., S.W. Asia
pratense	Timothy	$\left\{\begin{array}{l} 42 \\ (21) \\ (28\text{--}84) \end{array}\right.$	Myers 1944 Levan 1941 „ 1949	Fo	Eur., N. Asia

LIMNODEA $x = 7$

arkansana	14	Brown 1950	—	S.E: U.S.A.

COLEANTHUS $x = 7$

subtilis	14	Litardière 1950	—	Europe

AMMOPHILA (PSAMMA) $x = 7$

arenaria	Marram Grass	28	Westergaard 1941	Sb	W. Europe
breviligulata	Am. Beach G.	28	Church 1929a	Sb	N. America
baltica	Hybrid M. G.	28, 42	Westergaard 1942	Sb	W. Europe

(*A.* *arenaria* × *Calamagrostis epigeios*)

AGROSTIS * $x = 7$

alpina		14	Reese 1952a	—	Europe
biebersteiniana		14	Sokolovskaja 1938	Fo	S. Russia
elegans		14	„ „	Fo	S.W. Eur., N. Afr.
juressi		14	Gardé 1952b	—	Spain, Portugal
nebulosa	Cloud Grass	14	Avdulov 1931	FoH	„ „
reuteri		14	Björkman 1954	—	„ „
salmantica		14	Litardière 1950	—	„ „
setacea	Bristle Bent G.	14	Maude 1940	Fo	W. Europe
truncatula		14	Gardé 1952b	—	Europe
verticillata		14	Brown 1950	—	Temp. O.W.
rupestris		14, 28	Björkman 1954	—	Eur., N. Amer.
trinii		14, 28	Sokolovskaja 1938		
canina	Brown Bent	14, 28, 35, 42, 56	Björkman 1954	H	Temp. Eurasia
castellana		$\left\{\begin{array}{l} 42 \\ 28 + 0\text{--}3\mathbf{B} \end{array}\right.$	Rodrigues 1953 Björkman 1954	—	Spain, N. Afr.
matsumurae		28	Moriya & K. 1949a	—	Japan
mongolica		28	Sokolovskaja 1938	—	Sib., Mong.
rossae		28	Myers 1947	Fo	W: N. America
schraderiana		28	Björkman 1954	—	Alps, Pyrenees
tenuis	Fine Bent	28 (29–41)	Stuckey & B. 1946	FoH	Temp.
stolonifera	Marsh Bent	28, 35, 42 28–46	Björkman 1954 Juhl 1952b	FoH	N. Temp.
as *alba*		33–42	Stuckey & B. 1946		

AGROSTIS (*cont.*)

clavata	& 3 spp.	42	Sokolovskaja 1938	Fo	N. Eurasia
diegoensis	Thin G.	42	Stebbins & L. 1941	Fo	W: N. America
exarata	Spike Redtop	42	,, ,,	Fo	N. America
hallii		42	,, ,,	Fo	California
gigantea	Bl. Bent	42 + 0–4B	Björkman 1954	FoH	North Temp.
hendersoni		42	Stebbins, Beetle '45	Fo	Oregon
nevadensis	.	42 + 2–10B	Björkman 1954	—	Spain
borealis	Arctic Bent	56	,, ,,	Fo	N. & Arctic
lepida		56	Myers 1947	Fo	California
retrofracta		56	,, ,,	Fo	Hawaii, Polyn.

ALOPECURUS * $x = 7$

aequalis	Orange Foxtail	14	Johnsson 1941	Fo	N. Temp.
amurensis		14	Strelkova 1938	Fo	Siberia
bulbosus		14	Maude 1940	Fo	W. Eur., Algeria
gerardi		14	Johnsson 1941	Fo	Eur., S.W. Asia
heleochloides		14	,, ,,	Fo	Chile
myosuroides	Black Twitch	14	Kattermann 1930	—	Eur., Medit., W. Asia
utriculatus		14	Strelkova 1938	Fo	Eur., S.W. Asia
geniculatus	Water F.	28	Avdulov 1928	—	N. Temp.
japonicus		28	Tateoka 1954	—	Japan
ventricosus	& 4 spp.	28	Strelkova 1938	Fo	Eur., N. Asia
pratensis Mead. F.		28 + 0–2B, 42	Johnsson 1941	Fo	N. Temp.
aucheri	& 4 spp.	56	Strelkova 1938	Fo	S.W. Asia
roshevitzianus		70	Avdulov 1931	Fo	Siberia
borealis		98	Strelkova 1938	Fo	N. & Arctic
pseudobrachystachys		98	,, ,,	Fo	Siberia
antarcticus		112–116	Johnsson 1941	Fo	S. America
alpinus	Alpine F. {	119–122 / 112–130	,, ,, / Flovik 1940	Fo	Arctic
glaucus	{	130 / 130	S. & S. 1938, / Johnsson 1941	Fo	C. Asia

POLYPOGON $x = 7$

maritimus		14, 28	Gardé 1952b	—	Medit.
monspeliensis	Annual Beard G.	28	Avdulov 1931	FoH	Medit., Abyss., S Africa
semiverticillatus	Water Bent	28	Bjorkman 1954	Fo	Europe
littoralis		28	Rutland 1941	—	Eur., C. Asia
as *fugax*		42	Avdulov 1931		
lutosus		28, 42	Heiser & W. 1948	—	Europe

CINNA $x = 7$

latifolia	Drooping Woodreed	28	Ehrenberg 1945	Fo	N. Temp.

CALAMAGROSTIS* $x = 7$ (Some high polyploids apomictic)

arundinacea		28	Nygren 1946	Fo	N. Temp.
cainii	& 5 hybrids	28	,, 1954	—	Tennessee
canescens	Small Reed	28	,, 1946	—	Eur., Temp. Asia
koelerioides		28 + 0–2B	,, 1954	—	California
langsdorfii		28	Tateoka 1954	—	N. & E. Asia

437

CALAMAGROSTIS* (*cont.*)

longiseta		28	Ono & T. 1953	—	Japan
montanensis		28	Nygren 1954	Fo	C: N. Amer.
neglecta		28	,, 1946	Fo	N. Temp.
pseudophragmites		28	Ono & T. 1953	—	Eurasia
varia		28	Nygren 1946	Fo	Eur., N. Asia
breweri	Shorthair	28, 42	,, 1954	Fo	California
hakonensis		28, 56	Tateoka 1954	—	Japan
rubescens	Pinegrass	28, 42, 56	Nygren 1954	Fo	W. & C: N. Amer.
epigeios	Bush	⌠28, 42, 56	,, 1946	—	Eur., Temp. Asia
	Grass	⌡ *c.* 70	Avdulov 1931		
inexpansa	N. Reed G.	28, 56, 58, ⌉	Nygren 1954	Fo	Calif., Minn.
		84–105 ⌡			
chalybaea		42	Nygren 1946	—	Norway
canadensis	Bluejoint	42–66	,, 1954	Fo	N. America
purpurascens	Purp. Reed G.	40–57	,, ,,	—	,,
lapponica		42–112	,, 1946	Fo	N. Temp.
purpurea		(28) 56–91	,, 1946, 1949	Fo	N. Eurasia
bolanderi		56	,, 1954	—	California
perplexa		70	,, ,,	—	New York
fernaldii		84	,, ,,	—	Maine
porteri		84, 87	,, ,,	—	E: N. Amer.
crassigluma		140	,, ,,	—	W: N. Amer.

PHIPPSIA $x = 7$

algida	28	Flovik 1940	—	North & Arctic
concinna	28, 29	,, ,,	—	,, ,,

ARCTAGROSTIS $x = ?$

latifolia	62	Flovik 1938	—	Arctic

GARNOTIA $x = 10$

scoparia	20	Ramanathan 1950	—	India

TRIBE XV: PHALARIDEAE

ANTHOXANTHUM $x = 5$

alpinum		10	Östergren 1942	—	Europe
ovatum		10	,, ,,	—	Spain, Mor.
puelii (*aristatum*)		10	Avdulov 1928	—	Medit.
odoratum	Sw. Vernal	10 + 0–4B	Östergren 1947	FoHM	Eur., N. As., Cauc.
	G.	10, 20	,, 1942		N. Africa
japonicum		70	Tateoka 1954	—	Japan
amarum		80	Östergren 1942	—	S.W. Europe

PHALARIS $x = 6, 7$

canariensis	Canary G.	12	Hansen & H. 1953a	G	N. Afr., Can.
brachystachys		⌠12	Parthasarathy 1938	Fo	Medit., S.W. Asia
		⌡14	Miège 1939		
angusta		14	Saura 1943	Fo	Argentine
aquatica		14	Gardé 1952b	—	Europe
lemmoni		14	Parthasarathy 1938	Fo	California
paradoxa		14	Hansen & H. 1953a	Fo	Medit.
caroliniana		14	Brown 1950	—	S: U.S.A.

438

PHALARIS (*cont.*)

coerulescens		{ 14 { 28	Hansen & H. 1953a Miège 1939	Fo	Medit.

arundinacea	Reed Grass	{ 14, 28 { 27–31, 35 { 42	Church 1929b Hansen & H. 1953a Brock unp.	FoH	N. Temp.
californica		28	Stebbins & L. 1941	Fo	California
minor		28, 29	Hansen & H. 1953a	Fo	Medit., N. Asia
tuberosa	Toowoomba C.G.	28	,, ,, ,,	Fo	Medit.

HIEROCHLOË $x = 7$

odorata	Holy Grass	{ 28 { 42 { 28, 56	L. & L. 1948 Tateoka 1954 Church, Myers 1947	FoH	North & Arctic
occidentalis	Calif. Sweet G.	42	,, ,, ,,	Fo	W: U.S.A.
alpina		56	Flovik 1940	Fo	North & Arctic

TRIBE XVI: FESTUCEAE

BRIZA $x = 5, 7$

minor		10	Avdulov 1931	H	S. Eur., Medit.
glomerata		14	Saura 1947	—	Argentine
maxima		14	Kattermann 1933	H	Medit.
media	Quaking Grass	14	Avdulov 1931	FoH	Eur., Temp. Asia
elatior		14 + 1–3B	,, ,,	FoH	S.E. Eur., S.W. As.
stricta		28	Saura 1947	—	Chile
subaristata		28	,, ,,	—	Argentine

CATABROSA $x = 5$

aquatica		20	Avdulov 1931	Fo	N. Temp.

SCHIZACHNE (MELICA) $x = 5$

purpurescens	False Melic	20	Boyle 1944	Fo	N. Am., N.E. As.

DISTICHLIS $x = 5$

spicata	Saltgrass	40	Stebbins & L. 1941	—	America
stricta	Desert Saltgrass	40	,, ,, ,,	Fo	N. America
texana		40	Brown 1951	—	Texas, Mexico

GLYCERIA $x = 5$

alnasteretum		20	Tateoka 1954	Fo	Asia
lithuanica		20	,, ,,	Fo	N. Eur., Cauc.
borealis		20	Church 1949	Fo	N. America
declinata (*cookei*)		20	,, ,,	Fo	W. Europe
elata	Tall Manna G.	20	,, ,,	Fo	W: N. America
grandis	American M.G.	20	,, ,,	Fo	N. America
striata (*nervata*)	Fowl M.G.	20	,, ,,	Fo	,,
acutiflora		{ 20 { 40	Tateoka 1954 Church 1949	Fo	E: N. Amer., N.A. Asia
fluitans	Flote-grass, Manna G.	{ 40 { 40	Löve 1951 Church 1949	FoG	N. Temp.
leptostachya		40	,, ,,	Fo	W: U.S.A.
melicaria		40	,, ,,	Fo	E: N. America
nubigena		40	,, ,,	Fo	Tenn.
obtusa		40	,, ,,	Fo	E: N. America
occidentalis		40	,, ,,	FoG	W: N. America

439

GLYCERIA *(cont.)*

ischyoneura		40	Tateoka 1954	Fo	N. Temp.
hulteniana		40	A. Löve 1954	—	Alaska, Yukon
plicata		40	FitzPatrick 1946	Fo	N. Temp.
septentrionalis	Eastern M.G.	40	Church 1949	Fo	E: N. America
canadensis	Rattlesnake M.G.	60	,, ,,	Fo	,, ,,
maxima	Reed Grass	60	,, ,,	Fo	Eurasia
(aquatica)		c. 60	FitzPatrick 1946		

TORREYOCHLOA (GLYCERIA) $x = 7$

erecta		14	Church 1949	Fo	W: N. America
fernaldii (neogaea)		14	,, ,,	Fo	E: N. America
pallida		14	,, ,,	Fo	,, ,,
pauciflora	Weak M. G.	14	,, ,,	Fo	W: N. America
viridis	(3x)	21	Tateoka 1954	Fo	Japan

SPHENOPUS $x = 6$

divaricatus	12	Avdulov 1931	—	Medit.

BLEPHARIDACHNE $x = 7$

benthamiana	14	Covas 1945	—	Argentine
bigelovii	14	Brown 1950	—	Texas

BOISSIERA $x = 7$

pumilio (bromoides)	14	Avdulov 1931	—	E. Medit.

CATAPODIUM $x = 7$

loliaceum	14	Litardière 1950	—	Medit.
patens	14	,, ,,	—	,,
tenellum	14	,, ,,	—	,,

CUTANDIA $x = 7$

divaricata	14	Litardière 1950	—	Medit.
maritima	14	,, ,,	—	,,
memphitica	14	,, ,,	—	,,

CYNOSURUS $x = 7$

balansae		14	Avdulov 1928	Fo	N. Africa
cristatus	Crested Dogstail	14	,, 1931	FoH	Eur., Cauc., Asia Minor
echinatus	Rough D.	14	,, 1928	—	S. Eur., Medit.

DESMAZERIA $x = 7$

sicula	14	Avdulov 1931	—	N. & S. Africa

LAMARCKIA $x = 7$

aurea	14	Avdulov 1931	—	Europe

DACTYLIS $x = 7$

aschersoniana		14	Müntzing 1937a	Fo	N. Europe
glomerata	Cocksfoot	27–30 / 42 (28–39)	Myers & H. 1940 / Hanson & H. 1953b	Fo	O.W. Temp.

LOLIUM $x = 7$

loliaceum		14	Jenkin & T. 1938	Fo	S.E. Eur., S.W. As.
multiflorum	Italian Rye-Grass	14 / (28)	Peto 1933 / Shalygin 1941	Fo	Eur., Asia M.

440

LOLIUM (*cont.*)

perenne	Perennial Rye-G.	{ 14, (21) (28)	Müntzing 1937c Myers 1939	FoH	Eur., Temp. Asia, N. Africa
persicum		14	Avdulov 1931	Fo	S.W. Asia
remotum	Annual Rye-G.	14	Jenkin & T. 1938	Fo	Eur., Temp. Asia
rigidum		14	„ „	Fo	Eurasia
temulentum	Darnel	14	„ „	—	Temp. O.W.
subulatum		14	Myers 1947	Fo	Europe

SCLEROCHLOA $x = 7$

dura		14	Avdulov 1931	—	Eur., Asia

SCLEROPOA (FESTUCA) $x = 7$

rigida		14	Avdulov 1931	—	W. Eur., Medit.

BROMUS* $x = 7$

arvensis	Field Brome & 3 spp.	14	Cugnac & S. 1941	—	Eur., N. Asia
brizaeformis	Quaking B.	14	Avdulov 1928	FoH	S.W. Asia
ciliatus	Fringed B.	14	Stählin 1929	Fo	N. America
intermedius		14	Avdulov 1928	—	Medit.
japonicus (*abolini*)	Jap. B.	14	Moriya & K. 1949a	Fo	Eur., Asia
kalmii	Wild Chess	14	Stählin 1929	Fo	E. & C: U.S.A.
laevipes	& 2 spp.	14	Stebbins & L. 1941	Fo	W: N. America
porteri		14	Myers 1947	Fo	N. America
remotiflorus		14	Moriya & K. 1949a	—	Japan, W: N. A.
suksdorfii		14	Stebbins & T. 1944	Fo	W: U.S.A.
tectorum	Downy B.	14	Knowles 1944	Fo	Europe
vulgaris		14	Stebbins & T. 1944	Fo	W: N. America
anomalus	Nodding B.	{ 14 28	Elliott 1949 Nielsen & H. 1937	Fo	N. America
arduennensis		{ 14 28	Stählin 1929 Cugnac & S. 1941	Fo	Ardennes
ciliatus	Fringed B.	14, 28	Elliott 1949	Fo	N. America
macrostachys		{ 14 28	Stählin 1929 Litardière 1950	—	Medit.
purgans	Canada Brome	14, 28	Elliott 1949	Fo	N. America
ramosus	Hairy B.	14	Stählin 1929	Fo	Eur., N. Afr., T. Asia
secalinus	Rye Brome	{ 14 28	Nielsen 1939 Knowles 1944	—	Eur., Med., N. As.
commutatus	Smooth B.	{ 14 28 56	Felfoldy 1947a Litardière 1950 Nielsen 1939	Fo	Eur., N. Africa
adoensis		28	Cugnac & S. 1941	—	Abyssinia
albidus (*biebersteinii*)		28	Avdulov 1931	—	S.W. Asia
arenarius	Austr. B.	28	Knowles 1944	Fo	Australia
grossus		28	Cugnac & S. 1941	—	Eur., Med., N. As.
hordeaceus	Soft B.	28	„ „	—	Eur., N. Afr., N. Asia
interruptus		28	Maude 1940	Fo	Britain
lepidus		28	„ „	Fo	Europe
mollis		28	Knowles 1944	Fo	Eurasia
racemosus	Smooth B.	28	„ „	—	„
rubens		28	„ „	Fo	W: U.S.A.

441

BROMUS (*cont.*)

texensis		28	Myers 1947	Fo	Texas, Mexico
catharticus	Rescue Grass	⎰ 28	Moriya & K. 1949a	Fo	N. America
(*unioloides*)		⎱ 42	Stebbins & T. 1944		
madritensis	Wall B.	⎰ 28	Knowles 1944	—	Eur., N. Afr., W.
		⎱ 42	Stählin 1929		Asia
auleticus		42	Elliott 1949	—	Argentine
brevis		42	Covas & S. 1946	—	,,
cappadocicus		42	Stählin 1929	Fo	Asia Minor
macrantherus		42	Cugnac & S. 1941	Fo	Eur., Medit.
sitchensis		42	Stählin 1929	Fo	Sitcha Is.
trinii		42	Knowles 1944	Fo	Chile
uruguayensis		42	Stebbins, Myers '47	—	Uruguay
variegatus		42	Stählin 1929	Fo	Cauc., Medit.
erectus	Upright B.	⎰ 42	,,　　,,	Fo	Eur., Asia M.
v. *eu-erectus*		⎱ 56	Avdulov 1931		
marginatus		⎰ 42	Nielsen & H. 1937	Fo	W: N. America
		⎱ 56	Stebbins & T. 1944		
pumpellianus		⎰ 42	Stählin 1929	Fo	,,　　,,
		⎱ 56	Elliott 1949		
inermis	Smooth B.	28	Knobloch 1953	Fo	Temp. O.W.
		42, 56	,,　　1943		
		56 + 0–11B	Hill & M. 1948		
		56 (28)	Elliott 1949		
		56, 70	Nielsen 1939		
rigidus	Ripgut Grass	42	Cugnac & S. 1941	Fo	Eur., N. Afr.
(*villosus*)		56	Stebbins & L. 1941		
		56, 70	Beck & H. 1932		
breviaristatus		56	Stählin 1929	Fo	W: N. America
carinatus	Calif. B.	56	Stebbins & T. 1944	Fo	,,　　,,
gussonii	Great B.	56	Cugnac & S. 1941	Fo	,,　　,,
maritimus		56	Stebbins & W. 1949	Fo	California
pitensis		56	H. S. Walters 1952	—	Ecuador
riparius		70	Elliott 1949	—	Russia
arizonicus		84	Stebbins *et al.* 1944	Fo	Arizona

FESTUCA $x = 7$ (High Polyploids Apomictic)

amethystina		14	Litardière 1950	FoH	Europe
borderi		14	,,　　,,	—	,,
duriuscula		14	S. & S. 1940	—	Asia
geniculata		14	Avdulov 1931	Fo	Medit.
paniculata		14	Litardière 1950	—	
polesica		14	Bøcher 1947b	—	E. Europe
pratensis	Meadow Fes.	14 + 0–1B	Myers & H. 1947	Fo	Eur., N. Asia
(*elatior*)		14 + 0–16B	Bosemark 1954		
pumila		14	Litardière 1950	—	Europe
rigida		14	Maude 1939	—	Eur., N. Afr.
supina		14	S. & S. 1940		
tatrae		14	Brandberg 1948		
tenuifolia	Sheep's F.	14	Thomas, M. 1939	Fo	Europe
glauca		14, 28	Brandberg 1948	—	,,

442

FESTUCA (cont.)

Species	Common name	Chromosome no.	Author	Code	Distribution
pseudovina		14	Brandberg 1948	—	Europe
		28	Felfoldy 1947a		
altissima (*sylvatica*)	Reed Fescue	14	Litardière 1950	Fo	Eur., Asia
		42	Stählin 1929		
paniculata		14, 28, 42	Litardière 1950		
varia		14, 28, 42	Stählin 1929	—	Eur., Med., A.M.
ovina	Sheep's Fescue	14, 21, 28, 42	L. & L. 1942	FoH	Eurasia
		28, 35	Skalinska 1950a		
		56	Church 1929a		
		70	Turesson 1930		
v. *vivipara*		21, 28, 49	Flovik 1940		
		28, 35	Piotrowicz 1954		
rubra	Red Fescue	14, 28, 42, 56, 70	L. & L. 1942	FoH	N. Temp., Arctic
		28, 42	Brandberg 1948		
		42, 46, 53, 64	Juhl 1952b		
altaica		28	S. & S. 1940	—	Siberia
ciliata		28	Avdulov 1928	Fo	Eur., S.W. Asia
extremiorientalis		28	Ono & T. 1953	—	Korea
elmeri		28	Stebbins & L. 1941	Fo	W: U.S.A.
idahoensis	Bluebunch F.	28	,, ,, ,,	Fo	W: N. America
occidentalis	Western F.	28	,, ,, ,,	Fo	,, ,,
parvigluma		28	Moriya & K. 1949a	—	Japan
subuliflora		28	Maude 1940	Fo	W: N. America
valesiaca		28	Felfoldy 1947b	—	India
viridula		28	Stebbins, Myers '47	Fo	W: U.S.A.
heterophylla		28	Brandberg 1948	Fo	W. Europe
		42	Stählin 1929		
trachyphylla		28, 42	Bøcher 1947b	—	Europe
arundinacea (*elatior*)	Tall Fescue	28	Stählin 1929	Fo	,,
		42 + 0–2B	Myers & H. 1947		
		70	Lewitzky & K. 1927		
arizonica	Pinegrass	42	Brown 1951	Fo	S.W. U.S.A.
coelestis		42	S. & S. 1940	—	Arctic Eurasia
cryophila		42	Flovik 1940	—	,, ,,
fallax	Chewings F.	42	Maude 1940	Fo	Temp.
gigantea	Giant F.	42	Stählin 1929	Fo	Eur., N. As., Afr.
kirilovii		42	S. & S. 1940	—	C. Asia
longifolia	Hard F.	42	Maude 1940	FoH	Europe
sulcata		42	Felfoldy 1947b	—	,,
californica		56	Stebbins & L. 1941	Fo	W: N. America
kingii	Spike F.	56	Boyle 1950	Fo	,, ,,
kryloviana		70	S. & S. 1940	Fo	Pamir
maritima		70	Wulff 1937a	Fo	Medit.

VULPIA (FESTUCA) $x = 7$

Species	Common name	Chromosome no.	Author	Code	Distribution
alopecurus		14	Avdulov 1928	Fo	Medit.
bromoides	Squirrel tail F.	14	Stählin 1929	—	Temp.
geniculata		14	Rodrigues 1953	—	W. Medit.
pyramidata		14	Litardière 1950	—	Europe
myuros	Rat's-tail F.	14, 42	,, 1948d	Fo	Temp.
membranacea		14	,, 1950	Fo	Eur., Medit.
		42	Maude 1940		
ambigua		28	,, ,,	Fo	S.W. Eur., Med.

POA* $x = 7$ (High Polyploids Apomictic)

chaixii	Meadow Grass	14	Avdulov 1931	Fo	Eur., Asia M.
infirma (*exilis*)		14	Nannfeldt 1937	Fo	Medit.
remota		14	L. & L. 1942	—	N. Eur., Cauc.
supina		14	Nannfeldt 1937	Fo	Europe
annua	Annual M. G.	28	Litardière 1938	FoH	Cosmop.
trivialis	Rough-st. M. G.	14, 27, 28	Guinochet 1943	Fo	N. Temp.
alpina Alpine M. G.		{ 14 + 0–8B / 28–74 }	Müntzing 1948 / „ 1940, 1954	Fo	Arctic, Alpine
bulbosa		{ 14 / 28, 45 / 42 + 1B }	Guinochet 1943 / Akerberg 1942 / Hartung 1946	FoH	Temp. O.W.
acroleuca		28	Tateoka 1954	Fo	Japan
badensis		28	Armstrong 1937	Fo	C. Europe
bolanderi		28	Myers 1947	Fo	W: N. America
cuspidata		28	W. L. Brown 1939	Fo	E: U.S.A.
douglasii	& 4 spp.	28	Hartung 1946	Fo	California
iridifolia	& 5 spp.	28	Saura 1943, 1948a	Fo	Argentine
maroccana		28	Nannfeldt 1938	Fo	Morocco
rivulorum		28	„ „	Fo	„
sibirica		28	S. & S. 1938	Fo	Cauc., Siberia
sylvestris		28	W. L. Brown 1939	Fo	E: U.S.A.
violacea		28	Stählin 1929	Fo	S. Europe
wolfii		28	W. L. Brown 1939	Fo	E. & C: U.S.A.
altaica		28, 42	S. & S. 1940	Fo	Altai
cusickii	Bluegrass	{ 28 / 42 }	Stebbins & L. 1941 / Hartung 1946	Fo	W: N. America
palustris	Fowl B.G.	28–30, 42	L. & L. 1942	Fo	N. Temp.
nemoralis Wood M.G.		{ 28–38, 42, 43 / 47–49 / c. 70 }	„ „ / Bøcher & L. 1950 / Kato 1951	FoH	Eur., N. Asia
pratensis Smooth-stalked M.G.,	28, 56, 70		Avdulov 1931	FoH	N. Temp.
	Kentucky Blue G.	49–84 / 36–123 / 38–96	Hartung 1946 / Nissen 1950 / Juhl 1952a		
v. *vivipara*		42 + 4B	Flovik 1940		
v. *eupratensis*		50–124	Akerberg 1942		
sterilis		{ 28 / 42 }	Stählin 1929 / Armstrong 1937	Fo	E. Eur., N. Asia
confinis		42	Hartung 1946		W: N. America
longifolia		43	„ „	—	Caucasus
tibetica		42	S. & S. 1938	Fo	Tibet
laxa		28, 42, 43, 81	L. & L. 1948	Fo	N. Europe
caesia		42	Stählin 1929	Fo	„
arachnifera	Texas Bluegrass	42 / c. 54, 56, c. 63	W. L. Brown 1939 / Hartung 1946	Fo	S: U.S.A.
compressa Canada B. G.		{ 35, 42, 49 / 45, 49, 56 }	Akerberg 1942 / L. & L. 1948	Fo	North Reg.
glauca		{ 42–70 / 63 }	„ 1942 / Bøcher & L. 1950	Fo	N. Temp. & Arct.
herjedalica		47–64	L. & L. 1948	—	Scandinavia
scabrella Skyline B.G.		44+1B–104	Hartung 1946	Fo	W: U.S.A.
glaucifolia		50+0–1B, 56	„ „	Fo	W. & C: N. Amer.

POA (*cont.*)

conferta		56	Armstrong 1937	Fo	N. Europe
nipponica		{ 42	Tateoka 1954	—	Japan
		56	Moriya & K. 1949a		
bonariensis		56	Saura 1948a	—	Argentine
epilis	Skyline B.G. {	56	Armstrong 1937	Fo	W: N. America
		c. 84	Hartung 1946		
arctica	{	56	Flovik 1940		
	72–84, c. 100		L. & L. 1948	Fo	North Reg.
	38, 56, c. 68, 75		Nannfeldt 1940		
ampla	Big Bluegrass	62–100	Hartung 1946	Fo	W: N. America
arida	Plains B.G.	63–103	„ „	Fo	C: U.S.A.
fibrata		63, 64	„ „	—	California
juncifolia	Alkali B.G.	62–84	„ „	Fo	W: N. America
nervosa		62–70	„ „	Fo	„ „
nevadensis		62–70	„ „	Fo	W. & C: U.S.A.
canbyi		72–106	„ „	Fo	N. America
abbreviata		76	Flovik 1940	Fo	Arctic
secunda		74–87	Hartung 1946	Fo	W. & C: N. Am., Chile
gracillima	Slender B.G.	81–86	„ „	Fo	W: N. America
granitica		c. 80	Skalinska 1950a	—	C. Europe
irrigata		82–147	A. Löve 1952	Fo	Arctic
subfastigiata		91–97	Hartung 1946	Fo	Altai

PUCCINELLIA (GLYCERIA) $x = 7$

lemmoni		14	Church 1949	Fo	W: U.S.A.
parishii		14	„ „	Fo	California
vahliana		14	Flovik 1940	Fo	Arctic
distans	{	14	Avdulov 1931		
		28	Pólya 1948	Fo	Temp.
		42	L. & L. 1948		
fasciculata		28	Rutland 1941	Fo	W. Europe
phryganodes	{	28	Flovik 1940	Fo	Arctic
		20	L. & L. 1948		
angustata		42	Flovik 1940	Fo	„
retroflexa		42	L. & L. 1948	—	Europe
rupestris		42	Rutland 1941	—	W. Eur., Syria
paupercula (pumila)		42, 56	Church 1949	Fo	N: N. America
maritima	Sea Poa {	42, 56	„ „	Fo	W. Eur., N. Am., Sakhalin
		63	Maude 1940		
		c. 70	Wulff 1937a		
deschampsioides		56	Bøcher & L. 1950	—	—
laurentiana		56	Church 1949	Fo	N.E: N. Amer.
lucida		56	„ „	Fo	„ „
nuttalliana		56	„ „	Fo	N. America
simplex		56	„ „	Fo	California

SESLERIA $x = 7$

disticha		14	Reese 1953	—	Europe
autumnalis		28	Avdulov 1928	Fo	S. Eur., Asia M.
caerulea		28	Kattermann 1930	Fo	Europe
varia		28	Ujhelyi & F. 1948	—	„
tenuifolia		42	Avdulov 1928	Fo	S. Europe
sadleriana		56	Ujhelyi & F. 1948	—	Hungary

445

ARCTOPHILA $x = 7$
fulva 42 Flovik 1940 — North Reg.

FLUMINEA (SCOLOCHLOA) $x = 7$
festucacea {28 L. & L. 1944b / 42 Church 1949} Fo N. Temp.

PSEUDOBROMUS $x = 7$
africanus 28 de Winter 1951b — E: S. Afr., mtns.

ANTHOCHLOA (NEOSTAPFIA) $x = 7$
colusana 42 Church, Myers 1947 — California

VASEYOCHLOA $x = 7$
multinervosa 56 Brown 1950 — Texas

PLEUROPOGON $x = 7, 8$
californicus 14, 16 Church, Myers 1947 Fo California
davyi 16 ,, ,, ,, — ,,
refractus 16, 32 ,, ,, ,, Fo W: U.S.A.

BRACHYPODIUM $x = 7, 9, 15$
serpentinum 14 K. Jones unp. — Albania
flexum 18 P. T. Thomas unp. — S. Africa
sylvaticum False Brome 18 Ono & T. 1953 — Eur., S.W. Asia
phoenicoides 28 Mimeur 1950 — Medit.
pinnatum Heath F. B. 28 L. & L. 1944b — Eur., N. Afr., N. Asia

distachyon {28 Mimeur 1950 / 30 Avdulov 1931} — Medit.

MUNROA $x = 8$
mendocina 16 Covas 1949b — Chile

MELICA * $x = 9$
altissima 18 Hunter 1934 Fo S. Eur., N. Asia
andina 18 Covas 1945 — S. America
aristata & 5 spp. 18 Stebbins & L. 1941 Fo W: U.S.A.
bulbosa Onion grass & 6 spp. 18 Boyle 1945 Fo W: N. America
magnolii 18 Lorenzo-Andreu 1951 — Eur., N. Africa
minuta 18 Doulat, D. 1951 — S. Eur., Persia
nutans Mountain M. 18 Tateoka 1954 Fo Eur., N. Asia
onoei 18 ,, ,, — Japan
uniflora Wood Melic 18 L. & L. 1944b — Eur., S.W. Asia

ciliata 18, 30 Doulat, D. 1951 FoH Eur., N. Afr., S.W. Asia

amethystina 36 ,, ,, — Medit.
species 36 Melland 1945* Fo Chile

MOLINIA $x = 9$
caerulea Flying Bent, {18, 36 Mattick, T. 1950 / 36, 90 Guinochet & L. 1950} — Eur., N. Asia
Purple Melic

MOLINIOPSIS $x = ?$
japonica 50 Tateoka 1954 — Japan

DUPONTIA $x = 11$
fisheri 44 + 1–3B Flovik 1940 Fo Arctic
v. *psilosantha* 88 + 0–1B ,, ,,

446

ORCUTTIA $x = 12, 13, 16$

californica		24	Church, Myers 1947	Fo	California
greenei		24	,, ,, ,,	—	,,
tenuis		26	,, ,, ,,	—	,,
pilosa		32	,, ,, ,,	—	,,

TRIBE XVII: AVENEAE

AIROPSIS $x = 4$

tenella	8	Litardière 1948c	—	W. Medit.

HOLCUS $x = 4, 7$

gayanus		8	Litardière 1949b	—	Spain, Portugal
lanatus	Yorkshire Fog	14	,, ,,	H	Eur., Temp. Asia
mollis	Creeping Y. F.	14	Stählin 1929	—	Europe
		28	Litardière 1949b		
		28, 35, 42	Beddows & Jones '53		
		49	Jones unp.		

PERIBALLIA $x = 4, 7$

laevis	8	Litardière 1948c	—	Spain, Portugal
involucrata	14	,, ,,	—	Spain

SCHISMUS $x = 6$

calycinus	12	Avdulov 1931	—	Morocco

CORYNEPHORUS (AIRA) $x = 7$

canescens	Grey Hair G.	14	Avdulov 1931	FoH	S. & W. Europe
fasciculatus		14	Gardé 1952b	—	Algeria

GAUDINIA $x = 7$

fragilis	14	Gardé 1952b	—	Medit.

SPHENOPHOLIS $x = 7$

intermedia		14	Nielsen & H. 1937	Fo	N. America
obtusata	Prairie Wedgegrass	14	Brown 1950	Fo	,,

VENTENATA $x = 7$

macra	14	Avdulov 1931	—	Asia M., Mesopot.

AIRA $x = 7$

caryophyllea	Silver Hair G.	14	Wulff 1937b	H	Eur., S.W. Asia, Abyssinia
praecox	Early Hair G.	14	Hagerup 1939	—	Europe
multiculmis		28	,, ,,	Fo	,,

AVENA $x = 7$

brevis	Short Oat	14	Spier 1934	Fo	Europe
		(28)	Dorsey 1939		
bromoides		14	Litardière 1950	—	S.W. Europe
bruhnsiana		14	Emme 1930	—	Caspian
clauda		14	,, ,,	—	Greece, Asia M., N. Africa
decora		14	Litardière 1950	—	Europe
erianthus (*pilosa*)		14	Emme 1930	—	Asia M., Syria, N. Africa
hirtula		14	Shepeleva 1939	—	S. Europe
nudibrevis		14	Stanton 1936	G	,,

447

AVENA (*cont.*)

sedenensis (*montana*)		14	Litardière 1950	—	Alps
sempervirens		14	,, ,,	—	S. Europe
ventricosa		14	Emme 1930	Fo	Algeria
wiestii	Desert Oat	14	,, ,,	Fo	Egypt, Persia
strigosa	Sand Oat	14 (21), 28	Nishiyama 1936	Fo	*cult*, Medit.
abyssinica	Abyss. Oat	28	Spier 1934	GFo	Abyssinia
barbata	Slender Wild O.	28	Huskins 1927	Fo	Medit., Persia
vaviloviana		28	Emme 1930	G	*cult*, Russia
byzantina	Red Oat	42	Huskins 1927	G	Eur., N. Asia
chinensis (*nuda*)	Ch. Naked O.	42	,, ,,	G	*cult*, China
fatua	Wild Oat	42	Philp 1933a	GFoTo	S.W. Asia
ludoviciana	Wild Red Oat	42	Huskins 1927	G	Medit., S.W. Asia
sterilis	Animated Oat	42	Spier 1934	Fo	,, ,,
sativa	Oat	42	Emme 1930	FoG	*cult*, Persia
		(63)	Müntzing 1937c		
planiculmis		*c.* 126	Reese 1953	—	Eur., N. Asia

HELICTOTRICHON (AVENA) $x = 7$

hideoi		14	Tateoka 1954	—	Japan
pubescens	Downy Oat G.	$\begin{cases} 14 \\ 16 \end{cases}$	L. & L. 1948 Kattermann, T. 1936	Fo	Eur., N. Asia
pratense	Meadow Oat G.	$\begin{cases} 14, 28 \\ 42 \end{cases}$	Litardière 1950 Maude 1940	Fo	,, ,,
versicolor		60–62	Kattermann, T. 1936	Fo	S. Europe

ARRHENATHERUM $x = 7$

elatius	Tall Oat G.	28	Avdulov 1931	Fo	Eur., N. Afr., W.
v. *bulbosum*	Onion Couch	28	Rutland 1941		Asia

TRISETUM (AVENA) $x = 7, 12$?

sibiricum		14	Avdulov 1931	Fo	O.W. Arctic
flavescens	Golden Oat G.	$\begin{cases} 24 \\ 28 \end{cases}$	,, ,, Nakajima 1930	Fo	N. Temp.
bifidum		28	Moriya & K. 1949a	—	Japan
projectum		28	Stebbins, Myers 1947	Fo	W: N. America
spicatum		28	Flovik 1938	Fo	Arctic & Alpine
canescens		42	Stebbins & L. 1941	Fo	W: N. America
cernuum		42	Myers 1947	Fo	,, ,,

KOELERIA $x = 7$

glauca		14, 28	Bøcher 1943	Fo	Eur., N. Asia
cristata	June Grass	$\begin{cases} 14 + 2\mathbf{B} \\ 28 \end{cases}$	Tateoka 1954 Stebbins & L. 1941	Fo	Temp. O.W.
gracilis	Slender Hair G.	28, 30	Maude 1940	Fo	Eur., N. Asia
vallesiana		42	,, ,,	Fo	W. Eur., N. Afr.
pyramidata (*cristata*)		70, 84	Bøcher 1943	Fo	S. Europe

DESCHAMPSIA $x = 7, 13$ (High Polyploids Apomictic)

atropurpurea	Mtn. Hair G.	14	L. & L. 1948	Fo	North Reg.
setacea	Marsh Hair G.	14	Hagerup 1939	Fo	W. Europe
arctica		28	,, ,,	Fo	N. Amer., Arctic
bottnica		28	,, ,,	Fo	Temp.
flexuosa	Wavy H. G.	28	Tateoka 1954	FoH	N. Temp.
pumila		$\begin{cases} 28 \\ 39 \end{cases}$	Hagerup 1939 Bøcher & L. 1950	Fo	Arctic

DESCHAMPSIA (*cont.*)

caespitosa	Tufted H. G.	26	Lawrence 1945	Fo	Temp. & Arctic
		28	Hagerup 1939		
danthonioides		26	Myers 1947	Fo	W: N. Am., Chile
elongata	Slender H. G.	26	,, ,,	Fo	N. Temp.
holciformis		26	,, ,,	Fo	W: N. America
		26, 48, 52	L. & L. 1948		
alpina	Alpine H. G.	39, 41, 49	Flovik 1940	—	Arctic
		52	Lawrence 1945		
		56	Hagerup 1939		

DANTHONIA $x = 6, 7$

$x = 6$

curva		12	de Wet 1954a	—	S. Africa
disticha		12	,, ,,	—	,,
auriculata		24	,, ,,	—	Australia
carphoides		24	Myers 1947	—	,,
duttoniana		24	de Wet 1954a	—	E. Australia
forskalii		24	,, ,,	—	Egypt
gracilis		24	Calder 1937	Fo	New Zealand
nigricans		24	,, ,,	Fo	,, ,,
purpurea		24	de Wet 1954a	—	S. Africa
setifolia		24	Calder 1937	Fo	New Zealand
pilosa		24	Myers 1947	Fo	,, ,,
		48	Calder 1937		
semiannularis		24	Myers 1947	Fo	,, ,,
		48	Calder 1937		
australis		36	,, ,,	Fo	,, ,,
californica	Calif. Oat G.	36	de Wet 1954a	Fo	W. & C: N. Amer.
chilensis		36	,, ,,	Fo	Chile
compressa		36	,, ,,	Fo	E: N. America
crassiuscula		36	Calder 1937	Fo	New Zealand
intermedia		36	de Wet 1954a	Fo	W. & C: N. Amer.
oreophila		36	Calder 1937	Fo	New Zealand
spicata		36	de Wet 1954a	Fo	N. America
stricta		36	,, ,,	—	S. Africa
unispicata		36	,, ,,	Fo	W: N. America
bipartita		48	,, ,,	—	Australia
oresigena		48	,, ,,	—	S. Africa
richardsonii		48	,, ,,	—	S.E. Australia
buchanani	Desert D.	*c.* 72	Calder 1937	Fo	New Zealand

$x = 7$

cunninghamii		42	Calder 1937	Fo	New Zealand
ovata		42	,, ,,	Fo	,, ,,
raoulii	Red Tussock	42	,, ,,	Fo	,, ,,

PENTASCHISTIS $x = 7$

thunbergii		14	de Wet 1954a	—	S. Africa

SIEGLINGIA $x = 9$

decumbens	Heath G.	18	L. & L. 1944b	—	Eur., N. Afr., N. Asia
		36	Scheerer 1940		
		124	Maude 1940		

AEGILOPS $x = 7$

(i) *mutica*	14	Kihara 1954	Fo	Asia Minor
(ii) *bicornis*	14	,, ,,	Fo	Egypt, Palest.
longissima (incl. *sharonensis*)	14	,, ,,	Fo	N.E. Egypt, Pal.
speltoides Goat Gr. (incl. *aucheri*)	14	,, ,,	Fo	Asia M., Syria, Palestine
(iii) *comosa* (incl. *heldreichii*)	14	,, ,,	Fo	Asia M., Greece
uniaristata	14	,, ,,	Fo	Balkans
(iv) *caudata*	14	,, ,,	Fo	Asia M., Greece
cylindrica	28	,, ,,	Fo	E. Medit.—Afgh.
(v) *squarrosa*	14	,, ,,	Fo	Transcauc.—Afg.
ventricosa	28	,, ,,	Fo	W. Medit.
crassa	28, 42	,, ,,	Fo	Palest.—Persia
juvenalis (*turcomanica*)	42	,, ,,	Fo	Transcasp.
(vi) *umbellulata*	14	,, ,,	Fo	Asia M., Cauc.
biuncialis	28	,, ,,	Fo	E. Medit.—Casp.
columnaris	28	,, ,,	Fo	Asia Minor
ovata	28	,, ,,	Fo	S. Eur., N. Afr., S.W. Asia
triuncialis (incl. *persica*)	28	,, ,,	Fo	S. Eur., Medit.— Persia
variabilis (incl. *kotschyi*)	28	,, ,,	Fo	E. Medit.—Casp.
triaristata	28, 42	,, ,,	Fo	S. Eur., Medit.— Casp.

HAYNALDIA $x = 7$

villosa	14	Kostoff 1936	Fo	Eur., S.W. Asia

SECALE $x = 7$

ancestrale		14	Kostoff 1937	G	Anatolia
vavilovii		14	,, ,,	G	Armenia
kuprijanovii		14	Nakajima 1954	G	Caucasus
africanum	African Rye	14 / 14 + 1B	Gouws 1950 / Emme 1928	Fo	N. Africa
fragile	Hungarian R.	14 + 1–2B	,, ,,	G	S.E. Eur., N. Asi
montanum	Wild Rye	14 + 1–2B	,, ,,	Fo	Medit.—C. Asia
cereale	Rye	14 + 0–8B / (7) (21) / (28)	Müntzing 1943a / ,, 1937b, c / ,, 1951	G	*cult*, Persia

ELYMUS* $x = 7$

caput-medusae		14	Griffee 1927	Fo	Europe
junceus		14	Brown 1948	Fo	Kasakstan
akmolinensis		28	Litardière 1947	—	N. Asia
angustus		28	,, ,,	—	Siberia
canadensis	& 6 spp.	28	Brown 1948, 1950	GFo	N. America
glaucus	Blue Wild Rye	28	Stebbins & L. 1941	Fo	W: N. America
mollis	Amer. Dune G.	28	Suzuka 1950a	GSb	N.E. Asia, N. Am.
sibiricus		28	Avdulov 1928	Fo	N. Asia
villosus		28	Nielsen & H. 1937	Fo	E. & C: U.S.A.
virescens		28	Hartung 1946	Fo	W: N. America
dahuricus		28 / 42	Brown 1948 / Avdulov 1928	Fo	N. Asia
triticoides	Alkali Rye G.	28, 42	Stebbins & L. 1941	Fo	W: N. America
cinereus	Giant W. R.	28, 56	,, ,, ,,	Fo	N. America

ELYMUS (*cont.*)

giganteus		{ 28 { 56	Avdulov 1931 Brown 1948	Fo	Siberia
erianthus		42	Schnack & C. 1947	—	Chile
patagonicus		42	Hunziker 1955	Fo	S.W. Argentine
arenarius	Sea Lyme G.	56	S. & S. 1938	FoSbSu	Europe

HORDELYMUS $x = 7$

europaeus	Wood Barley	28	Wulff 1939b	Fo	Eur., Caucasus
(*El. eur., Hord. sylvaticum*)					

HORDEUM $x = 7$

agriocrithon		14	Aberg 1938	—	Tibet
californicum (*nodosum*)		14	Stebbins & L. 1941	—	California
comosum		14	Covas 1949a	—	Chile
chilense		14	Perak 1943	—	,,
compressum		14	Covas 1950a	—	Argentine
distichum	Two-Rowed B.	14	Kagawa 1929	G	*cult*
euclaston		14	Andres 1941	—	N. America
nudiramulosum		14	Ghimpu 1929a	—	*cult*
pavisi		14	Litardière 1926	—	France
pubiflorum		14	Covas 1952	—	S: S. America
spontaneum	Wild Sprat B.	14	Aase & P. 1926	Fo	S.W. Asia
stebbinsii		14	Covas 1949a	—	Medit., N. & S. America
stenostachys		14	,, 1950a	—	?
thyrosoideum		14	Ghimpu 1929a	—	*cult*
bulbosum		14, 28	Lein 1948	Fo	Medit.
hystrix		{ 14 { 28	Covas 1949a Chin 1941	Fo	,,
jubatum	Foxtail B.	{ 14 { 28	Tanzi 1925 Aase & P. 1926	—	N. & S. Amer.
marinum	Sea Barley	{ 14 { 28	Wulff 1937a Castro & F. 1946	—	Eur., S.W. Asia
murinum	Wall B.	{ 14 { 28	Stolze 1925 Aase & P. 1926	—	Eur., N. Afr., S.W. Asia
pusillum	Wild Barley	{ 14 { 28	Kihara 1924 Stählin 1929	Fo	N. & S. Amer.
vulgare	Barley	{ 14 { (28)	Kihara 1924 Karpechenko 1938	AG	*cult*, Abyssinia
nodosum	Meadow B.	{ 14, 28 { 42	Chin 1941 Griffee 1927	Fo	N. Temp.
brachyantherum (*nodosum*)		28	Covas 1952	Fo	W: N. America
canadense		28	Stählin 1929	—	*cult*
depressum		28	Covas 1949a	—	W: N. America
gussoneanum		28	Chin 1941	Fo	Sicily
leporinum		28	Covas 1952	—	Eur., N. Amer.
lechleri		42	Covas 1951	—	S. America
hexaploidum		42	,, ,,	—	Argentine
parodii		42	,, ,,	—	Patagonia

TRITICUM $x = 7$

aegilopoides	Wild Small S.W.	14	Darlington 1931c	—	Asia Minor
monococcum	Small Spelt W.	{ 14 { (7) { (28)	,, ,, Smith 1946 Dorsey 1939	G	*cult*, relic

451

TRITICUM (*cont.*)

armeniacum		28	Makushina 1938	—	Armenia
dicoccoides	Wild Emmer	28	Sachs 1953a	—	Syria
dicoccum	Emmer	28	Darlington 1931c	G	*cult*, relic
durum	Macaroni W.	28	Kihara 1936a	G	*cult*, N. Africa
		(56)	Dorsey 1936		
turanicum	Khorasan W.	28	Sachs 1953a	G	*cult*, Persia
(*orientale*)					
persicum (*carthlicum*)		28	,, ,,	G	,, ,,
polonicum	Polish W.	28	,, ,,	G	*cult*, Medit.
		(56)	Dorsey 1936		
pyramidale	Cone Wheat	28	Lilienfeld & K. '34	G	*cult*, Egypt
timopheevi		28	Sachs 1953a	G	*cult*, Persia
turgidum	Rivet W.	28	Darlington 1931c	G	*cult*, Medit.
compactum	Club W.	42	Sachs 1953b	G	*cult*, Afghan.
macha		42	,, ,,	G	*cult*, W. Georgia
sphaerococcum	Indian Dwarf W.	42	,, ,,	G	*cult*, N.W. India
spelta	Large Spelt W.	42	,, ,,	G	*cult*, relic
vavilovianum		42	,, ,,	G	*cult*
vulgare	Bread Wheat	42	,, ,,	G	*cult*
(*aestivum*)		(21) (63)	Y. Yamazaki '34, '37		
		(84)	Dorsey 1936		
edwardi (*durum* × *mon.*)		(42)	Zhebrak 1944	G	*expt*.
soveticum (*durum* × *timo.*)		(56)	,, ,,	G	,,
borisovi (*vulgare* × *timo.*)		(70)	,, ,,	G	,,

EREMOPYRON (AGROPYRON) *x* = 7

prostratum		14	Avdulov 1931	Fo	Eur., N. Asia

AGROPYRON * *x* = 7

elongatum	Couch Grass	14	Simonet 1935	Sb	Europe
gmelinii	Wheat Grass	14	Avdulov 1931	Fo	E. Siberia
velutinum		14	Hair unp.	Fo	Australia
cristatum	Crested Wh. G.	14, 28	Hartung 1946	Fo	Eur., N. Asia
spicatum	Blue Bunch W. G.	14, 28	,, ,,	Fo	N. America
caespitosum		14	Stebbins & P. 1953	—	S.W. Asia
borealis		28	Bøcher & L. 1950	—	Russia
caninum	Bearded W. G. & 8 spp.	28	Hartung 1946	Fo	Eur., N. Asia
ciliare		28	Nakajima 1936	—	
donianum		28	Bøcher & L. 1950	—	Scotland
japonicum		28	Nakajima 1936	—	Japan
junceiforme		28	Östergren 1940	—	W. & N. Europe
latiglume	& 2 spp.	28	Senn *et al.* 1949	—	N: N. America
mayebaranum		28	Moriya & K. 1949a	—	Japan
parishii		28	Stebbins *et al.* 1946	Fo	California
scabrifolium		28	Covas 1949b	—	Argentine
sibiricum	& 2 spp.	28	Avdulov 1930, 1931	Fo	Eur., N. Asia
turczaninovii		28	Ono & T. 1953	—	Turkestan
violacea		28	Bøcher & L. 1950	—	Scandinavia
junceum	Jointed Couch G.	28	Peto 1930	Sb	Europe
v. *mediterraneum*		42	Simonet 1935		
repens	Couch Grass	28, 42	Avdulov 1931	FoM	Eurasia
semicostatum		{ 28	Nielsen & H. 1937	Fo	C. Asia
		{ 42	Nakajima 1936		

AGROPYRON (cont.)

smithii	Bluestem	{ 28, 56 42	Hartung 1946 Stebbins, Myers 1947	Fo	N. America
acutum (*junceiforme* × *pungens*)		35	Simonet 1934c	Fo	Europe
duvalii		35, 42	,, 1935	Fo	*cult*, France
agroelymoides		42	Hunziker 1955	Fo	C. Argentine
enysii		42	Hair unp.	Fo	New Zealand
intermedium (*glaucum*)		42, 43	Hartung 1946	Fo	Europe
kirkii		42	Hair unp.	Fo	New Zealand
littorale		42	Simonet 1935	Sb	Europe
obtusiusculum		42	Peto 1930	Fo	N.W. Europe
pungens		42	Senn *et al.* 1949	Sb	Europe
racemiferum		42	Nakajima 1936	—	Japan
trichophorum		42	Hartung 1946	Fo	Europe
scabrum	(sexual)	42	Hair unp.	Fo	Austr., N.Z.
	(apo.)	41–84	,, ,,		
v. *tenue*		56	,, ,,	Fo	New Zealand
tallonii		49	Simonet 1935	Fo	*cult*, France
campestre		56	,, ,,	—	Europe
caespitosum	Couch Grass	70	Peto 1936	Sb	Armenia

HORDEOPYRUM $x = 7$

rouxii	49	Simonet 1954	—	W. Medit.
(*H. secalinum* × *A. littorale*)				(*nat. hybrid*)

SITANION $x = 7$

hanseni		28	Stebbins & L. 1941	Fo	W: U.S.A.
hystrix	Squirreltail	28	,, ,, ,,	Fo	W. & C: U.S.A., Mex.
jubatum		28	,, ,, ,,	Fo	W: U.S.A.

HYSTRIX $x = 7$

patula	Bottlebrush	28	Brown 1948	FoH	E: N. America
californica		56	Stebbins, Myers 1947	—	California

AEGILOTRICUM $x = 7$

Ae. ovata × *Tr. turgidum*	(46)	Percival 1936	G	*expt.*
Ae. squarrosa, etc. × *Tr. dicoccoides*, etc.	(42)	McFadden & S. '46, '47	—	,,

TRITICALE $x = 7$

Tr. vulgare × *S. cereale*	(56)	Müntzing 1939	G	*expt.*

AGROTRITICUM $x = 7$

Tr. vulgare × *Agr. glaucum*, etc.	(42)	Tzitzin 1933	Fo	*expt.*
Other intergeneric hybrids		Sears 1948	—	*expt.*

TRIBE XIX: STIPEAE

MILIUM $x = 4, 9, 14$

scabrum		8	Tutin 1950	—	W. Eur., Medit., W. Asia
vernale	Early Millet	18	Avdulov 1928	Fo	Medit.
effusum	Wood Millet	28	L. & L. 1944b	—	N. Temp.

453

STIPA *   x = 9, 10, 11, 12, 14, 16, 17
x = 7, 13

leucotricha	Texas N. G.	{ 26	Brown 1949	—	S.W: U.S.A.,
		28	Love, Myers 1947		Mexico
neesiana		28	Myers 1947	—	S. America
parviflora		28	Lorenzo-Andreu 1951	—	Medit.
pringlei		42	Love, Myers 1947	—	S.W: U.S.A., Mexico

x = 8, 9, 17

pinetorum		32	Myers 1947	—	W: U.S.A.
tenuissima		32	Brown 1951	—	Tex.—Mex., Arg.
webberi		32	Johnson 1945	—	N. America
robusta	Sleepy Grass	64	Love, Myers 1947	D	S.W: U.S.A., Mexico
pulchra	Nodding N.	{ 64	Love 1954		
		66	Nielsen 1939	Fo	California

lepida	Foothill Needlegrass	34	Love 1954	Fo	California
megapotomica		34	Myers 1947	—	Brazil
thurberiana		34	Stebbins & L. 1941	Fo	W: U.S.A.
lemmoni		34, 36	,, ,, ,,	Fo	,,
lettermani		{ 66	,, ,, ,,	Fo	
		68	Love, Myers 1947		W. & C: U.S.A.
speciosa	Desert N.	{ 68	,, ,, ,,	Fo	
		60	Stebbins & L. 1941		Calif., Chile

californica	Cal. Needlegrass	36	,, ,,	Fo	W: U.S.A.
elmeri		36	,, ,,	Fo	W: N. America
mucronata		36	Love, Myers 1947	—	Mexico
occidentalis	Western N.	36	Stebbins & L. 1941	Fo	W: N. America
philippii		36	Myers 1947	—	Chile

x = 10, 11

coronata		40	Stebbins & L. 1941	Fo	California
stillmanii		40	Myers 1947	—	,,
cernua		70	Love 1954	Fo	,,
latiglumis		70	Pohl 1954	Fo	,,
brachychaeta		{ 40	Saura 1943		
		44	Parodi 1946	Fo	Argentine
		44–46	Myers 1947		

capillata	& 6 spp.	44	Avdulov 1931	Fo	S. Eur., N. Asia
columbiana		44	Nielsen 1939	Fo	W: N. America
comechingoniana		44	Saura 1948a	—	
gynerioides		44	Covas 1945	—	Mexico
ichu		44	Saura 1948a	—	,,
juncea		44	Love, Myers 1947	—	Medit.
neomexicana		44	,, ,, ,,	Fo	S.W: U.S.A.
plumosa		44	Covas & B. 1945	—	Chile

comata	Needle & Thread G.	{ 44–46	Stebbins & L. 1941		
		46	Love, Myers 1947	Fo	N. America
humilis		{ 42–44	Stebbins, Myers 1947		
		66	Covas & B. 1945	—	S. America
neaei		66	,, ,,	—	Patagonia
speciosa		66	,, ,,	Fo	Calif., Chile

454

STIPA (cont.)
  x = 12, 13

sibirica	Sleepy Grass	24	Avdulov 1928	Fo	N. Asia, Himal.
extremiorientalis		24	Ono & T. 1953	Fo	Japan
eminens		46	Love, Myers 1947	Fo	Tex., Ariz., Mex.
spartea	Porcupine G.	46	,, ,, ,,	Fo	N. America
splendens		48	,, ,, ,,	—	Siberia
viridula		82	Johnson & R. 1943	Fo	C: U.S.A.

BRACHYELYTRUM   x = 11

erectum	22	Brown 1950	—	E: N. America

PIPTOCHAETIUM *   x = 11

bicolor		22	Covas & B. 1945	—	Chile
lasianthum	& 3 spp.	22	Parodi 1946	—	Argentine
napostaense		22	Covas & B. 1945	—	,,
fimbriatum		44	Brown 1951	Fo	S.W: U.S.A.

ORYZOPSIS   x = 11, 12. $x_2 = 23$

kingii		22	Johnson 1945	Fo	California
micrantha		22	,, ,,	Fo	W. & C: N. Amer.
pungens		22	,, ,,	—	N. America
holciformis		24	,, ,,	—	Persia
miliacea		24	Avdulov 1928	Fo	Medit.
paradoxa		24	Litardière 1950	Fo	Eur., Cauc.
virescens		24	Avdulov 1928	Fo	,, ,,
hymenoides	Indian Rice G.	48	Johnson 1945	FoG	N. America
asperifolia		46	,, ,,	—	,,
racemosa		46	,, ,,	—	E. & C: N. Amer.

STIPORYZOPSIS   x = (24 + 41)

caduca	65	Johnson & R. 1943	Fo	nat. hybrid
(O. hym. × S. vir.)				
Mandan Rice Grass	130	Nielsen & R. 1952	Fo	,, ,,
(S. caduca 4x)				

PHAENOSPERMA   x = 12

globosa	24	Avdulov 1931	Fo?	China

URACHNE (NASELLA)   x = 19

trichotoma	38	Avdulov 1928	Fo	Temp. S. Amer.

TRIBE XX: ORYZEAE

CHIKUSICHLOA   x = 12

aquatica	24	Hirayoshi 1937	Fo	Japan

HYDROCHLOA   x = 12

carolinensis	24	Brown 1948	Fo	S.E: U.S.A.

HYGRORYZA   x = 12

aristata	24	Hirayoshi 1937	Fo	Trop. Asia

POTAMOPHILA   x = 12

prehensilis	24	Winter 1951a	—	Australia

ZIZANIOPSIS $x = 12$

miliacea	Southern Wild Rice	24	Brown 1948	—	S.E: U.S.A., W.I.

EHRHARTA $x = 12$

erecta		{ 24	Parthasarathy 1939	Fo	S. Africa
		48	Nakamori 1933		
calycina	Veldt Grass	{ 24 (25–28)	Love 1948	Fo	,,
		48	Parthasarathy 1939		
longiflora		48	,, ,,	Fo	,,

ORYZA $x = 12$

australiensis		24	Sampath & R. 1949	—	Queensland
barthii	Afr. Per. W.R.	{ 24	Heyn 1936	FoG	Trop. Africa
		36	P. T. Thomas unp.		
brachyantha		24	Krishnaswamy *et al.* '54	—	Sudan
breviligulata		24	,, ,,	—	,,
granulata		24	,, ,,	—	India, Mal.
formosana		24	Hara 1942	—	Formosa
glaberrima		24	Ramanujam 1938	FoG	Trop. Africa
longistaminata		24	,, ,,	—	,, ,,
meyeriana		24	Heyn 1936, E.K.J.*	Fo	Trop. Asia
officinalis	Wild Rice	24	Nandi 1936	Fo	,, ,,
perennis	Cuban Rice	24	Gotoh & O. 1933	G	Trop. America
stapfi		24	Sampath & R. 1949	G	Trop. Africa
subulata		24	Saura 1948a	—	S. America
latifolia		{ 24	Heyn 1936	FoG	N. Amer., W.I.
		(48)	Gotoh & O. 1933		
sativa	Rice	{ 24	Avdulov 1931	AFoG	*cult*, India
		(36, 48)	Ichijima 1934		
coarctata	Wild Sind R.	48	Parthasarathy 1938	Fo	Sind, Bengal, Bur.
eichingeri		48	Pathak 1940	Fo	Trop. E. Africa
minuta		48	Nandi 1936	G	Philippines
sylvestris		48	Pathak 1940	—	Trop. Africa

MICROLAENA $x = 12$

stipoides		48	Parthasarathy 1939	Fo	Austr., N.Z.

LEERSIA $x = 12$

hexandra	Bareet G.	48	Brown 1948	Fo	Tropics
lenticularis	Catchfly G.	48	,, 1950	—	E: U.S.A.
monandra		48	,, ,,	—	S.E: U.S.A., W.I.
virginica	White grass	48	,, 1948	—	E. & C: N. Amer.
oryzoides	Cut G.	48	Tateoka 1954	Fo	N. Temp.
v. *japonica*		60	Hirayoshi 1937	Fo	Japan
japonica		96	,, ,,	—	,,

ZIZANIA $x = 15$

aquatica	Annual Wild R.	30	Brown 1948	G	E. & C: U.S.A.
latifolia	Manchurian W.R.	{ 30	Ramanujam 1938	GV	N. China
		34?	Hirayoshi 1937		
texana	Texas W.R.	30	Brown 1950	—	Texas

TRIBE XXI: ARUNDINEAE

PHRAGMITES $x = 12$

communis	⌠ 36	Tischler 1942		
	⟨ 48, *c.* 96	Avdulov 1931	DTToV	Cosmop.
	⌡ 48	Saura 1948a		
as *karka*	36	Ramanathan 1950		
japonica	48	Tateoka 1954	—	Japan

CORTADERIA (GYNERIUM) $x = 12$

selloana Pampas Gr.	⌠ 72 + 1B	Avdulov 1931	HT	S. America
(*argentea*)	⌡ 76	Hunter 1934		

ARUNDO $x = 12$?

donax	Spanish Reed	110	Hunter 1934	HT	Medit.—Japan

HAKONECHLOA $x = 12$?

macra	50	M. & S. 1935	H	Japan

AMPELODESMOS $x = 12$

mauritanicus	96	Myers 1947	Fo	W. Medit.

TRIBE XXII: CENTOTHECEAE

CENTOTHECA $x = 12$

lappacea	24	Avdulov 1931	Fo	O.W. Tropics

UNIOLA $x = 12$

laxa	24	Brown 1950	—	E: U.S.A.
sessiliflora	24	,, ,,	—	S.E: U.S.A.
latifolia	48	,, ,,	H	E: U.S.A.

TRIBE XXIII: BAMBUSEAE

ARUNDINARIA (SASAELLA) $x = 12$

iwatekensis	48	Uchikawa 1935	HTW	Japan
simonii	48	Parodi 1946	—	China

CHIMONOBAMBUSA $x = 12$

marmorea	48	Uchikawa 1933	HTW	China

INDOCALAMUS $x = 12$

wightianus Nilgiri Bamboo	48	E.K.J.*	HTW	India

PHYLLOSTACHYS $x = 12$

aurea Golden B. & 4 spp.	48	Uchikawa 1935	HW	China, Japan
striata	48	,, 1943	—	Japan
marliacea	⌠ 48	,, ,,	—	,,
	⌡ *c.* 72	Avdulov 1928		
flexuosa	54?	Hunter 1934	—	China

PLEIOBLASTUS (ARUNDINARIA) $x = 12$

fortunei	48	Hunter 1934	H	Japan
gramineus	48	Uchikawa 1935	—	,,
hindsii	48	,, ,,	H	Hong Kong
higoensis	48	,, 1943	—	Japan
communis	48	,, ,,	—	,,

457

PLEIOBLASTUS (ARUNDINARIA) (*cont.*)

chino (*maximowiczii*)		48	Tateoka 1954	H	China
simonii	Silverstripe B.	48	Uchikawa 1933	HW	,,
pygmaeus		54?	Hunter 1934	H	Japan

PSEUDOSASA *x* = 12

japonica	Arrow B.	48	Uchikawa '35, E.K.J.*	TW	Japan

SASA *x* = 12

sp. (3*x*)		36	Uchikawa 1943	—	
kozasa		48	Yamaura 1933	HW	Japan
kurilensis		48	,, ,,	HW	,,
paniculata		48	,, ,,	HW	,,

SASAMORPHA *x* = 12

purpurascens (*borealis*)	48	Tateoka 1954	HW	Japan

SEMIARUNDINARIA *x* = 12

yashadake	48	Uchikawa 1935	W	Japan

SINOBAMBUSA *x* = 12

tootsik	48	Uchikawa 1933	W	Japan

TETRAGONOCALAMUS (CHIMONOBAMBUSA) *x* = 12

angulatus	48	Uchikawa 1935	HTW	China

BAMBUSA *x* = 12

bambos	Common B.	⎰ 72	Janaki Ammal 1938	FoGHW	E. Indies
(*arundinacea*)		⎱ 70	Parthasarathy 1946		
floribunda		72	Uchikawa 1935	W	Java
multiplex	Henge B.	72	,, ,,	FoHW	Trop. Asia
as *nana*		72	Yamaura 1933	H	Japan
polymorpha		72	E.K.J.*	W	Burma
vulgaris	Feather B.	72	,,	FoHW	Trop. Asia

DENDROCALAMUS *x* = 12

giganteus	Giant Bamboo	72	E.K.J.*	HToW	Burma
longispathus		72	,,	W	,,
strictus	Male B.	⎰ 72	Richharia & K. '40,	HToW	India, Java
		⎱ 70	Parthasarathy 1946		
brandisii		72 + 2B	E.K.J.*	W	Burma

OCHLANDRA *x* = 12?

scriptoria	*c.* 72	E.K.J.*	TToW	India
travancoria	*c.* 72	,,	TToW	S. India

BIBLIOGRAPHY

ABBREVIATIONS

Cytologia, F.J.N.: *Fujii Jubilee Number* (1937).

P.N.A.S.: *Proceedings of National Academy of Sciences*, Washington.

Z.i.A.V.: *Zeitschrift für induktive Abstammungs-und Vererbungslehre.*

* References to Chromosome Lists.   See also p. x

Aase, H. C. & Powers, L. R.   1926.   *Amer. J. Bot.* **13,** 367.
Abele, K.   1923.   *Acta Univ. latv.* **8,** 371.
Aberg, E.   1938.   *Chron. bot.* **4,** 390.
Abraham, A.   1939.   *Ann. Bot., Lond.* n.s. **3,** 545.
—— 1942.   *Curr. Sci.* **11,** 282.
Adati, S.   1933.   *Cytologia,* **4,** 182.
—— 1935.   *Bot. & Zool., Tokyo,* **3,** 1445.
Adatia, R. D. & Chokshi, D. B.   1951.   *Curr. Sci.* **20,** 102.
Afzelius, K.   1924.   *Acta Hort. berg.* **8,** 123.
—— 1943.   *Svensk bot. Tidskr.* **37,** 266.
—— 1949.   *Acta Hort. berg.* **15,** 65.
Agharkar, S. P. & Bhaduri, P. N.   1935.   *Curr. Sci.* **3,** 615.
Aishima, T.   1934.   *Bot. Mag. Tokyo,* **48,** 150.
Akemine, T.   1935.   *J. Fac. Sci. Hokkaido Univ.* **5,** 25.
Åkerberg, E.   1942.   *Hereditas, Lund,* **28,** 1.
Alam, Z.   1936.   *Ann. Bot., Lond.* **50,** 85.
Aleskowsky, M. K.   1930.   *Zitologii roda Statice,* p. 374.
Allard, H. A. & Allard, H. F.   1940.   *J. Wash. Acad. Sci.* **30,** 335.
Almeida, J. L. F. de.   1946.   *Bol. Soc. Brot.* **20,** 201.
—— 1947a.   *Agron. lusit.* **9,** 129.
—— 1947b.   *Agron. lusit.* **9,** 265.
—— 1948.   *Agron. lusit.* **10,** 263.
Amano, Y.   1944.   *J. Fac. Sci. Hokkaido Univ.* **5,** 109.
Amico, A.   1947.   *Nuovo G. bot. ital.* **54,** 748.
Anderson, E.   1931.   *Ann. Mo. bot. Gdn.* **18,** 465.
—— 1936.   *Ann. Mo. bot. Gdn.* **23,** 457.
Anderson, E. & Sax, K.   1935.   *J. Arnold Arbor.* **16,** 40.
—— —— 1936.   *Bot. Gaz.* **97,** 433.
Anderson, E. & Whitaker, T. W.   1934.   *J. Arnold Arbor.* **15,** 28.
Andersson, A.   1931.   *Acta Univ. lund.* **27,** (7).
Andreas, C. H.   1947.   *Nederl. kruidk. Arch.* **54,** 138.
Andres, J. M.   1941.   *Rev. Fac. Agron. B. Aires,* **9,** 100.
Andres, J. M. & Saura, F.   1945.   *Rev. Fac. Agron. B. Aires (Inst. genet.),* **2,** 161.
Annen, E.   1945.   *Ber. schweiz. bot. Ges.* **55,** 81.
Araratian, A. G.   1939.   *C.R. Acad. Sci. U.R.S.S.* **25,** 777.
Araratian, A. G. and Tonian, C. R.   1945.   *Proc. Acad. Sci. Armen. S.S.R.* **2,** 141.
Arata, M.   1944.   *Nuovo G. bot. ital.* **51,** 39.
Arenkova, D. N.   1940.   *C.R. Acad. Sci. U.R.S.S.* **29,** 332.
Armand, L.   1912.   *C.R. Acad. Sci., Paris,* **155,** 1534.
Armstrong, J. M.   1937.   *Canad. J. Res.* § C, **15,** 281.
Asana, J. J. & Adatia, R. D.   1945.   *Curr. Sci.* **14,** 74.
Atchison, E.   1947a.   *J. Hered.* **38,** 311.

*ATCHISON, E. 1947b. *Amer. J. Bot.* **34,** 159.
—— 1947c. *Amer. J. Bot.* **34,** 407.
—— 1948. *Amer. J. Bot.* **35,** 651.
*—— 1949a. *J. Elisha Mitchell Sci. Soc.* **65,** 118.
—— 1949b. *Amer. J. Bot.* **36,** 364.
—— 1950. *J. Elisha Mitchell Sci. Soc.* **66,** 70.
—— 1951. *Amer. J. Bot.* **38,** 538
ATCHISON, E., MOORE, H. E. & WOOD, C. E. 1949. *Science,* **110,** 41.
ATWOOD, S. 1936. *Amer. J. Bot.* **23,** 674.
—— 1937. *Cellule,* **46,** 389.
ATWOOD, S. S. & HILL, H. D. 1940. *Amer. J. Bot.* **27,** 730.
AVANZI, M. G. 1948. *Caryologia,* **1,** 83.
—— 1949. *Caryologia,* **2,** 111.
AVDULOV, N. P. 1928. *Dnevn. Weecojusn. Ssed. Bot.* 1.
*—— 1931. *Bull. appl. Bot. Genet. etc.,* Suppl. 43.
—— 1933. *Bull. appl. Bot. Genet. etc.,* Ser. 2, **2,** 131.
AVDULOV, N. P. & TITOVA, N. 1933. *Bull. appl. Bot. Genet. etc.,* Ser. 2, **2,** 165.
AVERS, C. J. 1953. *Amer. J. Bot.* **40,** 669.
AYYANGAR RANGASWAMI, G. N. & KRISHNASWAMY, N. 1933. *Indian J. agric. Sci.* 3, 934.
—— —— 1935. *Curr. Sci.* **4,** 739.

BABCOCK, E. B. 1915. *P.N.A.S.* **1,** 535.
*—— 1947. *Univ. Calif. Publ. Bot.* **21,** 1.
—— 1951. *Univ. Calif. Publ. Bot.* **23,** 283.
BABCOCK, E. B., STEBBINS, G. & JENKINS, J. A. 1937. *Cytologia, F.J.N.* 188.
BABU, C. N. 1936. *Curr. Sci.* **4,** 739.
BACCHI, O. 1940. *J. Agron. S. Paulo,* **3,** 249.
BAEZ-MAJOR, A. 1934. *Cavanillesia,* **6,** 59.
BAILEY, P. C. 1951. *Bull. Torrey bot. Cl.* **78,** 324.
BALDWIN, J. T. 1935. *Bot. Gaz.* **96,** 558.
—— 1936. *J. Genet.* **33,** 455.
—— 1937. *Amer. J. Bot.* **24,** 126.
—— 1938. *Amer. J. Bot.* **25,** 572.
—— 1939. *J. Hered.* **30,** 169.
—— 1940. *Madroño,* **5,** 184.
—— 1941a. *J. Hered.* **32,** 249.
—— 1941b. *Bull. Torrey bot. Cl.* **68,** 615.
—— 1942a. *Bull. Torrey bot. Cl.* **69,** 134.
—— 1942b. *Amer. J. Bot.* **29,** 283.
—— 1943. *Bull. Torrey bot. Cl.* **70,** 26.
—— 1945. *Bull. Torrey bot. Cl.* **72,** 367.
—— 1946a. *Bull. Torrey bot. Cl.* **73,** 18.
—— 1946b. *Bull. Torrey bot. Cl.* **73,** 282.
—— 1947a. *J. Hered.* **38,** 54.
—— 1947b. *Amer. J. Bot.* **34,** 261.
BALDWIN, J. T. & CAMPBELL, J. M. 1940. *Amer. J. Bot.* **27,** 915.
BALDWIN, J. T. & CULP, R. 1941. *Amer. J. Bot.* **28,** 942.
BALDWIN, J. T. & SPEESE, B. M. 1947a. *Bull. Torrey bot. Cl.* **74,** 250.
—— —— 1947b. *Bull. Torrey bot. Cl.* **74,** 283.
—— —— 1949a. *Bull. Torrey bot. Cl.* **76,** 213.
—— —— 1949b. *Bull. Torrey bot. Cl.* **76,** 346.
—— —— 1951a. *Bull. Torrey bot. Cl.* **78,** 70.
—— —— 1951b. *Bull. Torrey bot. Cl.* **78,** 254.
—— —— 1951c. *Amer. J. Bot.* **38,** 153.
—— —— 1951d. *Bull. Torrey bot. Cl.* **78,** 161.
—— —— 1951e. *Rhodora,* **53,** 89.
—— —— 1952. *Bull. Torrey bot. Cl.* **79,** 293.
BALDWIN, J. T. & SPEESE, B. M. 1955a. *Amer. J. Bot.* **42,** 123.
—— —— 1955b. *Amer. J .Bot.* **42,** 406.

BALDWIN, J. T., SPEESE, B. M. & MIKULA, B. 1949. *Rhodora*, **51**, 368.
BAMBACIONE, V. M. 1940. *Sci. genet.* **1**, 326.
—— 1941. *Ann. di Bot.* **22**, 99.
BAMFORD, R. 1935. *J. Agric. Res.* **51**, 945.
—— 1941. *J. Hered.* **32**, 419.
BAMFORD, R. & WINKLER, F. B. 1941. *J. Hered.* **32**, 278.
BANACH, E. 1950. *Bull. Acad. Polon. Sci. Lett.* § B, **1**, 197.
BANACH-POGAN, E. 1954. *Acta Soc. bot. Polon.* **23**, 375.
BANERJI, E. A. R. 1936. *Sci. & Cult.* **1**, 653.
BANERJI, I. 1932. *J. Indian bot. Soc.* **11**, 82.
—— 1950a. *Curr. Sci.* **19**, 347.
—— 1950b. *Proc. 37th Indian Sci. Congr.* pt. 3, 44.
—— 1951. *Proc. Indian Acad. Sci.* § B, **34**, 172.
BANERJI, I. & HAKIM, A. 1954. *Proc. Indian Acad. Sci.* § B **39**, 128.
BANERJI, I. & HALDAR, S. 1942. *Proc. Indian Acad. Sci.* § B, **16**, 91.
BANGHAM, W. 1929. *J. Arnold Arbor.* **10**, 167.
BARANOV, P. & PODDUBNAJA, U. 1925. *Bull. Univ. Asie cent.* **11**, 1.
BARBER, H. N. 1941a. *Nature*, **148**, 227.
—— 1941b. *Ann. Bot., Lond.* **5**, 375.
—— 1942. *J. Genet.* **43**, 97.
BARDUCCI, T. B. & MADOO, R. M. 1941. Min. Fomento, Ecuador, Bol. 22.
BARNARD, C. 1949. *Austr. J. sci. Res.* Ser. B, **2**, 241.
BARTON, D. W. 1950. *Amer. J. Bot.* **37**, 639.
BATTAGLIA, E. 1940. *Nuovo G. bot. ital.* **47**, 271.
   1946. *Nuovo G. bot. ital.* **53**, 707.
—— 1947a. *R.C. Accad. Lincei*, Ser. 8, **2**, 63.
—— 1947b. *Nuovo G. bot. ital.* **54**, 560.
—— 1947c. *R. C. Accad. Lincei*, Ser. 8A, **2**, 463.
—— 1948. *Caryologia*, **1**, 1.
—— 1949a. *Caryologia*, **1**, 144.
—— 1949b. *Caryologia*, **1**, 269.
—— 1949c. *Caryologia*, **2**, 85.
—— 1949d. *Caryologia*, **2**, 23.
—— 1950a. *Caryologia*, **2**, 165.
—— 1950b. *Caryologia*, **3**, 126.
—— 1951. *Bot. Gaz.* **112**, 490.
—— 1952a. *Caryologia*, **5**, 113.
—— 1952b. *Atti Soc. tosc. Sci. nat.* § B, **49**, 130.
—— 1953. *Caryologia*, **5**, 237.
—— 1954. *Caryologia*, **6**, 63.
BAUR, E. 1932. *Züchter*, **4**, 57.
BAYLIS, G. T. S. 1954. *Trans. roy. Soc. N.Z.* **82**, 639.
BEADLE, G. W. 1930. *Cornell Univ. Agr. Exp. St.* **12**, 9.
BEAL, J. M. 1932. *Bot. Gaz.* **93**, 278.
—— 1937. *Bot. Gaz.* **99**, 400.
—— 1942. *Bot. Gaz.* **103**, 617.
BEAL, J. M. & OWNBEY, M. 1943. *Bot. Gaz.* **104**, 553.
BEALE, G. H. 1940. *J. Genet.* **40**, 337.
BEARD, E. C. 1937. *Bot. Gaz.* **99**, 1.
BEASLEY, J. O. 1940. *J. Hered.* **31**, 39.
—— 1942. *Genetics*, **27**, 25.
BEATUS, R. 1936. *Z.i.A.V.* **71**, 353.
BECK, C. 1953. Fritillaries, London.
BECK, P. & HORTON, J. S. 1932. *Bot. Gaz.* **93**, 42.
BEDDOWS, A. R. & JONES, K. 1953. *Nature*, **171**, 938.
BEETLE, A. A. 1945. *Bull. Torrey bot. Cl.* **72**, 541.
BEETLE, D. E. 1944. *Madroño*, **7**, 133.
BEHRE, K. 1929. *Planta*, **7**, 208.

31   461

BELL, C. R. 1949. *J. Elisha Mitchell Sci. Soc.* **65**, 138.
—— 1954. *Univ. Calif. Publ. Bot.* **27**, 133.
BELLING, J. 1926. *Biol. Bull., Wood's Hole,* **50**, 160.
BENOIST, E. 1937. *Rev. Cytol., Paris,* **2**, 415.
BERG, H. D. VON. 1933. *Anz. Akad. Wiss., Vienna,* **70**, 276.
BERGMAN, B. 1932. *Svensk bot. Tidskr.* **26**, 453.
—— 1935b. *Hereditas,* **20**, 214.
—— 1935c. *Svensk bot. Tidskr.* **29**, 155.
—— 1937. *Svensk bot. Tidskr.* **31**, 391.
—— 1941. *Svensk bot. Tidskr.* **35**, 1.
—— 1942. *Svensk bot. Tidskr.* **36**, 429.
—— 1944. *Svensk bot. Tidskr.* **38**, 240.
—— 1952. *Hereditas,* **38**, 367.
BERGNER, A. D. 1943. *Amer. J. Bot.* **30**, 431.
BERNSTRÖM, P. 1944. *Hereditas,* **30**, 257.
—— 1946. *Hereditas,* **32**, 514.
BHADURI, P. N. 1933. *J. Indian bot. Soc.* **12**, 56.
—— 1935. *J. Indian bot. Soc.* **14**, 133.
—— 1941. *Ann. Bot., Lond.* **5**, 1.
—— 1942. *Ann. Bot., Lond.* **6**, 229.
BHADURI, E. N. & BOSE, P. C. 1947. *J. Genet.* **48**, 237.
BHADURI, P. N. & BOSE, S. 1949. *Proc. 36th Indian Sci. Congr.* pt. 3, 139.
BHADURI, P. N. & ISLAM, A. S. 1949. *Proc. 36th Indian Sci. Congr.* pt. 3, 139.
BHADURI, P. N. & KAR, A. K. 1949. *Proc. 36th Indian Sci. Congr.* pt. 3, 140.
BHALLA, V. 1941. *Proc. Indian Sci. Congr.,* 1941.
BHATTACHARJEE, S. K. 1955. *Caryologia,* **6**, 333.
BIANCHI, R. 1946. *Ber. schweiz. bot. Ges.* **56**, 523.
BILLERI, G. 1954. *Caryologia,* **6**, 45.
BILLINGS, F. H. 1904. *Bot. Gaz.* **38**, 99.
—— 1937. *New Phytol.* **36**, 301.
BJÖRKMAN, S. O. 1951. *Hereditas,* **37**, 465.
—— 1954. *Hereditas,* **40**, 254.
BLACKBURN, K. B. 1928. *Z.i.A.V.* Suppl. **1**, 439.
—— 1933. *Proc. Univ. Durham phil. Soc.* **9**, 84.
—— 1953. *Rep. Soc. guernesiaise,* **15**, 169.
BLACKBURN, K. B. & BOULT, J. J. 1930. *Proc. Univ. Durham phil. Soc.* **8**, 260.
BLACKBURN, K. B. & HARRISON, J. W. H. 1921. *Ann. Bot.* **35**, 159.
—— —— 1924. *Ann. Bot., Lond.* **38**, 361.
BLEIER, H. 1925. *Jb. wiss. Bot.* **64**, 604.
—— 1928. *Z.i.A.V.* Suppl. **1**, 447.
—— 1930. *Z. Zellforsch.* **11**, 218.
BØCHER, T. W. 1932. *Bot. Tidskr.* **42**, 183.
—— 1936. *Hereditas,* **22**, 269.
—— 1938a. *Svensk bot. Tidskr.* **32**, 346.
—— 1938b. *Dansk bot. Ark.* **9**, 1.
—— 1940. *K. danske vidensk. Selsk. Biol. Medd.* **15**.
—— 1941. *Medd. Grønland,* **131**, 3.
—— 1943. *Hereditas,* **29**, 499.
—— 1944. *Dansk. bot. Ark.* **11**, 1.
—— 1945. *Hereditas,* **31**, 220.
—— 1947a. *K. danske vidensk Selsk. Biol. Medd.* **20**, 3.
—— 1947b. *Bot. Notiser,* 1947, 353.
—— 1949. *New Phytol.* **48**, 285.
—— 1950. *Bot. Notiser,* 1950, 353.
—— 1951. *K. danske vidensk Selsk. Biol. Skr.* **6** (7), 1.
—— 1954. *Svensk bot. Tidskr.* **48**, 31.
BØCHER, T. W. & LARSEN, K. 1950. *Medd. Grønland,* **147**, 3.
BØCHER, T. W., LARSEN, K. & RAHN, K. 1953. *Hereditas,* **39**, 289.
BOEHM, K. 1931. *Planta,* **14**, 411.

BOELCKE, O. 1951. *Darwiniana*, **9**, 348.
BOLTON, J. L. & GREENSHIELDS, J. E. R. 1950. *Science*, **112**, 275.
BOSCH, E. 1947. *Ber. Schweiz. bot. Ges.* **57**, 37.
BOSEMARK, N. O. 1950. *Hereditas*, **36**, 366.
—— 1954. *Hereditas*, **40**, 346.
BOUHARMONT, J. 1954. *Cellule*, **56**, 253.
*BOWDEN, W. M. 1940a. *Amer. J. Bot.* **27**, 357.
—— 1940b. *Chron. Bot.* **6**, 123.
*—— 1945a. *Amer. J. Bot.* **32**, 81.
*—— 1945b. *Amer. J. Bot.* **32**, 191.
—— 1948. *Amer. J. Bot.* **35**, 377.
—— 1954. *Genetics*, **39**, 959.
BOYLE, W. S. 1944. *Madroño*, **7**, 129.
—— 1945. *Madroño*, **8**, 1.
—— 1950. *Amer. J. Bot.* **37**, 291.
BRABEC, F. 1954. *Chromosoma*, **6**, 135.
BRANAS, M. 1932. *C. R. Acad. Sci. Paris*, **194**, 121.
BRANDBERG, B. 1948. *Ark. Bot.* **33B**, 1.
BRANDT, J. P. 1952. *Bull. Soc. neuchâtel. Sci. nat.* **75**, 179.
—— 1953. *Bull. Soc. neuchâtel. Sci. nat.* **76**, 111.
BREMER, G. 1923. *Genetica*, **5**, 97, 273.
—— 1924. *Arch. Suikerind. Ned.-Ind.* 1924, **16**, 477.
—— 1931. *Arch. Suikerind. Ned.-Ind.* 1931, nos. 13 & 31.
—— 1934. *Arch. Suikerind. Ned.-Ind.* 1934, **5**, 141.
BRESLAWETZ, L. 1926. *Bot. Arch.* **7**, 388.
BRESLAWETZ, L., MEDWEDEWA, G. & MAGILT, M. 1934. *Z. Zücht. A*, **19**, 229.
BRETT, O. E. 1955. *New Phytol.* **54**, 138.
BREVIGLIERI, N. & BATTAGLIA, E. 1955. *Caryologia*, **6**, 271.
BRINGHURST, R. S. 1954. *Proc. Amer. Soc. hort. Sci.*, **63**, 239.
BRITTINGHAM, W. H. 1934. *Amer. J. Bot.* **21**, 77.
*BRITTON, D. M. 1951. *Brittonia*, **7**, 233.
BROCK, R. D. 1952. *Ann. Rep. John Innes Hort. Inst.* **42**, 47.
—— 1953. *Nature*, **171**, 939.
BROWN, M. S. & MENZEL, M. Y. 1952. *Bull. Torrey bot. Cl.* **79**, 110.
BROWN, S. W. 1943. *Amer. J. Bot.* **30**, 686.
BROWN, W. H. 1908. *Bot. Gaz.* **46**, 445.
BROWN, W. L. 1939. *Amer. J. Bot.* **26**, 717.
BROWN, W. V. 1946. *Bot. Gaz.* **108**, 262.
*—— 1948. *Amer. J. Bot.* **35**, 382.
—— 1949. *Madroño*, **10**, 97.
*—— 1950. *Bull. Torrey bot. Cl.* **77**, 63.
*—— 1951. *Bull. Torrey bot. Cl.* **78**, 292.
—— 1953. *Kew Bull.* **1953**, 293.
BROWN, W. L. & CLARK, R. B. 1940. *Amer. J. Bot.* **27**, 237.
BROWN, W. V. & COE, G. E. 1951. *Amer. J. Bot.* **38**, 823.
BROWN, W. V., PONEWCZYNSKI, H. T. & SCARBOROUGH, H. H. 1951. *Bull. Torrey bot. Cl.* **78**, 66.
BROŽEK, A. 1932. *Preslia*, **11**, 1.
BRÜCHER, E. H. & ROSS, H. 1953. *Lilloa*, **26**, 453.
BRUMFIELD, R. T. 1941. *Amer. J. Bot.* **28**, 713.
BRUUN, H. G. 1932a. *Hereditas*, **16**, 63.
*—— 1932b. *Symb. bot. upsaliens.* **1**, 1.
BUCHHOLZ, J. T., WILLIAMS, L. F. & BLAKESLEE, A. F. 1935. *P.N.A.S.* **21**, 651.
BUKASOV, S. M. 1935. In Vavilov, 1935 (3, 1) *q.v.*
—— 1938. *C.R. Acad. Sci. U.R.S.S.* **20**, 177.
—— 1940. *Soviet Plant Ind. Rec.* **4**, 3.
BUKASOV, S. M. & LECHNOVICZ. 1935. *Rev. argent. Agron.* 1935, 173.
BURBANCK, M. P. 1941. *Bot. Gaz.* **103**, 247.
—— 1944. *Bot. Gaz.* **105**, 339.

BURKART, A.   1949a.   *Darwiniana*, **9**, 1.
—— 1949b.   *Darwiniana*, **9**, 63.
BURKART, A. & BRÜCHER, H.   1953.   *Züchter*, **23**, 65.
BURNS, G. W.   1942.   *Amer. Midl. Nat.* **28**, 127.
BURSTRÖM, H.   1929.   *Acta Hort. berg.* **9**, 293.
BURTON, G. W.   1940.   *J. agr. Res.* **60**, 193.
—— 1942.   *Amer. J. Bot.* **29**, 355.
BUSHNELL, E. P.   1936.   *Bot. Gaz.* **98**, 356.
BUXTON, B. H. & DARK, S. O. S.   1934.   *J. Genet.* **29**, 109.
BUXTON, B. H. & DARLINGTON, C. D.   1932.   *New Phytol.* **31**, 225.
BUXTON, B. H. & NEWTON, W. C. F.   1928.   *J. Genet.* **19**, 269.

CALDER, J. W.   1937.   *J. Linn. Soc. (Bot.)*, **51**, 1.
CALLAN, H. G.   1941.   *Ann. Bot., Lond.* **5**, 579.
CAMARA, A. & JESUS, A. DE.   1946.   *Agron. lusit.* **8**, 95.
CAMPIN, M. G.   1924.   *New Phytol.* **23**, 282.
CAPOOR, S. PR.   1937.   *Beih. bot. Zbl.* **57**, A, 233.
CARANO, E.   1926.   *Ann. Bot., Roma,* **17**, 50.
CÁRDENAS, M. & HAWKES, J. G.   1946.   *J. Linn. Soc. (Bot.)*, **53**, 91.
—— —— 1948.   *Rev. Agric. Cochabamba,* **4**, 30.
CARLETTO, G. M.   1948.   *Bull. Mus. Nac. Rio de Jan. Bot.* Ser. **9**, 1.
CARLSON, E. M. & STUART, B. C.   1936.   *New Phytol.* **35**, 68.
CARLSON, M. C.   1945.   *Bot. Gaz.* **107**, 107.
CARNIEL, K.   1952.   *Öst. Bot. Z.* **99**, 318.
CARPIO, M. D. A.   1952.   *Genet. Iber.* **4**, 47.
CARTER, K. M.   1928.   *J. R. micr. Soc.* **48**, 389.
CARVALHO, M. L. DE.   1948.   *Portug. acta biol.* **2A**, 255.
CASTETTER, E. F.   1930.   *Amer. J. Bot.* **17**, 41.
CASTRO, D. DE.   1941.   *Agron. lusit.* **3**, 104.
—— 1943.   *Agron. lusit.* **5**, 243.
—— 1944.   *Brot. Ciênc. nat.* **13**, 73.
—— 1945a.   *Bol. Soc. Brot.* **19**, 525.
—— 1945b.   *Bol. Soc. Brot.* **19**, 755.
—— 1949.   *Agron. lusit.* **11**, 85.
CASTRO, D. DE & FONTES, F. C.   1946.   *Brot. Ciênc. nat.* **15**, 38.
CASTRO, D. DE & WAGNER, N. M.   1950.   *Genet. Iber.* **2**, 75.
CASTRONOVO, A.   1945.   *Darwiniana,* **7**, 38.
CATCHESIDE, D. G.   1950.   *Genet. iber.* **2**, 139.
CAVE, M. S.   1948a.   *Madroño,* **9**, 257.
—— 1948b.   *Amer. J. Bot.* **35**, 343.
—— 1949.   *Madroño,* **10**, 95.
CAVE, M. S. & BRADLEY, M. V.   1943.   *Amer. J. Bot.* **30**, 142.
*CAVE, M. S. & CONSTANCE, L.   1942.   *Univ. Calif. Publ. Bot.* **18**, 205.
*—— —— 1944.   *Univ. Calif. Publ. Bot.* **18**, 293.
*—— —— 1947.   *Univ. Calif. Publ. Bot.* **18**, 449.
*—— —— 1950.   *Univ. Calif. Publ. Bot.* **23**, 363.
CELARIER, R. P.   1955.   *Bull. Torrey bot. Cl.* **82**, 30.
CHAKRAVORTI, A. K.   1948.   *Proc. Indian Acad. Sci.* **27**, § B, 74.
—— 1949.   *Proc. 36th Indian Sci. Congr.* pt. 3, 143.
—— 1952.   *Proc. 39th Indian Sci. Congr.* pt. 3, 30.
CHAMPAGNAT, M.   1952.   *Bull. Soc. bot. Fr.* **99**, 301.
CHANDLER, C.   1943.   *Bull. Torrey bot. Cl.* **70**, 612.
CHASE, S. S.   1947.   *Amer. J. Bot.* **34**, 581.
CHATELIER, G. GAZET DU.   1939.   *Rev. Cytol., Paris,* **4**, 1.
CHAUDURI, K.   1940.   *Curr. Sci.* **9**, 416.
CHEESEMAN, E. E.   1947.   *Kew Bull.* 1947, 97.
CHEESEMAN, E. E. & LARTER, L. N. H.   1935.   *J. Genet.* **30**, 31.
CHEVALIER, E.   1945.   *Rev. Cytol., Paris,* **8**, 77.
CHIARUGI, A. N.   1925.   *Nuovo G. bot. ital.* **32**, 223.

Chiarugi, A. N. 1926. *Nuovo G. bot. ital.* **33**, 501.
—— 1927b. *Nuovo G. bot. ital.* **34**, 783.
—— 1927c. *Nuovo G. bot. ital.* **34**, 864.
—— 1930b. *Boll. Soc. ital. Biol. sper.* **5**.
—— 1933. *Nuovo G. bot. ital.* **40**, 63.
—— 1937. *Nuovo G. bot. ital.* **44**, 641.
—— 1945. *Nuovo G. bot. ital.* **52**, 93.
—— 1949. *Caryologia*, **1**, 362.
—— 1950. *Caryologia*, **3**, 148.
Chin, T. C. 1941. *Ann. Bot., Lond.* **5**, 535.
Chin, T. C. & Youngken, H. W. 1947. *Amer. J. Bot.* **34**, 401.
Chittenden, R. J. 1928. *J. Genet.* **19**, 285.
Choudhuri, H. C. 1942. *Ann. Bot., Lond.* **6**, 183.
Christen, H. R. 1950. *Ber. schweiz. bot. Ges.* **60**, 153.
Christensen, H. M. & Bamford, R. 1943. *J. Hered.* **34**, 99.
Christiansen, H. 1950. *K. danske Vidensk. Selsk.* **18**, 1.
Christoff, M. 1929. *Bull. Soc. bot. Bulg.* **3**, 279.
—— 1940. *Planta*, **31**, 73.
Christoff, M. & Christoff, M. A. 1948. *Genetics*, **33**, 36.
Church, G. L. 1929a. *Bot. Gaz.* **87**, 608.
—— 1929b. *Bot. Gaz.* **88**, 63.
—— 1936. *Amer. J. Bot.* **23**, 12.
—— 1940. *Amer. J. Bot.* **27**, 263.
—— 1949. *Amer. J. Bot.* **36**, 155.
Clarke, A. E. 1932. *Proc. 6th intern. Congr. Genet. Ithaca*, **2**, 20.
—— 1934. *Univ. Calif. Publ. Bot.* **17**, 435.
Clausen, J. 1926. *Hereditas*, **8**, 1.
—— 1929. *Ann. Bot., Lond.* **43**, 741.
—— 1931a. *Hereditas*, **15**, 62.
—— 1931b. *Hereditas*, **15**, 67.
—— 1931c. *Bot. Tidskr.* **41**, 317.
—— 1931d. *Hereditas*, **15**, 219.
—— 1933. *Hereditas*, **18**, 65.
—— 1951. Stages in the Evolution of Plant Species. Ithaca.
Clausen, J., Keck, D. D. & Hiesey, W. M. 1934. *Ann. Rep. Pl. Biol., Yearb. Carneg. Instn.* 173.
—— —— —— 1937. *Ann. Rep. Pl. Biol., Yearb. Carneg. Instn.* 13.
—— —— —— 1940. *Carneg. Instn. Wash., Publ.* 520.
—— —— —— 1950. *Ann. Rep. Pl. Biol., Yearb. Carneg. Instn.* **49**, 101.
Clausen, R. E. & Goodspeed, T. H. 1925. *Genetics*, **10**, 278.
Clausen, R. T. & Uhl, C. H. 1943. *Brittonia*, **5**, 33.
—— —— 1944. *Madroño*, **7**, 161.
Cleland, R. E. 1950. *Ind. Univ. Publ.* **16**, 1.
Coe, G. E. 1953. *Amer. J. Bot.* **40**, 335.
—— 1954. *Bull. Torrey bot. Cl.* **81**, 141.
Coleman, L. C. 1940. *Amer. J. Bot.* **27**, 887.
Collins, E. J. 1933. *J. R. hort. Soc.* **58**, 17.
Collins, J. L. 1933. *Cytologia*, **4**, 248.
Collins, J. L. & Kerns, K. R. 1931. *J. Hered.* **22**, 139.
—— —— 1935. *Proc. Hawaii Acad. Sci.* **10**, 10.
—— —— 1936. *Amer. Nat.* **70**, 45.
Condit, I. J. 1928. *Univ. Calif. Publ. Bot.* **11**, 233.
—— 1933. *Univ. Calif. Publ. Bot.* **17**, 61.
Coonen, L. P. 1939. *Amer. J. Bot.* **26**, 49.
Cooper, D. C. 1931. *Amer. J. Bot.* **18**, 337.
—— 1932. *Amer. J. Bot.* **19**, 429.
1935a. *Amer. J. Bot.* **22**, 453.
—— 1935b. *J. Agr. Res.* **51**, 471.
—— 1936. *Amer. J. Bot.* **23**, 231.

465

COOPER, D. C.   1939.   *Bot. Gaz.* **100,** 362.
——   1941.   *Amer. J. Bot.* **28,** 755.
COOPER, D. C. & MAHONY, K. L.   1935.   *Amer. J. Bot.* **22,** 843.
COOPER, G. O.   1935.   *Bot. Gaz.* **97,** 169.
——   1936.   *Bot. Gaz.* **98,** 348.
CORTI, R. N.   1930b.   *Nuovo G. bot. ital.* **37,** 679.
——   1931a.   *Nuovo G. bot. ital.* **38,** 230.
——   1931b.   *Nuovo G. bot. ital.* **38,** 564.
——   1948.   *Nuovo G. bot. ital.* **55,** 446.
COULTER, J. M.   1908.   *Bot. Gaz.* **46,** 43.
COUTINHO, L. DE A.   1940.   *Agron. lusit.* **2,** 379.
——   1945.   *Bol. Soc. Brot.* **19,** 448.
COUTINHO, L. DE A. & LORENZO-ANDREU, A.   1948.   *An. Estac. exp. Aula Dei,* **1,** 3.
COUTINHO, L. DE A. & RIBEIRO, M. I. A.   1945.   *Rev. agron. Lisboa,* **33,** 354.
COUTINHO, L. DE A. & SANTOS, A.   1943.   *Agron. lusit.* **5,** 349.
COVAS, G.   1945.   *Rev. argent. Agron.* **12,** 315.
——   1949a.   *Rev. argent. Agron.* **16,** 173.
——   1949b.   *Darwiniana,* **9,** 158.
——   1950a.   *Rev. argent. Agron.* **17,** 78.
——   1950b.   *Rev. argent. Agron.* **17,** 257.
——   1950c.   *Bol. Soc. argent. Bot.* **3,** 83.
——   1951.   *Rev. argent. Agron.* **18,** 74.
——   1952.   *Rev. argent. Agron.* **19,** 52.
COVAS, G. & BOCKLET, M.   1945.   *Rev. argent. Agron.* **12,** 261.
COVAS, G. & CHERUBINI, C.   1946.   *Rev. argent. Agron.* **13,** 55.
COVAS, G. & SCHNACK, B.   1944.   *Rev. argent. Agron.* **11,** 89.
—— ——   1945.   *Rev. argent. Agron.* **12,** 57.
—— ——   1946.   *Rev. argent. Agron.* **13,** 153.
—— ——   1947.   *Rev. argent. Agron.* **14,** 224.
CRAMPTON, B.   1950.   *Madroño,* **10,** 95.
CRANE, M. B.   1936.   *Roy. Hort. Soc. Conf. on Cherries & Soft Fruits,* 121.
CRANE, M. B. & DARLINGTON, C. D.   1927.   *Genetica,* **9,** 241.
CRANE, M. B. & GAIRDNER, A. E.   1923.   *J. Genet.* **13,** 187.
CRANE, M. B. & LAWRENCE, W. J. C.   1938.   *Genetics of Garden Plants,* 2nd edn., London.
CRANE, M. B. & THOMAS, P. T.   1937.   *J. Genet.* **37,** 287.
—— ——   1939.   *Nature,* **143,** 684.
—— ——   1942.   *Nature,* **150,** 431.
CRUICHSHANK, R. H.   1953.   *Pap. roy. Soc. Tasm.* **87,** 13.
CUGNAC, A. & SIMONET, M.   1941.   *C.R. Soc. Biol.* **135,** 728.
CURTIS, W. M.   1952.   *New Phytol.* **51,** 398.

DAHL, A. O.   1937.   *Amer. J. Bot.* **24,** 732.
DAHLGREN, K. V. O.   1916.   *K. svenska Vetensk Akad. Handl.* **56,** no. 4.
——   1952.   *Hereditas,* **38,** 314.
D'AMATO, F.   1939.   *Nuovo G. bot. ital.* **46,** 470.
——   1940.   *Nuovo G. bot. ital.* **47,** 349.
——   1945.   *Nuovo G. bot. ital.* **52,** 86.
——   1946.   *Nuovo G. bot. ital.* **53,** 170.
——   1947b.   *Nuovo G. bot. ital.* **53,** 405.
——   1948.   *Caryologia,* **1,** 48.
——   1949a.   *Caryologia,* **2,** 60.
——   1949b.   *Caryologia,* **2,** 71.
——   1949c.   *Caryologia,* **1,** 194.
DANGEARD, P.   1937.   *Botaniste,* **28,** 291.
DANIELSSON, B.   1946.   *Sverig. pomol. Fören. Årsskr.* 1945, 7.
DANSEREAU, P.   1940.   *Ann. Épiphyt,* **6,** 7.
DARK S. O. S.   1932a.   *Ann. Bot., Lond.* **46,** 965.
—— ——   1932b.   *New Phytol.* **31,** 310.

DARK, S. O. S. 1934. *J. Genet.* **29**, 85.
—— 1936. *J. Genet.* **32**, 353.
DARLINGTON, C. D. 1927. *J. Pomol.* **6**, 242.
—— 1928. *J. Genet.* **19**, 213.
—— 1929a. *J. Genet.* **21**, 207.
—— 1929b. *Genetica*, **11**, 267.
—— 1930. *J. Genet.* **22**, 65.
—— 1931a. *J. Genet.* **24**, 65.
—— 1931b. *J. Genet.* **24**, 405.
—— 1931c. *Cytologia*, **3**, 21.
—— 1932b. *Biol. Bull., Wood's Hole*, **63**, 368.
—— 1933a. *Cytologia*, **4**, 229.
—— 1933b. *J. Genet.* **28**, 327.
—— 1936a. *Cytologia*, **7**, 242.
—— 1936b. *Cytologia*, **7**, 248.
—— 1936c. *Proc. Roy. Soc.* ser. B, **121**, 264.
—— 1937a. *Recent Advances in Cytology.* 2nd edn. London & Philadelphia.
—— 1937b. *J. Genet.* **35**, 259.
—— 1941. *Ann. Bot., Lond.* **5**, 203.
—— 1956. *Chromosome Botany*, Allen & Unwin, London.
DARLINGTON, C. D. & GAIRDNER, A. E. 1937. *J. Genet.* **35**, 97.
DARLINGTON, C. D., HAIR, J. B. & HURCOMBE, R. 1951. *Heredity*, **5**, 233.
DARLINGTON, C. D. & JANAKI AMMAL, E. K. 1945. *Ann. Bot., Lond.* **9**, 267.
DARLINGTON, C. D. & LA COUR, L. F. 1940. *J. Genet.* **40**, 185.
—— —— 1941. *Ann. Bot., Lond.* **5**, 547.
—— —— 1942. The Handling of Chromosomes. London.
—— —— 1950. *Heredity*, **4**, 217.
DARLINGTON, C. D. & MOFFETT, A. A. 1930. *J. Genet.* **22**, 129.
DARLINGTON, C. D. & THOMAS, P. T. 1941. *Proc. Roy. Soc. B.* **130**, 127.
DARLINGTON, C. D. & UPCOTT, M. B. 1941. *J. Genet.* **41**, 275.
DARMER, G. 1947. *Biol. Zbl.* **66**, 166.
DARROW, G. M. 1937. *Yearb. U.S. Dep. Agric.* 445.
*DARROW, G. M., CAMP, W. H., FISCHER, H. E. & DERMEN, H. 1944. *Bull. Torrey bot. Cl.* **71**, 498.
DATTA, P. C. 1952. *Caryologia*, **5**, 86.
DATTA, S. 1932. *Mem. Manchr. lit. phil. Soc.* **76**, 85.
—— 1933a. *J. Indian Bot. Soc.* **12**, 131.
—— 1933b. *Curr. Sci.* **1**, 364.
DAVIE, J. H. 1935. *Genetica*, **17**, 487.
DAVIES, E. W. 1953a. *Nature*, **171**, 659.
—— 1953b. *Watsonia*, **3**, 66, 70.
—— 1955. *Watsonia*, **3**, 129.
DAWSON, C. D. R. 1941. *J. Genet.* **42**, 49.
DAWSON, R. F. 1948. *Lloydia*, **11**, 81.
DELAUNAY, L. N. 1926. *Z. Zellforsch.* **4**, 338.
*DELAY, C. 1951. *Rev. Cytol., Paris*, **12**, 1.
DELISLE, A. L. 1937. *Amer. J. Bot.* **24**, 741.
DERMEN, H. 1931a. *Amer. J. Bot.* **18**, 250.
—— 1931b. *J. Arnold Arbor.* **12**, 281.
—— 1932a. *J. Arnold Arbor.* **13**, 50.
—— 1932b. *J. Arnold Arbor.* **13**, 410.
—— 1936a. *Cytologia*, **7**, 160.
—— 1936c. *J. Arnold Arbor.* **17**, 90.
—— 1949. *J. Hered.* **40**, 162.
DIANNELIDIS, T. 1949. *Prak. Acad. Athen*, **23**, 352.
—— 1951. *Portug. acta biol. A.* **3**, 151.
DILLEWIJN, C. VAN. 1939. *Ned. Boschb. Tijdschr.* **12**, 470.
—— 1942. *Genetica*, **22**, 131.
DILLMAN, A. 1933. *Science*, **78**, 409.

DIXIT, P. D. 1932. *Indian J. agric. Sci.* **2**, 385.
DNYANSAGAR, V. R. 1949. *J. Indian bot. Soc.* **28**, 95.
—— 1951 *J Indian. bot. Soc.* **30**, 100.
—— 1952. *Proc. Indian Acad. Sci. B*, **36**, 1.
DOBRONZ, K. 1935. *Diss. Univ., Berlin*, 61 pp.
DODDS, K. S. 1946. *Nature*, **157**, 729.
DODDS, K. S. & SIMMONDS, N. W. 1948. *J. Genet.* **48**, 285.
DOLCHER, T. 1947. *Nuovo G. bot. ital.* **54**, 648.
—— 1949. *Caryologia*, **2**, 55.
—— 1950. *Caryologia*, **2**, 127.
DORSEY, E. 1925. Thesis, Cornell Univ.
—— 1936. *J. Hered.* **27**, 155.
—— 1939. *J. Hered.* **30**, 393.
DOUGHTY, L. R. 1936. *J. Genet.* **33**, 197.
—— 1939. *Ann. Rep. E. Afr. Agric. Res. Sta. Amani*, 1939.
DOULAT, E. 1944. *Rev. Cytol., Paris*, **7**, 14.
—— 1946. *C.R. Acad. Sci., Paris*, **222**, 1510.
—— 1947. *C.R. Acad. Sci., Paris*, **225**, 354.
DOUWES, H. 1951. *J. Genet.* **50**, 179.
—— 1953. *J. Genet.* **51**, 611.
DOWRICK, G. J. 1952a. *Ann. Rep. John Innes Hort. Inst.* **42**, 47.
—— 1952b. *Heredity*, **6**, 365.
DRAHOWZAL, G. 1936. *Öst. Bot. Z.* **86**, 241.
DUDLEY, M. G. 1937. *Bot. Gaz.* **98**, 556.
DUFFIELD, J. W. 1940. *Amer. J. Bot.* **27**, 787.
—— 1943. *Chron. Bot.* **7**, 390.
DUGGAR, B. M. 1900. *Bot. Gaz.* **29**, 81.
DUNCAN, R. E. 1947. *Orchid Digest*, **11**, 199.
DUNCAN, R. E. & MCLEOD, R. A. 1948. *Bull. Amer. Orchid Soc.* **17**, 170.
—— —— 1949a. *Bull. Amer. Orchid Soc.* **18**, 84.
—— —— 1949b. *Bull. Amer. Orchid Soc.* **18**, 159.
—— —— 1949c. *Bull. Amer. Orchid Soc.* **18**, 573.
—— —— 1950. *Bull. Amer. Orchid Soc.* **19**, 489.
DUSSEAU, A. & MAGNANT, C. 1941a. *C.R. Acad. Sci., Paris*, **212**, 455.
—— —— 1941b. *C.R. Acad. Sci., Paris*, **213**, 276.
DUTT, M. 1952a. *Curr. Sci.* **21**, 168.
—— 1952b. *Sci. & Cult.* **17**, 527.

EARNSHAW, F. 1942. *New Phytol.* **41**, 151.
EAST, E. M. 1933. *Genetics*, **18**, 324.
EDMAN, G. 1929. *Acta Hort. berg.* **9**, 165.
—— 1931. *Acta Hort. berg.* **11**, 13.
EHRENBERG, L. 1945. *Bot. Notiser*, 1945, 430.
EHRENDORFER, F. 1949. *Öst. Bot. Z.* **96**, 109.
—— 1952. *Carneg. Inst. Wash. Yearb.* **51**, 125.
EICHHORN, A. 1937a. *C.R. Acad. Sci., Paris*, **204**, 1669.
—— 1937b. *Cytologia, F.J.N.* 447.
—— 1938. *C.R. Acad. Sci., Paris*, **206**, 1266.
—— 1943. *Bull. Mus. Hist. nat. Paris*, Ser. 2, **15**, 461.
—— 1949. *Rev. Cytol., Paris*, **11**, 333.
—— 1950. *Rev. gén. Bot.* **57**, 209.
EICHHORN, A. & FRANQUET, R. 1936. *C.R. Acad. Sci., Paris*, **202**, 1609.
EIGSTI, O. J. 1936. *Bot. Gaz.* **98**, 363.
—— 1942. *Amer. J. Bot.* **29**, 626.
EINSET, J. 1944. *Amer. J. Bot.* **31**, 336.
—— 1947. *Gentes Herbarum*, **7**, 181.
EINSET, J. & IMHOFE, B. 1947. *Proc. Amer. Soc. hort. Sci.* **50**, 45.
—— —— 1949. *Proc. Amer. Soc. hort. Sci.* **53**, 197.
EINSET, J. & LAMB, B. 1951. *Proc. Amer. Soc. hort. Sci.* **58**, 103.

EKLUNDH-EHRENBERG, C. 1949. *Hereditas*, **35**, 1.
ELLERSTRÖM, S. & TJIO, J. H. 1950. *Bot. Notiser*, 1950, 463.
ELLIOT, E. 1950. *New Phytol.* **49**, 344.
ELLIOTT, F. C. 1949. *Iowa St. Coll. J. Sci.* **24**, 44.
ELVERS, I. 1932a. *Svensk bot. Tidskr.* **26**, 13.
—— 1932b. *Acta Hort. berg.* **11**, 81.
EMERSON, S. H. 1938. *Genetics*, **23**, 190.
EMME, H. 1928. *Z.i.A.V.* **47**, 99.
—— 1930. *Züchter*, **2**, 65.
EMME, H. & SCHEPELJEWA, H. 1927. *Bull. appl. Bot. Pl. Breed*, **17**, 265.
EMSWELLER, S. L. & BRIERLEY, P. 1940. *J. Hered.* **31**, 223.
EMSWELLER, S. L. & LUMSDEN, D. V. 1943. *Proc. Amer. Soc. hort. Sci.* **42**, 593.
ERLANDSSON, S. 1939a. *Hereditas*, **25**, 27.
—— 1939b. *Bot. Notiser*, 1939, 261.
—— 1942a. *Ark. Bot.* **30**, 1.
—— 1942b. *Hereditas*, **28**, 503.
—— 1942c. *Acta Hort. berg.* **13**, 117.
—— 1946. *Svensk bot. Tidskr.* **40**, 427.
ERLANSON, E. W. 1929. *Bot. Gaz.* **87**, 443.
—— 1932. *Amer. Rose Ann.* **17**, 83.
—— 1933. *Bot. Gaz.* **94**, 551.
—— 1934. *Bot. Gaz.* **96**, 197.
—— 1938. *New Phytol.* **37**, 72.
ERITZIAN, A. 1932. *Bull. appl. Bot.* Ser. 5, 47.
ERWIN, A. T. & HABER, E. S. 1930. *Bull. agric. Exp. Sta., Iowa*, **263**, 343.
EYSTER, W. H. 1939. *Proc. 7th Int. Genet. Congr.* 117.

FABERGÉ, A. C. 1935. *Nature*, **135**, 876.
—— 1944. *J. Genet.* **46**, 125.
FAGERLIND, F. 1934. *Hereditas*, **19**, 223.
—— 1937. *Acta Hort. berg.* **11**, 195.
—— 1938. *Svensk bot. Tidskr.* **32**, 139.
—— 1940. *Hereditas*, **26**, 23.
—— 1947. *Acta Hort. berg.* **14**, 221.
FARDY, A. 1940. *Bull. Mus. Hist. nat., Paris*, **12**, 132.
FAVARGER, C. 1946. *Ber. schweiz. bot. Ges.* **56**, 365.
—— 1949a. *Ber. schweiz. bot. Ges.* **59**, 62.
—— 1949b. *Bull. Soc. neuchâtel. Sci. nat.* **72**, 15.
—— 1952a. *Ber. schweiz. bot. Ges.* **62**, 5.
—— 1952b. *Ber. schweiz. bot. Ges.* **62**, 244.
—— 1953. *Bull. Soc. neuchâtel. Sci. nat.* **76**, 133.
FAVERGER, C. & SÖLLNER, R. 1949. *Ber. schweiz. bot. Ges.* **59**, 87.
FEDOROVA, N. J. 1946. *C.R. Acad. Sci. U.R.S.S.* **52**, 545.
FEDOTOV, V. S. 1935. *Bull. appl. Bot., Pl.-Breed.* **9**, 165.
FEINBRUN, N. 1939. *Palest. J. Bot. Rehovot*, **1**, 42.
—— 1950. *Palest. J. Bot., Jerusalem*, **5**, 13.
FELFÖLDY, L. J. M. 1947a. *Archiv. Biol. Hung.* **17**, 101.
—— 1947b. *Rep. Hung. agric. Exp. Sta.* **47-49**, 11.
FERGUSON, M. C. & COOLIDGE, E. B. 1932. *Amer. J. Bot.* **19**, 644.
FERGUSON, N. 1926. *Phil. Trans. Roy. Soc.* Ser. B, **215**, 225.
FERNANDES, A. 1931. *Bol. Soc. Brot.* **6**, 294.
—— 1934. *Bol. Soc. Brot.* **11**, 1.
—— 1936. *Bol. Soc. Brot.* **11**, 267.
—— 1937a. *Bol. Soc. Brot.* **12**, 93.
—— 1937b. *Bol. Soc. Brot.* **12**, 159.
—— 1939a. *Sci. genet.* **1**, 16.
—— 1939b. *Bol. Soc. Brot.* **13**, 487.
—— 1939c. *Sci. genet.* **1**, 141.
—— 1940. *Bol. Soc. Brot.* **14**, 53.

FERNANDES, A. 1943. *Bol. Soc. Brot.* **17,** 5.
—— 1949a. *Bol. Soc. Brot.* **23,** 1.
—— 1949b. *Bol. Soc. Brot.* **23,** 177.
—— 1950a. *Bol. Soc. Brot.* **24,** 291.
—— 1950b. *Agron. lusit.* **12,** 551.
—— 1951. *Bol. Soc. Brot.* **25,** 113.
FERNANDES, A. & FERNANDES, R. 1945. *Herbertia,* **12,** 85.
—— —— 1946. *Acta Univ. Conim.* **1.**
FERNANDES, A., GARCIA, J. & FERNANDES, R. 1948. *Mem. Soc. Brot.* **4,** 5.
FERNANDES, A. & NEVES, J. B. 1941. *Bol. Soc. Brot.* **15,** 43.
FIKRY, M. A. 1930. *J.R. micr. Soc.* **50,** 387.
FICKER, T. 1951. *Plant Life,* **7,** 68.
FINN, W. 1937. *J. Inst. bot. Acad. Sci. Ukr.* **12,** 83.
FINN, W. W. 1928. *Ber. dtsch. bot. Ges.* **46,** 235.
FISHER, W. D., BASHAW, E. C. & HOLT, E. C. 1954. *Agron. J.* **46,** 401.
FISK, E. L. 1931. *P.N.A.S.* **17,** 511.
FITZPATRICK, J. M. 1946. *New Phytol.* **45,** 137.
FLORIN, R. 1932. *Svensk bot. Tidskr.* **26,** 205.
FLORY, W. S. 1934. *Cytologia,* **6,** 1.
—— 1936. *J. Arnold Arbor.* **17,** 83.
—— 1937. *Cytologia, F.J.N.* 171.
—— 1940. *Texas Agr. Exp. Sta. Ann. Rep.* **53,** 28.
—— 1943. *Herbertia,* **10,** 114.
—— 1948. *Amer. J. Bot.* **35,** 791.
—— 1950. *Virginia J. Sci.* **1,** 111.
FLOTO, E. V. & GUDJONSSON, G. 1947. *K. VetHøjsk. Aarsskr.* 1947, 31.
FLOVIK, K. 1938. *Hereditas,* **24,** 265.
—— 1940. *Hereditas,* **26,** 430.
FOGELBERG, S. O. 1938. *Bull. Torrey bot. Cl.* **65,** 631.
FORBES, I. 1952. *Agron. J.* **44,** 194.
FORD, C. E. 1938. *Genetica,* **20,** 431.
FOSTER, R. C. 1933. *J. Arnold Arbor.* **14,** 386.
—— 1937. *Contr. Gray Herb. Harv.* no. 119.
FOTHERGILL, P. G. 1936. *Proc. Univ. Durham phil. Soc.* **9,** 205.
—— 1938. *Genetica,* **20,** 159.
—— 1944. *New Phytol.* **43,** 23.
FRAHM-LELIVELD, J. A. 1953. *Euphytica,* **2,** 46.
FRANCINI, E. N. 1931. *Nuovo G. bot. ital.* **38,** 155.
FRANDSEN, N. H. & WINGE, O. 1932. *Herèditas,* **16,** 212.
FRANKEL, O. H. 1940. *J. Genet.* **40,** 171.
—— 1941. *Nature,* **147,** 117.
FRANKEL, O. H. & HAIR, J. B. 1937. *N.Z. J. Sci. Tech.* **18,** 669.
FREIBURG, M. 1933. *Planta,* **20,** 659.
FRETER, L. E. & BROWN, W. V. 1955. *Bull. Torrey bot. Cl.* **82,** 121
FRIESNER, R. C. 1930. *Butler Univ. bot. Stud.* **1,** 77.
FRISENDAHL, A. 1927. *Acta Hort. gothoburg.* **3,** 99.
FRISENDAHL, A. K. 1912. *Svensk Vet. Akad. Handl.* **48,** 62.
FRITSCH, R. 1935. Diss. Univ. Berlin.
FROST, H. B. 1931. *P.N.A.S.* **17,** 434.
FRÖST, S. 1948. *Hereditas,* **34,** 255.
FRYER, J. R. 1930. *Canad. J. Res.* **3,** 3.
FUKUDA, Y. 1933. *Jap. J. Bot.* **6,** 489.
FULTS, J. L. 1942. *Amer. J. Bot.* **29,** 45.
FURUSATO, K. 1940. *Bot. & Zool., Tokyo,* **8,** 1303.

GAISER, L. O. 1927. *Trans. roy. Soc. Can.* **21** (5), 1.
—— 1949. *Amer. J. Bot.* **36,** 122.
—— 1950a. *Amer. J. Bot.* **37,** 414.
—— 1950b. *Amer. J. Bot.* **37,** 763.

GAISER, L. O. 1951a. *Madroño*, **11**, 10,
—— 1951b. *Evolution*, **5**, 52.
GAISER, L. O., SUTHERLAND, M. & MOORE, R. 1943. *Amer. J. Bot.* **30**, 543.
GAJEWSKI, W. 1946. *Acta Soc. Bot. Polon.* **17**, 129.
—— 1947. *Acta Soc. Bot. Polon.* **18**, 33.
—— 1949. *Proc. 8th Int. Congr. Genet.* 578.
GANESAN, D. 1939. *J. Genet.* **38**, 493.
GANGULY, J. K. 1946. *Curr. Sci.* **15**, 112.
GARBER, E. D. 1944a. *Amer. J. Bot.* **31**, 161.
—— 1944b. *Amer. Nat.* **78**, 89.
—— 1950. *Univ. Calif. Publ. Bot.* **23**, 283.
—— 1954. *Bot. Gaz.* **115**, 336.
GARBER, E. D. & SNYDER, L. A. 1951. *Madroño*, **11**, 6.
GARCIA, J. G. 1942. *Bol. Soc. Brot.* **16**, 183.
GARDÉ, A. 1948. *Genet. iber.* **1**, 69.
—— 1952a. *Genet. iber.* **3**, 133.
—— 1952b. *Genet. iber.* **3**, 145.
* GARDÉ, A. & GARDÉ, N. 1949. *Agron. lusit.* **11**, 91.
*—— —— 1951. *Genet. iber.* **3**, 23.
GARDÉ, A. & MALHEIROS-GARDÉ, N. 1952. *Genet. iber.* **4**, 91.
—— —— 1953. *Genet. iber.* **5**, 115.
—— —— 1954. *Brotéria*, **23**, 5.
GASSNER, G. G. 1941. *Beih. bot. Zbl. A.* **61**, 237.
GAUGER, W. 1937. *Planta*, **26**, 529.
GEISLER, F. 1931. *Butler Univ. bot. Stud.* **2**, 53.
GEITLER, L. 1929a. *Öst. bot. Z.* **78**, 242.
—— 1929b. *Züchter*, **1**, 243.
—— 1936. *Jb. wiss. Bot.* **83**, 707.
—— 1939. *Öst. bot. Z.* **88**, 226.
—— 1940. *Chromosoma*, **1**, 554.
GELIN, O. E. V. 1936. *Svensk bot. Tidskr.* **30**, 324.
—— 1934. *Acta Hort. berg.* **11**, 99.
GENTSCHEFF, G. 1938. *Genetica*, **20**, 398.
GENTCHEFF, G. & GUSTAFSSON, A. 1940a. *Bot. Notiser*, 1940, 109.
—— —— 1940b. *Hereditas*, **26**, 209.
GENTSCHEFF, G. 1937a. *Planta*, **27**, 165.
—— 1937b. Diss. Univ. Sofia.
GERSHOY, A. 1934. *Bull. Vt. agric. Exp. Sta.* no. 367.
GHIMPU, V. 1928. *C.R. Acad. Sci., Paris*, **187**, 245.
GHIMPU, V. C. R. 1929a. *C.R. Soc. Biol., Paris*, **100**, 187.
—— 1929b. *Congr. int. Agric., Bucarest*, 1929.
—— 1930. *Arch. Anat. micr.* **26**, 135.
GHOSE, A. K. 1952. *Sci. & Cult*, **17**, 384.
GIFFIN, M. H. 1936. *Trans. roy. Soc. S. Afr.* **24**, 203.
GILES, N. H. 1942. *Amer. J. Bot.* **29**, 637.
GIUFFRIDA, C. 1950. *Caryologia*, **3**, 113.
GLOTOV, V. 1940. *C.R. Acad. Sci. U.R.S.S.* **28**, 450.
GOLDSMITH, E. P. & KRUPKO, S. 1948. *J. S. Afr. Bot.* **14**, 107.
GOLUBINSKI, I. N. 1936. *Sovetsk. Bot.* 1936, 49.
—— 1937. *C.R. Acad. Sci. U.R.S.S.* **15**, 261.
GOODSPEED, T. H. 1930. *Univ. Calif. Publ. Bot.* **11**, 299.
—— 1940. *Herbertia*, **7**, 17.
*—— 1945. *Univ. Calif. Publ. Bot.* **18**, 335.
GOODSPEED, T. H., UBER, F. M. & AVERY, P. 1935. *Univ. Calif. Publ. Bot.* **18**, 33.
GOODWIN, R. H. 1937. *Amer. J. Bot.* **24**, 425.
GOPINATH, D. M. 1944. *Proc. Indian Acad. Sci. B*, **20**, 175.
—— 1945. *Proc. Indian Acad. Sci. B*, **22**, 225.
GOTOH, K. 1937. *Jap. J. Genet.* **13**, 209.
GOTOH, K. & KIKKAWA, R. 1937. *Jap. J. Genet.* **13**, 241.

GOTOH, K. & OKURA, E. 1933. *J. Soc. trop. Agric., Taihoku Univ., Formosa*, **5**, 363.
GOULD, F. W. 1953. *Amer. J. Bot.* **40**, 297.
GOUWS, J. B. 1949. *Plant Life*, **5**, 54.
—— 1950. *Natuurwet. Tijdschr.* **32**, 139.
GOW, J. E. 1908. *Bot. Gaz.* **46**, 35.
GRAM, K., LARSEN, C. M., LARSEN, C. S. & WESTERGAARD, M. 1941. *K. Vet Højsk. Aarrskr.* 1941, 44.
GRANER, E. A. 1935. *Contr. cytol. da Manioca Univ., S. Paulo, Escol. Sup. de Agric. 'Luiz de Querioz'.*
—— 1942. *Bragantia, S. Paulo*, **2**, 23.
GRANICK, E. B. 1944. *Amer. J. Bot.* **31**, 283.
GRANT, V. 1950. *Yearb. Carneg. Inst. Wash.* **49**, 111.
—— 1953. *Evolution*, **7**, 51.
GRANT, W. F. 1953. *Amer. J. Bot.* **40**, 729.
—— 1954. *Bot. Gaz.* **115**, 323.
—— 1955. *Brittonia*, **8**, 121.
GRAZE, H. 1933. *Jb. wiss. Bot.* **77**, 507.
—— 1935. *Jb. wiss. Bot.* **81**, 609.
GRECO, R. N. 1929. *Nuovo G. bot. ital.* **36**, 57.
GREENLEAF, W. H. 1942. *J. Genet.* **43**, 69.
—— 1947. *Proc. Amer. Soc. hort. Sci.* **49**, 231.
GREGOR, J. W. & SANSOME, F. W. 1930. *J. Genet.* **22**, 373.
GREGORY, P. J. 1936. *J. Linn. Soc. (Bot.)*, **50**, 363.
*GREGORY, W. C. 1941. *Trans. Amer. Phil. Soc.* n.s. **31**, 443.
*GRIESINGER, R. 1937. *Ber. dtsch. bot. Ges.* **55**, 556.
GRIESINGER, R. & KLINKOWSKI, M. 1939. *Züchter*, **11**, 147.
GRIFFEE, F. 1927. *Stud. biol. Sci. Univ. Minn.* **6**, 319.
GRIMM, J. 1912. *Flora*, **104**, 309.
GUARD, A. T. & HOBBES, C. H. 1941. *Proc. Ind. Acad. Sci.* **50**, 68.
GUDJONSSON, G. 1941. *Bot. Tidskr.* **45**, 352.
GUINOCHET, M. 1935. *Rev. Cytol., Paris*, **1**, 131.
—— 1942. *Bull. Soc. bot. Fr.* **89**, 153.
—— 1943. *Rev. Cytol., Paris*, **6**, 209.
—— 1945. *Rev. Cytol., Paris*, **8**, 87.
—— 1946. *C.R. Acad. Sci., Paris*, **222**, 1131.
GUINOCHET, M. & LEMÉE, G. 1950. *Rev. gen. Bot.* **57**, 565.
GULLINE, H. F. 1952. *Pap. roy. Soc. Tasm.* **86**, 131.
GUSTAFSSON, A. 1932. *Hereditas*, **16**, 41.
—— 1933. *Hereditas*, **18**, 77.
—— 1935a. *Hereditas*, **20**, 1.
—— 1935b. *Hereditas*, **21**, 1.
—— 1939. *Hereditas*, **25**, 33.
—— 1942. *Hereditas*, **28**, 249.
—— 1943. *Acta Univ. lund*, n.s. 2, **39**, 3.
—— 1947. *Acta Univ. lund*, n.s. 2, **43**, 1.
GUSTAFSSON, A. & HÅKANSSON, A. 1942. *Bot. Notiser*, 1942, 331.
GUSULEAC, M. & TARNAVSCHI, J. T. 1935. *Bull. Fac. Sci. Cernauti*, **9**, 387.

DE HAAN, I. & DOORENBOS, J. 1951. *Meded. Landb.Hoogesch., Wageningen*, **51**, 151.
HAASE-BESSEL, G. 1928. *Planta*, **6**, 767.
HAFLINGER, E. 1943. *Ber. schweiz. bot. Ges.* **53**, 317.
HAGA, T. 1937a. *Cytologia*, **8**, 137.
—— 1937b. *Jap. J. Genet.* **13**, 135.
—— 1951. *Cytologia*, **16**, 243.
HAGERUP, O. 1927. *Dansk bot. Ark.* **5**, 1.
—— 1928. *Dansk bot. Ark.* **6**, 1.
*—— 1932. *Hereditas*, **16**, 19.
—— 1933. *Hereditas*, **18**, 122.
—— 1938. *Hereditas*, **24**, 258.

HAGERUP, O. 1939. *Hereditas*, **25**, 185.
—— 1940. *Hereditas*, **26**, 399.
—— 1941a. *Planta*, **32**, 6.
—— 1941b. *Bot. Tidskr.* **45**, 385.
—— 1944. *Hereditas*, **30**, 152.
—— 1947. *K. dansk. vidensk. Selsk. Biol. Medd.* **20** (9), 1.
HAIR, J. B. 1942. *Trans. roy. Soc. N.Z.* **71**, 271.
HÅKANSSON, A. 1926. *Acta Univ. lund.* n.s. 2, **21**, 471.
—— 1928. *Hereditas*, **10**, 277.
—— 1929. *Hereditas*, **13**, 1.
—— 1931. *Ber. dtsch. bot. Ges.* **49**, 228.
—— 1933. *Hereditas*, **18**, 199.
—— 1945. *Bot. Notiser*, 1945, 1.
—— 1946. *Acta Univ. lund.* **42**, 1.
—— 1949. *Hereditas*, **35**, 375.
—— 1952. *Bot. Notiser*, 1951, 143.
—— 1953. *Bot. Notiser*, 1953, 301.
—— 1954. *Hereditas*, **40**, 325.
HAMACHER, H. 1947. *Mem. Inst. Osw. Cruz*, **45**, 373.
HAMBLER, D. J. 1954. *Nature, Lond.* **173**, 547.
HAMEL, J. L. 1937. *Rev. Cytol., Paris*, **2**, 392.
—— 1938. *Rev. Cytol., Paris*, **3**, 153.
—— 1939. *Bull. Mus. Hist. nat., Paris*, **11**, 271.
—— 1948a. *Bull. Mus. Hist. nat., Paris*, **20**, 198.
—— 1948b. *Bull. Mus. Hist. nat., Paris*, **20**, 558.
—— 1949a. *Bull. Mus. Hist. nat., Paris*, **21**, 749.
—— 1949b. *Bull. Mus. Hist. nat., Paris*, **21**, 752.
—— 1950. *Bull. Mus. Hist. nat., Paris*, **22**, 785.
—— 1951a. *Bull. Mus. Hist. nat., Paris*, **23**, 548.
—— 1951b. *Bull. Mus. Hist. nat., Paris*, **23**, 651.
—— 1952. *Bull. Mus. Hist. nat., Paris*, **24**, 588.
—— 1953. *Rev. Cytol., Paris*, **14**, 113.
—— 1954. *Mem. Soc. bot. Fr.*, 1953-4, 106.
HANCOCK, B. L. 1942. *New Phytol.* **41**, 70.
HANSEN, A. A. & HILL, H. D. 1953a. *Bull. Torrey bot. Cl.* **80**, 16.
—— —— 1953b. *Bull. Torrey bot. Cl.* **80**, 113.
HANSON, C. H. 1953. *Agron. J.* **45**, 200.
HAQUE, A. 1946. *Curr. Sci.* **15**, 78.
—— 1951. *Bot. Gaz.* **112**, 495.
—— 1952. *Rep. John Innes hort. Instn.* **42**, 47.
HARA, S. 1942. *Jap. J. Genet.* **18**, 183.
HARADA, I. 1942. *Jap. J. Genet.* **18**, 92.
—— 1943. *Jap. J. Genet.* **19**, 120.
—— 1944. *Jap. J. Genet.* **20**, 127.
—— 1947. *Cytologia*, **14**, 214.
—— 1948. *Jap. J. Genet.* **23**, 13.
—— 1951. *Jap. J. Genet.* **26**, 226.
HARDAS, M. W. & JOSHI, A. B. 1954. *Indian J. Genet.* **14**, 47.
HARLAN, J. R. 1949. *Amer. J. Bot.* **36**, 495.
HARLAND, S. C. 1940. *Trop. Agriculture, Trin.* **17**, 53.
HARLING, G. 1945. *Bot. Notiser*, 1945, 114.
—— 1946. *Svensk bot. Tidskr.* **40**, 257.
—— 1950. *Acta Hort. berg.* **15**, 135.
—— 1951a. *Acta Hort. berg.* **16**, 1.
—— 1951b. *Acta Hort. berg.* **16**, 73.
HARMSEN, L. 1939. *Medd. Grønland, Copenhagen*, **125**, 1.
—— 1943. *Medd. Grønland, Copenhagen*, **131**, 1.
HARRISON, H. H. 1930. *Proc. Univ. Durham phil. Soc.* **8**, 252.
HARRISON, J. W. H. 1920. *Trans. nat. Hist. Soc. Northumb.* **5**, 244.

HARRISON, J. W. H. 1926. *Nature*, **117**, 50.
HARTUNG, M. E. 1946. *Amer. J. Bot.* **33**, 516.
HASEGAWA, N. 1932. *Cytologia*, **3**, 350.
—— 1933. *Bot. Mag., Tokyo*, **47**, 901.
—— 1934. *Cytologia*, **6**, 68.
HASKELL, G. & MARKS, G. E. 1952. *New Phytol.* **51**, 382.
HÄUSER, R. 1916. *Beitr. allg. Bot.* **1**, 115.
HAWKES, J. G. 1944. *Bull. Imp. Bur. Pl. Br. & Genet.*
—— 1954. *Ann. Mag. nat. Hist.*, ser. 12, **7**, 689.
HEASLIP, M. B. 1951. *Ohio J. Sci.* **51**, 62.
HECHT, A. 1949. *Bull. Torrey bot. Cl.* **76**, 7.
HEILBORN, O. 1921. *Ark. Bot.* **17** (12).
—— 1926. *Svensk bot. Tidskr.* **20**, 414.
—— 1927. *Hereditas*, **9**, 59.
—— 1939. *Hereditas*, **25**, 224.
—— 1941. *Svensk bot. Tidskr.* **35**, 141.
HEIM, P. 1941. *Botaniste*, **31**, 66.
—— 1950. *Encycl. Mycol.* 1950.
HEIMANS, J. 1938. *Chron. Bot.* **4**, 389.
HEIMLICH, L. F. 1927. *P.N.A.S.* **13**, 113.
HEISER, C. B. 1947. *Madroño*, **9**, 103.
—— 1948. *Bull. Torrey bot. Cl.* **75**, 512.
HEISER, C. B. & WHITAKER, T. W. 1948. *Amer. J. Bot.* **35**, 179.
HEITZ, E. 1926. *Hab. Schr. Hamburg*, cit. T. 1927.
—— 1927. *Abh. Naturw. Hamburg*, **21**, 47.
—— 1929. *Ber. dtsch. bot. Ges.* **47**, 274.
—— 1931a. *Planta*, **12**, 775.
—— 1931b. *Planta*, **15**, 495.
—— 1932. *Planta*, **18**, 571.
HEITZ, E. & RESENDE, F. 1936. *Bol. Soc. Brot.* **11**, 5.
HERIBERT-NILSSON, N. 1928. *Acta Univ. lund.* n.s. 2, **24**, 89.
—— 1935. *Hereditas*, **20**, 339.
HESLOP-HARRISON, J. 1953. *Ann. Bot., Lond.* **17**, 539.
HESLOP-HARRISON, Y. 1953a. *New Phytol.* **52**, 22.
—— 1953b. *Watsonia*, **3**, 7.
HESLOT, H. 1953. *C.R. Acad. Sci., Paris*, **237**, 433.
HEUSSER, C. 1938. *Ber. schweiz. bot. Ges.* **48**, 562.
HEYN, A. N. J. 1936. *Landbouw.* **12**, 11.
HICKS, G. C. 1929. *Bot. Gaz.* **88**, 132.
HILL, H. D. & MYERS, W. M. 1948. *J. Amer. Soc. Agron.* **40**, 466.
HIORTH, G. 1933. *Z.i.A.V.* **66**, 106.
—— 1941. *Z.i.A.V.* **79**, 199.
HIRAYOSHI, I. 1937. *Jap. J. Genet.* **13**, 215.
—— 1942. *Seiken Zihô*, 1942, 88.
HIRAYOSHI, I. & MATSUMURA, M. 1952. *Jap.J. Breed.* **1**, 219.
HIRAYOSHI, I. & NAKAMURA, Y. 1943. *Bot. & Zool., Tokyo*, **11**, 73.
HJELMQVIST, H. 1951. *Bot. Notiser*, 1951, 180.
HOAR, C. S. 1931. *Bot. Gaz.* **92**, 396.
HOAR, C. S. & HAERTL, E. J. 1932. *Bot. Gaz.* **93**, 197.
HOCQUETTE, W. 1922. *C.R. Soc. Biol., Paris*, **87**, 1301.
HOFELICH, A. 1935. *Jb. wiss. Bot.* **81**, 541.
HOFFMANN, K. M. 1930. *Planta*, **10**, 523.
HOFMEYR, J. D. J. 1945. *S. Afr. J. Sci.* **41**, 225.
HOLLINGSHEAD, L. 1942. *Bull. Torrey bot. Cl.* **69**, 41.
HOLLINGSHEAD, L. & BABCOCK, E. B. 1930. *Univ. Calif. Publ. Agr. Sci.* **6**, 1.
HOLMGREN, J. 1919. *K. svenska VetenskAkad. Handl.* **59**, No. 7.
HOLZER, K. 1952. *Öst. bot. Z.* **99**, 118.
HOMBURG, O. 1931. Skandinaviens Flora, Stockholm, 1931.
HOMEDES, R. J. 1943. *An. Esc. Perit. agric. Barcelona*, **3**.

HOMEYER, H. 1932. *Planta*, **18**, 640.
—— 1935. *Bot. Jahrb.* **67**, 238.
HONING, J. A. 1928. *Meded. LandbHoogesch.*, *Wageningen*, **32**, 1
HORN, K. 1938. *Avh. norske VidenskAkad.* **5**, 1.
—— 1948. *Blyttia*, **6**.
HOWARD, H. W. 1938. *J. Genet.* **35**, 383.
—— 1939. *Cytologia*, **10**, 77.
—— 1942. *J. Genet.* **43**, 105.
—— 1947. *Nature*, **159**, 66.
HOWARD, H. W. & MANTON, I. 1946. *Ann. Bot., Lond.* **10**, 1.
HRISHI, N. J. 1952. *Genetica*, **26**, 280.
HRUBY, K. 1932. *Preslia*, **11**, 1.
—— 1933. *Vest. Kral. Ces. Spol. Nauk (Prague)*, **2**, 1.
—— 1934a. *Beih. bot. Zbl.* § A. **52**, 298.
—— 1934b. *Bull. int. Acad. Sci. Boheme*, 1.
—— 1935. *Stud. Pl. physiol. Lab. Charles Univ.* **5**, 1.
—— 1941. *Vest. Kral. Ces. Spol. Nauk (Prague)*, 1941, 9.
—— 1948. *J. Genet.* **48**, 316.
HUBER, A. W. 1927. *Jb. wiss. Bot.* **66**, 359.
HUMPHREY, L. M. 1932. *Amer. Nat.* **66**, 471.
—— 1934. *Amer. Nat.* **68**, 184.
HUNTER, A. W. S. 1934. *Canad. J. Res.* **11**, 213.
HUNZIKER, J. H. 1955. *Amer. J. Bot.* **42**, 459.
HURCOMBE, R. 1946. *S. Afr. J. Sci.* **42**, 144.
—— 1947. *J. S. Afr. Bot.* **13**, 107.
HURST, C. C. 1928. *Z.i.A.V.* Suppl. 2, 866.
—— 1931. *Proc. Roy. Soc. B.* **109**, 126.
HÜSER, W. 1930. *Planta*, **11**, 485.
HUSKINS, C. L. 1927. *J. Genet.* **18**, 315.
—— 1930. *Genetica*, **12**, 531.
HUSKINS, C. L. & LA COUR, L. 1930. *Amer. Nat.* **64**, 382.
—— —— 1934. *J. Genet.* **28**, 387.
HUSKINS, C. L. & SMITH, S. G. 1932. *J. Genet.* **25**, 241, 250.
HUSTED, L. 1933. *Cytologia*, **5**, 109.
—— 1936. *Cytologia*, **7**, 396.
HUTCHINSON, J. B. 1943. *Trop. Agric.* **20**, 4.
HUTTLESTON, D. G. 1949. *Bull. Torrey bot. Cl.* **76**, 307.
HYDE, B. B. 1953. *Amer. J. Bot.* **40**, 809.

IBARRA, F. E. & LA PORTE, J. 1947a. *Rev. argent. Agron.* **14**, 94.
—— —— 1947b. *Rev. argent. Agron.* **14**, 261.
—— —— 1948. *Rev. argent. Agron.* **15**, 81.
ICHIJIMA, K. 1926. *Genetics*, **11**, 590.
—— 1930. *Z.i.A.V.* **55**, 300.
—— 1934. *Proc. Imp. Acad. Tokyo*, **10**, 388.
IKENO, S. 1929. *Jap. J. Bot.* **4**, 303.
INARIYAMA, S. 1937. *Sci. Rep. Tokyo Univ. B.* **3**, 95.
—— 1944. *Jap. J. Genet.* **20**, 87.
INOUE, S. 1952. *J. Sci. Hiroshima Univ. B.* ser. 2, **6**, 59.
ISHIDA, Y. 1951. *Sci. Bull. Fac. Agric. Kyushu*, **13**, 49.
ISHII, T. 1930. *Cytologia*, **1**, 335.
*ISHIKAWA, M. 1916. *Bot. Mag. Tokyo*, **30**, 404.
ISLAM, A. S. 1950. *J. Indian bot. Soc.* **29**, 79.
—— 1953. *Curr. Sci.* **22**, 118.
ISLAM, A. S. & BATEN, A. 1952. *Nature*, **169**, 457.
ISLAM, A. & SAHA, B. 1951. *Curr. Sci.* **20**, 332.
ITO, T. 1942. *Cytologia*, **12**, 313.
IVANOV, V. I. 1939. *C.R. Acad. Sci. U.R.S.S.* **24**, 486.

IYENGAR, G. S.   1937.   *J. Indian bot. Soc.* **16**, 175.
IYENGAR, K.   1937.   *J. Indian bot. Soc.* **16**, 99.
IYENGAR, N. K.   1939.   *Ann. Bot., Lond.* **3**, 271.

JACKSON, W.   1951.   *Naturalist*, 1951, 114.
JACOB, K. T.   1940.   *Ann. Bot., Lond.* **4**, 201.
—— 1941.   *Bibliogr. genet.* **13**, 225.
JACOBSEN, P.   1954.   *Hereditas*, **40**, 252.
JAKOB, K. M.   1949.   *Madroño*, **10**, 95.
JAKOWSKA, S.   1949.   *Amer. J. Bot.* **36**, 98.
JALAS, J.   1948.   *Hereditas*, **34**, 414.
JAMES, L. E.   1951.   *Contr. Dudley Herb.* **4**, 63.
JANAKI AMMAL, E. K.   1933.   *Curr. Sci.* **1**, 328.
—— 1934.   *Cytologia*, **5**, 453.
—— 1936.   *Indian J. agric. Sci.* **6**, 1.
—— 1938.   *Nature*, **141**, 925.
—— 1940a.   *Nature*, **145**, 464.
—— 1940b.   *Nature*, **146**, 839.
—— 1941.   *J. Genet.* **41**, 217.
—— 1948.   *J. R. hort. Soc.* **73**, 117.
—— 1950.   *J. R. hort. Soc.* **75**, 23.
—— 1951a.   *J. R. hort. Soc.* **76**, 269.
—— 1951b.   *J. R. hort. Soc.* **76**, 365.
—— 1952a.   *J. R. hort. Soc.* **77**, 287
—— 1952b.   *Yearb. Amer. Camellia Soc.* 1952, 106.
—— 1953a.   *Curr. Sci.* **22**, 4.
—— 1953b.   *Indian J. Genet.* **12**, 44.
JANAKI AMMAL, E. K. & BRIDGWATER, M.   1951.   *J. R. hort. Soc.* **76**, 372.
JANAKI AMMAL, E. K., ENOCH, I. C. & BRIDGWATER, M.   1950.   *Rhodod. Yearb.* **5**, 78.
JANAKI AMMAL, E. K. & SAUNDERS, B.   1952.   *Kew Bull.* (1952), 539.
JANAKI AMMAL, E. K. & SELIGMAN, R.   1952.   *J. R. hort. Soc.* **77**, 221.
JARETZKY, R.   1928a.   *Jb. wiss. Bot.* **68**, 1.
—— 1928b.   *Jb. wiss. Bot.* **69**, 357.
—— 1929.   *Ber. dtsch. bot. Ges.* **47**, (82).
—— 1930.   *Planta*, **10**, 120.
—— 1932.   *Jb. wiss. Bot.* **76**, 485.
JEDRYCHOWSKA, A. & SROCZYNSKA, A.   1934.   *Acta Soc. Bot. Polon.* **11**, 423.
JENKIN, T. J. & THOMAS, P. T.   1938.   *J. Bot.* **76**, 10.
JENSEN, H. W.   1936.   *Cytologia*, **7**, 1.
—— 1937.   *Cytologia, F.J.N.* 96.
—— 1939.   *Cellule*, **48**, 49.
—— 1941.   *Cytologia*, **11**, 591.
—— 1944.   *Amer. Nat.* **78**, 375.
—— 1951.   *Cellule*, **54**, 133.
JENSEN, H. & LEVAN, A.   1941.   *Hereditas*, **27**, 220.
JINNO, T.   1951a.   *La Kromosomo*, **9-10**, 360.
—— 1951b.   *Jap. J. Genet.* **26**, 133.
JOHANSEN, D. A.   1929c.   *P.N.A.S.* **15**, 882.
—— 1929d.   *Cactus & Succ. J., Los Angeles,* **1**, 592.
—— 1931a.   *Ann. Bot., Lond.* **45**, 111.
—— 1931b.   *Amer. J. Bot.* **18**, 134.
—— 1931d.   *Amer. J. Bot.* **18**, 854.
—— 1932.   *Amer. J. Bot.* **19**, 779.
—— 1933a.   *Bull. Torrey bot. Cl.* **60**, 1.
—— 1933b.   *Bot. Gaz.* **95**, 177.
—— 1936.   *Amer. J. Bot.* **23**, 95.
JOHN, C. M. & NARASINGA RAO, U.   1941.   *Curr. Sci.* **10**, 364.
JOHNSON, B. L.   1945.   *Bot. Gaz.* **107**, 1.

JOHNSON, B. L. & ROGLER, G. A. 1943. *Amer. J. Bot.* **30,** 49.
JOHNSON, D. S. 1910. *Jb. exp. Zool.* **9,** 715.
—— 1914. *Amer. J. Bot.* **1,** 323.
JOHNSSON, H. 1940a. *Hereditas,* **26,** 321.
—— 1940b. *Svensk PappTidn.* 1940.
—— 1941. *Acta Univ. lund.* NF. Avd. 2, **37,** 3.
—— 1942a. *Hereditas,* **28,** 228.
—— 1942b. *Hereditas,* **28,** 306.
—— 1944. *Bot. Notiser,* 1944, 85.
JONES, K. L. 1943. *Bot. Gaz.* **105,** 226.
JONES, Q. 1951. *Contr. Gray Herb. Harv.* **173,** 1.
JÖRGENSEN, C. A. 1923. *Dansk bot. Tidskr.* **38,** 81.
—— 1927a. *Hereditas,* **9,** 126.
—— 1927b. *J. Genet.* **18,** 63.
—— 1928. *J. Genet.* **19,** 133.
JOSHI, A. B. & HARDAS, M. W. 1953. *Curr. Sci.* **22,** 384.
JOSHI, A. C. 1934. *Nature,* **134,** 29.
—— 1935. *J. Indian bot. Soc.* **14,** 349.
JUHL, H. 1952a. *Flora,* **139,** 462.
—— 1952b. *Ber. dtsch. bot. Ges.* **65,** 330.
JUNELL, S. 1934. *Symb. bot. upsaliens.* 1934, 1.

KACHIDZE, N. 1929. *Planta,* **7,** 482.
—— 1935. *Bull. appl. Bot. Select.* **11,** 99.
KADRY, A. el R. 1951. *Svensk bot. Tidskr.* **45,** 414.
KAGAWA, F. 1929. *J. Coll. Agric. Tokyo,* **10,** 173.
KAMEMOTO, H. 1950. *Bull. Amer. Orchid Soc.* **19,** 366.
—— 1952. *Bull. Pacif. Orchid Soc. Hawaii,* **10,** 141.
KAMERAZ, A. J. 1940. *Soviet Plant Ind. Rec.* no. 4, 13.
KANEZAWA, R. 1951. *Bull. Tokyo Univ. For.* **39,** 21.
KANO, T. 1929. *Proc. Crop, Sci. Soc. Japan,* **4,** 15.
KARASAWA, K. 1936. *Jap. J. Bot.* **8,** 113.
—— 1943. *Jap, J. Bot.* **12,** 475.
—— 1950. *Genetica,* **25,** 188.
KARPECHENKO, G. D. 1924a. *Bull. appl. Bot. Pl.-Breed.* **13,** 4.
—— 1924b. *J. Genet.* **14,** 375.
—— 1925. *Bull. appl. Bot. Pl.-Breed.* **14,** 143.
—— 1927. *Hereditas,* **9,** 349.
—— 1928. *Z.i.A.V.* **48,** 1.
—— 1930. *Proc. U.S.S.R. Congr. Genet.* **2,** 277.
—— 1938. *C.R. Acad. Sci. U.R.S.S.* **21,** 59.
KARPER, R. E. & CHISHOLM, A. T. 1936. *Amer. J. Bot.* **23,** 369.
KATAGIRI, S. 1952. *Jap. J. Breeding,* **1,** 233.
KATAYAMA, Y. 1936. *J. Coll. Agric. Tokyo,* **13,** 431.
KATO, Y. 1951. *La Kromosomo,* **9-10,** 342.
KATTERMANN, G. 1930. *Planta,* **12,** 19.
—— 1933. *Jb. wiss. Bot.* **78,** 43.
KAUSIK, S. B. 1938. *Ann. Bot., Lond.* **2,** 899.
—— 1939. *Proc. Indian Acad. Sci. B.* **9,** 39.
KAWAKAMI, I. 1930. *Bot. Mag. Tokyo,* **44,** 319.
KAWATANI, T. & OHNO, T. 1950. *Jap. J. Genet.* **25,** 177.
KAZAO, N. 1929. *Sci. Rep. Tôhoku Univ.* (b) *Biol.* **4,** 543.
KECK, D. D. 1945. *Amer. Midl. Nat.* **33,** 128.
KEDARNATH, S. 1950. *Indian J. Genet.* **10,** 96.
KESSELER, E. 1932. *Amer. J. Bot.* **19,** 128.
KHAN, I. R. 1951. *Pakist. J. Forestry,* **1,** 326.
KIHARA, H. 1924. *Mem. Coll. Sci. Kyoto,* **1,** 1.
—— 1927. *Bot. Mag. Tokyo,* **41,** 124.

KIHARA, H. 1929. *Jap. J. Genet.* **4**, 55.
—— 1937. *Mem. Coll. Agric. Kyoto*, **41**, 61.
—— 1954. *Cytologia*, **19**, 336.
KIHARA, H. & HIRAYOSHI, I. 1932. *Jap. Assoc. Adv. Sci. 8th Congr.* 1932, 363.
KIHARA, H. & ONO, T. 1926. *Z. Zellforsch.* **4**, 475.
KIHARA, H. & YAMAMOTO, Y. 1935. *Agric. Hort.* **10**, 2485.
*KIHARA, H., YAMAMOTO, Y. & HOSONO, S. 1931. *A list of Chromosome Numbers of Plants cultivated in Japan.* Tokyo.
KIKUCHI, M. 1926. *J. Soc. Agric. For. Sapporo*, p. 26.
KING, J. R. & BAMFORD, R. 1937. *J. Hered.* **28**, 279.
KISHIMOTO, E. 1936. *Cont. Genet. Imp. Univ. Kyoto*, 105.
—— 1938. *Cytologia*, **9**, 23.
—— 1941. *Bot. & Zool., Tokyo*, **9**, 433.
KISHORE, H. 1951. *Indian J. Genet.* **11**, 217.
KJELLMARK, S. 1934. *Bot. Notiser*, 1934, 136.
KLIMOCHKINA, L. V. 1940. *C.R. Acad. Sci. U.R.S.S.* **27**, 584.
KLINKOWSKI, M. & GRIESINGER, R. 1939. *Züchter*, **11**, 313.
KNOBLOCH, I. W. 1943. *Bull. Torrey bot. Cl.* **70**, 467.
—— 1953. *Bull. Torrey bot. Cl.* **80**, 131.
KNOWLES, P. F. 1944. *Genetics*, **29**, 128.
KOBEL, F. 1927. *Arch. Klaus-Stift. VererbForsch.* **3**, 1.
—— 1928. *Z.i.A.V.* Suppl. 2, 927.
—— 1929. *Züchter*, **1**, 197.
KOEPERICH, J. 1930. *Cellule*, **39**, 307.
KONDO, N. & MEGATA, M. 1943. *Seiken Zihô*, **2**, 69.
KÖNIG, D. 1939. *Planta*, **29**, 361.
KOOPMANS, A. 1951. *Genetica*, **25**, 193.
KOSHY, T. K. 1934. *J. R. micr. Soc.* **54**, 104.
KOSTOFF, D. 1936. *Z.i.A.V.* **72**, 115.
—— 1937. *C.R. Acad. Sci. U.R.S.S.* **14**, 213.
—— 1940. *Phytopath. Z.* **13**, 91.
KOSTOFF, D., DOGADKINA, H. & TICHONOWA, A. 1935. *Dokl. Acad. Nauk. U.R.S.S.* **3** (8), 401.
KOSTOFF, D. & KENDALL, J. 1933. *Arch. Microbiol.* **4**, 487.
KOTLIAREWSKAJA, M. 1931. *Z. Zellforsch.* **14**, 465.
KOVALEV, N. V. 1939. *C.R. Acad. Sci. U.R.S.S.* **23**, 284.
KOZHUCHOW, Z. A. 1925. *Bull. appl. Bot. Pl.-Breed.* **14**, 96.
—— 1930. *Bull. appl. Bot. Pl.-Breed.* **23**, 357.
—— 1934. *J. Inst. Bot. Acad. Sci., Ukraine*, **9**, 63.
KRAJEVOY, S. 1934. *C.R. Acad. Sci. U.R.S.S.* **4**, 224.
KRAPOVICKAS, A. 1949. *Lilloa*, **17**, 179.
—— 1950. *Darwiniana*, **9**, 248.
—— 1951a. *Bol. Soc. argent. Bot.* **4**, 105.
—— 1951b. *Bol. Soc. argent. Bot.* **4**, 107.
KRAPOVICKAS, A. & KRAPOVICKAS, A. M. F. 1951. *Darwiniana*, **9**, 612.
KRAPOVICKAS, A. & RIGONI, V. A. 1951. *Rev. Invest. Agric.* **5**, 289.
KRAUSE, O. 1930. *Ber. dtsch. bot. Ges.* **48**, 9.
—— 1931. *Planta*, **13**, 29.
KRENKE, N. P. 1930. *Pros. U.S.S.R. Congr. Genet.* **2**, 319.
KREUTER, E. 1930. *Planta*, **11**, 1.
KRIJTHE, N. 1939. *Tijdschr. PlZiekt.* **45**, 63.
KRISHNASWAMY, N. 1940. *Beih. bot. Zbl.* § A, **60**, 1.
KRISHNASWAMY, N. & AYYANGAR, R. 1935b. *Curr. Sci.* **3**, 559.
—— —— 1935c. *Curr. Sci.* **4**, 106.
—— —— 1940. *Curr. Sci.* **9**, 461.
—— —— 1941. *Proc. Indian Acad. Sci.* § B. **13**, 9.
KRISHNASWAMY, N. & RAMAN, V. S. 1948a. *J. Indian bot. Soc.* **27**, 77.
—— —— 1948b. *Curr. Sci.* **17**, 153.

KRISHNASWAMY, N., & RAMAN, V. S. 1949. *Curr. Sci.* **18**, 376.
KRISHNASWAMY, N., RAMAN, V. S., SHETTY, B. V. & CHANDRASEKHARAN, P. 1954. *Curr. Sci.* **23**, 64.
KRUCKEBERG, A. R. 1948. *Madroño*, **9**, 258.
—— 1955. *Amer. J. Bot.* **42**, 373.
KRUG, C. A. 1934. *Züchter*, **6**, 166.
—— 1936. *Bol. Techn. S. Paulo*, **22**, 1.
—— 1937. *J. Genet.* **34**, 399.
—— 1943. *Bot. Gaz.* **104**, 602.
KRUG, C. A. & ALVES, A. S. 1949. *J. Hered.* **40**, 133.
KRUG, C. A. & BACCHI, O. 1943. *J. Hered.* **34**, 277.
KRUPKO, S. 1953. *J. S. Afr. Bot.* **19**, 31.
KUHN, E. 1928a. *Jb. wiss. Bot.* **68**, 382.
—— 1928b. *Ber. dtsch. bot. Ges.* **46**, 682.
KUMAR, L. S. S. & ABRAHAM, A. 1941. *Proc. Indian Acad. Sci.*, § B. **14**, 509.
—— —— 1942a. *Curr. Sci.* **11**, 58.
—— —— 1942b. *Curr. Sci.* **11**, 112.
—— —— 1942c. *Proc. Indian Acad. Sci.*, § B. **15**, 253.
KUMAR, L. S. S. & RANADE, S. G. 1952. *Curr. Sci.* **21**, 75.
KUMAR, L. S. S. & RANDIVE, K. 1941. *J. Univ. Bombay*, 10 B, **31**, 9.
KUMAR, L. S. S. & SRINIVASAN, V. K. 1944. *Curr. Sci.* **13**, 15.
KUMAR, L. S. S. & VISHVESHWARA, S. 1951. *Curr. Sci.* **20**, 211.
KUMAR, L. S. S. & VISHVESHWARAIAH, V. 1952. *Nature*, **170**, 330.
KUMAZAVA, M. & KIMURA, M. 1947. *Jap. J. Genet.* Suppl. 1, 100.
KURAKUBO, Y. 1940. *Bot. & Zool., Tokyo*, **8**, 1492
KURITA, H. 1940. *Bot. & Zool., Tokyo*, **8**, 72.
KURITA, M. 1939. *Bot. Mag. Tokyo*, **53**, 505.
KUWADA, Y. 1915. *Bot. Mag. Tokyo*, **29**, 83.
—— 1919. *J. Coll. Sci. Tokyo*, **39** (10).
—— 1928. *Bot. Mag. Tokyo*, **42**, 117.
KUZMINA, N. A. 1935. *Bull. appl. Bot., U.S.S.R.* **11**, 81.

LA COUR, L. F. 1931. *J. R. micr. Soc.* **51**, 119.
—— 1946. *Rep. John Innes Hort. Instn.* **36**, 19.
—— 1951a. *Heredity*, **5**, 37.
—— 1951b. *Rep. John Innes Hort. Instn.* **41**, 23.
—— 1952. *Rep. John Innes Hort. Instn.* **42**, 47.
LAMM, R. 1937. *Svensk bot. Tidskr.* **31**, 217.
LANG, A. 1940. *Bibliothec. Bot.* **118**.
LANGLET, O. F. J. 1925. *Svensk bot. Tidskr.* **19**, 215.
—— 1927a. *Svensk bot. Tidskr.* **21**, 1.
1927b. *Svensk bot. Tidskr.* **21**, 397.
—— 1928. *Svensk bot. Tidskr.* **22**, 169.
—— 1932. *Svensk bot. Tidskr.* **26**, 381.
—— 1934. *Svensk Skog. Tidskr.* **1934**, 87.
—— 1936. *Svensk bot. Tidskr.* **30**, 288.
LANGLET, O. F. J. & SÖDERBERG, E. 1927. *Acta Hort. berg.* **9**, 85.
LAPIN, W. 1937a & b. *Trud. vsesoj. nauch. issled. Inst. vlazn. subtrop.* **1**, 1 & 69.
—— 1939. *C.R. Acad. Sci. U.R.S.S.* **23**, 84.
LARSEN, C. S. & WESTERGAARD, M. 1938. *J. Genet.* 36, 523.
LARSEN, K. 1953. *Bot. Tidsskr.* **50**, 91.
LARTER, L. N. H. 1932. *J. Genet.* **26**, 255.
—— 1935. *J. Genet.* **31**, 297.
DE LATTIN, G. 1951. *Naturwiss.* **38**, 531.
LAWALRÉE, A. 1943. *Cellule*, **49**, 337.
LAWRENCE, W. E. 1945. *Amer. J. Bot.* **32**, 298.
—— 1947. *Amer. J. Bot.* **34**, 538.
LAWRENCE, W. J. C. 1929. *J. Genet.* **21**, 125.
—— 1930. *Genetica*, **12**, 269.

LAWRENCE, W. J. C.   1931a.   *J. Genet.* **24**, 257.
—— 1931b.   *Cytologia*, **2**, 352.
—— 1931.   *Genetica*, **13**, 183.
—— 1936.   *Genetica*, **18**, 109.
LAWRENCE, W. J. C., SCOTT-MONCRIEFF, R. & STURGESS, V. C.   1939.   *J. Genet.* **38**, 299.
LAWS, D.   1930.   Diss. Univ. Berlin.
LAY, K. K.   1950.   *Ann. Mo. Bot. Gard.* **37**. 315.
LECHTOVA-TRNKA, M.   1931.   *Botaniste*, **23**, 301.
LEDINGHAM, G. F.   1940.   *Genetics*, **25**, 1.
LEE, C. L.   1954.   *Amer. J. Bot.* **41**, 545.
LEHMANN, E.   1944.   *Jb. wiss. Bot.* **91**, 395.
LEIN, A.   1948.   *Züchter*, **19**, 6.
LELIVELD, J. A.   1933.   *Genetica*, **15**, 425.
LENZ, L. W.   1950.   *El Aliso*, **2**, 317.
LEONCINI, M. L.   1951.   *Caryologia*, **3**, 336.
—— 1952.   *Caryologia*, **4**, 367.
LESZCZAK, W.   1950.   *Acta Soc. Bot. Polon.* **20**, 647.
LEUNG, T. C. & LI, H. W.   1949.   *J. Sugarcane Res. Taiwan*, **3**, 211.
LEVAN, A.   1931.   *Hereditas*, **15**, 347.
—— 1932.   *Hereditas*, **16**, 257.
—— 1934.   *Hereditas*, **18**, 349.
—— 1935.   *Hereditas*, **20**, 289.
—— 1936.   *Hereditas*, **22**, 1.
—— 1937a.   *Hereditas*, **23**, 99.
—— 1937b.   *Hereditas*, **23**, 317.
—— 1940a.   *Hereditas*, **26**, 317.
—— 1940b.   *Hereditas*, **26**, 353.
—— 1941.   *Hereditas*, **27**, 243.
—— 1942a.   *Hereditas*, **28**, 245.
—— 1942b.   *Hereditas*, **28**, 345.
—— 1943.   *Hereditas*, **29**, 255.
—— 1944a.   *Hereditas*, **30**, 217.
—— 1944b.   *Hereditas*, **30**, 401.
—— 1949.   *Proc. 8th Int. Congr. Genet.* 46.
LEVAN, A. & LOVE, A.   1942.   *Hereditas*, **28**, 495.
LEVAN, A. & STEINEGGER, E.   1947.   *Hereditas*, **33**, 552.
LEVYNS, M. R.   1934.   *Ann. Bot., Lond.* **48**, 355.
LEWIS, H.   1945.   *Brittonia*, **5**, 276.
—— 1951.   *Evolution*, **5**, 142.
—— 1953a.   *Evolution*, **7**, 1.
—— 1953b.   *Evolution*, **7**, 102.
LEWIS, H., EPLING, C., MEHLQUIST, G. A. L. & WYCKOFF, C. G.   1951.   *Ann. Mo. Bot. Gard.* **38**, 101.
LEWIS, H. & ERNST, W. R.   1953.   *Madroño*, **12**, 89.
LEWIS, H. & LEWIS, M.   1953.   *Madroño*, **12**, 33.
LEWIS, H. & SNOW, R.   1951.   *Madroño*, **11**, 141.
*LEWITZKY, G. A.   1931a.   *Bull. appl. Bot., Pl.-Breed.* **27**, 19.
*—— 1931b.   *Bull. appl. Bot., Pl.-Breed.* **27**, 187.
—— 1934.   *C.R. Acad. Sci. U.R.S.S.* **1**, 84.
—— 1940.   *Bot. J. U.S.S.R.* **25**, 292.
LEWITZKY, G. A. & KUZMINA, N. A.   1927.   *Bull. appl. Bot., Pl.-Breed.* **17**, 3.
LI, C. H. & LI, H. W.   1943.   *Chinese J. Sci. Agric.* **1**, 139.
LI, H. W. & LEE, C. L.   1948.   *J. Sugarcane Res. Taiwan*, **2**, 5.
LI, H. W. & MA, T. H.   1951a.   *Rep. Taiwan Sugar Exp. Sta.* **7**, 47.
—— —— 1951b.   *Proc. 7th Congr. Int. Soc. Sugarcane Techn.* 1950, 277.
LILIENFELD, F. A.   1936.   *Jap. J. Bot.* **8**, 119.
LILIENFELD, F. A. & KIHARA, H.   1934.   *Cytologia*, **6**, 87.
LILJEFORS, A.   1934.   *Svensk bot. Tidskr.* **28**, 290.

LINCOLN, F. B. & McCANN, L. P. 1937. *Proc. Amer. Soc. hort. Sci.* **34**, 26.
LINDENBEIN, W. 1932. *Ber. dtsch. bot. Ges.* **50**, 399.
—— 1937. *Ang. Bot.* **19**, 313.
LINDQVIST, K. 1950. *Hereditas*, **36**, 94.
LINDSAY, R. H. 1930. *Amer. J. Bot.* **17**, 152.
LINDSCHAU, M. 1933. *Planta*, **20**, 5C6.
LINDSTROM, E. W. 1929. *J. Hered.* **20**, 23.
LITARDIÈRE, R. DE. 1926. *Bull. Soc. bot. Fr.* **73**, 218.
—— 1938. *Rev. Cytol., Paris*, **3**, 134.
—— 1943. *Boissiera*, **7**, 155.
—— 1947. *C.R. Acad. Sci., Paris*, **224**, 981.
—— 1948a. *Candollea*, **11**, 175.
—— 1948b. *C.R. Acad. Sci., Paris*, **226**, 1327.
—— 1948c. *C.R. Acad. Sci., Paris*, **227**, 1071.
—— 1949a. *C.R. Acad. Sci., Paris*, **228**, 349.
—— 1949b. *C.R. Acad. Sci., Paris*, **228**, 1786.
—— 1950. *Bol. Soc. Brot.* **24**, 79.
LITARDIÈRE, R. DE & DOULAT, E. 1942. *Bull. Soc. bot. Fr.* **89**, 123.
LJUNGDAHL, H. 1922. *Svensk bot. Tidskr.* **16**, 103.
LONGLEY, A. E. 1924a. *Amer. J. Bot.* **11**, 249.
—— 1924b. *Amer. J. Bot.* **11**, 295.
—— 1925. *J. Wash. Acad. Sci.* **15**, 347.
—— 1927b. *Science*, **66**, 566.
—— 1932. *J. agric. Res.* **44**, 317.
—— 1933. *J. agric. Res.* **46**, 217.
—— 1937. *J. agric. Res.* **54**, 835.
LONGLEY, A. E. & DARROW, G. M. 1924. *J. agric. Res.* **27**, 737.
LONGLEY, A. E. & SANDO, W. J. 1930. *J. agric. Res.* **40**, 683.
LOPANE, F. 1951. *Caryologia*, **4**, 44.
LORENZO-ANDREU, A. 1951. *An. Estac. Exp. Aula Dei*, **2**, 195.
LORENZO-ANDREU, A. & GARCIA-SANZ, P. 1950. *An. Estac. Exp. Aula Dei*, **2**, 12.
LORZ, A. 1937. *Cytologia*, **8**, 241.
LOTFY, T. 1951. *Nature*, **168**, 338.
LÖVE, A. 1942. *Hereditas*, **28**, 289.
—— 1944a. *Bot. Notiser*, 1944, 237.
—— 1944b. *Hereditas*, **30**, 1.
—— 1944c. *Svensk bot. Tidskr.* **38**, 381.
—— 1951. *Bot. Notiser*, 1951, 229.
—— 1952. *Hereditas*, **38**, 11.
—— 1954. *Svensk bot. Tidskr.* **48**, 211.
*LÖVE, A. & LÖVE, D. 1942. *Bot. Notiser*, 1942, 19.
—— —— 1944a. *Ark. Bot.* **31** B (1), 1.
*—— —— 1944b. *Ark. Bot.* **31** A (12), 1.
—— —— 1947. *Rep. Dep. Agric. Univ. Inst. appl. Sci. Iceland*, Ser. B, **2**, 1.
*—— —— 1948. Chromosome Numbers of Northern Plant Species, Reykjavik.
—— —— 1951. *Svensk bot. Tidskr.* **45**, 368.
—— —— 1954. *Amer. Midl. Nat.* **52**, 88.
LÖVE, D. 1942. *Svensk bot. Tidskr.* **36**, 262.
—— 1953. *Hereditas*, **39**, 225.
LOVE, R. M. 1948. *Amer. J. Bot.* **35**, 358.
—— 1954. *Amer. J. Bot.* **41**, 107.
LÖVKVIST, B. 1947. *Hereditas*, **33**, 421.
LUBBERT, G. 1951. *Beitr. Biol. Pfl.* **28**, 254.
LUCKWILL, L. C. 1943. *Aberd. Univ. Stud.* no. 120.
LUTKOV, A. N. 1930. *Proc. U.S.S.R. Congr. Genet.* **2**, 353.

McAULAY, A. L. & CRUICKSHANK, F. D. 1937. *Pap. roy. Soc. Tasm.* 1937, 41.
McAULAY, A. L., CRUICKSHANK, F. D. & BRETT, R. G. 1936. *Nature*, **138**, 550.

McCullagh, D. 1934. *Genetica*, **16**, 1.
McFadden, E. S. & Sears, E. R. 1946. *J. Hered.* **37**, 81 & 107.
—— —— 1947. *J. Amer. Soc. Agron.* **39**, 1011.
*McKay, J. W. 1930. *Bot. Gaz.* **89**, 416.
—— 1931. *Univ. Calif. Publ. Bot.* **16**, 339.
McKay, J. W. & McKay, H. H. 1941. *Amer. J. Bot.* **28**, suppl. 4.
MacKelvey, S. D. & Sax, K. 1933. *J. Arnold Arbor.* **14**, 76.
McLeish, J. 1953. *Heredity*, **6** (suppl.), 125.
MacMahon, B. 1936. *Cellule*, **45**, 209.
MacMillan, C. 1949. *Madroño*, **10**, 95.
McMinn, H. E. 1951. *Madroño*, **11**, 33.
McQuade, H. A. 1949. *Ann. Mo. Bot. Gdn.* **36**, 433.
Majumdar, A. 1953. *Caryologia*, **5**, 306.
Makushina, E. N. 1938. *C.R. Acad. Sci. U.R.S.S.* **21**, 345.
Malheiros, N. 1942. *Agron. lusit.* **4**, 231.
Malheiros, N. & Gardé, A. 1947. *Agron. lusit.* **9**, 75.
Malvesin-Fabre, G. & Eymé, J. 1949. *C.R. Acad. Sci., Paris*, **228**, 2050.
Mangelsdorf, P. C. & Reeves, R. G. 1939. *Texas Agric. Exp. Sta. Bull.* **574**, 75.
Mangenot, G. 1947. *C.R. Acad. Sci., Paris*, **224**, 587.
Manshard, E. 1936. *Planta*, **25**, 364.
Manton, I. 1932. *Ann. Bot., Lond.* **46**, 509.
—— 1937. *Ann. Bot., Lond.* n.s. **1**, 439.
—— 1949. *Watsonia*, **1**, 36.
Makino, I. 1951. *La Kromosomo*, **8**, 318.
Marchal, E. 1920. *Mem. Acad. R. Belg. Cl. sci. II*, **4**, 3.
Marks, G. E. 1950. *Rep. John Innes Hort. Instn.* **40**, 7.
—— 1952. *Rep. John Innes Hort. Instn.* **42**, 47.
Marshak, J. A. G. 1934. *Amer. J. Bot.* **21**, 592.
Martini, E. 1939. *Nuovo G. bot. ital.* **46**, 197.
Martinoli, G. 1939. *Nuovo G. bot. ital.* **46**, 259.
—— 1940. *Nuovo G. bot. ital.* **47**, 287.
—— 1942. *Nuovo G. bot. ital.* **49**, 472.
—— 1943. *Nuovo G. bot. ital.* **50**, 1.
—— 1948. *Nuovo G. bot. ital.* **55**, 235.
—— 1949. *Caryologia*, **1**, 329.
—— 1950a. *Caryologia*, **3**, 72.
—— 1950b. *Caryologia*, **3**, 156.
—— 1951. *Caryologia*, **4**, 86.
—— 1953. *Caryologia*, **5**, 253.
Martzenitzina, K. K. 1927. *Bull. appl. Bot., Pl.-Breed.* **17**, 253.
Masima, I. 1947. *Jap. J. Genet.* suppl. **1**, 122.
Mason, C. T. 1952. *Univ. Calif. Publ. Bot.* **25**, 455.
Mather, K. 1932. *J. Genet.* **26**, 129.
—— 1934. *Hereditas*, **19**, 303.
—— 1935. *Cytologia*, **6**, 354.
—— 1937. *Genetica*, **19**, 143.
Mathews, A. C. 1932. *J. Elisha Mitchell Sci. Soc.* **48**, 101.
Matsuura, H. 1935. *J. Fac. Sci. Hokkaido Univ.* 3 (5), 219.
—— 1937. *Bot. & Zool, Tokyo*, **5**, 15.
Matsuura, H. & Okuno, S. 1936. *Jap. J. Genet.* **12**, 42.
—— —— 1943. *Cytologia*, **13**, 1.
*Matsuura, H. & Suto, T. 1935. *J. Fac. Sci. Hokkaido Univ.* 5 (5), 33.
Matsuura, H. & Toyohuko, T. 1937. *Jap. J. Genet.* **13**, 21.
*Maude, P. F. 1939. *New Phytol.* **38**, 1.
—— 1940. *New Phytol.* **39**, 17.
Maugini, E. 1950. *Caryologia*, **3**, 221.
—— 1952. *Caryologia*, **5**, 101.
—— 1953a. *Caryologia*, **5**, 167.

MAUGINI, E. 1953b. *Caryologia*, **5**, 282.
—— 1953c. *Caryologia*, **5**, 313.
MECHELKE, F. 1954. *Kulturpflanze*, **2**, 143.
MEDVEDEVA, G. B. 1935. *Z.i.A.V.* **70**, 170.
—— 1936. *J. Bot. U.R.S.S.* **21**, 533.
—— 1937. *Biol. J.* **6**, 93.
MEGATA, M. 1941. *Eine Liste von Chromosomenzahlen bei Kakteen und anderen Sukkulenten*, Imp. Univ., Kyoto.
MEHLQUIST, G. A. L. 1947. *Bull. Mo. Bot. Gdn.* **35**, 211.
—— 1952. *Cymbidium Soc. News*, **7**, 17.
MEHLQUIST, G. A. L., BLODGETT, C. O. & BRUSCIA, L. 1943. *J. Hered.* **34**, 187.
MEHRA, P. N. 1934. *Curr. Sci.* **3**, 11.
—— 1946. *Proc. Nat. Acad. Sci. India*, Ser. B, **16**, 259.
MEHRA, P. N. & KHOSHOO, T. N. 1948a. *Curr. Sci.* **17**, 242.
—— —— 1948b. *Proc. 34th Indian Sci. Congr.* pt. 3, 167.
MELCHERS, G. 1935. *Z.i.A.V.* **69**, 263.
MELDERIS, A. 1930. *Acta Hort. bot. Univ. latv.* **5**, 1.
MELDERIS, A. & VIKSNE, A. 1931. *Acta Hort. bot. Univ. latv.* **6**, 90.
MELINOSSI, R. 1937. *Monit. Zool. ital.* **47**, 318.
MENDES, A. J. T. 1945. *Rev. Agric. Piracicaba*, **20**, 412.
—— 1947. *Bragantia*, **7**, 257.
MENDES, L. O. T. 1946. *Bol. Tecn. Inst. Agron. Norte*, **7**, 1.
MENSINKAI, S. W. 1939a. *Ann. Bot., Lond.* **3**, 763.
—— 1939b. *Cytologia*, **10**, 59.
—— 1940. *J. Genet.* **39**, 1.
MENZEL, M. Y. 1950. *Amer. J. Bot.* **37**, 25.
—— 1951. *Proc. Amer. Phil. Soc.* **95**, 133.
MEREMINSKI, H. 1936. *Bull. Acad. Polon.* Ser. B, Sci. Nat. 53.
MESSERI, A. 1928. *Nuovo G. bot. ital.* **34**, 1037.
—— 1931. *Nuovo G. bot. ital.* **38**, 409.
MEURMAN, O. 1924. *Soc. Sci. Fenn. Comment. Biol.* **2**, (2).
—— 1925. *Soc. Sci. Fenn. Comment. Biol.* **2**, (3).
—— 1928. *Hereditas*, **11**, 289.
—— 1929a. *Hereditas*, **12**, 179.
—— 1929b. *J. Genet.* **21**, 85.
—— 1930. *Memor. Soc. Fauna Flor. fenn.* **6**, 95.
—— 1931. *Rep. 5th Int. Bot. Congr.* 235.
—— 1933. *Hereditas*, **18**, 145.
MEURMAN, O. & SUOMALAINEN, E. 1946. *Ann. Ak. Sci. Fenn.* 4 (11).
MEURMAN, O. & THERMAN, E. 1939. *Cytologia*, **10**, 1.
MEYER, J. R. 1944. *Genetics*, **29**, 199.
MICHALSKA, A. 1953. *Acta Soc. Bot. Polon.* **22**, 169.
MIDUNO, T. 1938. *Cytologia*, **8**, 505.
—— 1939. *Cytologia*, **9**, 447.
—— 1940. *Cytologia*, **11**, 179.
—— 1943. *Jap. J. Genet.* **19**, 123.
—— 1954. *Cytologia*, **19**, 239.
MIÈGE, J. 1939. *Bull. Soc. Hist. nat. Afr. N.* **30**, 223.
MILLER, E. W. 1930. *Proc. Univ. Durham Phil. S:oc.* **8**, 267.
MILOVIDOV, P. F. 1932. *Preslia*, **11**, 62.
—— 1941. *Planta*, **32**, 38.
MIMEUR, G. 1950. *Bull. Mus. Hist. nat., Paris*, **22**, 130.
MIRANDA, F. 1931. *Bol. Soc. esp. Hist. nat.* **31**, 403.
MITRA, J. 1947. *J. Indian bot. Soc.* **26**, 105.
—— 1949. *Proc. 36th Indian Sci. Congr.* pt. 3, 140.
MITSUKURI, Y. 1947. *Jap. J. Genet.* **22**, 18.
MITSUKURI, Y. & HAYASHI, M. 1951. *Jap. J. Genet.* **26**, 225.
MIYAJI, Y. 1929. *Cytologia*, **1**, 28.
—— 1930. *Planta*, **11**, 631.

MIYAKI, K. 1934. *Ann. Bot., Lond.* **17**, 351.
MODILEWSKI, J. 1934. *Visn. Kiewsk. Botan. Sad.* **17**, 3.
—— 1937. *J. Bot. Acad. Sci. Ukr.* **13-14**, 63.
MOFFETT, A. A. 1931a. *J. Pomol.* **9**, 100.
—— 1931b. *Proc. Roy. Soc.* Ser. B, **108**, 423.
—— 1932a. *Cytologia*, **4**, 26.
—— 1932b. *J. Genet.* **25**, 315.
—— 1936. *Cytologia*, **7**, 490.
—— 1944. *Rhod. agric. J.* **41**, 11.
* MOFFETT, A. A. & HURCOMBE, R. 1949. *Heredity*, **3**, 369.
MOHRBUTTER, C. 1936. *Planta*, **26**, 64.
DE MOL, W. E. 1922. *Proc. Kon. Akad. Wettensch. Amst.* **25**, 216.
MOOKERJEA, A. 1951. *Curr. Sci.* **20**, 328.
MOORE, R. J. 1946. *Canad. J. Res.* **24** C, 66.
—— 1947. *Amer. J. Bot.* **34**, 527.
MOORE, R. J. & FRANKTON, C. 1954. *Canad. J. Bot.* **32**, 182.
MOORE, R. J. & LINDSAY, D. R. 1953. *Canad. J. Bot.* **31**, 152.
MORINAGA, T. 1929. *Cytologia*, **1**, 16.
MORINAGA, T., FUKUSHIMA, E., KANO, T. & YAMASAKI, Y. 1929. *Bot. Mag., Tokyo*, **43**, 589.
MORINAGA, T. & FUKUSHIMA, E. 1931. *Bot. Mag., Tokyo*, **45**, 140.
MORINAGA, T. & KURUJAMA, H. 1937. *Cytologia, F.J.N.* 967.
MORAN, R. 1951. *Bull. S. Calif. Acad. Sci.* **50**, 57.
MORIYA, A. & KONDO, A. 1949a. *Jap. J. Genet.* **25**, 126.
—— —— 1949b. *Jap. J. Genet.* **25**, 131.
MORLEY, T. 1949. *Madroño*, **10**, 95.
MORRISON, J. W. 1952. *Rep. John Innes Hort. Instn.* **42**, 47.
MORTON, J. K. 1955. *New Phytol.* **54**, 68.
MOYER, L. S. 1934. *Bot. Gaz.* **95**, 678.
—— 1936. *Bot. Gaz.* **97**, 860.
MUKHERJEE, S. K. 1950. *Nature*, **166**, 196.
—— 1952a. *Sci. & Cult.* **18**, 91.
—— 1952b. *Curr. Sci.* **21**, 77.
MÜLLER, C. 1912. *Arch. Zellforsch.* **8**, 1.
MULLER, F. S. 1945. *Publ. Univ. Pretoria*, **2**, 27.
MÜNTZING, A. 1931. *Hereditas*, **15**, 166.
—— 1932. *Hereditas*, **16**, 73, 105.
—— 1937a. *Hereditas*, **23**, 113.
—— 1937b. *Hereditas*, **23**, 401.
—— 1937c. *Cytologia, F.J.N.* 211.
—— 1939. *Hereditas*, **25**, 387.
—— 1943a. *Hereditas*, **29**, 91.
—— 1948. *Heredity*, **2**, 49.
—— 1951. *Hereditas*, **37**, 17.
—— 1954. *Hereditas*, **40**, 459.
MUNTZING, A. & MÜNTZING, G. 1941. *Bot. Notiser*, 1941, 237.
MURTHY, K. L. 1934. *Curr. Sci.* **3**, 258.
MURTHY, S. N. K. 1933. *J. Mysore Univ.* **7**, 1.
MUTO, A. 1929. *Mem. Coll. Sci. Kyoto*, Ser. B, **4**, 265.
MYERS, W. M. 1939. *J. Hered.* **30**, 499.
—— 1941. *J. agric. Res.* **63**, 649.
—— 1944. *J. agric. Res.* **68**, 21.
*—— 1947. *Bot. Rev.* **13**, 319.
MYERS, W. M. & HILL, H. D. 1947. *Bull. Torrey bot. Cl.* **74**, 99.

NAGAI, K. & SASAOKA, T. 1930. *Jap. J. Genet.* **5**, 151.
NAGAO, M. 1941. *Jap. J. Genet.* **17**, 109.
NAGAO, S. 1929. *Mem. Coll. Sci. Kyoto*, Ser. B, **4**, 177.

NAGAO, S. 1933. *Mem. Coll. Sci. Kyoto*, Ser. B, **8**, 81.
—— 1938. *Comment. Pap. Agron.* Akemine.
—— 1941. *J. Sapporo Soc. Agric. For.* **32**, 28.
NAGAO, S. & MASIMA, I. 1943a. *Jap. J. Genet.* **19**, 110.
—— —— 1943b. *Trans. Sapporo N.H. Soc.* **17**, 131.
NAKAJIMA, G. 1930. *Jap. J. Genet.* **5**, 172.
—— 1931. *Bot. Mag. Tokyo*, **45**, 7.
—— 1933. *Jap. J. Genet.* **9**, 1.
—— 1936. *Jap. J. Genet.* **12**, 211.
—— 1937. *Cytologia, F.J.N.* 282.
—— 1942. *Cytologia*, **12**, 262.
—— 1944. *Jap. J. Genet.* **20**, 131.
—— 1954. *Bot. Mag. Tokyo*, **67**, 69.
NAKAMORI, E. 1933. *Proc. imp. Acad. Japan*, **9**, 340.
NAKAMURA, M. 1941. *Studia Citrol.* **10**, 12.
—— 1942. *J. Hort. Assoc.* **13**, 30.
NAKAMURA, T. 1929. *Mem. Coll. Sci. Kyoto*, Ser. B, **4**, 353.
NAKAMURA, W. 1934. *Bull. Kagoshima Coll. Agric. For.* **1**, 11.
NAMIKAWA, J. & HIGASHI, M. 1928. *Bot. Mag. Tokyo*, **42**, 436.
NANDI, H. K. 1936. *J. Genet.* **33**, 327.
NANNFELDT, J. A. 1937. *Bot. Notiser*, 1937, 238.
—— 1938. *Svensk bot. Tidskr.* **32**, 295.
—— 1940. *Symb. bot. upsaliens.* **4**, no. 4.
NARASINGA RAO, V. 1936. *Curr. Sci.* **4**, 654.
NASCIMENTO, A. C. 1941. *Bol. Soc. brasil. Agron.* **4**, 67.
NATIVIDADE, J. V. 1937. *Publ. Dir. Serv. Flor. agric.* **4**, 74.
NAVASHIN, M. 1930. *Nature*, **126**, 604.
NAVASHIN, M. & GERASSIMOVA, H. 1941. *C.R. Acad. Sci. U.R.S.S.* **31**, 43.
NAWA, N. 1928. *Bot. Mag. Tokyo*, **42**, 33.
NEBEL, B. R. 1929. *Gartenbauwiss.* **1**, 549.
NEGODI, G. 1930. *Ann. di Bot.* **18**, 325.
—— 1935. *Atti Soc. Nat. Mat. Modena*, **67**, 3.
—— 1936a. *Riv. Biol.* **20**, 15.
—— 1936b. *Arch. bot., Forli*, **12**, 82.
—— 1937. *Nuovo G. bot. ital.* **44**, 667.
—— 1939. *Sci. genet.* **1**, 168.
—— 1940. *Sci. genet.* **2**, 1.
—— 1951. *Sci. genet.* **4**, 94.
NEMEC, B. 1910. Das Problem der Befruchtungsvorgänge. Berlin.
NETO, E. 1948. *Herbertia*, **15**, 25.
NEUMANN, M. 1935. *Öst. Bot. Z.* **84**, 1.
NEVES, J. DE B. 1939. *Boll. Soc. Brot.* **13**, 547.
—— 1944. Diss. Univ. Coimbra.
—— 1950. *Bol. Soc. Brot.* **24**, 335.
—— 1952. *Bol. Soc. Brot.* **26**, 1.
—— 1953. *Bol. Soc. Brot.* **27**, 203.
NEWCOMER, E. H. 1941. *Proc. Amer. Soc. hort. Sci.* **38**, 468.
NEWTON, W. C. F. 1924. *Ann. Bot., Lond.* **38**, 197.
—— 1927. *J. Linn. Soc. (Bot.)*, **47**, 339.
NIELSEN, E. L. 1939. *Amer. J. Bot.* **26**, 366.
—— 1944. *J. agric. Res.* **69**, 327.
NIELSEN, E. L. & HUMPHREY, L. M. 1937. *Amer. J. Bot.* **24**, 276.
NIELSEN, E. L. & ROGLER, G. A. 1952. *Amer. J. Bot.* **39**, 343.
NIELSEN, N. 1924. *Hereditas*, **5**, 378.
NIETSCH, H. 1941. *Öst. Bot. Z.* **90**, 31.
NIKOLAJEWA, A. 1923. *Bull. appl. Bot., Pl.-Breed.* **13**, 33.
NIRULA, R. L. 1945. *Proc. Indian Acad. Sci.* § B, **21**, 174.
NISHIYAMA, I. 1936. *Cytologia*, **7**, 276.

NISHIYAMA, I. & KONDO, N. 1942. *Seiken Zihô*, 1, 26.
NISSEN, ∅. 1950. *Agron. J.* 42, 136.
NITZSCHKE, J. 1914. *Beitr. Biol. Pfl.* 12, 223.
NOACK, K. L. 1937. *Biol. Zbl.* 57, 383.
—— 1939. *Z.i.A.V.* 76. 569.
NOBS, M. A. 1942. In McMinn, H. E., *Ceanothus*. California.
NODA, K. 1946. *Jap. J. Genet.* 21, 93.
NOGUCHI, T. 1936. *Bot. Mag. Tokyo*, 50, 225.
NORDENSKIÖLD, H. 1937. *Hereditas*, 23, 304.
—— 1941. *Bot. Notiser*, 1941, 12.
—— 1951. *Hereditas*, 37, 325.
NYGREN, A. 1946. *Hereditas*, 32, 131.
—— 1954. *Hereditas*, 40, 377.

OCCHIONI, P. 1945. *Rodriguesia, Rio de Jan.* 9, 37.
OEHM, G. 1924. *Beih. bot. Zbl.* § 1, 40, 237.
OFFERIJNS, F. I. M. 1935. Diss. Utrecht.
OGAWA, K. 1929. *Mem. Coll. Sci. Kyoto*, 4, 309.
OHGA, T. & SINOTO, Y. 1932. *Bot. Mag. Tokyo*, 46, 311.
OIKAWA, K. 1942. *Jap. J. Genet.* 18, 157.
OINUMA, T. 1949. *Jap. J. Genet.* Suppl. 2, 29.
OKABE, S. 1928. *Sci. Rep. Tôhoku Univ.* Ser. 4, 3, 733.
—— 1934. *Bot. Mag. Tokyo*, 48 (7).
—— 1937. *Cytologia, F.J.N.* 527.
OKE, J. G. 1950. *Proc. Indian Acad. Sci.* § B, 32, 227.
OKSIJUK, P. 1929. *Mem. phys.-mat. Acad. Sci. Ukr.* 15, 37.
—— 1935. *J. Bot. Acad. Sci. Ukr.* 4, 15.
OKUNO, S. 1937. *Cytologia, F.J.N.* 897.
—— 1940. *Jap. J. Genet.* 16, 164.
OLDEN, E. J. 1945. *Svensk Pomol. Foren. Arsskr.* 46, 105.
OLESON, E. M. 1941. *Bot. Gaz.* 103, 198.
OLMO, H. P. 1937. *Cytologia, F.J.N.* 606.
OLSZEWSKA, M. J. 1954. *Acta Soc. bot. Polon.* 23, 699.
ONO, H. 1937. *Cytologia, F.J.N.* 535.
—— 1941. *Bot. Mag. Tokyo*, 55, 17.
—— 1943. *Cytologia*, 13, 61.
ONO, H. & TATEOKA, T. 1953. *Bot. Mag. Tokyo*, 66, 18.
ONO, R. 1953. *Jap. J. Genet.* 28, 129.
ONO, T. 1926. *Sci. Rep. Tôhoku Univ.* 2, 93.
—— 1928. *Bot. Mag. Tokyo*, 42, 542.
—— 1930. *Bot. Mag. Tokyo*, 44, 168.
ONO, Y. 1935. *Jap. J. Genet.* 11, 238.
OSAWA, J. 1913. *J. Coll. Agric. Tokyo*, 1, 264.
—— 1920. *Bull. Imp. Agric. Exp. Sta. Tokyo*, 1, 318.
ÖSTERGREN, G. 1940. *Hereditas*, 26, 305.
—— 1942. *Hereditas*, 28, 242.
—— 1947. *Hereditas*, 33, 261.
OWNBEY, G. B. 1951a. *Amer. Midl. Nat.* 45, 184.
—— 1951b. *Bull. Torrey bot. Cl.* 78, 233.
OWNBEY, M. 1950. *Amer. J. Bot.* 37, 487.
—— 1953. *Rhodora*, 55, 61.

PAETOW, W. 1931. *Planta*, 14, 441.
PAL, B. B., RAMANUJAM, S. & JOSHI, A. B. 1941. *Indian J. Genet.* 1, 28.
PAL, N. 1952. *Proc. Nat. Inst. Sci. India*, 18, 363.
PALMGREN, O. 1939. *Bot. Notiser*, 1939, 246.
—— 1943. *Bot. Notiser*, 1943, 348.
PANJE, R. R. 1934. Thesis, Univ. Madras.

PANNOCCHIA-LAJ, F. 1938. *Nuovo G. bot. ital.* **45**, 157.
PANTULU, J. V. 1940. *Curr. Sci.* **9**, 416.
—— 1942. *Curr. Sci.* **11**, 152.
—— 1943. *Curr. Sci.* **12**, 274.
—— 1946. *Curr. Sci.* **15**, 255.
—— 1948. *Proc. 34th Indian Sci. Congr.* pt. 3, 167.
PANUTINA-MUSCHINA, W. N. 1933. *Bull. Soc. Nat. Moscou, Biol.* **42**, 162.
PARDI, P. N. 1934. *Nuovo G. Bot. ital.* **40**, 576.
PARODI, L. R. 1946. Gramineas Bonariensis. Buenos Aires.
PARTHASARATHY, N. 1938. *Cytologia*, **9**, 307.
—— 1939. *Ann. Bot., Lond.* **3**, 43.
—— 1946. *Curr. Sci.* **15**, 233.
PASSAMORE, S. F. 1930. *Bot. Gaz.* **90**, 213.
PASTRANA, M. D. 1932. *Amer. J. Bot.* **19**, 365.
PATEL, G. I. & OLMO, H. P. 1955. *Amer. J. Bot.* **42**, 141.
PATHAK, G. N. 1940. *J. Genet.* **39**, 437.
PATHAK, G. N. SINGH, B., TINARI, K. M., SRIVASTAVA, A. N. & PANDE, K. K. 1949. *Curr. Sci.* **18**, 347.
PATHAK, G. N. & YADAVA, R. S. 1951. *Curr. Sci.* **20**, 304.
PATEL, J. S. & NARAYANA, G. V. 1937. *Curr. Sci.* **5**, 479.
PAUL, A. K. 1937. *Cytologia*, **8**, 48.
PEARSON, H. H. W. 1912. *Ann. Bot., Lond.* **26**, 603.
PEARSON, O. H., HOPP, R. & BOHN, G. W. 1951. *Proc. Amer. Soc. hort. Sci.* **57**, 310.
PERAK, J. T. 1940. *Rev. argent. Agron.* **7**, 364.
—— 1943. *An. Inst. fitotec. S. Catalina*, 1941, 3, 7.
PERCIVAL, J. 1926. *J. Genet.* **17**, 49.
—— 1936. *Ann. Bot., Lond.* **50**, 427.
PEREIRA, A. DE L. 1940. *Bol. Soc. Brot.* **14**, 67.
—— 1942. *Bol. Soc. Brot.* **16**, 5.
—— 1948. *Portug. acta biol.* Ser. A, **2**, 101.
PERLOVA, R. L. 1939. *C.R. Acad. Sci. U.R.S.S.* **25**, 419.
*PERRY, B. A. 1943. *Amer. J. Bot.* **30**, 527.
PETERSON, D. 1936. *Bot. Notiser*, 1936, 281.
PETO, F. H. 1930. *Canad. J. Res.* **3**, 428.
—— 1933. *J. Genet.* **28**, 113.
—— 1938. *Canad. J. Res.* § C, **16**, 445.
PFEIFFER, H. 1942. *Veröff. dtsch. KolonMus. Bremen*, **3**, 238.
PHILLIPS, H. M. 1938. *Chron. Bot.* **4**, 385.
PHILP, J. 1933a. *J. Genet.* **27**, 133.
—— 1933b. *J. Genet.* **28**, 169.
—— 1934a. *J. Genet.* **29**, 197.
—— 1934b. *Daffodil Yearb.* 1934, 52.
PIENAAR, R. DE V. 1952. *Trans. roy. Soc. S. Afr.* **33**, 223.
PIERCE, W. P. 1939. *Amer. J. Bot.* **26**, 736.
PIGOTT, C. D. 1954. *New Phytol.* **53**, 470.
PIJL, L. VAN DER. 1934. *Rec. Trav. Bot. Neerland*, **31**, 113.
PINTO-LOPES, J. 1944. *Agron. lusit.* **6**, 129.
—— 1946. *Portug. acta biol.* Ser. A, **1**, 187.
PIOTROWICZ, M. 1954. *Acta Soc. Bot. Polon.* **23**, 43.
PIRSCHLE, K. 1942. *Z.i.A.V.* **80**, 247.
PODDUBNAJA (ARNOLDI), V. 1931. *Beih. bot. Zbl.* § 2, **48**, 141.
—— 1933a. *Planta*, **19**, 46.
—— 1933b. *Planta*, **21**, 381.
PODDUBNAJA (ARNOLDI), V. & DIANOWA, V. 1934. *Planta*, **23**, 19.
—— —— 1937. *J. Bot. U.R.S.S.* **22**, 267.
PODDUBNAJA (ARNOLDI), V., STESCHINA, N. & SOSNOVETZ, A. 1935. *Beih. bot. Zbl.* Ser. A, **53**, 309.
PODDUBNAJA, W. 1927. *Planta*, **4**, 284.

Pogliaga, H. H.   1952.   *Rev. argent. Agron.* **19**, 171.
Pohl, R. W.   1954.   *Madroño*, **12**, 145.
Pólya, L.   1948.   *Arch. Biol. Hungarica*, **18**, 145.
Popoff, A.   1935.   *Planta*, **24**, 510.
Poucques, M. L. de.   1945.   *Rev. Cytol., Paris*, **8**, 117.
—— 1949a.   *Rev. gen. Bot.* **56**, 5, 74, 172.
—— 1949b.   *Bull. Mus. Hist. nat. Paris*, **21**, 147.
—— 1949c.   *Bull. Soc. Sci. Nancy.*
—— 1950.   *Bull. Soc. Sci. Nancy.*
—— 1951.   *Bull. Soc. bot. Fr.* **98**, 89.
Powers, L.   1944.   *J. agric. Res.* **69**, 435.
Pratasenja, G. D.   1937.   *C.R. Acad. Sci. U.R.S.S.* **14**, 449.
Proctor, M. C. F.   1955.   *Watsonia*, 3, 154.
Proos, A. G.   1938.   *Sovetsk. Subtrop.* 3, (43), 78.
Propach, H.   1934.   *Z. Zellforsch.* **21**, 357.
—— 1935.   *Planta*, **23**, 349.
—— 1939.   *Gartenbauwiss.* **14**, 642.
Purcell, N. I.   1953.   *Pap. roy. Soc. Tasm.*
Purewal, S. S. & Randhawa, G. S.   1947.   *Indian J. agric. Sci.* **17**, 129.
Puri, V. & Singh, N. B.   1935.   *Proc. Indian Acad. Sci.* § B, **1**, 93.

Quintanilha, A. & Cabral, A.   1947.   *S. Afr. J. Sci.* **43**, 167.

Radermacher, A.   1925.   *Ann. Jard. bot. Buitenz.* **35**, 1.
Raghavan, T. S.   1935.   *J. Indian bot. Soc.* **14**, 151.
—— 1938.   *Ann. Bot., Lond.* n.s. **2**, 75.
Raghavan, T. S. & Krishnamurthy, K. V.   1945.   *Curr. Sci.* **14**, 152.
—— —— 1947.   *Proc. Indian Acad. Sci.* § B, **26**, 236.
Raghavan, T. S. & Rangaswamy, K.   1941.   *J. Indian bot. Soc.* **20**, 341.
Raghavan, T. S. & Srinivasan, A. R.   1941a.   *Proc. Indian Acad. Sci.* § B, **14**, 412.
—— —— 1941b.   *Proc. Indian Acad. Sci.* § B, **14**, 472.
Raghavan, T. S. & Srinivasan, V. K.   1940a.   *Ann. Bot., Lond.* **4**, 651.
—— —— 1940b.   *Cytologia*, **11**, 37.
—— —— 1941.   *Proc. Indian Acad. Sci.* § B, **13**, 24.
—— —— 1942.   *Proc. Indian Acad. Sci.* § B, **15**, 83.
Raghavan, T. S. & Venkatasubban, K. R.   1939a.   *Cytologia*, **10**, 23.
—— —— 1939b.   *Cytologia*, **10**, 189.
—— —— 1940a.   *Cytologia*, **11**, 55, 71.
—— —— 1940b.   *J. Indian bot. Soc.* **19**, 293.
—— —— 1941a.   *Cytologia*, **11**, 319.
—— —— 1941b.   *Proc. Indian Acad. Sci.* § B, **13**, 85.
—— —— 1943.   *Proc. Indian Acad. Sci.* § B, **17**, 118.
Rajagopalan, V. R.   1949.   *Proc. 36th Indian Sci. Congr.* pt. 3, 137.
Raju, M. V. S.   1952.   *Curr. Sci.* **21**, 107.
Ramaer, H.   1935.   *Genetica*, **17**, 193.
Raman, V. S.   1955.   *Cytologia*, **20**, 19.
Ramanathan, K.   1950.   *Curr. Sci.* **19**, 155.
Ramanujam, S.   1938.   *Ann. Bot., Lond.* n.s. **2**, 107.
—— 1940.   *Curr. Sci.* **9**, 325.
Ramanujam, S. & Joshi, A. B.   1948.   *Nature, Lond.* **161**, 99.
Ramanujam, S., Parthasarathy, K. & Ramiah, K.   1933.   *Proc. 20th Indian Sci. Congr. Agric. Sect.* 53.
Ramanujam, S. & Srinivasachar, D.   1943.   *Indian. J. Genet.* **3**, 73.
Randolph, L. F.   1928.   *Cornell Univ. Exp. Sta. (Ithaca) Mem.* **117**, 1.
—— 1932.   *P.N.A.S.* **18**, 222.
—— 1934.   *Bull. Amer. Iris Soc.* **52**, 63.
—— 1935.   *J. agric. Res.* **50**, 591.
—— 1944.   *Bull. Amer. Iris Soc.* **95**, 37.
Rangaswamy, K.   1941.   *Proc. Indian Acad. Sci.* § B, **14**, 149.

RANGASWAMY, K. 1949. *Proc. 36th Indian Sci. Congr.* pt. 3, 137.
RANGASWAMI-AYYANGAR, G. N. See AYYANGAR.
RAO, C. V. & RAO, K. V. S. 1952. *J. Indian bot. Soc.* **31**, 56.
RAO, K. V. R. 1940. *J. Indian bot. Soc.* **19**, 53.
RAO, L. N. 1942. *Ann. Bot., Lond.* n.s. **6**, 131.
RAO, N. S. 1947a. *Curr. Sci.* **16**, 156.
—— 1947b. *Curr. Sci.* **16**, 229.
RAO, N. S. & DATTA, R. M. 1953. *Nature, Lond.* **171**, 754.
RAO, V. S. 1936a. *J. Indian bot. Soc.* **15**, 105.
—— 1936b. *J. Indian bot. Soc.* **15**, 335.
RAO, Y. S. 1943. *Indian J. Genet.* **3**, 64.
—— 1945. *J. Indian bot. Soc.* **24**, 42.
—— 1946. *Curr. Sci.* **15**, 78.
—— 1950a. *Curr. Sci.* **19**, 384.
—— 1950b. *Proc. 37th Indian Sci. Congr.* pt. 3, 67.
—— 1953a. *Sci. & Cult.* **18**, 336.
—— 1953b. *Proc. Nat. Inst. Sci. India,* **19**, 563.
RATERA, E. L. 1938. *Rep. Inst. Genet. B. Aires,* **1**, 88.
—— 1943. *Rev. Fac. Agron. B. Aires,* **10**, 318.
—— 1947. *Bol. Soc. argent. Bot.* **2**, 43.
RATTENBURY, J. A. 1948. *Madroño,* **9**, 258.
RAU, M. A. 1941. *Beih. bot. Zbl.* **61A**, 1.
*RAU, N. S. 1929a. *J. Indian bot. Soc.* **8**, 126.
*—— 1929b. *J. Indian bot. Soc.* **8**, 201.
RAUCH, K. V. 1936. *Ber. schweiz. bot. Ges.* **46**, 61.
RAVES, J. F. 1926. *J. R. micr. Soc.* **46**, 193.
RAY, C. 1944. *Amer. J. Bot.* **31**, 241.
RAY, P. M. 1954. *Rapp. & Comm. 8th Int. Bot. Congr.* § 10, 188.
RAYNOR, L. A. 1952. *Amer. J. Bot.* **39**, 713.
REDDY, N. S. 1952. *J. Hered.* **43**, 233.
REED, H. S. 1950. *Madroño,* **10**, 139.
REESE, G. 1950. *Planta,* **38**, 324.
—— 1952a. *Ber. dtsch. bot. Ges.* **64**, 241.
—— 1953. *Ber. dtsch. bot. Ges.* **66**, 66.
—— 1954. *Planta,* **44**, 203.
REGNART, H. C. 1935. *Genetica,* **17**, 145.
REMSKI, M. F. 1954. *Bot. Gaz.* **116**, 163.
RESENDE, F. 1937. *Planta,* **26**, 757.
—— 1938. *Ber. dtsch. bot. Ges.* **56**, 533.
—— 1940. *Chromosoma,* **1**, 486.
RESENDE, F. & FRANCA, P. DA. 1946. *Portug. acta biol.* **1**, 289.
RESENDE, F. & RIJO, L. 1948. *Portug. acta biol.* **2**, 117.
RHOADES, M. M. 1950. *J. Hered.* **41**, 58.
RICHARDS, P. W. & CLAPHAM, A. R. 1941. *J. Ecol.* **29**, 385.
RICHARDSON, M. M. 1933. *Univ. Calif. Publ. Bot.* **17**, 51.
—— 1935. *Bot. Gaz.* **97**, 400.
RICHHARIA, R. H. 1937. *J. Genet.* **34**, 45.
RICHHARIA, R. H. & GHOSH, P. N. 1953. *Curr. Sci.* **22**, 17.
RICHHARIA, R. H. & KALAMAR, W. J. 1938. *Cytologia,* **9**, 249.
RICHHARIA, R. H. & KOTWAL, J. P. 1940. *Indian J. agric. Sci.* **10**, 1033.
RICHHARIA, R. H. & PERSAI, D. P. 1940. *Curr. Sci.* **9**, 542.
RICK, C. M. 1945. *Genetics,* **30**, 347.
—— 1951. *P.N.A.S.* **37**, 741.
—— 1953. *Proc. Amer. Soc. hort. Sci.* **61**, 459.
RILEY, H. P. 1948a. *J. S. Afr. Bot.* **14**, 97.
—— 1948b. *Amer. J. Bot.* **35**, 645.
—— 1950. *Trans. Ky. Acad. Sci.* **13**, 111.
RISSE, K. 1928. *Bot. Arch.* **23**, 266.
RIZET, G. 1945. *C.R. Soc. Biol., Paris,* **139**, 140.

RODOLICO, A. 1933. *Nuovo G; bot. ital.* **40**, 421.
RODRIGUES, J. E. DE M. 1950. *Mem. Soc. Brot.* **6**, 113.
—— 1953. Diss. Univ. Coimbra.
ROHWEDER, H. 1934. *Engler's bot. Jb.* **66**, 249.
*—— 1937. *Planta*, **27**, 500.
—— 1939. *Beih. bot. Zbl* § B, **59**, 1
ROLLINS, R. C. 1939a. *Amer. J. Bot.* **26**, 419.
—— 1939b. *Lloydia*, **2**, 109.
—— 1953. *Rhodora*, **55**, 109.
ROMANENKO, V. 1937. *J. Bot. Acad. Sci. Ukr.* **11**, 3.
ROMANOV, I. D. 1936. *Planta*, **25**, 438.
RORK, C. L. 1949. *Amer. J. Bot.* **36**, 687.
ROSCOE, M. V. 1927. *Bot. Gaz.* **84**, 392.
ROSEN, W. 1931. *Acta Hort. gothoburg.* **7**, 31.
ROSENTHAL, C. 1936. *Jb. wiss. Bot.* **83**, 809.
ROSS, J. G. & DUNCAN, R. E. 1949. *Bull. Torrey bot. Cl.* **76**, 414.
ROY, B. 1933. *Indian J. agric. Sci.* **3**, 1098.
—— 1936. *Cytologia*, **7**, 424.
—— 1937. *J. Genet.* **35**, 89.
ROZANOVA, M. A. 1939. *C.R. Acad. Sci., U.R.S.S.* **24**, 58.
—— 1940a. *C.R. Acad. Sci., U.R.S.S.* **29**, 143.
—— 1940b. *Zh. Bot. U.S.S.R.* **25**, 304.
RÜMKE, C. L. 1934. *Arch. Suikerind. Ned.-Ind.* 1934, 211.
RUNQUIST, E. 1937. *Hereditas*, **23**, 279.
RUTISHAUSER, A. 1943. *Ber. schweiz. bot. Ges.* **53**, 5.
*RUTLAND, J. P. 1941. *New Phytol.* **40**, 210.
RUTTLE, M. L. 1931a. *Gartenbauwiss.* **4**, 428.
—— 1931b. *Tech. Bull. N.Y. St. agric. Exp. Sta.* **186**, 1.
—— 1932. *Gartenbauwiss.* **7**, 154.
RYBERG, M. 1950. *Acta Hort. berg.* **15**, 207.
RYBIN, V. A. 1926. *Bull. appl. Bot., Pl.-Breed.* **16**, 187.
—— 1927. *Bull. appl. Bot., Pl.-Breed.* **17**, 101.
—— 1930. *Z.i.A.V.* **53**, 313.
—— 1933. *Bull. appl. Bot., Pl.-Breed.* S. 2, **2**, 3.
—— 1936. *Planta*, **25**, 22.
—— 1939. *C.R. Acad. Sci., U.R.S.S.* **24**, 368, 483.
RYKA, C. 1954. *Acta Soc. bot. Polon.* **23**, 321.

SACHS, L. 1953a. *Heredity*, **7**, 49.
—— 1953b. *J. agric. Sci.* **43**, 204.
SAEZ, F. A. 1949a. *Lilloa*, **19**, 97.
—— 1949b. *Lilloa*, **19**, 105.
SAEZ, F. A. & NUNEZ, O. 1943. *Notas. Mus. La Plata*, **8**, 333.
SAKAI, B. 1951. *La Kromosomo*, **11**, 425.
—— 1952. *Cytologia*, **17**, 104.
SAKAI, K. 1934. *Jap. J. Genet.* **9**, 226.
—— 1935. *Jap. J. Genet.* **11**, 68.
—— 1940. *Jap. J. Bot.* **11**, 68.
SALOMON, E. S. 1940. *An. Inst. fitotec. S. Catalina*, **2**, 13, 1940 (1942).
SAMPATH, S. & RAMANATHAN, K. 1949. *Curr. Sci.* **18**, 408.
SAMUELSSON, G. 1914. *Svensk bot. Tidskr.* **8**, 181.
SANDO, W. J. 1939. *J. Hered.* **30**, 271.
SANSOME, E. R. 1933. *Cytologia*, **5**, 15.
SANSOME, E. R. & LA COUR, L. 1934. *Lily Yearb.* 40.
SANTOS, A. C. DOS. 1945. *Bol. Soc. Brot.* **19**, 519.
SANTOS, J. K. 1924. *Bot. Gaz.* **77**, 353.
SASAKI, M. 1937. *Jap. J. Genet.* **13**, 260.
SATCZEK, K. 1951. *Bull. Acad. Polon. Sci. Lett.* Ser. B (1951), 285.
SATINA, S. 1953. *Amer. J. Bot.* **40**, 638.

SATINA, S., BERGNER, A. D. & BLAKESLEE, A. F. 1941. *Amer. J. Bot.* **28**, 383.
SATO, D. 1935a. *Bot. Mag. Tokyo*, **49**, 298.
—— 1935b. *Jap. J. Genet.* **11**, 272.
—— 1936. *Cytologia*, **7**, 521.
—— 1938. *Cytologia*, **9**, 203.
—— 1942. *Jap. J. Bot.* **12**, 57.
—— 1946. *Cytologia*, **14**, 174.
—— 1948. *Jap. J. Genet.* **23**, 44.
—— 1952. *Pap. Coord. Comm. Res. Genet.* **3**, 91.
SATO, M. 1932. *Bot. Mag. Tokyo*, **46**, 68.
—— 1934. *Bot. Mag. Tokyo*, **48**, 823.
SAURA, F. 1941. *Rep. Inst. Genet. B. Aires*, **2**, 41.
—— 1943. *Rev. Fac. Agron. B. Aires*, **10**, 344.
—— 1944. *Ingen. Agron.* **6**, 188.
—— 1947. *Rev. Fac. Agron. B. Aires*, **11**, 330.
—— 1948a. *Rev. Fac. Agron. B. Aires*, **12**, 51.
—— 1948b. *Cienc. Invest.* 1948, 435.
SAVCHENKO, P. F. 1935. *Bull. appl. Bot. Select.* II, **8**, 105.
SAX, H. J. 1930. *J. Arnold Arbor.* **11**, 220.
—— 1954. *J. Arnold Arbor.* **35**, 334.
SAX, H. J. & SAX, K. 1947. *J. Arnold Arbor.* **28**, 137.
SAX, K. 1929. *Proc. Amer. Soc. hort. Sci.* **26**, 32.
—— 1930a. *J. Arnold Arbor.* **11**, 7.
—— 1931a. *J. Arnold Arbor.* **12**, 3.
—— 1931b. *J. Arnold Arbor.* **12**, 198.
—— 1932. *J. Arnold Arbor.* **13**, 363.
—— 1933a. *J. Arnold Arbor.* **14**, 82.
—— 1933b. *J. Arnold Arbor.* **14**, 274.
—— 1936. *J. Arnold Arbor.* **17**, 352.
SAX, K. & ABBE, E. C. 1932. *J. Arnold Arbor.* **13**, 37.
SAX, K. & BEAL, J. M. 1934. *J. Arnold Arbor.* **15**, 225.
SAX, K. & HUSTED, L. 1936. *Amer. J. Bot.* **23**, 606.
SAX, K. & KRIBS, D. A. 1930. *J. Arnold Arbor.* **11**, 147.
SAX, K. & SAX, H. J. 1933. *J. Arnold Arbor.* **14**, 356.
SAXTON, W. T. 1909. *Bot. Gaz.* **47**, 406.
SCHAEPPI, H. & STEINDL, F. 1937. *Ber. schweiz. bot. Ges.* **47**, 369.
SCHAFER, B. & LA COUR, L. 1934. *Ann. Bot., Lond.* **48**, 693.
SCHEEL, M. 1931. *Bot. Arch.* **32**, 148.
SCHEERER, H. 1939. *Planta*, **29**, 636.
—— 1940. *Planta*, **30**, 716.
SCHIEMANN, E. 1929. *Ber. dtsch. bot. Ges.* **47**, 164.
—— 1951. *Z. Pflanzenzücht.* **30**, 464.
SCHLENKER, G. 1936. *Flora*, **130**, 305.
SCHLOSSER, L. A. 1936. *Züchter*, **8**, 75.
SCHNACK, B. 1940. *An. Inst. fitotec. S. Catalina*, **2**, 9, 1940 (1942).
—— 1944. *An. Inst. fitotech. S. Catalina*, **4**, 17.
SCHNACK, B. & COVAS, G. 1944. *Darwiniana*, **6**, 469.
—— —— 1945a. *Rev. argent. Agron.* **12**, 222.
—— —— 1945b. *Darwiniana*, **7**, 71.
—— —— 1947. *Haumania*, **1**, 32.
SCHNACK, B. & FERNANDEZ, O. 1946. *Bol. Soc. argent. Bot.* **1**, 285.
SCHNACK, B. & GONZALEZ, F. F. 1945. *Rev. argent. Agron.* **12**, 285.
SCHNARF, K. & WUNDERLICH, R. 1939. *Flora*, **33**, 297.
SCHOENNAGEL, E. 1931. *Bot. Jahrb.* **64**, 266.
SCHOTSMAN, H. D. 1954. *Acta bot. Neerl.* **3**, 313.
SCHTSCHAVINSKAJA, S. A. 1937a. *Bull. appl. Bot., Pl.-Breed.* **7**, 69.
—— 1937b. *Bull. appl. Bot., Pl.-Breed.* **7**, 101.
SCHULLE, H. 1933. *Flora*, **127**, 140.
SCHULZ-GAEBEL, H. 1930. *Beitr. Biol. Pfl.* **18**, 345.

SCHÜRHOFF, P. N.   1926.   Die Zytologie der Blütenpflanzen.   Stuttgart.
—— 1929a.   *Beitr. Biol. Pfl.* **17**, 72.
—— 1929b.   *Arch. Pharm. Berl.* **267**, 515.
—— 1931.   *Engler's bot. Jahrb.* **64**, 324.
SCHÜRHOFF, P. N. & MÜLLER, H.   1937.   *Cytologia, F.J.N.* 551.
SCHWARZENBACH, F.   1922.   *Flora,* **115**, 393.
SCHWEMMLE, J.   1924.   *Ber. dtsch. bot. Ges.* **42**, 238.
SEALY, J. R. & WEBB, D. A.   1950.   *J. Ecol.* **38**, 223.
SEARS, E. R.   1948.   *Adv. Genet.* **2**, 239.
SEKI, H.   1950.   *Jap. J. Genet.* **25**, 123.
SENJANINOVA (KORCZAGINA), M.   1930.   *Bull. appl. Bot., Pl.-Breed.* **26**, 453.
—— 1932a, b.   *Bull. appl. Bot., Pl.-Breed.* **28**, 1, 91.
*SENN, H. A.   1938.   *Bibl. Genet.* **12**, 175.
SENN, H. A., BOWDEN, W. M. & MOORE, R. J.   1949.   *Lilloa,* **19**, 119.
SEPELEVA, E. M.   1937.   *C.R. Acad. Sci. U.R.S.S.* **15**, 207.
—— 1939.   *C.R. Acad. Sci. U.R.S.S.* **25**, 228.
SESHAGIRIAH, K. N.   1941.   *J. Indian bot. Soc.* **20**, 357.
SETHI, M. L.   1928.   *J. Indian bot. Soc.* **7**, 105.
—— 1930.   *J. Indian bot. Soc.* **9**, 126.
SHAH, G. L.   1953.   *Curr. Sci.* **22**, 50.
SHALYGIN, I. N.   1941.   *C.R. Acad. Sci. U.R.S.S.* **30**, 527.
SHARMA, A. K.   1955.   *Genetica,* **27**, 323.
SHARMA, A. K. & DAS, N. K.   1954.   *Agron. lusitan.* **16**, 23.
SHARMA, A. K. & GHOSH, C.   1954.   *Genetica,* **27**, 17.
SHARMA, Y. M. L.   1939.   *Ann. Bot., Lond.* n.s. **3**, 861.
SHCHIBRA, N.   1936.   *C.R. Acad. Sci. U.R.S.S.* **11**, 189.
SHERIFF, A.   1946.   *Curr. Sci.* **15**, 354.
SHERIFF, A. & MURTHY, M. H. S.   1946.   *Curr. Sci.* **15**, 319.
SHIBUKAWA, T.   1930.   *Bot. Mag. Tokyo,* **44**, 561.
SHIFRISS, O.   1941.   *Thesis Cornell Univ.* 1941, 363.
—— 1942.   *J. Hered.* **33**, 144.
SHIMAMURA, T.   1941.   *Bot. Mag. Tokyo,* **55**, 553.
—— 1951.   *Jap. J. Genet.* **26**, 226.
SHIMOTOMAI, N.   1925.   *Bot. Mag. Tokyo,* **39**, 159.
—— 1929.   *Sci. Rep. Tôhoku Univ.* Ser. 4, **4**, 369.
—— 1933.   *J. Sci. Hiroshima Univ.* Ser. B, 2, **2**, 1.
—— 1937b.   *Z.i.A.V.* **74**, 30.
SHIMOTOMAI, N. & HARA, K.   1935.   *Bot. & Zool., Tokyo,* **3**, 1759.
SHIMOTOMAI, N. & HUZIWARA, Y.   1942.   *Cytologia,* **12**, 206.
SHIMOTOMAI, N. & INOUE, S.   1951.   *J. Sci. Hiroshima Univ.* Ser. B, 2, **6**, 1.
SHIMOTOMAI, N. & TAKEMOTO, T.   1936.   *Bot. Mag. Tokyo,* **50**, 324.
SHINKE, N.   1929.   *Mem. Coll. Sci. Kyoto,* Ser. B, **9**, 367.
SHOWALTER, H. M.   1935.   *Amer. J. Bot.* **22**, 594.
SIDOROV, B. N. & SOKOLOV, N. N.   1941.   *C.R. Acad. Sci. U.R.S.S.* **31**, 264.
SIKKA, S. M.   1940.   *J. Genet.* **40**, 441.
SIMMONDS, N. W.   1953.   *Kew Bull.* 1953, 571.
—— 1954.   *Heredity,* **8**, 139.
SIMMONDS, N. W. & DODDS, K. S.   1949.   *J. Genet.* **49**, 221.
SIMON, S. V. & LOWIG, E.   1930.   *Jb. wiss. Bot.* **72**, 466.
SIMONET, M.   1932c.   *C.R. Acad. Sci., Paris,* **195**, 738.
—— 1934a.   *Ann. Sci. nat. Bot.* s. 10, **16**, 229.
—— 1934c.   *Bull. Soc. bot. Fr.* **81**, 273, 801.
—— 1934d.   *C.R. Soc. Biol., Paris,* **117**, 1153.
—— 1935.   *C.R. Acad. Sci., Paris,* **201**, 1210.
—— 1938.   *C.R. Acad. Agric. Fr.* **24**, 846.
—— 1952.   *C.R. Acad. Sci., Paris,* **235**, 1244.
—— 1954.   *C.R. Acad. Sci., Paris,* **237**, 1755.
SIMONET, M. & MIEDZYRZECKI, CH.   1932.   *C.R. Soc. Biol., Paris,* **111**, 969.
SIMURA, T.   1935.   *Proc. Crop. Sci. Soc. Japan,* **7**, 121.

SINGH, B. 1951. *Curr. Sci.* **20**, 105.
SINGH, T. S. N. 1934. *Indian J. agric. Sci.* **4**, 290.
SINHA, N. P. 1950a. *Indian J. Genet.* **10**, 36.
—— 1950b. *Curr. Sci.* **19**, 348.
—— 1951a. *J. Indian bot. Soc.* **30**, 92.
—— 1951b. *Curr. Sci.* **20**, 70.
SINNOTT, E. W., BLAKESLEE, A. F. & WARMKE, H. E. 1939. *Genetics,* **24**, 84.
SINOTO, Y. 1928b. *Proc. imp. Acad. Japan,* **4**, 231.
—— 1929. *Cytologia,* **1**, 109.
—— 1938. *Cytologia,* **9**, 254.
SINOTO, Y. & KIKKAWA, R. 1932. *Jap. J. Genet.* **7**, 194.
SINOTO, Y. & SATO, D. 1940. *Sci. genet.* **1**, 354.
SIROTINA, M. 1936. *Nautsch. Sapisk. Sacharn. promytlennosti,* **2**, 56.
*SISA, M. 1929. *Jap. J. Genet.* **5**, 88.
SKALINSKA, M. 1931. *Proc. 5th Int. Bot. Congr.* 250,
—— 1947. *J. Linn. Soc. (Bot.),* **53**, 159.
—— 1950a. *Acta Soc. Bot. Polon.* **20**, 45.
—— 1950b. *Bull. Acad. Pol. Sci. Lett.* Ser. B, **1**, 149.
—— 1951. *Bull. Acad. Pol. Sci. Lett.* Ser. B, **1**, 119.
SKOVSTED, A. 1933. *Ann. Bot., Lond.* **47**, 227.
—— 1934a. *J. Genet.* **28**, 407.
—— 1934b. *Dansk bot. Ark.* **8**, 1.
—— 1935. *J. Genet.* **31**, 263.
*—— 1941. *C.R. Lab. Carls. S. Physiol.* **23**, 195.
SLADE, B. F. 1953. *Trans. roy. Soc. N.Z.* **81**, 1.
SMITH, B. W. 1937. *Bull. Torrey bot. Cl.* **64**, 189.
SMITH, C. M. 1929. *Bot. Gaz.* **87**, 507.
SMITH, E. C. 1941. *J. Arnold Arbor.* **22**, 219.
—— 1943. *J. Arnold Arbor.* **24**, 275.
SMITH, F. H. 1933. *P.N.A.S.* **19**, 605.
—— 1934. *Proc. Amer. phil. Soc.* **74**, 193.
—— 1938. *Amer. J. Bot.* **25**, 220.
—— 1942. *Amer. J. Bot.* **29**, 657.
—— 1955. *Amer. J. Bot.* **42**, 213.
SMITH, H. B. 1927. *Genetics,* **12**, 84.
SMITH, L. 1946. *J. agric. Res.* **73**, 291.
SMITH, S. G. 1932. *Bot. Gaz.* **94**, 394.
SMITH-WHITE, S. 1942. *Proc. Linn. Soc. N.S.W.* **67**, 335.
—— 1948a. *Proc. Linn. Soc. N.S.W.* **73**, 16.
—— 1948b. *Proc. Linn. Soc. N.S.W.* **73**, 37.
—— 1950. *Proc. Linn. Soc. N.S.W.* **75**, 99.
—— 1954a. *Proc. Linn. Soc. N.S.W.* **79**, 21.
—— 1954b. *Aust. J. Bot.* **2**, 287.
—— 1955. *Aust. J. Bot.* **3**, 48.
SNOAD, B. 1951. *Heredity,* **5**, 279.
—— 1952. *Rep. John Innes Hort. Instn.* **42**, 47.
—— 1955. *Heredity,* **9**, 129.
SNYDER, L. A. & HARLAN, J. R. 1953. *Amer. J. Bot.* **40**, 702.
SOBOLEWSKA, H. 1926. *Acta Soc. Bot. Polon.* **4**, 64.
SÖDERBERG, E. 1919. *Svensk bot. Tidskr.* **13**, 204.
SOEDA, T. 1944. *J. Fac. Sci. Hokkaido Univ.* **5**, 221.
SOKOLOVSKAJA, A. 1932. *Trud. petergof. est-nauch. Inst.* **8**, 149.
—— 1938. *Cytologia,* **8**, 452.
*SOKOLOVSKAJA, A. & STRELKOVA, O. 1938. *C.R. Acad. Sci. U.R.S.S.* **21**, 68.
—— —— 1940. *C.R. Acad. Sci. U.R.S.S.* **29**, 415.
—— —— 1941. *C.R. Acad. Sci. U.R.S.S.* **32**, 144.
SÖLLNER, R. 1950. *Experientia,* **6**, 335.
—— 1952. *Experientia,* **8**, 104.
—— 1953. *C.R. Acad. Sci. Paris,* **236**, 1503.
33   493

SÖRENSEN, T. & GUDJONSSON, G. 1946. *K. danske vidensk. Selsk. Skr. (Biol.)*, 4 (2), 1
SPARROW, A. H., POND, V. & SPARROW, R. C. 1952. *Amer. Nat.* 86, 277.
SPEESE, B. M. 1939. *Amer. J. Bot.* 26, 853.
SPEESE, B. M. & BALDWIN, J. T. 1952. *Amer. J. Bot.* 39, 685.
SPIER, J. D. 1934. *Canad. J. Res.* 11, 347.
SPRUMONT, G. 1928. *Cellule*, 38, 271.
SRINATH, K. V. 1940. *Cytologia*, 10, 467.
SRINIVASAN, A. R. 1941. *Proc. Indian Acad. Sci.* § B, 14, 529.
—— 1942. *Proc. Indian Acad. Sci.* § B, 16, 155.
SRINIVASAN, V. K. 1952. *Curr. Sci.* 21, 224.
SRINIVASACHAR, D. 1940. *Proc. Indian Acad. Sci.* § B, 11, 107.
SRIVASTAVA, G. D. 1939. *Proc. Nat. Acad. Sci. India*, 9, 58.
STÄHLIN, A. 1929. *Pflanzenbau*, 1, 330.
STANTON, T. R. 1936. *Yearb. Agric. U.S. Dept. Agric.* 1936, 375.
STEBBINS, G. L. 1932. *Bot. Gaz.* 94, 134, 322.
—— 1938. *Genetics*, 23, 83.
—— 1948. *Science*, 108, 5.
STEBBINS, G. L., JENKINS, J. A. & WALTERS, M. S. 1953. *Univ. Calif. Publ. Bot.* 26, 401.
STEBBINS, G. L. & KODANI, M. 1944. *J. Hered.* 35, 163.
STEBBINS, G. L. & LOVE, R. M. 1941. *Amer. J. Bot.* 28, 371.
STEBBINS, G. L. & PADDOCK, E. P. 1949. *Madroño*, 10, 70.
STEBBINS, G. L. & PUN, F. T. 1953. *Amer. J. Bot.* 40, 444.
STEBBINS, G. L. & TOBGY, H. A. 1944. *Amer. J. Bot.* 31, 1.
STEBBINS, G. L., TOBGY, H. A. & HARLAN, J. R. 1944. *Proc. Calif. Acad. Sci.* 25, 307.
STEBBINS, G. L., VALENCIA, J. I. & VALENCIA, R. M. 1946. *Amer. J. Bot.* 33, 338.
STEBBINS, G. L. & WALTERS, M. S. 1949. *Portug. Acta Biol.* Ser. A, R. B. Goldschmidt
  vol., 106.
STEINDL, FR. 1935. *Ber. schweiz. bot. Ges.* 44, 343.
STEINER, E. 1944. *Bot. Gaz.* 105, 374.
STENAR, H. 1927. *Bot. Notiser*, 1927, 104.
—— 1928. *Bot. Notiser*, 1928, 357.
—— 1935. *Ark. Bot.* 26 (8).
STEPHENS, S. G. 1942. *J. Genet.* 44, 272.
STERN, F. C. 1944. *Proc. Linn. Soc. London, Bot.* 155, 76.
STEWART, R. N. 1943. *Bot. Gaz.* 104, 620.
—— 1947. *Amer. J. Bot.* 34, 19.
STEWART, R. N. & BAMFORD, R. 1942. *Amer. J. Bot.* 29, 301.
STEWART, W. S. 1939. *Amer. J. Bot.* 26, 730.
STIFF, M. L. 1951. *Virginia J. Sci.* 2, 317.
STOCKAR, A. 1946. *Rev. argent. Agron.* 13, 253.
STOCKWELL, P. 1935. *Bot. Gaz.* 96, 565.
STOKES, J. 1937. *Bot. Gaz.* 99, 387.
STOLZE, K. V. 1925. *Bibl. genet. Lpz.* 8, 71.
STOREY, W. B. 1941. *Hawaii Agric. Exp. Sta. Bull.* 87, 6.
—— 1950. *Pacific Science*, 4, 37.
—— 1953. *Bull. Pacif. Orchid Soc. Hawaii*, 11, 17.
STOUT, A. B. 1932. *Cytologia*, 3, 250.
STRASBURGER, E. 1909. *Z. Bot.* 1, 507.
—— 1910. *Flora*, 100, 398.
STRAUB, J. 1937. *Ber. dtsch. bot. Ges.* 55, (160).
—— 1938. *Ber. dtsch. bot. Ges.* 56, 406.
—— 1939. *Ber. dtsch. bot. Ges.* 57, 531.
STRELKOVA, O. 1938. *Cytologia*, 8, 468.
STREY, M. 1931. *Planta*, 14, 682.
SUBRAMANYAM, K. 1944. *Proc. Indian Acad. Sci.* § B, 19, 115.
—— 1946. *J. Mysore Univ.* Ser. B, 7, 1.
—— 1951. *Proc. 38th Indian Sci. Congr.* pt. 3, 145.
STUCKEY, I. H. & BANFIELD, W. G. 1946. *Amer. J. Bot.* 33, 185.
SUESSENGUTH, K. 1920. *Beih. bot. Zbl.* 38 (2), 1.

SUESSENGUTH, K. 1921. *Flora,* **114,** 313.
SUGIHARA, Y. 1940. *Sci. Rep. Tôhoku Univ.* **15,** 13.
—— 1941. *Sci. Rep. Tôhoku Univ.* **16,** 187.
—— 1943. *Sci. Rep. Tôhoku Univ.* **17,** 125.
SUGIURA, T. 1927. *Bot. Mag. Tokyo,* **41,** 219.
—— 1928a. *Bot. Mag. Tokyo,* **42,** 504.
—— 1931. *Bot. Mag. Tokyo,* **45,** 353.
—— 1936a. *Proc. imp. Acad. Japan,* **12,** 144.
—— 1936b. *Cytologia,* **7,** 544.
—— 1937a. *Cytologia, F.J.N.* 845.
—— 1937b. *Bot. Mag. Tokyo,* **51,** 425.
*—— 1939a. *Proc. imp. Acad. Japan,* **14,** 391.
*—— 1940, including 1939. *Cytologia,* **10,** 73, 205, 324, 363, 558.
—— 1942. *Cytologia,* **12,** 418.
—— 1944. *Cytologia,* **13,** 352.
SULLIVAN, T. D. 1947. *Bull. Torrey bot. Cl.* **74,** 453
SUOMALAINEN, E. 1947. *Ann. Acad. Sci. Fenn.* Ser. A, **13,** 1.
SUTO, T. 1936. *Jap. J. Genet.* **12,** 107.
—— 1944. *J. Fac. Sci. Hokkaido Univ.* Ser. 5, **5,** 249.
SUTTON, E. 1935. *Ann. Bot., Lond.* **49,** 689.
SUZUKA, O. 1950a. *Rep. Kihara Inst. Biol. Res.* **4,** 57.
—— 1950b. *Jap. J. Genet.* **25,** 17.
—— 1951. *Jap. J. Genet.* **26,** 226.
SUZUKA, O. & KORIBA, S. 1949. *Jap. J. Pharmacog.* **3,** 68.
SVENSSON, H. G. 1925. *Uppsala Univ. Arsskr.* no. 2, 1925.
SVESHNIKOVA, I. N. 1927. *Bull. appl. Bot., Pl.-Breed.* **17,** 37.
—— 1930. *Proc. U.S.S.R. Congr. Genet.* **2,** 441.
—— 1940. *J. Hered.* **31,** 349.
SWAMINATHAN, M. S. 1954. *Genetics,* **39,** 59.
SWAMINATHAN, M. S. & HOUGAS, R. W. 1954. *Amer. J. Bot.* **41,** 645.
SWAMY, B. G. L. 1941. *Proc. Indian Acad. Sci.* § B, **14,** 454.
SYMON, J. L. 1926. *Bot. Gaz.* **81,** 121.
SZELUBSKY, R. 1950. *Palest. J. Bot. Jerusalem,* **5,** 1.
SZWABOWICZ, A. 1954. *Acta Soc. bot. Polon.* **23,** 243.

TÄCKHOLM, G. 1914. *Svensk bot. Tidskr.* **8,** 223.
—— 1922. *Acta Hort. berg.* **7,** no. 3.
TÄCKHOLM, G. & SÖDERBERG, E. 1917. *Ark. Bot.* **15,** no. 8.
—— —— 1918. *Svensk bot. Tidskr.* **12,** 189.
TAHARA, M. 1910. *Bot. Mag. Tokyo,* **24,** 281.
—— 1921. *J. Coll. Sci. Tokyo,* **43** (7).
—— 1937. *Cytologia, F.J.N.* 14.
TAHARA, M. & SHIMOTOMAI, N. 1916. *Bot. Mag. Tokyo,* **40,** 132.
TAKAGI, F. 1928. *Sci. Rep. Tôhoku Univ.* Ser. 4, **3,** 665.
—— 1933. *Bot. Mag. Tokyo,* **47,** 556.
TAKAGI, N. 1938. *Bull. Miyazaki Coll. Agric. For.* **10,** 83.
TAKENAKA, V. 1931. *J. Tyosen. nat. Hist. Soc.* **12,** 1.
TAKENAKA, Y. 1941. *Bot. Mag. Tokyo,* **55,** 319.
—— 1950. *Cytologia,* **16,** 95.
—— 1952. *Pap. Coordin. Commit. Res. Genet.* **3,** 71.
TAKIZAWA, S. 1940. *Jap. J. Genet.* **16,** 18.
—— 1952a. *J. Fac. Sci. Hokkaido Univ.* Ser. 5, **6,** 249.
—— 1952b. *Kromosomo,* **14,** 509.
TAMAMSCHJAN, S. 1933. *Bull. appl. Bot.* Ser. 2, **2,** 137.
TANAKA, N. 1935. *Bot. Mag. Tokyo,* **49,** 709.
—— 1937. *Cytologia, F.J.N.* 814.
—— 1938. *Cytologia,* **8,** 515.
—— 1939a. *Bot. Mag. Tokyo,* **53,** 480.

TANAKA, N. 1939b. *Cytologia*, **10**, 51.
—— 1939c. *Jap. J. Genet*. **15**, 153.
—— 1941. *Bot. Mag. Tokyo*, **55**, 55.
—— 1949. *Cytologia*, **15**, 15.
TANG, P. S. & LOO, W. S. 1940. *Science*, **91**, 222.
TANZI, SH. 1925. *Bot. Mag. Tokyo*, **39**, 459.
TARNAVSCHI, I. T. 1935. *Bull. Fac. St. Cernauti*, **9**, 47.
—— 1938. *Bull. Fac. St. Cernauti*, **12**, 68.
TATEOKA, T. 1954. *Cytologia*, **19**, 317.
*TAYLOR, H. 1945. *Brittonia*, **5**, 337.
TAYLOR, W. R. 1920. *Contr. bot. Lab. Univ. Pa.* **5**, 111.
—— 1925a. *Amer. J. Bot*. **12**, 104.
—— 1925b. *Amer. J. Bot*. **12**, 219.
—— 1925c. *Amer. J. Bot*. **12**, 238.
TERNOVSKY, M. F. 1935. *Z. Zücht. A.* **20**, 268.
TESHIMA, T. 1933. *J. Fac. Agric. Hokkaido Univ.* **34**, 155.
TETRY, A. 1941. *Rev. Sci.* **79**, 190.
THATHACHAR, T. 1942. *J. Indian bot. Soc.* **21**, 185.
THERMAN, E. 1950. *Amer. J. Bot*. **37**, 407.
—— 1951. *Heredity*, **5**, 253.
—— 1953. *Ann. Bot. Soc. Vanamo*, **25** (6), 1.
THOMAS, P. T. 1936. *Nature*, **138**, 402.
—— 1940. *J. Genet*. **40**, 141.
THOMAS, P. T. & REVELL, S. H. 1946. *Ann. Bot., Lond.* **10**, 159.
THOMPSON, H. J. 1953. *Contr. Dudley Herb. Calif.* **4**, 73.
THOMPSON, R. C., WHITAKER, T. W. & KOSAR, W. F. 1941. *J. agric. Res.* **63**, 91.
TIMM, F. W. & CLAPHAM, A. R. 1940. *New Phytol.* **39**, 1.
TING, Y. C. & KEHR, A. E. 1953. *J. Hered.* **44**, 207.
*TISCHLER, G. 1922. *Allg. Pflanzenkaryologie, Hb. Pflanzenanat.* 2, Berlin.
*—— 1927a. *Tabul. biol., Hague*, **4**, 1.
—— 1927b. *Planta*, **4**, 617.
—— 1928. *Biol. Zbl.* **48**, 321.
—— 1929. *Planta*, **8**, 685.
—— 1930. *Z. Bot.* **23**, 150.
*—— 1931. *Tabul. biol., Hague*, **7**, 109.
—— 1931b. *Ber. dtsch. bot. Ges.* **47**, (30).
*—— 1936 & 1937. *Tabul. biol., Hague*, **11**, 281 and **12**, 57.
*—— 1938. *Tabul. biol., Hague*, **16**, 162.
—— 1942. *Naturwiss.* **30**, 713.
*—— 1950. Chromosomenzahlen der Gefässpflanzen Mitteleuropas. Hague.
TIXIER, P. 1953. *Rev. Cytol., Paris*, **14**, 1.
TJEBBES, K. 1928. *Hereditas*, **10**, 328.
TJIO, J. H. 1948. *Hereditas*, **34**, 135.
TOMÉ, G. A. 1947. *Rev. Fac. Agron. B. Aires*, **11**, 299.
TONGIORGI, E. 1935. *Nuovo G. bot. ital.* **42**, 261.
—— 1942. *Nuovo G. bot. ital.* **49**, 242.
TÖREN, J. 1950. *Rev. Fac. Sci. Univ. Istanbul*, Ser. B, **15**, 239.
TOXOPEUS, H. J. 1933. *Genetica*, **15**, 241.
—— 1952. *Euphytica*, **1**, 175.
TRAUB, H. P. 1942. *Herbertia*, **9**, 53.
TRAUB, H. P. 1945. *Herbertia*, **12**, 38.
TSCHECHOW, W. 1930. *Planta*, **9**, 673.
—— 1931. *Izv. Tomskog. otd. Russk. Bot.* **3**, 121.
—— 1933. *Bull. appl. Bot., Pl.-Breed.* Ser. 2, **1**, 119.
—— 1935. *Trud. biol. nautschn. issledov. Inst.* **1**, 143.
TSCHECHOW, T. & KARTASCHOWA, N. 1932. *Cytologia*, **3**, 221.
TURESSON, G. 1930. *Hereditas*, **13**, 177.
—— 1938. *Ann. Agric. Coll. Sweden*, **5**, 405.

TURNER, B. L. & BEAMAN, J. H.   1953.   *Field & Lab.* **21,** 47.
TUSCHNJAKOWA, M.   1929.   *Planta,* **7,** 29.
—— 1935.   *Züchter,* **7,** 169.
TUTIN, T. G.   1950.   *Watsonia,* **1,** 345.
TZITZIN, N. V.   1933.   *Lenin Ac. Agric. Sci. Sib. Inst. Grain Cult. Omsk,* 101.   *Cf.* Pl. Br. Abst. **8,** 350 (1936).

U, N., NAGAMATU, T. & MIDUSIMA, N.   1937.   *Cytologia, F.J.N.* 437.
UCHIKAWA, I.   1933.   *Mem. Coll. Agric. Kyoto,* 25, **2,** 11.
—— 1935.   *Jap. J. Genet.* **11,** 308.
—— 1943.   *Jap. J. Genet.* **19,** 112.
UDDLING, A.   1929.   *Hereditas,* **12,** 294.
UFER, M.   1937.   *Z.i.A.V.* **73,** 390.
UHL, C. H.   1948.   *Amer. J. Bot.* **35,** 695.
—— 1952.   *Evolution,* **6,** 81.
—— 1953.   *Cactus & Succ. J., Los Angeles,* **25,** 4.
UHL, C. H. & MORAN, R.   1953.   *Amer. J. Bot.* **40,** 492.
UJHELYI, J. & FELFÖLDY, L. J. M.   1948.   *Arch. Biol. Hung.* **18,** 52.
UPCOTT, M.   1935.   *J. Genet.* **31,** 1.
—— 1936a.   *Cytologia,* **7,** 118.
—— 1936b.   *J. Genet.* **33,** 135.
UPCOTT, M. & LA COUR, L.   1936.   *J. Genet.* **33,** 237.

VAARAMA, A.   1939.   *J. sci. agric. Soc., Finland,* **11,** 72.
—— 1941.   *Ann. Bot. Soc. Vanamo,* **16** (2).
—— 1943.   *Hereditas,* **29,** 191.
—— 1947a.   *Arch. Soc. Zool. Bot. Fennicae Vanamo,* **2,** 55.
—— 1947b.   *Hereditas,* **33,** 422.
—— 1949a.   *Hereditas,* **35,** 136.
—— 1949b.   *Hereditas,* **35,** 251.
—— 1950.   *Hereditas,* **36,** 342.
—— 1951.   *Hereditas,* **37,** 290.
—— — 1954.   *Arch. Soc. zool.-bot. fenn. Vanamo,* **8,** 192.
VACHELL, E. & BLACKBURN, K. B.   1939.   *J. Bot.* **77,** 65.
VAKAR, B. A.   1936.   *Cytologia,* **7,** 293.
VALCANOVER, R.   1927.   *Cellule,* **37,** 203.
VALENTINE, D. H.   1949.   *Rep. Conf. Bot. Soc., Brit. Isles,* 1949, 48.
—— 1950.   *New Phytol.* **49,** 193.
VAVILOV, N. I.   1935.   *Theoretical Bases of Plant Breeding* (Russian), **1,** 17.
VAZART, J.   1950.   *Rév. gén. Bot.* **57,** 517.
VEATCH, C.   1934.   *Bot. Gaz.* **96,** 189.
VELSER, I.   1913.   Diss. Univ. Bonn.
VENKATASUBBAN, K. R.   1944.   *Annamalai Univ. Publ.* **1-3,** 1.
—— 1945a.   *Proc. Indian Acad. Sci.* § B, **21,** 77.
—— 1945b.   *Proc. Indian Acad. Sci.* § B, **22,** 193.
—— 1946.   *Proc. Indian Acad. Sci.* § B, **23,** 281.
—— 1950.   *Proc. Indian Acad. Sci.* § B, **31,** 308.
VENKATESWARLU, J.   1946.   *Curr. Sci.* **15,** 142.
VENUGOPALAN, S.   1949.   *Proc. 36th Indian Sci. Congr.* pt. 3, 137.
VERMEULEN, P.   1947.   Studies on Dactylorchids. Utrecht.
VIGNOLI, L.   1933.   *Lav. Ist. bot. Palermo,* **4,** 5.
—— 1936.   *Lav. Ist. bot. Palermo,* **7,** 3.
—— 1939.   *Lav. Ist. bot. Palermo,* **10,** 54.
—— 1945a.   *Nuovo G. bot. ital.* **52,** 1.
—— 1945b.   *Nuovo G. bot. ital.* **52,** 11.
VILKOMMERSON, H.   1943.   *Bull. Torrey bot. Cl.* **70,** 430.
VILMORIN, R. DE & SIMONET, M.   1927a.   *C.R. Acad. Sci., Paris,* **184,** 164.
—— —— 1927b.   *C.R. Soc. Biol., Paris,* **96,** 166.

VILMORIN, R. DE & SIMONET, M. 1928. *Z.i.A.V.* Suppl. 2, 1520.
VIVEIROS, A. 1949. *Portug. Acta Biol.* Ser. A, R. B. Goldschmidt vol., 200.
—— 1951. *Rev. Fac. Cienc. Lisb.* C, 1, 215.
VOS, M. P. DE. 1943. *S. Afr. J. Sci.* 40, 113.
—— 1947. *Ann. Univ. Stellenbosch,* A, 25, 1.
—— 1951. *J. S. Afr. Bot.* 17, 77.

WAGNER, S. 1932. *Z.i.A.V.* 61, 76.
WAGNER, M. DE N. 1948. *Agron. lusit.* 10, 171.
—— 1949. *Genet. Iber.* 1, 59.
WAHL, H. A. 1940. *Amer. J. Bot.* 27, 458.
WAKAKUWA, S. H. 1931. *Jap. J. Genet.* 7, 17.
WALKER, R. I. 1942. *Bot. Gaz.* 103, 625.
—— 1944. *Bull. Torrey bot. Cl.* 71, 529.
WALLISCH, R. 1930. *Öst. bot. Z.* 79, 97.
WALTERS, J. L. 1952. *Amer. J. Bot.* 39, 145.
WALTERS, M. S. 1952. *Amer. J. Bot.* 39, 619.
WALTERS, M. S. & GERSTEL, D. U. 1948. *Amer. J. Bot.* 35, 141.
WALTERS, S. M. 1949. *J. Ecol.* 37, 192.
WANG, F. H. 1948. *Amer. J. Bot.* 35, 21.
WANNER, H. 1943. *Planta,* 33, 637.
WANSCHER, J. H. 1931. *Hereditas,* 15, 179.
—— 1932. *Bot. Tidskr.* 42, 49.
*—— 1933. *Bot. Tidskr.* 42, 384.
—— 1934. *New Phytol.* 33, 58.
WARBURG, E. F. 1938. *New Phytol.* 37, 189.
—— 1952. In Clapham, A. R. *et al. Flora of the British Isles,* Cambridge.
WARD, G. H. 1953. *Contr. Dudley Herb.* 4, 155.
WARMKE, H. E. 1937. *Amer. J. Bot.* 24, 376.
—— 1951. *Agron. J.* 43, 143.
WARMKE, H. E., PEREZ, J. R. & MONGE, J. A. F. 1946. *4th Ann. Rep. Inst. Trop. Agric. Univ. Puerto Rico,* 1945-46, 19.
WARTH, G. 1925. *Z.i.A.V.* 38, 200.
WATANABE, K. 1934. *Proc. imp. Acad. Japan,* 10, 421.
—— 1935. *Proc. imp. Acad. Japan,* 11, 283.
—— 1939. *Proc. Crop Sci. Soc. Japan,* 11.
WATKINS, G. M. 1936. *Amer. J. Bot.* 23, 328,
WCISŁO, H. 1951. *Bull. Acad. Pol. Sci. Lett.* Ser. B, 1, 147.
WEBBER, J. M. 1932. *Amer. J. Bot.* 19, 411.
—— 1934. *J. agric. Res.* 49, 223.
—— 1936. *Cytologia,* 7, 313.
WEBER, W. A. 1946. *Amer. Midl. Nat.* 35, 400.
WEBER, W. A. & BREWBAKER, J. L. 1950. *Univ. Colo. Stud. Biol.* 1, 24.
WEDDLE, C. 1941. *Proc. Amer. Soc. hort. Sci.* 39, 393.
WEEKS, W. D. 1941. *Proc. Amer. Soc. hort. Sci.* 38, 141.
WEIJER, J. 1952. *Genetica,* 26, 1.
WEINEDEL-LIEBAU, F. 1928. *Jb. wiss. Bot.* 69, 636.
WELLER, D. M. 1939. Hawaii Sugar Planters' Assoc., pp. 121.
WELSH, D. A. 1950. *J. Ecol.* 38, 185.
WESTERGAARD, M. 1936. *C.R. Lab. Carlsberg, Physiol.* 21, 195, 437.
—— 1938. *Dansk bot. Ark.* 9 (5).
—— 1940. *Dansk bot. Ark.* 10 (5).
—— 1941. *Bot. Tidskr. Copenh.* 45, 338.
—— 1942. *K. danske vidensk Selsk. Skr. (biol.),* 2, (4).
—— 1946. *Hereditas,* 32, 419.
—— 1948. *K. danske vidensk. Selsk. Biol. Medd.* 18, 3.
WESTFALL, J. J. 1949. *Amer. J. Bot.* 36, 805.
—— 1950. *Amer. J. Bot.* 37, 667.

DE WET, J. M. J. 1954a. *Amer. J. Bot.* **41**, 204.
—— 1954b. *Cytologia*, **19**, 97.
WETMORE, R. H. & DELISLE, A. L. 1939. *Amer. J. Bot.* **26**, 1.
WETZEL, R. 1929. Diss. Marburg, 60 pp.
WEXELSEN, H. 1928. *Univ. Calif. Publ. Agric. Sci.* **12**, 355.
WHEELER, H. M. 1935. *Univ. Calif. Publ. Bot.* **18**, 45.
—— 1945. *P.N.A.S.* **31**, 177.
WHITAKER, T. W. 1933a. *J. Arnold Arbor.* **14**, 113.
—— 1933b. *Bot. Gaz.* **94**, 780.
—— 1933c. *J. Arnold Arbor.* **14**, 376.
—— 1934a. *J. Arnold Arbor.* **15**, 135.
—— 1934c. *J. Arnold Arbor.* **15**, 353.
—— 1941. *Proc. Amer. Soc. hort. Sci.* **39**, 346.
—— 1950. *Madroño*, **10**, 209.
WHITAKER, T. W. & JAGGER, I. C. 1939. *J. agric. Res.* **58**, 297.
WHITE, O. E., TAYLOR, J. H. & SPEESE, B. M. 1946. *J. Hered.* **37**, 66.
WHYTE, R. O. 1929. *New Phytol.* **28**, 319.
WILKINSON, J. 1941. *Ann. Bot., Lond.* n.s. **5**, 149.
—— 1944. *Ann. Bot., Lond.* n.s. **8**, 269.
WILSON, G. B. 1946. *Genetics*, **31**, 475.
—— 1947. *Nature*, **160**, 121.
WILSON, G. B. & BOOTHROYD, E. R. 1941. *Canad. J. Res.* § C, **19**, 400.
WINGE, Ø. 1917. *C.R. Trav. Lab. Carlsberg*, **13**, 131.
—— 1925. *Cellule*, **35**, 303.
—— 1926. *Beretn. Nord. Jordbrugs-forsk. Kongr. Oslo*, 592.
—— 1940. *C.R. Trav. Lab. Carlsberg*, **23**, 41.
WINKLER, H. 1906. *Ann. Jard. bot. Buitenzorg*, Ser. 2, **5**.
WINTER, B. DE. 1951a. *Bothalia*, **6**, 117.
—— 1951b. *Bothalia*, **6**, 139.
WITKUS, E. R. 1951. *Bull. Torrey bot. Cl.* **78**, 80.
WITSCH, H. 1932. *Öst. bot. Z.* **81**, 108.
WITTE, M. B. 1947. *Bull. Torrey bot. Cl.* **74**, 443.
WITTLAKE, E. H. 1940. *Herbertia*, **7**, 166.
WOESS, E. T. 1947. *Chromosoma*, **3**, 66.
—— 1948. *Öst. bot. Z.* **95**, 270.
—— 1949. *Öst. bot. Z.* **96**, 56.
WOESS, F. V. 1941. *Z.i.A.V.* **79**, 444.
WOLCOTT, G. B. 1937. *Amer. Nat.* **71**, 190.
WOLF, P. 1929. *Beitr. Biol. Pfl.* **17**, 351.
WOOD, C. E. 1949. *Rhodora*, **51**, 193, 233, 305, 369.
WOODARD, J. W. 1951. *Bull. Amer. Orchid Soc.* **20**, 356.
—— 1952. *Bull. Amer. Orchid Soc.* **21**, 247.
WOODWORTH, R. H. 1929a. *Bot. Gaz.* **87**, 331.
—— 1929b. *Bot. Gaz.* **88**, 383.
—— 1930c. *Amer. J. Bot.* **17**, 863.
—— 1931. *J. Arnold Arbor.* **12**, 206.
WOYCICKI, Z. 1906. *Bull. Acad. Sc. Cracovie Sc. Math. & Nat.* 506.
—— 1937. *Cytologia, F.J.N.* 1094.
WRIGHT, F. R. E. 1936. *J. Bot.* **74**, suppl. 1.
—— 1938. *J. Bot.* **76**, suppl. 1.
WRIGHT, J. W. 1944. *J. For.* **42**, 489.
WU, S. H. 1942. *Pap. Mich. Acad. Sci. Art. Lett.* **27**, 117.
WULFF, H. D. 1933. *Planta*, **21**, 12.
—— 1934a. *Ber. dtsch. bot. Ges.* **52**, 43.
—— 1935. *Beih. bot. Zbl.* **54**, Abt. A, 83.
—— 1936. *Planta*, **26**, 275.
*—— 1937a. *Jb. wiss. Bot.* **84**, 812.
—— 1937b. *Ber. dtsch. bot. Ges.* **55**, 262.

WULFF, H. D. 1938. *Ber. dtsch. bot. Ges.* **56**, 247.
—— 1939a. *Ber. dtsch. bot. Ges.* **57**, 84.
WULFF, H. D. 1939b. *Ber. dtsch. bot. Ges.* **57**, 424.
—— 1940a. *Planta*, **31**, 478.
—— 1944. *Bot. Arch.* **45**, 149.
—— 1950. *Ber. dtsch. bot. Ges.* **63**, 64.
—— 1954. *Arch. Pharm.* **287**, 529.
WUNDERLICH, R. 1937. *Flora*, **132**, 48.
WYLIE, A. P. 1952. *Heredity*, **6**, 137.
—— 1954. *Am. Rose Annual*, **39**, 36.

YAKAR, N. 1945. *Rev. Fac. Sci. Univ. Istanbul*, Ser. B, **10**, 299.
YAKOVLEVA, S. V. 1933. *Bull. appl. Bot.* Ser. II, **5**, 207.
YAMAHA, G. & SUEMATSU, S. 1936. *Sci. Rep. Tokyo Univ.* Ser. B, **3**, 21.
YAMAMOTO, K. & SAKAI, K. 1932. *Jap. J. Genet.* **8**, 27.
YAMAMOTO, Y. 1934. *Cytologia*, **5**, 317.
—— 1937. *Cytologia, F.J.N.* 181.
YAMANE, Y. 1950. *Jap. J. Genet.* **25**, 220.
YAMASHITA, K. 1935. *Jap. J. Genet.* **11**, 360.
—— 1937. *Agric. & Hort.* **12**, 1219.
YAMAURA, A. 1933. *Bot. Mag. Tokyo*, **47**, 551.
YAMAZAKI, R. 1936. *Jap. J. Genet.* **12**, 101.
YAMAZAKI, Y. 1934. *Agric. Hort.* **9**, 156.
—— 1937. *Jap. J. Genet.* **13**, 393.
YARNELL, S. H. 1929. *Genetics*, **14**, 78.
—— 1931a. *Genetics*, **16**, 422.
—— 1931c. *Proc. Amer. Soc. hort. Sci.* **28**, 114.
—— 1936. *J. agric. Res.* **52**, 385.
YASUI, K. 1935. *Cytologia*, **6**, 484.
—— 1936a. *Cytologia*, **7**, 535.
—— 1937. *Bot. Mag. Tokyo*, **51**, 539.
—— 1939. *Cytologia*, **10**, 180.
—— 1941. *Cytologia*, **11**, 452.
YATES, J. J. & BRITTAN, N. H. 1952. *Austr. J. Agric. Res.* **3**, 300.
YEO, P. F. 1954. *Watsonia*, **3**, 101.
YOUNG, J. O. 1940. *Bot. Gaz.* **101**, 839.
YOUNGMAN, W. 1927. *Ann. Bot., Lond.* **41**, 755.
—— 1931. *Ann. Bot., Lond.* **45**, 49.

ZAIKOVSKAJA, N. E. 1939. *C.R. Acad. Sci. U.R.S.S.* **23**, 944.
ZAITZEW, G. S. 1927. *Bull. appl. Bot., Pl.-Breed.* **18**, 1.
ZEEUW, J. DE. 1936. *Cellule*, **44**, 389.
ZERPA, D. M. DE. 1951. *Agron. Trop. Venezuela*, **1**, 83.
—— 1952. *Agron. Trop. Venezuela*, **2**, 215.
ZHEBRAK, A. 1944. *Nature*, **153**, 549.
ZIELINSKI, Q. B. 1953. *Bot. Gaz.* **114**, 265.
ZIMMERMANN, W. 1932. *Jb. wiss. Bot.* **77**, 393.
ZINNAI, I. & CHIBA, S. 1951. *Jap. J. Breed.* **1**, 43.
ZOHARY, M. 1953. *Palest. J. Bot. Jerus.* **5**, 4.
ZOSSIMOVICH, V. P. 1939. *C.R. Acad. Sci. U.R.S.S.* **24**, 69.
ZUNDORF, W. 1939. *Z.i.A.V.* **77**, 195.

INDEX TO FAMILIES AND GENERA

Family names, capitals
Genus names asterisked—counts summarised
Page references to figures in italics

BALANOPHORACEAE 190
Baldellia 336
Baliospermum 128
Ballota 329
BALSAMINACEAE 85
Balsamorrhiza 255
Bambusa 458
Banisteria 126
Banksia 90
Baptisia 166
Barbarea* 43
Bartonia 36, 276
Bartschia 316
Bartsia 316
Bartlingia 368
Basella 78
BASELLACEAE 78
Bassia* 75, 225
Bastardia 121
Bauera 133
Bauhinia 150
Beckmannia 432
Begonia 100
BEGONIACEAE 100
Belairia 169
Belamcanda 388
Bellevalia 351
Bellis 255, 257
Bellium 257
Benincasa 100
Benzoin 16
BERBERIDACEAE 27
Berberis* 28
Bergenia 59
Bergeranthus* 68
Bergia 59
Berkheya 265
Bernardia 130
Berteroa 42
Berula 205
Beschorneria 394
Beta 76
Betonica 324
Betula 175, 180
BETULACEAE 179
Bidens 254
Bifora 210
Bignonia 319, 320
BIGNONIACEAE 318
Bijlia 66
Billbergia* 343
Biscutella* 38
Biserrula 163
Bivonaea 39
Bixa, 95
BIXACEAE 95
Blackstonia 276

Blennosperma 264
Blepharidachne 440
Bletia 406
Bletilla 406
Bloomeria 355
Blumenbachia 36
Blysmus 416
Blyxa 335
Bocconia 34
Boehmeria 185
Boenninghausenia 195
Boissiera 440
Boltonia 257
Bomarea 373
BOMBACACEAE 120
Bombax 120
Bongardia 28
Boöphone 381
Bootia 335
BORAGINACEAE 294
Borago 296
Borassus 398
Borderea 393
Boronia* 194
Borzicactus 102
Bothriochloa 421
Bougainvillea 90
Boussingaultia 77
Bouteloua 432
Bouvardia 235
Bowenia 3
Bowiea 369
Bowlesia 209
Boykinia 58
Brabeium 90
Brachiaria 424
Brachychilus 346
Brachycyrtis 370
Brachyelytrum 455
Brachyloma 220
Brachypodium 446
Brahea 396
Brassavola 407
Brassica 46
Bravoa 394
Braya 41
Bredemeyera 50
Brevoortia 355
Breynia 130
Bridelia 130
Briza 439
Brodiaea 354, 355
Bromelia 343
BROMELIACEAE 343
Bromus* 441
Brosimum 183
Broussonetia 183
Browallia 302

Brownea 149
Bruckenthalia 215
Brunella 328
Brunfelsia 303
Brunnera 294
Brunsvigia 381
Bryonia 99
Bryophyllum* 55
Buchloë 434
Buckleya 190
Buddleia 226
Bulbine 365
Bulbinella 364
Bulbocodium 368
Bulbostylis 414
Bulnesia 82
Bumelia 225
Bunias 44
Buphthalmum 258
Bupleurum 205
BURSERACEAE 197
Butia 397
BUTOMACEAE 335
Butomus 335
BUXACEAE 177
Buxus 177

Cabomba 27
Cacalia 262, 264
Caccinia 294
CACTACEAE 101
CAESALPINACEAE 147
Caesalpinia 149
Caiophora 35
Cajanus 171
Cakile 47
Caladium 376
Calamagrostis* 437
Calamintha 328, 329
Calamus 396
Calandrinia 71
Calanthe* 407
Calathea 347
Calceolaria 313
Calendula 266
Calepina 45
Calla 373
Calliandra 150
Callianthemum 25
Callicarpa 323
Callichlamys 319
Callipeltis 236
Callirhoë 121
Callisia 338
Callistemma 244
Callistemon* 112
Callistephus 257
CALLITRICHACEAE 89

512

GEORGE ALLEN & UNWIN LTD
London: 40 Museum Street, W.C.1

Auckland: 24 Wyndham Street
Sydney, N.S.W.: Bradbury House, 55 York Street
Cape Town: 58–60 Long Street
Bombay: 15 Graham Road, Ballard Estate, Bombay 1
Calcutta: 17 Chittaranjan Avenue, Calcutta 13
New Delhi: 13–14 Ajmere Gate Extension, New Delhi 1
Karachi: Haroon Chambers, South Napier Road, Karachi 2
Toronto: 91 Wellington Street West
Sao Paulo: Avenida 9 de Julho 1138–Ap. 51

by C. D. Darlington

CHROMOSOME BOTANY

Cr. 8vo about 12*s.* 6*d. net*

In the last twenty years chromosomes have penetrated into every kind of plant study. In his new book, which he begins with a simple account of chromosome behaviour, Professor Darlington reviews the effects of this penetration on genetics and systematics, ecology, plant geography and plant breeding. The effect of this treatment is in a sense to turn the science upside down. All the various branches of botany are seen from a new angle, and it is not surprising that several unexpected evolutionary principles are brought to light. This is especially true of what concerns the origins of species and the origins of cultivated plants. The book will serve as an introduction to a wide range of biological problems. It is illustrated by 36 drawings, diagrams and maps, mostly unpublished.

by C. D. Darlington and L. F. La Cour

THE HANDLING OF CHROMOSOMES

Revised Second Edition. Cr. 8*vo.* 9*s.* 6*d. now—net*

The chromosomes are the machinery of organic inheritance and evolution, the chemical organizers of life. In every plant and animal cell they are continually at work controlling and organizing development. Here for the first time is a simple account of how to make them visible. Darlington and La Cour's work is well known in this field of research. Their book will enable teachers in schools and universities to demonstrate chromosomes to their pupils. It describes every stage of the treatment from dissecting an anther or salivary gland to making a camera lucida drawing or microphotograph. Diagrams, schedules, formulae, bibliography and lists of equipment are provided. This book will be indispensable alike in botany and zoology, medicine and agriculture.

'One of the writers of this book has probably done more than any other living man to increase our knowledge of chromosomes, the other has made useful contributions to the technique of studying them. They have collaborated to the advantage of fellow cytologists in preparing this authoritative account.'—*Lancet.*

'This is more than a manual for students. Research workers will find indications as to when and how more elaborate methods should be used. They will also find a most useful bibliography of recent reviews together with much information, some unpublished hitherto, which has never before been collected in a single volume.'—*British Medical Journal.*

by C. D. Darlington and K. Mather

THE ELEMENTS OF GENETICS

Second Impression.   Demy 8vo.   30s. net

Genetics has undergone many transformations since it began with the re-discovery of Mendel in 1900.   Drosophila and the chromosomes, population studies, human heredity and statistical methods, the chemistry of mutations and finally the great revelations of the genetics of micro-organisms have, each of them, meant a revolution in the study of heredity.   The last has meant its combination with the study of development and infection also.

The Elements of Genetics by Darlington and Mather represents for the first time the whole length and breadth of this history.   It is a concise text book of genetics.   But it is written by two workers who in their 15 years' collaboration have done as much as any others to make this new science.   It is therefore bound to be a book for the research worker as well as for the student.

There are a great number of new figures, diagrams and tables, and a glossary with the author's definitions of 500 terms gives clarity and precision to the whole work.

' Most stimulating, fascinating for the breadth of its ideas . . . a most important book of lasting value. . . . Packed with information and ideas from which all will profit and it should have the widest of publics.'—*Eugenics Review.*

' Seldom within the confines of a single volume does one find a lucid ex-position of a whole discipline. . . . Darlington and Mather understand genetics; they do not merely know it.   In this book they have set down in admirably clear language the elements, the ultimate parts of which genetics is made.'—*Biology and Human Affairs.*

by C. H. Waddington

AN INTRODUCTION TO MODERN GENETICS

Demy 8vo.   Third Impression.   about 30s. net.

' In the interests of genetics and of biology as a whole, we hope that Waddington's book will be widely used.'   J. B. S. HALDANE, J. S. HUXLEY, H. J. MULLER in *Nature.*

' An enormous mass of information from many different fields, but his pre-sentation of the various investigations is frequently better and more lucid than that of the original authors.'—*Animal Breeding Extracts.*

by C. D. Darlington

THE FACTS OF LIFE

Demy 8vo. 35s. *net*

This book begins as a history of man's attempts to discover the facts about himself. It goes on to deal in detail with heredity, sex and reproduction, and with their bearing on the great problems of society, with race, class and mating; with education, health and crime; with evolution and the interpretation of history; and with the never-ending war between superstition and scientific method. The conclusion is a philosophy of determinism which is very old so far as the name goes. But the evidence on which Dr. Darlington bases his argument has been brought together only in the last thirty years. The result is therefore in effect a new philosophy of life.

' The vigour of Darlington's thought, and prose, and the combination of a highly individual point of view with a wide field of scientific knowledge, will, I think, cause this book to be quoted for a long time as an important mid-twentieth century opinion about the cultural influence of biology.'—*Heredity*.

' This is a brilliant and stimulating book. The story of the growth of our knowledge and the defeat of our superstitions and prejudices about human reproduction and heredity has never been better told; and the chapters on the social and historical implications of modern genetics are admirably provocative.'—*Dr. Julian Huxley*.

by C. D. Darlington and K. Mather

GENES, PLANTS AND PEOPLE

Demy 8vo. 16s. *net*

Here is a collection of essays covering a large part of the field of genetics. They announce the generalizations and hypotheses developed over a period of twenty years during which they have served as some of the main signposts in the astonishing advance of this science. They deal with plants and animals, medicine and agriculture. They offer new interpretations of evolution, development and disease. Indeed they sketch out a rigorous framework of causation which is now being applied to the whole of biology.

Scattered in many journals these essays have long been out of reach to the general reader. Now in compact form they serve as an introduction and as a history of the subject which the two authors have presented with more detail in their *Elements of Genetics*.

by Roger Pilkington

SONS AND DAUGHTERS

Demy 8vo.   18s. net

Sons and Daughters tells the story of the development of the human baby from conception to birth and explains the remarkable and complex events of the early stages of development in simple and non-technical language. The present knowledge of human heredity is clearly stated, and there are sections dealing with the effects of the environment upon characters controlled by genes, the possibility of inducing mutations chemically, and the accuracy with which genetic forecasting of a child's talents and physical features can be done. There are scores of photographs of unusual excellence, and the work is written with a lively humour which marks it as a book of outstanding merit.

'We follow with absorbed interest the growth of the human baby from conception to birth and learn of the remarkable events in the early stages of its development. The factors which determine the physical, mental and emotional entity which is a human being are clearly outlined and the degree to which these can be predicted examined. . . . It brings to a difficult yet momentous subject the illuminating power of a lively enquiring mind.'—*School Government Chronicle.*

by Julian Huxley

EVOLUTION : THE MODERN SYNTHESIS

Fifth Impression.   Demy 8vo.   25s. net

It is proclaimed in some quarters that Darwinism is dead. This book by Professor Julian Huxley completely refutes the assertion. Owing to a combination of historical accidents Darwinism suffered an eclipse in the early years of this century: but recent progress in various fields has led to a new synthesis of biological knowledge, which has made it evident that the Darwinian principle of Natural Selection must still be regarded as the main factor in evolutionary change, although recent developments in our knowledge of hereditary constitution have shed new light on the precise method of its operation.

The author deals at some length with these modern developments of Mendelism and their bearings on Evolution, and discusses the general problems of adaptation. A large section of the book is devoted to the various methods by which new species may be formed. In these chapters, data from Systematic zoology and botany and from field natural history have been analysed in the light of modern genetic and evolutionary theory on a scale not hitherto attempted.

'. . . most important book. . . . Dr. Huxley presents a fascinating and extremely complex picture of that fascinating and extremely complex thing called living nature, painted in genes. His picture is essentially dynamic.'— *New Statesman and Nation.*

'. . . there is certainly no more complete and no more satisfactory work on evolution.'   *Times Literary Supplement.*

LONDON : GEORGE ALLEN AND UNWIN LTD

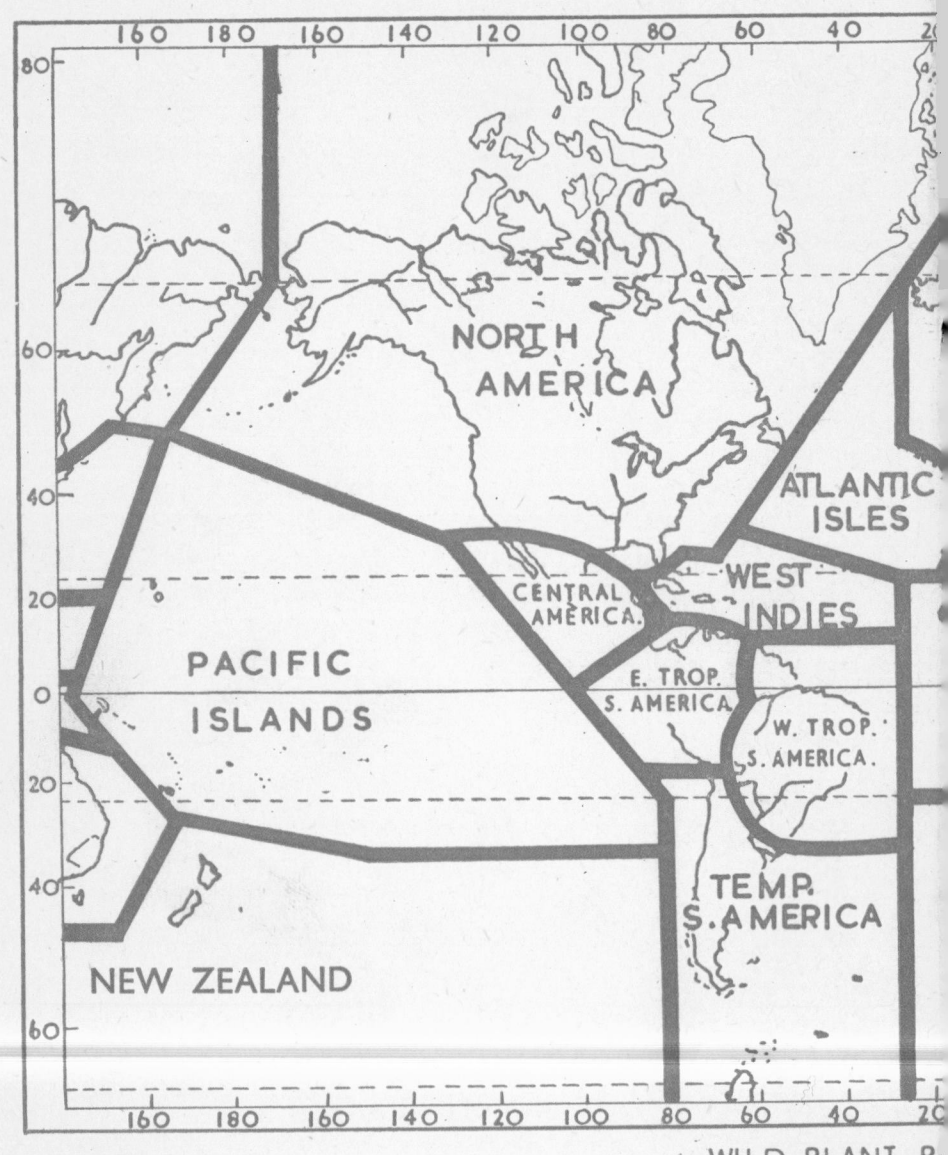

WILD PLANT R.